5

GOLD

HISTORICAL AND ECONOMIC ASPECTS

GOLD

HISTORICAL AND ECONOMIC ASPECTS

Advisory Editor

KENNETH CARPENTER

THE AUTOBIOGRAPHY OF

JOHN HAYS HAMMOND

Volumes I & II

ARNO PRESS

A New York Times Company

New York • 1974

Library of Congress Cataloging in Publication Data

Hammond, John Hays, 1855-1936.
   The autobiography of John Hays Hammond.

   (Gold: historical and economic aspects)
   Reprint of the ed. published by Farrar & Rinehart,
New York.
   Bibliography: p.
   1. Hammond, John Hays, 1855-1936. I. Series.
CT275.H3585A3 1974   622'.092'4 [B]   74-351
ISBN 0-405-05913-2

The Autobiography of John Hays Hammond

JOHN HAYS HAMMOND

THE AUTOBIOGRAPHY OF

JOHN HAYS HAMMOND

Illustrated with Photographs

VOLUME

1

FARRAR & RINEHART · INCORPORATED

On Murray Hill, New York

To My Wife

1881-1931

Contents Volume One

List of Illustrations

ix

x

List of Illustrations

Foreword

California, with its changing history, vital yet romantic, derives its very name from a fabled island. Garci Ordoñez de Montalvo wrote of this mythical region in the early years of the sixteenth century: "Know that on the right hand of the Indies there is an island called California, very close to the side of the Terrestrial Paradise . . . the strongest in all the world, with its steep cliffs and rocky shores." The arms of its inhabitants, he went on to relate, "were all of gold, and so was the harness of the wild beasts which they tamed to ride; for in the whole island there was no metal but gold."

Throughout the legendary years of California, the gold lure seems to have beckoned repeatedly. When Hernando Cortez heard of this country north of Mexico, his impelling desire was to journey thither that he might explore for gold. He sent expeditions by both land and sea, but all failed and his desire was never fulfilled. Other conquistadores likewise attempted to open up a way to the alleged wealth of California, but it remained for the heroic Franciscans—men of the church—actually to settle the country.

In 1769, Miguel José Serra Junipero—a vigorous and dauntless priest—led a party of missionaries from Old and New Spain into California, for the purpose of converting the savages. They were not seeking gold and they did not find it. Instead, they found disorganized, warring tribes of Indians, whose civilization was unbelievably primitive. They ate anything available. Acorns and roots were their chief diet, supplemented occasionally by fish and wild game, reptiles, insect larvae and worms: "almost everything, in fact, except dogs and men." The men wore skins wrapped around their loins; the women, from either modesty or vanity, wore double petticoats or aprons, nothing more.

The Spanish friars settled down to work. They had brought with them grain, fruits, vegetables and cattle. They tilled the virgin fields, they irrigated the dry savannas. Indefatigably they educated the Indians in an attempt to build up an agrarian culture under the

xi

*church. Olive groves and vineyards and pasture lands replaced
tangled wilderness. The teaching and training of the Indians kept
pace with the material development: laboring together, padre and
Indian built and planted, and slowly the California missions came
into being.*

*Visitors today can see shaded cloisters, campanarios, patios, foun-
tains, vineyards, and gardens developed by the Franciscans at the cost
of bloodshed and untold sacrifice.*

*The Hispanic-California era definitely was born when colonists
arrived from Spain and Mexico. Pasture lands were plentiful and
rich. Gradually the great ranchos and haciendas were built up. As
the country developed and became wealthy, the hacendados revived
the culture of Castile and Asturias. These men of Spain, in colorful
and splendid attire, were noble in their bearing, they were gallant,
they were gay. Their music was tuneful; their dances were spirited;
their fiestas were gorgeous in color. Within their hacienda walls
they built up small worlds of activity and contentment. Wayfarers,
riding through the country, never failed to receive a cordial welcome,
genuine hospitality, and often gracious bounty at the ranchos. In
those days, the Californios found life warm and generous.*

*But their civilization was destined to be transient. Gold lay hid-
den in the hills and its existence was known long before the Forty-
niners. There are well-authenticated stories of Indians coming to
the missions from the back-country with small nuggets. One of the
old Franciscan padres, whom I knew very well, told me that the mission fathers opposed the Indians in their search for brightly-speckled
nuggets and so far as they were able smothered the reports of gold.
They were interested only in Christianizing and civilizing the savages.
The rancheros were accomplices of the Franciscans, in hushing
rumors of gold. They also feared the arrival of gringos, since they
knew what sudden wealth might do to the country. They hoped to
preserve their leisurely life at the haciendas.*

*In 1841, Francisco Lopez, who was employed at the San Fernando
Mission not far from the thriving village of El Pueblo de Nuestra
Señora la Reina de Los Angeles, was tracking his strayed burros
through Santa Feliciana Canyon in the San Fernando hills. He
picked up a large nugget, which some years later was sent to the*

United States Mint at Philadelphia. This was the first California gold to be minted, and when stamped into coin had a value of $344.75.

As the result of the Lopez find, local prospectors of some previous experience in Sonora and other parts of Mexico started placer mining in the canyon, and during the course of the next two years panned out a hundred thousand dollars' worth of gold. This did not in any way stimulate the search for other gold deposits, however, and played no part in the development of the country.

The few non-Spanish settlers who had come to this simple and peaceful country were not Argonauts. They had come as pioneers to farm the river valleys and to graze their cattle on the hills. A very few with unusual imagination, such as Johann August Sutter, a Swiss settler, had succeeded in creating great landed estates on the model of the Old World. Chance intervened to terminate abruptly this pastoral life and early development.

On January 24, 1848, James Marshall, a carpenter, was erecting a sawmill for Johann Sutter on a creek running through his princely estate. A few yellow specks shone in the sand of the mill race. Marshall realized that he had found gold. Swearing the mill crew to secrecy, he hurried to tell Sutter of his find. But a discovery of this magnitude could not be concealed. While Marshall was gone, the mill crew whispered among themselves at first, and then confided in their wives and neighbors. The news spread with incredible rapidity up and down the west coast, across the Pacific Ocean. Within six months it had reached the eastern seaboard of the United States.

Towards the end of 1848 a huge tide of gold-seekers, adventurers, and traders set out for California. The peaceful mission life, the quiet plenty of hacendados and early colonists was over; the western Annus Mirabilis had arrived—The Year of the Gold! The Age of Gold had succeeded the Golden Age, and, as the historian Bancroft observes, "how different!"

CHAPTER ONE

Heritage of a Californian

THE FORTY-NINERS AND OTHERS—SAN FRANCISCO
EMERGES FROM THE FLATS—EMPEROR NORTON—
"COUSIN LILY" ANSWERS THE FIRE ALARM—
CHINATOWN AND THE BARBARY COAST—JUDGE LYNCH
AND THE VIGILANTES—THE PIONEER CREED—SAN
FRANCISCO OF THE SIXTIES—MY FIRST EARTH-
QUAKE—THE PONY EXPRESS BRINGS NEWS OF WAR

On April 1, 1849, the steamer *Oregon*, out of Panama, slipped into the quiet waters of the harbor of San Francisco. This small side-wheeler was bearing the first, or nearly the first, of the Argonauts answering the call of gold. As she cleared the Golden Gate, her bow was black with tense figures gazing eagerly over the mud flats and sand hills towards the mountains in which lay El Dorado.

Among the adventurers who streamed down the gangplank was my father, Richard Pindell Hammond, major of artillery in the United States Army, who had been ordered to the new territory of California for garrison duty.

Precluded by his position from joining the rush to the diggings, he yet, by virtue of the date of his arrival, was entitled to hold the full rank of a Forty-niner.

While a distinction between the pioneer of 1849 and the pioneer of 1850 might seem purely arbitrary, the first comers affected to see a great difference, and made of it a point of pride. They asserted that they alone had broken the trail and others, coming even as recently

3

as Fifty or Fifty-one, were merely followers. One was either a Forty-niner, or one was not. To the former category belonged the elect who had led the way to fame and fortune; if so benighted as to have been a follower instead of a leader in the memorable hegira, one was, to say the least, unfortunate.

This distinction of priority was sometimes carried to inordinate lengths. When Stephen J. Field, afterwards associate justice of the United States Supreme Court, offered himself as a candidate for the newly created office of alcalde of Marysville, a small village on the Yuba River above Sacramento, the supporters of a rival candidate objected to him on the ground that he was a newcomer. Field had been there only three days; his opponent had been there six.

In spite of its stately name, the village of San Francisco was in 1849 no more than a heterogeneous collection of huts and canvas shelters, sprawling over the flats bordering the bay. In the wake of the gold discovery, California began to receive the mounting tide of fortune hunters, and San Francisco was the distributing point of all those who came by sea.

My father's military duties in San Francisco could not have been onerous; during the first few months after his arrival he found time to embark in other activities. In partnership with General William Tecumseh Sherman, a West Point collegemate who had already been a year in California, he made a survey for the promoters of a new city. In the heated imagination of the forward-looking California real estate men of 1849, their town was to rival the Atlantic metropolis and to become the "New York of the Pacific." According to their theory, and looking back it would seem reasonable, all traffic inland would have to stop at its wharves to equip for expeditions to the outlying mining districts up the Sacramento and San Joaquin rivers. This dream city never materialized; in fact, during 1850 it had a post office just long enough to postmark one envelope.

In spite of this initial failure, the idea of converting waste land into home sites had so captured my father's imagination that in 1851 he resigned from the army and formed a partnership with Captain Charles M. Webber. As surveyors and engineers, these two young men laid out the city of Stockton, which grew and prospered. Located at the head of navigation of the San Joaquin River, it became the logical outfitting station for miners heading for the central part of the state. They also planned Tuolumne which, having no raison d'être, soon disappeared.

By this time my father had become a man of mark in the community and was shortly after elected to the State Assembly; in 1852 he was chosen speaker of the House. His main interest thereafter was in the political organization of his adopted city and state.

Many of his fellow officers in the Mexican War had likewise followed the swing westward. Among them was John Coffee Hays, former colonel of the Texas Rangers, known to his admiring contemporaries and to history as Colonel Jack. In 1851 he became the first sheriff of the turbulent community of San Francisco. This honor was by no means uncontested. The colonel's opponent, a storekeeper, proved to be a serious rival. With great political sagacity, he hired a brass band to play in front of his store on election day and was fast polling all the votes.

When Colonel Hays realized the emergency, he mounted his horse, a beautiful, spirited, black animal, perfectly trained to obey the slightest word or touch. Galloping into the middle of the plaza, where the voting was taking place, the colonel put his mount through one fancy turn after another, and continued to make him dance to his rival's music until the polls were finally closed. The votes were counted—and the colonel had won.

The tide of pioneers was steadily mounting during the early fifties. Whether the western adventurers came "the Horn around, the Isthmus across, or the land over," the trip entailed hardship and heartbreak. In 1852 my mother, Sarah E. (Hays) Lea, a widow with a small daughter, started out on the hazardous journey to California to visit her brother, Colonel Hays.

Leaving her ship at Aspinwall, now Colon, in company with the throngs of gold-seekers she crossed the Isthmus by donkey-train through the pestilential jungles. It took a lot of courage as well as physical endurance to survive this trip. Many people died on the way. Although my mother and her daughter Lucy were fortunate in avoiding the deadly yellow fever, they were, like all the pilgrims, ill and exhausted when at last they reached San Francisco.

Soon after her arrival, she met my father, and in 1854 they were married.

My introduction to this world occurred in San Francisco, March 31, 1855, just seven years after Marshall's joyous eureka had startled the globe. Although the oldest of seven children, I was necessarily relegated to the inferior category of "followers" of the Forty-niners, who could hope to achieve only reflected glory, and whose duty it was to regard the Ancients with the reverence and the solemnity which were their due.

The San Francisco of my infancy was greatly changed from the straggling little settlement my father had seen from the crowded deck of the side-wheeler barely six years earlier. In spite of the constant traffic to and from the mines, there was an air of settled business. The town had been on several occasions almost entirely destroyed by fire, and each time, by the undefeatable energy of its sturdy citizens, had been rebuilt and better built. In the business section the stores, saloons, and lodging houses of canvas or rough boards had given way for the most part to brick buildings, sometimes as much as two stories high. With almost incredible rapidity the haphazard village of the gold year had climbed up Telegraph, Russian, and Rincon hills. Seven years later there was a population of 70,000.

The houses on Rincon Hill, then the fashionable section of San Francisco and the one in which our home was located, were constructed of wood. The dusty, unpaved streets were soon covered with planks, slivers from which would catch in the women's long dresses of the period. Although prairie schooners and springless dead-ax wagons were still to be seen, they were no longer in danger of being mired to the hub; and the humorous signs, "This street is not passable—not even jackassable," had disappeared.

The sidewalks were constantly crowded with human beings of every class and description. Sunday was a gala day, with gambling halls, theaters, and saloons wide open and crowded. Sailors of every nationality rolled arm in arm along the streets, miners lounged in saloon doorways, Chinese in native costume, with pigtails swinging, padded along unobtrusively, dark-skinned hacendados wearing broad sombreros clattered in from their great ranchos. Noticeable among the crowd, by virtue of the great diamonds glittering in their cravats

GOLDEN GATE, SAN FRANCISCO, 1855

MY FATHER, RICHARD PINDELL HAMMOND,
ON LEAVING WEST POINT

and on their conspicuously white hands, were the gamblers. The black felt hat, the Prince Albert coat, and the golden cable looped across the waistcoat was the exaggerated uniform of their trade.

The odd and picturesque features of San Francisco life in the early sixties were naturally those which most deeply imprinted themselves on my boyish mind. Many were the conspicuous characters to be seen on the streets of San Francisco, but most vivid to my youthful recollection was that remarkable character known as "Emperor" Norton, whose story illustrates the freehanded generosity and kindliness of the time.

Although born in Pennsylvania, the emperor had long been a California fixture. It was said that, after one of the fires of the fifties, in which he lost all his property, his mind went astray, and he announced himself Emperor of the United States and Proctector of Mexico. There is also good authority that he once offered his hand in marriage to Queen Victoria. In any case, he was accustomed to bear himself as much like an emperor as an American could, walking majestically and speaking to all in graciously royal tones. As well as ancient and shabby clothes would permit, he dressed his part, often completing his costume with tarnished gold epaulets of great magnificence, and a marshal's hat.

Even boys like myself were generous and indulgent to the old fellow. He had become an institution, and editors were glad to insert in their newspapers his "proclamations" to his loyal subjects:

Know ye whom it may concern that W. Norton I, Emperor Dei gratia of the United States and Protector of Mexico, have heard serious complaints from our adherents and all that our imperial wardrobe is a national disgrace, and even His Majesty the King of Pain has had his sympathy excited so far as to offer us a suit of clothing, which we have a delicacy in accepting. Therefore we warn those whose duty it is to attend to these affairs that their scalps are in danger if our said need is unheeded.

At long intervals, when his well-worn suit of clothes became too obviously unfitted to his exalted rank, the Board of Supervisors presented him with a new one He was allowed to order meals in restaurants, and regally charge them to the imperial account. The fact that he could draw checks of from fifty cents to five dollars and find bank tellers kind enough to honor them might indicate that he was not completely deranged.

For twenty years his make-believe kingdom endured, and when he died in 1880 he was given a public funeral.

After all these years San Francisco has remained loyal to the memory of Norton. Recently he was reburied in Woodland Memorial Park, and a battalion of United States infantry fired a three-gun salute over the grave of Emperor Norton I.

There was no paid fire department in the city; each ward had its own engine and volunteer fire company. One of the companies, called the Occidental, was made up of younger members of prominent San Francisco families. As a young boy it was my greatest delight to hear the fire alarm tolling from the tower of the City Hall where a lookout was posted day and night. All the boys of the neighborhood answered the call and ran behind the engine for what seemed to us miles. At the scene of the fire we were very much in the way but we enjoyed the excitement hugely.

Our most honored honorary member was the daughter of a retired army officer, Dr. Charles Hitchcock. Cousin Lily, as I called her, was a high-spirited girl, who roused an individual conflagration in the breast of each member of the company. She was so earnest a devotee that even at a ball she wore her fire badge. When the alarm sounded, she always sat with the driver on the fire engine.

In those days everybody employed Chinese servants and found them remarkably reliable, faithful, and efficient. When a tong war was not raging, or the yellow plague flag had not been run up in the Chinese quarter, I was allowed to go there with our cook. Even in so colorful and so bizarre a place as San Francisco the Chinese section struck a gaudy alien note—shrill piping music and unfamiliar smells, slant-eyed children tumbling around the streets, and sometimes a woman toddling on miniature bound feet, looking as though she were about to capsize. I always came home laden with firecrackers and exotic sweets.

There was one place strictly forbidden to me but from which faint echoes constantly drifted into my world. This was the Barbary Coast. Crowded with saloons, dance halls, brothels, gambling dens, sailors' boarding houses, and doss joints, it gave San Francisco the reputation of being the "Wickedest City in the World." Gamblers, harlots, press gangs, and confidence men kept wary eyes upon gold-seekers and battened on them. Since the Barbary Coast was outside the pale of the respectable community, however, it represented but a small and unobtrusive part of the life of the city.

By the time I was ten years old the problem of controlling the criminal and lawless elements in this frontier society had already been solved by the Vigilantes. I often heard tales of their deeds from Colonel Hays, General Sherman, and William T. Coleman, a prominent merchant and former leader.

The issue between crime and order had been fought out chiefly in San Francisco. The three outlying river towns, Marysville, Sacramento, and Stockton, each a terminus of steamer transportation towards the gold-bearing foothills, had yielded precedence to the seaport, which was now indisputably a city. In its turbulent population the slow and peaceful method of developing orderly government, as practiced in the New England town meeting, had been obviously impossible. The efforts of the elected authorities had grown constantly more feeble and ineffectual.

The irregular endeavors to establish order in 1849 and 1851 culminated in the movement of 1856. At that time the government of California, headed by a governor, a legislature, and a supreme court, had been completely paralyzed by corrupt politics. In San Francisco, session after session of the court meted out no justice; murder after murder went unpunished; crime after crime against property was committed in places high and low. Merchants, bankers, and professional men, disgusted by the very word "law," decided to defy the rankly unjust decisions of the supreme court as well as the grossly illegal and partisan orders of Governor J. Neely Johnson.

Angered beyond endurance by the murder of a San Francisco editor, the great Vigilance Committee of 1856 was formed under the leadership of W. T. Coleman. Its members assumed every responsibility. In the harbor they seized coastwise schooners laden with arms which they believed had been sent against them by Governor Johnson. Known criminals were tracked down, captured, and tried in orderly fashion. If convicted, they were publicly hanged from a beam protruding from a headquarters' window. The executions were carried out in the presence of the Vigilantes and of curious crowds. San Francisco was swept as clean of crime as was ever possible in any such frontier city.

On the day the committee felt its object had been accomplished, the total membership, accompanied by its artillery, marched in column through the town. But, as the procession broke ranks and mingled with the crowd, the word was passed from mouth to mouth that the Committee of Vigilance was "fully prepared to reassemble and resume duty whenever necessary!" Not only did the memory of its stern justice continue as a restraining force over the evil impulses of our farthest west communities, but the substantial citizens who had led the revolt against constituted law continued to operate individually as protective influences.

Years later, in 1880, acts of violence again became frequent. The loud-mouthed rantings of Dennis Kearney, the Sand Lot Orator, were directed principally against the wealthy man and the Chinese laborer. Kearney's followers were brawny malcontents who, because of their numbers, constituted a serious menace. They gathered around him on the sand lots throughout the city and gave vociferous approval to his threats to bomb the mansions on aristocratic Nob Hill and to do away with their owners.

At that time my father was chairman of the Board of Police Commissioners of the city. Although obviously, under these conditions, the office was not a sinecure, my father and his associates (William Alvord, president of the Bank of California, and Richard Tobin, president of the Hibernia Bank), men of brains, firmness, and courage, took a determined stand for the preservation of law and order in San Francisco.

My younger brother Harry, who had graduated from West Point in 1877, was then practicing law in San Francisco, and accepted the position of colonel in the state militia. In order to be prepared for any serious uprising of the Kearney followers, he stipulated that, if his soldiers were attacked, there was to be no firing of blank cartridges or aiming over the heads of the rioters. This warning undoubtedly had a deterrent effect on the mob element.

Coleman finally decided that some action must be taken to curb Kearney. With this in mind he arranged a meeting with him at the Grand Hotel in Market Street.

"Kearney," he stated firmly, "you know I'm a man of my word. I was the head of one of the vigilance committees of the early days and helped to hang a lot of damned scoundrels. Now, I want to warn you: if anybody who lives on Nob Hill is injured or any house is blown up, I'll catch you and hang you on the lamppost you see outside this window!"

What Coleman told Dennis Kearney in the Grand Hotel was effective. No outbreak took place. The spirit of the Vigilante still survives as is evidenced by the events in San Francisco in 1934.

In addition to the criminal outbreaks which cast a lurid glare over early San Francisco society, another phase of violence grew naturally from the almost universal habit of carrying a gun. Duels took place with great frequency.

The most famous of the California duels occurred on September 13, 1859, between United States Senator David C. Broderick and Judge Davis S. Terry of the state supreme court. During an acrimonious political campaign insults had been exchanged and a challenge followed. The two principals met in a gray fog in an open space by Lake Merced, just outside San Francisco. Broderick was shot through the lungs and died within a few hours.

I was only four years old at the time, but I later became a close friend of the Terry boys who would repeat the details of the duel to me. Furthermore, my uncle, Dr. William H. Hammond, was the surgeon attending Terry. I have never forgotten his description of how Broderick's German physician, Dr. Loehr, displayed a somewhat tactless efficiency in laying out on the ground under a tree his whole equipment of knives, scissors, bandages, and bottles.

My uncle always opposed the orthodox view that Broderick was so helpless against the superior skill of Terry that he was, in effect, murdered. As a matter of fact, Broderick was the better shot. Terry had a bad reputation for getting into trouble, and his favorite weapon was the Bowie knife, with which he was very skillful; he was no expert with the pistol. The error was actually made by Broderick's own second who did not ascertain that the pistols were unequal in action. The one given to Broderick was exceptionally light on the trigger; it went off before Broderick had taken proper aim. Terry then had a free shot and Broderick was killed. I have often seen these pistols and held them in my hands. They were old dueling pistols belonging to Dr. Dan Aylette, a friend of my father.

There was poetic justic in Terry's own end several decades later. He emerged from the cloud under which he had been living since the duel to become attorney for Sarah Althea Hill, commonly referred to as the Rose of Sharon because of her relations with Senator Sharon of Nevada, multimillionaire Comstock mine owner. During the suit Terry became very angry at the ruling of Justice Stephen J. Field, who was trying the case. He threatened to retaliate whenever the opportunity should present itself. Although Terry lost the case, he married his client.

By chance, Field and Terry later met in the lunchroom at Lathrop, on the Southern Pacific Railway. Justice Field, accompanied by a United States marshal assigned to him as bodyguard, had seated himself at a table. Terry approached Field and, after a few words, struck him in the face. The marshal thereupon shot Terry dead. Mrs. Terry ended her days in an asylum.

The Terry-Broderick duel was the last of any importance in California, although dueling persisted in other parts of the country. As a matter of fact, the men who originally introduced dueling in the Far West had in the main come from the South and had brought the code duello with them.

Since public affairs were generally conducted in the Balkan fashion in those times, it was often unwise for any man to take too radical a stand unless he was prepared to vindicate his principles by ordeal of combat. Dueling did have one good effect. The risk of incurring a challenge undoubtedly encouraged prudence in speech. It behooved every man to guard his tongue carefully, for the words "liar" and "scoundrel" were not used idly; they were intended as affronts and accepted as such. Dueling was, in fact, so inextricably bound up with one's personal character and social standing that, as Judge Edward McGowan remarked long afterwards, "It required more bravery to decline than to accept a challenge, and the man in California in those early days who refused to fight when challenged was considered outside the pale of genteel society."

By the time I was old enough to go alone to the wharves, the original mud flats had been filled in, and new land extended from Sansome Street toward the bay. Rather than take the trouble or go to the expense of removing the hulks which had been beached on the flats, earth had been dumped around them. The old steamer *Niantic* had even been turned into a hotel and was so used until finally destroyed by fire.

In place of the Civic Center, with its municipal buildings, opera house, library, and gardens, were sand hills overgrown with sparse brush. On the site of the present Golden Gate Park I hunted rabbits and quail, and even caught a wildcat now and then.

Regular steamer days came only about once a month. As soon as a steamer was sighted outside Golden Gate, the flag was run up on Telegraph Hill. Everybody who could possibly leave his duties hurried to the wharf. If we were lucky enough to be free of school at the moment, my schoolmates and I would rush to see the steamer dock and watch the cargo being unloaded.

In the sixties and seventies the so-called bonanza kings began to build enormous homes on Rincon and Nob hills. The fact that these houses were pretentious did not establish for their owners any social superiority. San Francisco was pre-eminently known for the spirit of democracy that prevailed there.

There was no such thing as planned architecture. W. T. Coleman owned a Roman villa, George Hearst (later a senator) erected a Spanish palace, James Ben Ali Haggin, his partner, lived in a huge gray mansard structure, and Jim Flood, of Nevada silver fame, inhabited a huge brownstone mansion surrounded by a brass fence, the polishing of which was one man's full-time job. This is now the Pacific-Union Club, of which my father was the first president. The houses which had come around the Horn in sections from New England were curiosities in architecture. When they were put together again, the pieces somehow did not seem to match.

The influence of the many Southerners in the community undoubtedly was a contributing factor to the generous and gay flavor which San Francisco possesses. For many years the city has been renowned for its incomparable restaurants, surpassing even those of New Orleans. This was not because the chefs and cuisines were superior to those of Paris, Vienna, and other parts of the world, but because the climate and the other unique characteristics of the country made available an extraordinary variety of rare meats, fruits, vegetables, and wild game. Complementary to this the cosmopolitan character of the population was responsible for variety and color in the changing customs and amenities of the city. Each racial unit had its own types of food, and expert methods of preparing them. French, German, Mexican, Chinese, and Italian restaurants catered to gourmets of all nationalities. Among the more famous cafés of the seventies and eighties were Jacks, Maison Dorée, Poodle Dog, Pup, and Jules for wild duck.

At the age of eleven I had my share in a type of excitement common to Californians. Prior to 1906, an earthquake was called an earthquake and not a fire. One morning, with other boys, I was playing baseball, and, while running to catch a fly, I was tumbled suddenly to the ground by a sharp shock. The batter was too frightened to take advantage of his base hit. Several "bad" little Mexican boys, who were clandestinely smoking cigarettes on a platform they had built in a tree for a secret refuge, fell on their knees and prayed loudly for the intervention of the saints, promising complete reform.

During the next few days there were many quakes and, much to our delight, school was dismissed for the week.

On the following Sunday in church, I remember that we were startled by a slight tremor, and a slow but definite foreboding filled our minds. The minister appealed to the congregation to remain seated, saying, not very convincingly, that there was no danger. At that moment the building shook again. Seeing his previous statement had not quieted the evident alarm of his congregation, he said, even less convincingly, that there could be no safer place than the House of the Lord.

Just then came a shock that rocked the building. The pastor tumbled down from his pulpit and fled precipitately up the aisle and out, muttering, as he outdistanced his flock, "I'll take my chances outside!"

MY MOTHER, SARAH E. (HAYS) LEA HAMMOND

MY BROTHERS AND MYSELF:
JOHN, RICHARD, HARRY, WILLIAM

As a youthful but enthusiastic stamp collector, I was particularly interested in the incoming foreign mail. After each boat was docked I made what for me was a considerable journey to the various mercantile houses on California, Montgomery, and Sansome streets. Hat in hand, after mustering up the necessary nerve, I bolted into the establishment, introduced myself and asked whether I might have some stamps from the newly arrived mail. Since my father was known to every merchant in town, I usually had good luck. If the merchant happened to be busy, I would tactfully excuse myself and unfailingly return next day.

My early collection was destroyed in the San Francisco fire and I never had another collection hobby until I started a gallery of signed photographs of men whom I admired for their achievements.

My father often had to go on business to Sacramento. I was sometimes allowed to accompany him on the overnight boat trip. Although it was the capital of the state, Sacramento was only a straggling village, and frequently the river overflowed and we had to make our calls in rowboats through the flooded streets.

Sacramento was built around what had formerly been Sutter's Fort and was not only the point at which the prospectors outfitted, but also the terminus of the Pony Express, and the Overland Stage line. It was thrilling for me to see the six-horse stagecoach start off on the two thousand mile trip to the railhead at St. Joseph, Missouri, colloquially known as St. Joe. Inside were the passengers, high up on top was the luggage; in front was the driver, and directly behind him the Wells-Fargo shotgun messenger.

Even more exciting was the arrival of the Pony Express, which covered the same distance in nine days. Whenever I had the good fortune to be in Sacramento the day it was due, I was always to be found among the yelling crowd as the jingling, sweating little cayuses came pounding in to the station.

Up to August, 1860, the through rates on the Pony Express were $5.00 per half-ounce or under, but from that date letters weighing a quarter-ounce or under were carried for $2.50. At one time I had the largest collection of Pony Express franks of any philatelist of my acquaintance.

The Pony Express service owned several hundred horses and employed upwards of a hundred plucky riders, who made their way through country infested with Indians, over snow-clad mountains, and across arid deserts. Now an airmail letter can be sent for six cents from New York to San Francisco in twenty-four hours, and the trip has been made in less than twelve hours.

It was the Pony Express that brought from the Missouri River the first faint rumblings of impending civil conflict.

CHAPTER TWO

A Boy on the Frontier

THE YOUNG SECESH — THE MARTIAL HAYS' AND
HAMMONDS — COLONEL JACK — THE ENCHANTED
ROCK — HEROES AND HERO WORSHIP — LEARNING
TO ROUGH IT — REHABILITATING SILVER —
THE BRET HARTE COUNTRY AND THE
YOSEMITE VALLEY — PANNING MY FIRST GOLD

I began my formal education during the Civil War. I was sent to the Lincoln public school, in San Francisco, which at that time contained about two hundred pupils. It was an excellent school and we received good training. It was not because of the fact that my father was president of the Board of Education that I went to a public school, but because he could not afford a tutor or private school. Possibly as a result of my own experience, I have always been a great believer in sending children to public schools.

Because our parents were from the South, we considered ourselves Southerners, and my brothers and I had many a fist fight with the Yankees of our own age.

My mother's family came from Tennessee and, like my father's, included many soldiers. Her grandfather, and other relatives, served under Jackson at the Battle of New Orleans in 1815. It was he who built the Hermitage, near Nashville, which he later sold to President Jackson.

One of my mother's brothers was General Harry T. Hays, commander of the famous Louisiana Tigers in the Confederate Army.

Another brother was John Coffee Hays—Colonel Jack, of the Texas Rangers, for whom I was named. He was sixteen when both his parents died within a few days of each other, of yellow fever. The seven orphans were taken by an uncle to his plantation in Mississippi. One morning in 1837 Jack's aunt found attached to her pincushion a note in which Jack said: "I have decided to lighten the burden of so large a family by making my own way in the world, and I have gone away."

Although California was a Union state, and the Southerners there were viewed with suspicion during the Civil War, yet we were so far removed from the scene of actual conflict that the bitterness of personal animus was greatly lessened. Some Southerners, including my uncle, Colonel Jack Hays, were paroled, after giving their word to the northern officers that they would not join the southern cause.

My father found his business enterprises made difficult by the war; his political activities ceased. Many northern officers in command in California were his West Point friends, and they were as considerate as possible of my mother's feelings. The progress of the war was so tactfully touched upon when they visited at our house that friendly relations were maintained throughout the struggle.

In later years I asked my father why he had not joined one army or the other. His answer was that, although then reputed a wealthy man, he had at the moment lost so heavily in a worthless gold mine and other ventures that he did not feel justified in leaving a wife and small children.

Of far more importance than this, however, was the fact that he could not give whole-hearted allegiance to either side. He believed firmly that the war had been brought on by northern and southern politicians: had it not been for the intemperate attitude of the leaders on both sides, some compromise could have been worked out and war averted. Unfortunately for his peace of mind, he was a Unionist, in that he opposed dismemberment of the Union, while his natural sympathies were with the South.

Most of the Hammonds had led adventurous lives from the time they first left England and settled down in Maryland where they intermarried with the Ringgolds, Tilghmans, Lloyds, Galloways, and

MY UNCLE, COLONEL JACK HAYS, ON ENCHANTED ROCK

MY SISTER, MARY-ELIZABETH: BETTY

other prominent families who have their roots in the foundations of the colony.

Major General John Hammond had been vice-admiralty judge, member of the House of Burgesses, and one of His Majesty's Council in that colony. His tomb is still to be seen in Annapolis at the entrance of St. Ann's Protestant Episcopal Church. The ground on which it stands had been deeded by him "in evidence of the love I bear my fellow man." On his death in 1707 he left a sum of money to be expended in the purchase of a brass-bound Bible, cherished to this day in the archives of St. Ann's.

His great-grandson, Mathias, built at Annapolis the house still known as the Hammond-Harwood house, one of the finest examples of Colonial architecture extant in America. The story is that this home, planned and constructed by him for his future wife, finally led to the breaking of their engagement. He became so much interested in the building and its furnishings, which he collected with exquisite taste, that he failed to pay his fiancée the attentions she thought due her. After suffering what she considered his neglect for some time, the young lady finally lost patience and sent her negro servant to return ring and presents to young Mathias. Neither ever married.

My grandfather, Dr. William Hammond, army surgeon, was a Forty-niner in the same sense as my father. He had arrived in San Francisco in the autumn of 1849 and was stationed at Benicia, where he died in 1851. Two other sons, my uncles, came to California about this time. William Hammond, Jr., was first surgeon in the United States Army and later a well-known practitioner in San Francisco. George H. Hammond, surgeon in the navy, served under Commodore Farragut at Mare Island and was lost under the same command in the Civil War. My father and my uncles had been with my grandfather in the Mexican War.

My father was born in 1820 in Hagerstown, Maryland. At the age of twenty-nine when he came to California, his life had already been full of adventure. At seventeen, he had been appointed a cadet to West Point by President Jackson, a personal friend of my grandfather. After his graduation in 1841 he was sent to Fort McHenry, in Baltimore. He was still there when, just after the Seminole War,

Inspector General Quitman came through on a tour of inspection of the South. The general attached my father to his staff and then inquired: "Do you know any West Pointer who can write a good legible report, and who has a legal trend of mind? I'd like to take him along with us."

My father replied: "There's William T. Sherman who's recruiting out in Ohio. I've just had a letter from him and he doesn't like his work there."

Sherman was sent for and joined them on the tour of inspection. Years later Sherman told me that the working knowledge of the topography of the South obtained at this time proved of inestimable value to him on his March to the Sea. At the beginning of the Mexican War, in 1846, Sherman was ordered to California, and consequently had no part in it.

My father was summoned to West Point but found a substitute for that unwelcome detail and went instead to Mexico, where he served under General James Shields. After participating with his regiment in the siege of Vera Cruz, he was made captain for gallant and meritorious conduct at Cerro Gordo. Later at Contreras and Churubusco his gallantry won him the further rank of brevet major. During the storming of Chapultepec, as related by the *United States Army Register,* he narrowly escaped death, his horse being shot under him, and he himself being slightly wounded. The *Register* continues:

> When the city of the Montezumas fell into the hands of the Americans, Major Hammond was appointed Secretary of the State Government, and acting Judge Advocate. After the close of the war, Major Hammond was ordered to California, and resigned from the Army, May 31, 1851.

My father was fortunate in his military career, in having as his associates many officers who later, in a far more terrible conflict, were to rise to fame on one side or the other. He won the enduring friendship of Robert E. Lee and Joseph Eccleston Johnston. Many of their letters to him, which have been preserved, show the mutually affectionate relations founded during the stormy days of the Mexican campaign.

The friendship with Lee was particularly close. In the National Palace in Mexico City the two shared the same room. I still have a yellowed slip of paper in Lee's handwriting, which reveals an unexpected touch of humor in this period before sadder days descended upon the great Confederate leader. Written from Mexico City, it imitated the manner of army regulations, and was facetiously entitled "Memo for Sir Richard," who was about to depart for the States. Lee adjured him:

1. Not to go mad, either from joy or drink.
2. To eschew all tigers, etc.
3. The three boxes, marked 'G. W. P. Custis, etc.' to be shipped to the Dist. of Columbia, to Mr. Custis, or to Baltimore to Mr. L. Marshall, Esq., U. S. Dist. Attorney.
4. The *grey* pony, to have the same destination. Particular directions to be given about his *tail,* and *mane,* and being *covered* at sea. He is provided with *two* covers.
5. All bills of expense to be forwarded to the consigners. The Pony has fifty dollars, for current expenses.
6. Get Miss Follie, or Virginia Mason, to ride out to *Arlington* with him when he is in the *District.* Any other pretty girl will do as well.
7. Sometimes think of

R. E. LEE

When the Civil War broke out, Lee and Johnston wanted my father's services for the South, while his old commander, Shields, demanded him for the Union Army.

"I wish to God you were here," wrote General Shields from Washington when about to take the field with his division in March, 1862:

> I would give half my pay to have you with me as Adjutant. If I thought you would, I would leave it open. I find no such soldier as you in the army, and you are not so well fitted for anything else. The President and Secretary of War are as honest and Democratic

as I want. God never made an honester man than Lincoln, nor a nobler, truer man than Stanton. Either of them has more honesty in his finger than Jeff Davis in his body. By the way, Jeff has killed the southern revolution. He has made it as tame as a meeting house conventicle. I knew he would do that and the South has found it out too late. Jeff for President, and a Jew for Secretary of War, and drunken M. for Secretary of the Navy, you can easily figure out the end. If you want to come telegraph. I know what your friends will say, but if they knew all I know now, they would advise you to do it.

I would not give you as a soldier for any two I have met here. You are a born soldier and a made soldier, and cannot be anything else.

A month later Shields sent him another message from his headquarters at Strasburg, Virginia:

We have had an interesting fight. I wish you could have been there. It would have reminded you of old times . . . The war is not over yet. There will be many a hard fight before the South goes down. They fight hard, at least their Potomac Army does.

I learned to appreciate the value of my father's army connections when, after the war, I was privileged to meet on terms of friendship such men as Sherman, Grant, McClellan, McDowell, Halleck, Sheridan, Longstreet, Beauregard, Johnston, Hancock, Rosecrans, Gibson, and other heroes of the Civil War. I listened eagerly as these men gave their views of the problems facing the country in the difficult period of reconstruction.

Of all these generals I knew Sherman best. In fact, I persuaded him to send his son Tom to Yale, and I always felt a certain responsibility to look out for Tom while he was there. This didn't prove irksome.

During the eighteen-eighties McClellan, then living in New York, often dropped in at my office and took me to a little restaurant in Hanover Square where they served excellent Mexican food.

On my return from a Central American mining trip in the middle eighties I stopped off at New Orleans. There I spent a delightful day with Beauregard and Longstreet. The state had asked these two generals to head the huge Louisiana lotteries; because of their unquestioned honesty, it was believed this choice would inspire public confidence. A few years later the lotteries were abandoned, not on account of any chicanery in their management but because of the disapproval of the federal government of such legalized games of chance.

When I was twelve my mother died and I was sent to a boarding school in Oakland. Two years later I attended the preparatory department of the University of California. While I was in what was known as the fifth class of the university, in 1870-71, I formed a close friendship with a classmate, Josiah Royce, who became one of America's leading philosophers and the author of one of the best histories of early days in California.

In spite of these excellent opportunities for academic education, a valuable part of my early training was my friendship and association with my uncle, Colonel Jack Hays. Almost every Friday afternoon I walked out to his ranch, about three miles from Oakland, and back again on Monday morning.

> Were an account of the Indian fights, skirmishes, and adventures of Colonel Hays to be given to the world,

says a quaint history of the Texas Rangers published in 1847,

> it would fill a volume, and the work would be looked upon rather as the effusion of a fertile imagination, consisting of legendary tales, and the adventures of some fictitious knight-errant, than the faithful account of the achievements of a man, living and moving among us, and that, too, comparatively unknown.

The stories Uncle Jack told us were better than a whole library of books of adventure. Shortly after he left his uncle's home in Mississippi, he turned up at San Antonio where he found work in surveying frontier lands.

Since his ability to lead men was soon recognized, he was chosen to captain several independent forays against the Indian tribes who roamed the border. So great was his success in fighting the savages that eventually the Texas Congress appointed him captain of a scout company, and in 1840 promoted him to the rank of major, charging him with the defense of the frontier. Soon afterwards he was advanced to the rank of colonel.

In 1844 he was the hero of an historic frontier exploit. He became separated from his party of Rangers while tracking an Indian tribe which had gone on the warpath. He climbed to the top of a large rock to survey the surrounding country. The entire party of Indians had apparently seen him as he climbed. They were following him.

Ordinarily in those days, the Rangers were armed with muzzle-loading, double-barreled pistols. But by some freak of fortune he had with him a Colt six-shooter, incidentally the first gun of this kind ever manufactured. This revolver had been designed for his use and presented to him by its maker. As the braves attacked him at the summit of the rock, he shot them down, one by one, rapidly and with calm precision. The Indians fell back in utter confusion, leaving a half dozen dead warriors behind them. The speed and accuracy of Colonel Jack's firing completely bewildered them. They charged again and once more a spatter of bullets checked them. He was able to hold them at bay for several hours until the other Rangers came to his assistance.

The Indians, dismayed by this new and unfamiliar weapon, were so firmly convinced that some supernatural power had been at work that they named the colonel's place of refuge The Enchanted Rock.

At the outbreak of the Mexican War, Colonel Hays formed a regiment of his old Texan fighters and they, on many fields of battle, rendered conspicuous service to General Taylor's army.

Uncle Jack sometimes took two or three of us boys and some of his own friends on a camping trip lasting several weeks. During the day he taught us the rudiments of camping; around the fire at night we listened eagerly to his stories. Since he was a singularly modest man, it was only with great difficulty that we could induce him to recount the exciting exploits of his own life. But he knew that his friends would tell the stories should he persistently refuse.

One incident made a particularly deep impression on me. A Mexican colonel of cavalry who had a large reputation for his truculence had challenged Colonel Hays to single combat before their regiments clashed in battle. Colonel Hays accepted without hesitation and they engaged in a duel on horseback. As my uncle described the scene, I could hear the occasional stamp or whinny of a nervous horse and see the men of both regiments, silent but watchful, drawn up in battle array on each side of the cleared space.

Colonel Jack always assured us that he really regretted having been obliged to kill the Mexican colonel, as he had greatly admired his enemy's bravery. The regimental battle followed the course of the duel, the Americans emerging victorious.

I remember the excitement I felt whenever Uncle Jack would let me run my fingers gingerly over the sharp edge of the sword he had obtained in the defeat of the Mexican colonel or even hold the weapon on my knees.

Later in the war, Colonel Hays won a national reputation by storming Independence Hill and the Bishop's Palace at Monterey; while on the march to Mexico City his military skill and brilliance were demonstrated once more.

On the conclusion of the war Uncle Jack went to San Francisco where he served as sheriff. When Franklin Pierce was elected president in 1853, my father and Colonel Jack, neither of them then aware that they were to be brothers-in-law, went to Washington for the inauguration of the Mexican War general. It was said that the handsome figure and the fame of young Jack Hays drew about him such a crowd at the official reception that there was danger of his "stealing the show." The two Californians were cordially received and each was rewarded with office: Colonel Hays was made surveyor general of California; my father, collector of the port of San Francisco.

The latter appointment was made on personal as well as political grounds. My father was held in high regard; the many honors which came to him were unsought. Nevertheless, the President felt himself peculiarly indebted to him. When Pierce, as a young officer in the Mexican War, came under fire for the first time, he was seized with that fear to which the bravest men have often confessed. My father, who had broader vision and sounder balance than any other man with whom I have ever come in contact, talked to him, joked with him, and restored his confidence. This good service the President never forgot.

When Colonel Jack gave up his position as surveyor general, he retired to the ranch he had bought near Oakland.

My father also owned several acres there, which he one day exchanged for an old bobtailed white horse. As Oakland grew and prospered and the land increased in value, I tried to figure out the price he would have received from the sale of this land. Compared with the value of the old bobtailed horse, it was unbelievable that it could have mounted to such a sum. Since that time I've never regarded a bobtailed horse with any great degree of affection.

Uncle Jack was not allowed to remain quiet on his ranch. Within a few years the people of Nevada asked him to come to their relief against the Piute Indians who were plundering and murdering. The soldiers of the regular army were unfamiliar with Indian warfare and consequently not trained to deal with the Piutes. Colonel Hays was made commander in chief. Using the strategy he had learned from the Indians themselves, he succeeded in ambushing and exterminating the Piute warriors.

In gratitude for his services, the people of Nevada presented him with a handsome silver service, and at the same time sent to my aunt a beautiful black horse named Piute, which I often rode at the ranch.

During my boyhood, every country place was called a ranch, but my uncle's was really a ranch de luxe. Although in extent not comparable with some of the enormous ranches of the day, it held cattle and, of course, many horses. With its alternating hills and wild ravines, it was an ideal place for a boy with an adventurous spirit. I suppose my lifelong desire for exploration and discovering was transmitted to me from my pioneer ancestry and was fostered

A CHINESE PLACER MINER

by those days spent in the woods with only my young brothers and cousins as companions.

I roamed over the hills of that section until I had learned every foot of them. In fact, I knew them so thoroughly that, when I was fifteen, I was able to guide my father, then a regent of the University of California, and a committee looking for a new site for the university foundation over the slopes of what is now Berkeley. The university was moved there in 1875.

Interesting people came constantly to my uncle's ranch. Outstanding among them was Captain John C. Freaner, who had served in Texas under Colonel Hays. He and Uncle Jack taught my brothers and myself, as boys of five or six, to ride and later to shoot and generally to take care of ourselves in what was still a frontier country.

Bravery was one thing Captain Freaner insisted upon, and ingeniously devised various tests which he never would permit us to flunk. For example, he would leave his pipe, hat, or some similar object in a graveyard located a mile or so down a lonely canyon. Then he would send us boys out into the night each in turn and quite alone, to retrieve the article he had purposely abandoned there. It took all our physical courage to accomplish this feat.

Explorers' blood was so strong in my brothers and myself that there was always a rivalry as to which of us had been in the greatest number of counties in California. After our summer vacation, we would compare notes as to our relative standing in this competition. The entrance into each new county provided us with a thrill as great as that which must have come to Balboa, the famous stowaway from Spain, when from the heights of Darien he first saw the great Pacific.

Our common ambition to visit the entire fifty counties then included in California was not realized by any of us during our younger days. Even when we went east to school we were still immature enough to keep tabs on the different states through which we passed on our trips to college and back. My brothers used to accuse me of taking circuitous routes in order to add an additional state or two to my record. Very likely this was true, and time has not weakened my wanderlust. I have been many times in every state in the Union, and in nearly every section of every state.

A large part of my vacation was customarily spent at the Fairfax ranch in Marin County, California. There, when I was eleven or twelve, I learned to lead the life of a typical young cowboy, which naturally included herding cattle and busting broncos.

Charles Snowden Fairfax, my father's friend and later mine, was the lineal descendant of the famous Virginia earl whose offspring can claim the unique distinction of holding the only "American peerage" ever recognized by this government. Preferring to be known as a plain American citizen, "Uncle Charley" had waived the right of his title. I was greatly influenced by him and he was one of my first heroes. It was on a trip with him that I killed my first deer.

Possessed of the same type of adventuresome spirit as Colonel Hays, the baron—as he was commonly called—had been captain of a company serving under my uncle in the Piute War. His patrician origin was displayed not only in his handsome and athletic appearance, but in his nobility of character.

On one occasion Fairfax was stabbed in the back by a man who bore him a grudge. As he fell to the ground, onlookers thought he was mortally wounded. Nevertheless, he raised himself painfully on his elbow, drew his pistol, pointed it at his assailant, and said, "I curse you for your cowardly attack, but I spare your life for the sake of your wife and children!" Thereupon he fired the pistol into the air.

Fairfax lived some years longer, although without doubt the wounds received at this time hastened his death.

California youngsters of those days took to horse and gun almost instinctively. Shooting was my favorite sport, while riding was only a method of locomotion. Our chief diversion during the summer vacations was to make up an exploring party. Three or four of us would load a horse with grub, blankets, and guns, then hike out to the hills twelve or fifteen miles away and camp there for days at a time. We would kill quail and sometimes even a deer, and fish the brooks for trout.

These pursuits led us far and wide, and I thus learned to rough it with fair success before I was fifteen years old. It was fortunate for me that I acquired early in life the art of taking care of myself, because in later years the practice of my profession involved much hardship in various parts of the world where the novice was, to say the least, out of place. I suppose I never was a tenderfoot.

It must have been in 1870 that I made the long trip of five days and nights by stagecoach from San Francisco to Los Angeles to visit my schoolmate, Billy Fitzhugh. The stage, suspended on leather straps and drawn by the traditional six horses, traveled continuously day and night. The coach was so heavy that the horses had to be changed every ten or fifteen miles.

Los Angeles was then a village of about five thousand inhabitants, largely Mexican, and the county itself had a population of only fifteen thousand.

Billy Fitzhugh, two other boys, and I hired a pack horse and went camping on the old Wilson ranch, a Spanish grant on part of which Pasadena now stands. The only sign of civilization along the route was the San Gabriel Mission.

One morning I rose early and set out alone to try to find some quail for lunch. The hunting ground was a small canyon, just about where the Pony Express Museum now stands. I had not gone far into the gulch before I chanced upon a bear. Thoroughly startled, I raced back to camp shouting, "Bear! Bear! Bear!" and the four of us immediately sought safety in the nearest trees. We never discovered in which tree the bear found refuge.

The best trip of my boyhood came when I was fifteen and my young brother Bill was thirteen. Our father had gone east on business, leaving us in the care of an aunt. With school just out, forty dollars in our pockets, and the whole summer before us, we felt truly that the world was ours.

First we went to visit General David Douglass at his ranch in San Joaquin County, where we had often been before. Since neither of us had ever seen the Calaveras grove of big trees, which was about forty miles away, we decided one day to have a look at it.

My brother Bill owned a fast roan mustang with one white eye, named Kitty. He made sure of being her sole user by teaching her to buck all strangers who might attempt to ride her. I had no horse of my own and had to borrow one for the week's trip. Near the Douglass ranch lived the Washington Trains, friends of our family, and from them I borrowed Silver, the old horse on which the Train children had learned to ride. Silver was an unfortunate choice; he was not only stupid and nearsighted, but he was subject to splints and the periodic necessity for repairs delayed us considerably.

When I went to catch and saddle him one morning there was Kitty grazing peacefully, but no Silver was to be seen. I might have thought he had been stolen except that I knew no one could possibly want such a horse. First I called and then I hunted and finally I located him. He had started across the field towards a beckoning haystack and walked straight into a muddy ravine about fifteen feet deep. There he was at the bottom—unhurt, but a sorry sight. It took the better part of the morning to hoist Silver out with ropes and get him rehabilitated. Then Bill whirled away down the trail, shouting tactlessly over his shoulder, "Old plug!"

All my heel thumpings and my exhortations of "Get up, Silver!" were of little avail. I was not riding a horse like Piute. I gripped the double-barreled shotgun (from which my father had made me remove one lock) in such a furious temper that in later years Bill used to say he believed I would certainly have peppered him if I could have caught up with him. But he and Kitty took care of that. By evening my temper had cooled enough for us to make camp together peaceably. A ride of fifty miles in one day may have accounted for my diminished rage; but I have never liked a white-eye since.

Occasionally we slept under the skies or in abandoned prospectors' shanties; more often miners, hotelkeepers, or livery stable men gave us shelter. The fame of our wanderings had preceded us and, at every stop, a hearty welcome awaited us. Everyone was friendly and helpful and glad to show these two youngsters what free-handed western hospitality was like. Though we offered to pay our way, our forty dollars remained practically intact; seldom was money accepted for lodging or food.

Our trip, which we had expected would last the usual five or six days, kept lengthening as we were lured on and on by the prospect of new adventures. At a leisurely pace, stopping here for a day and there for a day when we discovered something that interested us, or when Silver needed to be repaired, we rode through the Sierra Nevadas and the district now known as the Bret Harte country.

I came to know Bret Harte a little later when he was secretary to General E. F. Beale. In spite of his apparently intimate knowledge of conditions in the mining camps, Harte had in reality but little firsthand knowledge of the scenes of his stories. Yet he was able to construct a character almost from the inflection of a voice or make up a tale from the barest hint of a plot.

Leaving the mining camps behind, and jogging along through the wild mountains, we finally penetrated into the yet trackless Yosemite Valley and were, so far as we could tell, the only visitors there in 1870. Now the Yosemite is visited yearly by more people than the half million who were then living on the Pacific coast. Our food supply was derived mainly from the game we were able to shoot, and from the fish we caught without flies, in the Indian fashion.

Fortunately for me we were not quite alone when we moved on to the Mariposa grove of big trees. There I met with misfortune. I fell into the mill race at Clark's sawmill, and, although I could swim, the water was running too fast for a boy's strength. While rapidly being carried into eternity, I was fished out by some of the men working the mill.

Old Galen Clark, its owner, had been the discoverer of the Mariposa Grove. When I visited the Yosemite with President Taft in 1909, I found Clark still living in the valley. He was ninety or over and still sound enough of mind to remember my narrow escape from drowning.

Our expedition carried us even into Nevada. The summer was now nearly over, and we had traveled about seven hundred miles. Our father had returned from the East and discovered that we were missing. After weeks had passed without word from us, he became alarmed and notified Wells, Fargo Express Company messengers to be on the alert. We were making a leisurely return trip, quite unconscious of our family's distress. In fact, by that time we had entirely forgotten we had borrowed Silver for a week and had been gone nearly all summer. Word that our father was scouring the country finally reached us and we streaked for home as fast as our horses could carry us.

The expedition was invaluable to us both. We had been taught by actual experience how to forage for food in wild places, how to take care of the horses upon whom our safety depended, and most important, how to meet on friendly terms all sorts and conditions of men.

It also gave me my first intimate knowledge of how a real gold mine was operated. So fascinated was I by my first descent into this mine, called Hite's Cove, that I persuaded the owner to allow me to spend several days there, during which time I went down frequently. Hite was said to have married an Indian squaw out of gratitude, because she had rescued him when he had been overtaken by a heavy snow-storm. She was also reported to have shown him the outcroppings of the vein he subsequently developed with so much profit.

Prior to this experience my mining education, though begun at an early age, had been rudimentary. When I was eleven years old, I had gone to pay one of my first visits to General Douglass. Adjoining the general's ranch were gold-placer washings, which a group of Chinese were patiently working over. Because of racial discrimination, the industrious and peaceable Chinaman was not allowed to work virgin gravels; he was limited to reworking the ground already gone over by the masterful white man. While there was no written law, the custom of the camps was sufficient to define his rights. The Chinese miner toiled away unobtrusively in the corners allotted him, but often, through dogged persistence, he made what was to him a modest fortune.

I watched these Chinese working along the streams tributary to the San Joaquin River, and, of course, I could not rest until I had duly inspected the washings and had tried my hand at a little panning. I had not been at it long before my excited gaze encountered some gold dust in the bottom of the pan, and I vociferously acclaimed my great discovery with all the enthusiasm of James Marshall himself. The picture of that eventful moment was later evoked for me by the imagination of the New York *Globe* cartoonist, Camillus Kessler, in his book, *At the Bottom of the Ladder*. It may not be a faithful portrait, but I am sure the air of jubilation is by no means overdrawn.

Thus it was that I became a "miner." As I washed the gravel, sometimes finding as much as fifty cents' worth of gold, dreams of fortune filled my head. I imagined myself a real miner, hiring hordes of Chinese to work for me. I was caught by the lure of gold.

CHAPTER THREE

In Pursuit of an Education

*W*hen I was sixteen my father decided that I should go east to school. He thought, and justly so, that I was growing altogether too provincial. Although at the time I was reluctant to leave the West, I can now see the wisdom of his decision and have become a firm believer in the advisability of sending Westerners to eastern colleges, and vice versa.

During the summer of 1871 I was packed off in charge of an uncle, Colonel Sprague. In was an exciting day for me when I boarded a train on the new transcontinental railway line which had been completed only two years before. We traveled slowly, so slowly, indeed, that it was not a difficult stunt for an agile boy to jump off near the head of the train and catch on to the platform of the rear car. Few modern improvements had as yet been introduced on the railroads. Old-fashioned hand brakes were still in use, while the wood-burning locomotives had huge cone-shaped smokestacks.

I was delighted by the fact that the conductor of our train had been scalped by Indians. It was not, of course, the "massacre" scalping which would have taken off the entire scalp; it was merely the removal from the head of the small round piece of epidermis, which signified victory in open warfare.

Traveling across the continent was an interesting and an involved process. The trip to Washington took seven days. We changed trains at Ogden and again at Omaha. From there we crossed the Missouri River on a ferry to Council Bluffs, where the next train connection was made. We changed once more at Chicago. As we crossed the plains we could see in the distance an occasional herd of buffalo, while large herds of antelope galloped alongside the train for miles. Three times a day we stopped for meals. Since the train was often late, the passengers had worked up a fine appetite by the time an eating-station was reached. Frequently, just as we were well into our meal and eating as fast as possible, by some unaccountable arrangement the whistle would blow, the conductor would stick his head in at the station dining room door long enough to shout "All aboard!" and everyone would rush from the tables. I usually scrambled on to the train with a scalded throat but still clutching a piece of bread from which I resolutely refused to be separated.

I shall never forget the thrill I experienced soon after our arrival at Washington. My uncle took me to the White House and introduced me to President Grant. A Cabinet meeting had just been concluded and the members had not yet left. When I was presented to the President he turned to his brother-in-law, General Frederick Dent, and asked him if he did not recall my father from West Point days. General Dent replied that he remembered him only too well, because of a certain escapade in which both had been involved and which had very nearly caused their expulsion. The President then said to his Cabinet: "Gentlemen, if this young man's father had gone north instead of west, he would probably have the position I hold today."

In early October I was enrolled in the Hopkins Grammar School at New Haven to prepare for Yale. The very first day, during the morning recess, I was accosted by some eastern boys who, in typical schoolboy fashion, began to badger me about my part of the world. Although I looked and dressed as they did, something indefinable in my manner or speech made them feel that I was "different," since any deviation from the norm is always a challenge to the young. A boy named Jackson asked me whether I had seen the big trees of California; he had heard about them and demanded to know how large they were. I had visited the big trees many times since that first memorable trip with my brother Billy and had even measured some of them myself. I told him their exact dimensions. Since he had never seen a tree larger than an elm, he called me a liar. Like any true Californian, I promptly showed my resentment by thrashing him. Immediately after this, and before we had time to dust ourselves off, class was reassembled. I, the newcomer, was promptly reprimanded by the headmaster and expelled.

It is not difficult to imagine my humiliation. I walked the old Green for hours, not knowing what to do and afraid to write home of my disgrace. Finally, I decided to see Professor William P. Trowbridge, an old army friend of my father's who at this time was on the Yale faculty. After listening attentively and in silence to my story, he asked me whether I was positive I had done nothing to Jackson before he called me a liar. I assured him I was guiltless on that count. Professor Trowbridge then asked, "What would your father have done if you had not fought young Jackson because of the insult?"

"He wouldn't have liked it," I replied ingenuously.

Greatly to my relief, Professor Trowbridge not only agreed with me that I could not have acted differently but even went with me to the principal of the school, "Buck" Johnson, to whom he explained the situation. I was reinstated, but from then on the mere words, "big trees," could always be invoked as a *casus belli*. Nevertheless, I managed to keep my enthusiasm for my native state under such restraint that it never again got me into serious trouble at school.

Several of my college friends prepared at the old Hopkins Grammar School and one of the closest of them was Arthur Twining Hadley, later president of Yale. After graduating from Yale, we saw much of each other in Germany while he was studying at Berlin and I at Freiberg. Although often separated by thousands of miles, our friendship remained unbroken until his death in 1930.

Hadley was a man of extraordinary intellectual attainments and great versatility of mind. No one who knew him could forget his ready wit and his phenomenal stock of stories, gay and serious.

His memory was prodigious. He could quote pages verbatim from innumerable books. Facts of all sorts could be drawn at will from the storehouse of his mind. He knew, it seemed, every Yale graduate, and his ability to place a man, and remember his name and some especial characteristic or undergraduate attainment, added greatly to his popularity. Occasionally this memory proved embarrassing for others. Once, glancing over the pages of the *Yale Literary Magazine,* he saw an article on China. He went to his library, pulled down a book and demonstrated that much of the article was plagiarized. It was practically impossible to trick him in an argument. The wide knowledge he could bring to bear on any point made the less skillful man hesitant to enter into a debate.

Yet he was intellectually generous and always ready to listen to the other man's opinions. Unlike many minds capable of absorbing unlimited numbers of facts, he had the ability to relate and use them, he was imaginative as well as objective. Although he was one of our foremost economists, a director of railroads, and consulted by the great business men of the country, he was appreciative of literature and to the day of his death could read Latin and Greek as well as he could read English.

In spite of his memory, he was absent-minded; while he could recognize a man he had not seen for years, he was capable of passing his own wife on the street without recognizing her if he was deeply gripped in thought. In appearance he was quixotic and aware of the fact. His gestures were awkward, his body nervous. His voice was hesitant, strange, and often came to the ear as though from some throaty struggle. Yet once the listener had succumbed to the charm of the man, this was forgotten and, in spite of every handicap on the platform, generations of Yale graduates will testify that he was one of the greatest orators they have ever heard.

The Hadley home was always filled with undergraduates, mingling freely with great visitors from all over the world. Their Sunday midday dinners were famous and I have often sat at table there with bishops, politicians, undergraduates, athletes, ambitious young writers, and scholars. To these Mrs. Hadley added her amazing genius as a hostess. Adept at drawing her husband out and quite capable of silencing him if she thought he was running away with the party, she balanced the conversation and kept every guest a part of the scene. The closeness of President Hadley's contacts with undergraduates has perhaps not been generally realized. He often joined them in long walks over the Connecticut countryside, and where a mind or a personality interested him, he would talk hour on hour, stimulating, advising, always the friend and rarely the preceptor.

One incident that occurred in California, in 1901, illustrates Hadley's ability to make friends. I was spending the winter at Del Monte with my family and the Hadleys came to visit us for a few days before going to Los Angeles. I wanted them to stay a day longer than originally planned. Hadley said this would be impossible because he had to be in Los Angeles on a certain date to make connections with the train going east. I suggested his going over the coast road of the Southern Pacific, which, although completed from Del Monte south, was not yet open for traffic. He replied that he had already tried to make such an arrangement but without success.

J. A. Fillmore, the general manager of the railroad, was then in Monterey on his way south. I got in touch with him at once and asked whether he could take the Hadleys along on his private train. He promptly excused himself on the ground that, as he had already turned down so many applications, it would be impossible for him to make an exception in this case. Suspecting that what was really frightening him was the prospect of taking a college president in his private car, I reiterated my request, stressing the friendship we had formed when I was consulting engineer for the road in the eighties. So insistent was I that he finally agreed to take President and Mrs. Hadley with him.

When Fillmore returned, I asked him what sort of time he had had with Hadley. "Fill" was a diamond in the rough, who had worked his way up from the lowest position in the company to that of general manager, and he answered in his customary forceful way: "He's the damned best fellow I've met for a long time. We hit it off like that! As a matter of fact, he told me a lot of things about railroading I didn't know." This was indeed great praise for a practical railroad man to give one whose experience had been largely academic, even though he was the author of the best known text on railroads.

Every Yale man was proud of Hadley, and fond of repeating, among countless stories about him, his characterization of the Harvard man. Hadley had been one of the guests at a banquet of Harvard alumni when President Eliot wound up his speech by saying, "You can always tell a Harvard man."

Hadley said in his response: "I agree with Dr. Eliot perfectly. You can always tell a Harvard man, but you can't tell him much."

By autumn, 1873, I was ready for college, and entered Sheffield Scientific School of Yale University, known familiarly to all connected with it as "Sheff."At my father's insistence I had been given a good foundation in Latin and Greek, which would have qualified me to enter the academic class had I so desired. I was, indeed, as much interested in general and cultural subjects as in science. Geology, astronomy, botany, chemistry, physics, history, political economy, English, French, German, and, strangely enough, comparative philology were the main subjects in the Select Course in which I enrolled.

Mathematics was not stressed then as it is now. Even at Freiberg my stock of information on it was increased but little. That I should neglect a subject now considered such an integral part of engineering training may seem surprising, but my opinion has always been that too much emphasis is laid on higher mathematics for mining engineers.

Years later when I was serving on the staff at Sheffield as professor of mining—professor, indeed, for about twenty-four hours—I made this clear in my first talk to the students. I said: "Don't be discouraged because you cannot pass your examination in mathematics. That is not so important in mining engineering, but it is important in other kinds of engineering."

Later in faculty meeting I had an argument over the mining curriculum with some of the leading professors. They were especially desirous of maintaining a high standard of mathematics in that department. From long practical experience I was convinced that certain other subjects were much more important to the mining engineer than higher mathematics, though I realized that for mechanical, electrical, and civil engineering such knowledge was indispensable. After a long discussion on this subject, Professor Augustus Dubois, an old friend and member of my Yale society, addressed me as Professor Hammond. "That is all right, to call me professor at a meeting like this," I said. "But as soon as I leave the meeting I am no longer professor."

"Why?" asked another faculty member.

"Because a professor in mining is looked on with high contempt and suspicion by the practical engineers of the country."

Professor Dubois, a great mathematician and an authority on mechanical engineering, asked me, as consulting engineer of the famous Camp Bird mine, what I would do in case the hoisting works should burn down. Would I not require a knowledge of mathematics to determine the tensile strength of materials? Otherwise how could I have the hoisting works rebuilt?

I answered promptly: "I'll tell you what I'd do under those circumstances. I'd call up one of the big manufacturers of mining machinery in Denver, and say, 'Our headgear has burned down; am sending you the blueprints of the headgear and wish you'd let me know by phone how long it will take you to erect another, and what the cost will be.'" I then went on: "The consulting engineer of a mining property has experts whose duty it is to work out such problems for him, while he devotes his time to the development of ore reserves, the metallurgical treatment of ores, or the administration of the company's business."

I then addressed the chair, demanding, "President Hadley, what is your opinion of the importance of mathematics in the education of a mining engineer?"

He replied: "I am not an engineer and cannot give any firsthand opinion, but I recall a conversation I had some years ago with one of the great railroad executives of the country. I asked him which made the better railroad man, one who was proficient in mathematics or one who was well equipped in the Greek language. Much to my surprise he answered, 'The one who is well equipped in Greek, because he forgets the Greek sooner.'"

Although my views did not prevail with the Sheffield faculty, I had better luck later at Harvard. When I was chairman of the Board of Visitors for the Harvard Scientific School, this same question of mathematics came up and I was backed up in my opinion by other members of the Board, which included such noted mining engineers as B. B. Thayer, Rudolph Agassiz, Hennen Jennings, and Charles Perrin.

In my own undergraduate days, the academic life was concentrated, the faculty was limited but the professors were widely recognized authorities in their particular subjects. Many of them had received offers to go to other colleges, but they preferred to remain at Yale. Our classes were not large, and we became intimately acquainted with our teachers. Not a few of them called us by our first names, even occasionally letting a "Tom" or a "Jack" slip out in the classroom. We were guests in their homes—we knew their wives. Their daughters were our friends.

Some of these professors were great scholars, but forbidding, like Lounsbury; some were unorthodox, like Brewer. But as I recall them, they—most of them—seem to have had force and individuality and to have been able to win our attention and admiration in one way or another and to inspire interest in their subjects which continued long after graduation.

Noah Porter was president of Yale at the time. He served in that office from 1871 to 1886. I had great admiration and, in common with other students, a real affection for him: this, in spite of a most unfortunate experience.

During one winter vacation some of us whose homes were far away remained at New Haven. One evening there was a "quiet" celebration in my room in Divinity Hall. This was a new building and students of Sheff were eager to room there. On this particular night several of us had been indulging, perhaps not wisely but too well, in a concoction at that time popularly known as "Tom and Jerry." Perhaps it still is. We realized that we were in Divinity Hall and in deference to such a saintly atmosphere restrained our normal desire to "roughhouse."

The janitor evidently was acutely aware of the dignity of the building and determined to preserve it. We found him listening at the keyhole, and thought it better for him to get a close view of the proceedings. I was commissioned to climb over the transom and to drop down on him and take him unawares. This I did.

The door was then opened by my friends and the janitor was taken into the room and subjected to what he characterized as "considerable indignity." He immediately reported the matter to President Porter, who dismissed us from the building. It was a serious matter with us as we had gone to great expense to establish ourselves comfortably for what we thought would be two years' occupation.

However, the kindly president did not expel us from college as he undoubtedly would have been justified in doing, and I have always felt grateful to him for his forbearance.

The teacher who influenced me most at Yale was Francis A. Walker. He had been a general in the Civil War on the northern side. He was professor of political economy and history. His poise, breadth of view, and even his temperament made him an ideal for me. He developed my interest in broad questions of public policy. I worked hard in his courses and I have never lost this interest.

On the question of the war, he was invariably fair to both sides, preferring to treat the subject from the constitutional rather than the political angle. He was equally impartial on the tariff question as it stood in the seventies. It was, however, his masterly presentation and analysis of the effects of various economic policies that made me a supporter of a protective tariff. In the opinion of H. H. Powers, a recent writer, Francis Walker was the first to point out that the United States, with internal free trade and the protective boundary of a tariff, was an example of what Adam Smith meant by free trade.

Although geology was one of my subjects at Yale, chance first opened to my mind its fascinating possibilities. On one of my vacation trips home, a locomotive accident in Wyoming caused a delay of several hours. It so happened that Professor Joseph Leidy, geologist and paleontologist of the University of Pennsylvania, was on the train. He asked whether I would like to accompany him to a geological deposit of great interest near the point at which the train had stopped. Naturally, I accepted eagerly. He explained to me how the ages of geological formations are determined by the presence of certain fossils, and during the last two days of our journey continued his instructions in so stirring a fashion that geology became one of my favorite studies.

Also I became well acquainted with Professor James Dwight Dana, then the world's leading geologist and mineralogist. In my junior year, when John Tyndall, the English physicist, was his guest, Professor Dana made up a party to visit East Rock, a Gibraltar-like formation of trap rock near New Haven. Professor Tyndall, who prided himself on his renown as an Alpinist, attempted to climb the face of the rock, which rises precipitously two hundred feet from its base. After failing to accomplish the impossible ascent, he inquired how the inscription YALE '76, painted in letters so large as to be visible for a mile or more, could have been placed there.

I had been partially responsible for the inscription, so I explained to Professor Tyndall that a party of us had drawn lots to see who should be lowered by a rope from the top of the cliff to do the lettering, and the honor had fallen to me. After I had painted assiduously for an hour, one of the fellows went down to inspect progress. He reported that the painting was so bad he could not make out whether the letters spelled HELL or YALE, whereupon it was unanimously voted that I should be recalled. I made an ineffectual but not sincere protest. My successor apparently had more artistic ability, for he was allowed to finish, and the letters remained there for many years as a challenge to other classes. In his lecture that evening, Tyndall referred to the East Rock episode and turned it into a graceful compliment to Yale by saying that, in his effort to reach the heights, Yale was ever before him beckoning him on.

My last meeting with Professor Dana occurred in 1883 when he was visiting California. As I was particularly anxious to discuss with him certain geological questions connected with the genesis of ore deposits, I boarded the train some hours before it reached San Francisco and continued the journey with him. I would have considered his opinion ex cathedra but, like all great men, Professor Dana was extremely modest and told me that in an expression of opinion on that subject he would defer to me who had specialized in its study. He talked most interestingly of his first passage through the Sacramento Valley in 1841 on his way to join the Wilkes Expedition at the Pacific Ocean. Even at that early date, seven years before Marshall's discovery, Dana was on record as having expressed his belief in the existence of gold deposits in that part of California.

Thomas R. Lounsbury was another of the great teachers of his time. His profound scholarship, combined with keen literary appreciation, made him unusually successful in introducing generations of students to the varied excellencies of English and American literature. My deep and abiding love of Shakespeare is entirely due to him although I never stood in his good graces. "Tommy" was not a supporter of college athletics. All students who, like myself, had athletic ambitions were put into one section of the room, and were invariably treated as mentally inferior. Doubly handicapped by being an athlete and also slightly deaf, I fared badly.

I also fell under Lounsbury's displeasure for insisting on graduating with my class, in spite of having lost ten weeks through an injury received in the gymnasium. I managed to pass my examination with credit, but had no compliments from Tommy Lounsbury. I well remember his meeting James L. Houghteling and me the day after graduation. Addressing Jim, he said warmly, "Mr. Houghteling, I wish you every success in life; I predict great things for you." Then turning to me, he uttered gruffly: "Good day, Mr. Hammond." I never quite forgave him for the slight, although in later years he was cordial enough.

William Dwight Whitney was professor of German. He was brother of Josiah D. Whitney, Harvard professor of geology. Whitney certainly qualified for his position: he had won a competitive examination test for the best grammar published in German, and this grammar had been adopted and used by the schools of Berlin.

Professor Whitney also gave us courses in comparative philology, in which subject he ranked among the greatest authorities of his time. His controversy with Professor Max Müller, of Oxford, as to the origin of speech created wide comment among those interested in the subject.

Later, when I was a student in Germany, I met Professor Whitney in Dresden and enjoyed showing him the sights of that pleasant city, and particularly the art collections. One day we dropped in at a bierkeller for luncheon and Professor Whitney took the menu and studied it carefully. Now, I thought, I can safely leave the ordering to him and shall not have to use my stumbling German on the waiter. Much to Whitney's chagrin, however, and to my ill-concealed amusement, the waiter blandly but firmly refused to understand a word of the orders poured out to him. By employing the sign language and a few phrases in the vernacular, I made our wants known, and I did not lose the opportunity to impress solemnly upon my former professor the necessity for "getting close to the people" in order to learn their language.

All of our professors were not giants of intellect, of course, nor were they all popular. There were the "tough" ones along with the "easy" ones.

For example, there was a mathematics instructor named Wells.

At the end of my freshman year the class had its annual supper at Savin Rock, on the outskirts of New Haven, a resort which still lures the Yale undergraduate with shore dinners, and less conventional pleasures. We had heard that Wells was to leave Yale, which was a great relief as he was most difficult to satisfy and, moreover, was unpopular personally with the class. So, when I was asked to propose a toast at the supper, I said enthusiastically, "All's well that ends Wells."

The unfortunate aftermath was that Mr. Wells changed his mind and decided to remain at Yale. Naturally my standing with him was not improved when he heard of the toast, as he inevitably did.

And there were the "soft," or "cinch," courses in those days. I dare say there still are. Among our most pleasantly disposed friends were John H. Niemeyer, professor of drawing, and William H.

Brewer, whose actual title I do not remember but who struck me as being professor of "general information."

Brewer we admired because of his really broad knowledge on many subjects, but we were especially delighted by his funny stories. He told the same ones year after year, and we naturally encouraged him even though they were chestnuts. In his younger days he had been one of two geologists to examine our western country. In fact, Mount Brewer is named for him. He had many interesting tales to tell about his experiences. One of his favorites was about a soldier who had been stationed for many years at Yuma, Arizona, one of the hottest spots on earth. The soldier died. Later a letter was received by his friends at the post asking them to express him his blankets to hell.

Our class heard this story from Brewer for two years and when, in our senior year, he started telling it again, it was too much for us and we raised our fingers to indicate that this was the third time. Brewer saw the joke, laughed, and said: "Well, my young friends, it's a good story anyhow and this will be the last year you will hear it, but I am going to keep it up on succeeding classes."

Professor Brewer remained a favorite for many years. Even when he was seventy or over, he rode an old bicycle around the streets of New Haven. Years later when I was in Denver, he stopped off at the Denver Country Club and I gave him a big dinner. He loved it. It gave him a chance to tell his favorite yarn once more.

I am not only the world's worst freehand drawer, I cannot even draw with a ruler. I was particularly grateful to the liberality of Niemeyer who passed me in freehand drawing. The class had been told to submit a drawing of an eye and an ear. My exhibit was the most amazing one shown; in fact, when I took it to Niemeyer he said, "Mr. Hammond, you have failed to indicate which is the eye and which is the ear. Would you mind marking each one so that I can distinguish between them?" It was fortunate for me that he had a sense of humor.

A few years ago Rube Goldberg, who is a Californian, wrote an article for the *Saturday Evening Post* in which he told how he became an artist. He said that his father was averse to his studying drawing as he did not believe in it. Goldberg said, "Father, how would you like me to become an engineer like John Hays Hammond?" His father said, "That would suit me fine." Goldberg went to the University of California and registered in engineering, but instead of studying engineering he studied drawing—at least so he wrote me years afterwards.

I said to him, "How did you ever think you could learn drawing from engineering?" and told him the story of my freehand drawing in Niemeyer's class. People have an idea that an engineer should be a great drawer and that business men should be great mathematicians, but fortunately for some of them, this is not always so.

The smaller size of the college in my time naturally influenced its social and athletic life, as well as its academic studies. I understand that with the development of the new College Plan, splitting into smaller social groups, there is a return of some of the delightful intimacy that we enjoyed, and since men from "Academic" and "Sheff" are now rooming under the same roofs a greater unity is being achieved. We knew intimately almost everyone in both schools, including the faculties and the heads of the colleges.

In the years of contact with various schools and colleges after my graduation from Yale, it seemed to me that this intimacy was vanishing from American education. I have always thought that as much if not more can be learned through friendly conversation with men of intelligence than from any library in the world. President Hopkins, of Amherst, well defined this idea when he said, "The ideal college consists of a log of wood with an instructor at one end and a student at the other." It is encouraging to see that in many colleges other than Harvard and Yale—where Mr. E. S. Harkness by his gifts has made the new housing program possible—the small seminar course, often conducted in the professor's home or over a table in the most informal manner, is bringing back this free exchange of ideas between the great teachers and their students. Too much cannot be done in this direction.

Partly the problem of formality has arisen through the mushroom growth of our colleges. Simultaneously another difficulty occurs. Entirely too many boys go to college who never ought to be within the gates. They have no idea of what they want. Many are seeking social prestige, fame in athletics, or the benefits they feel college contacts will bring them later in business life. During my long experience in employing graduates of various colleges, English boys in South Africa and Americans here, I have found them often ridiculously unable to adjust themselves to practical circumstances and utterly unprepared to undertake what seems to me to be their actual education. The source of this unfitness lies in the trivial, I believe, aims they harbored in their academic careers.

I have found that students of the technical schools take their education more seriously and are not so disposed to attend recitations without attention. Requirements for admission and graduation in professional schools—engineering, law, medicine, and so on—are nearly always much stiffer than in other institutions and the tuition is much more costly.

But my opinion is that even in technical schools a certain amount of time should be given to a study of the humanities. I have never been particularly interested in the controversies over requirements of Latin and Greek in a curriculum and I do not think that one should concentrate on a study of either of them. But I have never regretted the time I devoted to these subjects. In Russia I was amused to find that my college Greek—alas! largely forgotten—proved of practical value since Greek characters are used in the Russian language. Moreover, the ability to trace the meaning of unfamiliar words through their Latin or Greek roots has been a decided pleasure to me and has stimulated my interest in all kinds of reading. To be dogmatic, the broader one lays the foundation, the higher one can raise the monument to achievement. Broad culture not only enables one to understand more thoroughly the miner or the Pullman porter, but also to enjoy the conversation of wise, witty, well-educated people and to know better the great minds of the past through their works.

By far the most important part of a college education is the interest created by the professors in the various subjects. A professor or a lecturer recognized nationally or internationally as an authority on his subject can command attention and effectively supplement the work of the young instructor. I can think of no more worthy philanthropy, no more urgent and pleasurable duty for the man of standing and wide experience than to pass on his knowledge to the young. Lecturing in colleges is the most practical means of accomplishing this.

Today, many of the collegiate tourist lecturers have axes to grind. All shades of opinion could be expressed if outstanding financiers, executives, politicians, medical and other professional men were invited and demanded by the colleges. This seems to me a healthy antidote for so-called academic license—a matter which college trustees might well include among their responsibilities.

No one attitude should continually and unchallenged hold the floor in any college course. A radically-minded professor might well conduct a course in history or economics, but only so long as other attitudes may simultaneously be expressed. Particularly in the teaching of such controversial subjects as economics, the perspective in the presentation should be as broad as possible.

Few facts are sure, and all attitudes are debatable. And controversy soundly launched is the best possible means of teaching one to think. Beyond the actual knowledge college can give a man, if it can expose him thoroughly to many types of men and to many casts of belief, if it can stimulate and accelerate his processes of thought, it has been of inestimable value to him. It has given him the equipment with which to go out into life and learn.

I had been at the Hopkins Grammar School with many of my Yale classmates and may perhaps be allowed to boast that, with the exception of Ned Ryerson, I had passed the highest entrance examination. I had also been on several of the athletic teams, so that I was assured of election to a club. I heard that the Chicago fellows had gone to Sigma Delta Chi, and as I thought it would be a fine thing to know some Midwesterners well, I went along with them. Later, because of the monastic character of the life at the club building where I lived during my senior year, I suggested the name by which this fraternity is now known: "The Cloister."

It was then at 36 Elm Street, an old brownstone house with a long flight of steps going from the sidewalk to the door. One day I hired an old plug and started riding him up the steps, which were crowded with the boys. They scattered in all directions. I had no difficulty in getting the horse up the steps, but when I started to back him down the trouble began. I finally had to slide off him! When the boys accused me of becoming an eastern tenderfoot, I replied that horses were "more versatile in the West."

The various clubs ate at different restaurants, or at least had separate dining rooms as was the case at the place on Orange Street where we ate. This was the scene of the provocation of the fight made famous by William Howard Taft in an article he wrote for one of the Yale magazines.

One day when I was calling on President Roosevelt, he said, "I don't think I should have a man like you here at the White House." I asked "Why?" supposing he referred to my connection with the Jameson Raid.

"Taft told me this morning about a fight which you refereed at Yale. Of course, I take no stock in fights. What was it?"

I repeated the story to him. The fight occurred in my senior year between James L. Houghteling and George Creighton Webb. Webb was president of the Yale Athletic Association, of which I was secretary; Houghteling was editor of one of the college papers.

Houghteling had officially commented unfavorably on the activities of the association. I upbraided him for this, and jokingly made the statement that Webb had threatened to whip the entire editorial staff, if provoked by further unfair criticisms. Houghteling said, "That is a lie! Webb never made such a threat."

Unfortunately, one of Webb's brothers in an adjoining room overheard Houghteling's remark and went immediately to report it to Creighton. Creighton then threatened to horsewhip Houghteling publicly. Finally, Chester Dawes and Walker Blaine, who greatly enjoyed a little diversion in the way of a fight, prevailed upon Webb to accompany them to my room in the Cloister, where Houghteling also roomed. I heard of the plan a few hours before the appearance of Webb, with his two seconds. As I had been a faithful pupil of Lett Dole, I was able to give Houghteling a few points in boxing, but he did not seem to avail himself of these lessons when the fight actually took place. I was induced to act as referee. Both opponents were large men, but had no knowledge whatever of boxing. After a half-hour during which no damage was done, Webb, somewhat out of breath, said, "Mr. Houghteling, I am here to give you satisfaction."

"On the contrary, Webb," I said, "he is here to give you satisfaction."

Then Webb said, "We are here to fight according to Marquis of Queensberry rules."

"No," I told him, "you are here to fight according to my rules, and if you don't finish soon I will put you both out as I have to hurry to a recitation. I haven't many cuts left."

In the end both had black eyes, Houghteling did not apologize, and they had to go into hiding until they were more presentable, as it was of supreme importance to keep the faculty from discovering this disgraceful row.

President Roosevelt laughed and said, "I agree with you; that is the worst boxing I ever heard of. As a matter of fact, they should both have been expelled for such a bad exhibition."

Houghteling became one of the leaders of the younger generation of businessmen in Chicago. As to Webb's valor there can be no question, since he later distinguished himself as a staff officer in the Spanish-American War. He received letters of commendation from many generals and one in particular from General Joseph Wheeler, who said Webb was one of the bravest men he had ever known. During one of the battles before Santiago, Webb went about his duties in apparent unconcern although the enemy's bullets were flying all about him. Wheeler said this was the most courageous act it had ever been his pleasure to witness.

It must not be assumed that all our time at Yale was spent in fighting. Nevertheless, a recent Yale football victory over Harvard reminded me of how I quite accidentally started my first revolution. The Town and Gown riots are famous at New Haven; there have been many of them through the years. The relations between the students and the townspeople are not always cordial, and often break into fisticuffs around the time of the big games. In 1875, for the first time in many years we beat Harvard at baseball in New Haven, and we beat them with a disabled team; several of our men were not in condition as the result of a hard game played the week before.

THE STEPS OF "THE CLOISTER"—YALE 1876

Copyright Secured.   Photographed by H. Buchholz, Springfield, Mass.

YALE UNIVERSITY CREW,
Champions of 1873.

Henry Meyer.   Willis F. McCook.   Herbert G. Fowler. *Bow.*
  '73   Jeremiah Day.   Julian Kennedy. '76 R. J. Cook. '74
      '73   S. S. S.   '76
                    Stroke & Capt.

Yale celebrated the victory by building a big bonfire on the old campus. This was not only against the rule of the college, but also against the law of the town. I had nothing do with the bonfire part of it, as I had been at a dance and had gone to take the Mitchell girls home.

On my way back to the Cloister I passed the campus. There was a great commotion and out of curiosity I went across the street to see what was happening. There I saw an officer—"a peeler," we called them—reading the riot act to a lot of the boys.

I remembered this peeler very well; I had had a little disagreement with him after our freshman dinner. I reached the campus just in time to hear him say, "Did some one of you men call me a liar?"

No one replied, so I stepped up to him and said: "Yes, I called you a liar. You *are* a liar."

At that he grabbed me. I hit him on the chin and he keeled over.

The policemen patrolling that section then came running and immediately there was a riot. I was grabbed at each arm by a policeman. They began pushing me through the crowd, waving their pistols.

I said, "You damn fools, put those guns up, someone will get shot." By the time they got me across the Green my new frock coat was badly torn. A big crowd of students followed us, and soon the cry "Yale! Yale!" went up. Just as we got near the New Haven jail Durbin Horne, a quiet kind of fellow, came up and asked, "Jack, what is happening?"

I said, "These fellows have arrested me."

Horne said, "I will go bail for you." This was amazing, as Durb was close with his money.

He protested to the officers; they paid no attention, but opened the door to the back cell of the jail and shoved Durb in with me. He argued loudly, but it made no difference. Within an hour the whole jail was full of Yale men. It was hard luck for them that I had come along the campus just when I did.

Along towards midnight college professors and many of the alumni who were in town for the game came to the jail. Some of them were among the best lawyers in New York. They came to use their influence for us.

The following morning we were all haled into court and fined $8.29. I have never known to this day just how the judge arrived at the twenty-nine cents.

Our social life in the seventies was informal, as a rule, interesting, and intellectually stimulating.

It was rare for students to leave New Haven during term time; the week-end habit came with the advent of the automobile. The atmosphere was convivial, and it is decidedly a moot question whether at that time there was more or less drinking than there is at present. According to my recollection, hard liquor was rarely used, the chief indulgence being in beer and ale. Excessive drinking was invariably frowned upon by college sentiment, and it was unheard of for students under the influence of liquor to be allowed to participate in social functions at which ladies were present.

When there were no ladies in the group we went to Moriarty's. Moriarty and his wife were Welsh, I think, although the name sounds Irish enough. They were both huge in size. The old gentleman liked to sit around and tell us stories, while we drank beer and ate Welsh rabbits and grilled sardines. It was a restaurant then but, of course, has since become a club and "Mory's" is still known for its food and ale. In our day the famous convivial "green cup," fortunately, had not been devised.

Most of the girls with whom we talked and walked and danced were the daughters of professors and of the gentler citizens of "The Town"—among them Miss Delia Lyman, the Misses Trowbridge, Miss Sargent, and the Mitchell girls, one of whom later married Ned Ryerson. We had a small dancing club, some sixteen couples. On Saturday nights we had dances that we called "Germans." These were held at the girls' homes. On such an occasion the young lady who was hostess did the cooking herself, helped by the other girls. It was entertainment in the simplest and most gracious fashion.

Among the houses we visited, one of the most interesting was the Mitchell home at Edgewood. Donald Grant Mitchell, who wrote *Reveries of a Bachelor* under the nom de plume of Ik Marvel, was then enormously popular and perhaps lent a special aura of romance to the household. Mr. Mitchell was simple and genial. He dressed informally and liked to go out and putter in his garden in the most unconventional old clothes. One of my classmates once went to the house on horseback to call on one of the daughters. Not recognizing Mr. Mitchell in his gardening clothes, the boy threw the reins to him and asked him to hold the horse. Mitchell did this and my friend, when he left, handed him a quarter. The famous writer kept his silence—and the quarter.

The boys of the club were so intimate with the families of the girls that the parents would allow us to escort them to any of the dances or other entertainments.

Of course, the proms were held at the university and were slightly more formal, although we danced mostly waltzes and square dances. One of the strangest experiences I ever had at a college dance was at a junior prom.

Among my college friends was Elijah Thien Foh Laisun, a Chinese in the class below me. Although we knew each other fairly well, I was somewhat taken aback when Laisun asked if I would be kind enough to help escort his sisters, then studying at a Connecticut private school, to the prom. Naturally, I agreed to do what I could to entertain them but inwardly I felt considerable embarrassment—such is the superself-consciousness of a boy of that age—in making myself responsible for them. For moral support I inveigled another chap into standing by me.

When the sisters arrived, we were in thorough consternation. There was no doubt that they were pretty, but, dressed as they were in colorful Chinese costume of embroidered slippers and jackets, trousers, headdresses, and all, it was inevitable for them to be the cynosure of all student eyes. Obviously my friends were enjoying my all-too-apparent discomfiture.

As soon as the dancing began, the young ladies asked to be excused for a few minutes. After a truly uncomfortable wait, they reappeared in American evening dresses. As the strains of a beautiful waltz filled the air, my friend and I bowed dutifully to our partners and swung into the dance. I rather fancied myself as a waltzer. At the first step my spirits rose with a bound, and before we had circled the room it was obvious to all bystanders that the sisters were perfect dancers. In no time they were besieged. Joyfully I claimed a prior right, and it was only with much reluctance that I relinquished my partners for an occasional dance with someone else.

The Chinese girls had been thoroughly posted in the type of conversation that appealed to college boys. They knew the names of the captains of the baseball nine, the crew, and the football team. In fact, they were so well informed about athletics and school activities that it is little wonder they were popular.

Laisun himself came to Freiberg to study mining the year after I went there. He had graduated from Yale with high honors and was, in addition, the class poet. At Freiberg also he was an excellent student and, after his graduation, passed on to a distinguished career in China. I received an occasional letter from him for a few years; I then lost all track of him.

More than fifty years later, Dr. Wu, son of an old friend, Wu Ting-Fang, was minister to Washington as his father had been before him. I once asked him whether by any remote possibility he had ever heard of Laisun. He smiled. "He was my first cousin. He died just a few years ago." This was indeed a long shot out of four hundred million Chinese.

College life for me, then, was a pleasant mélange of books, professors, comradeships, social diversions, and athletics. At Hopkins Grammar School I had been captain of the baseball team and had given Walter Camp, three classes behind me, his first education in baseball. I continued athletics at Yale, spending some time in track events and playing as captain on the Sheff football and baseball teams. The effort involved was not so great in those days as it is today when athletics are overemphasized and commercialized. I had much free time for other activities.

The rowing situation was an interesting one in my day, and the banner period of Yale rowing commenced in the latter part of my college years. The races were six-oar races: there was no coxswain; the steering was done by the bow oar. Yale had consistently lost up to '73.

The '72 Yale crew was one of the worst I have ever seen and Yale was badly beaten. Bob Cook, a freshman, rowed No. 3 in that race.

After this defeat, President Porter was persuaded to grant Cook a three months' leave of absence, so that he could go to England and study the English stroke at Oxford and Cambridge.

Bob Cook is the greatest figure in the history of Yale rowing. His father was a prosperous farmer in Fayette, Pennsylvania, and strenuously opposed the idea of his coming to Yale. The boy was very poor, since the only financial assistance he had was what his mother could manage to give him.

The expenses of the trip to England were made up by contributions given by Bob's friends. I was one of those friends, though still at Hopkins Grammar School, and was glad to contribute in a small way. Many helped, even to the extent of pawning their personal belongings or raising loans on the furniture in their rooms.

When Bob returned from England in April, 1873, he was made captain of the Yale crew and retained this position during '74, '75, and '76. Since he had overstayed his leave, he was dropped from the class of '75 and joined '76, as he said, "in order to promote Yale's success in rowing."

At first Bob had much difficulty in getting Yale to adopt the new stroke he had learned in England. He did all the coaching himself, but there was so much opposition to the stroke that the freshman crew sent outside and hired a professional coach. However, Yale varsity crew won in '73.

The '74 race, held at Saratoga, will never be forgotten by Yale men of that time. The distance was three miles. Yale had perfected the Cook stroke by then, and Yale men were confident of victory. When the crews reached the two-mile mark it was signaled to the large crowd at the finishing line that Yale was ahead. Under ordinary circumstances this would mean that the race was a walkover for Yale, as the advantage of the slower Yale stroke left the crew comparatively fresh for the finishing spurt. After several minutes the crews reached the finishing line—and no Yale boat in sight. It was not until some time afterwards that Yale, with a crippled crew, arrived. This is the story I have often heard from my close friend George L. Brownell ("Browny"), who rowed bow on the Yale crew.

He said that Yale was rowing the Cook stroke and taking things easy, and was leading at the end of the second mile. The Harvard boat came close alongside and Bob Cook yelled tauntingly to Richard Dana, captain of the Harvard crew, "You better come up to Yale and learn how to row."

As the rudder of the Yale boat passed, the bow oarsman of Harvard struck it with his oar; this broke the rudder and caused the Yale boat to veer sharply, snapping Brownell's oar and putting Yale out of the race. Cook then called to Bob Cornell, captain of Columbia, "Go ahead and win the race." Columbia did.

In those days, as stated before, steering was done by the bow oar. It is difficult to believe that the damage was done deliberately by the Harvard oarsman, but the majority of Yale men believed that to be the case. There is no question but that Yale would have been several lengths ahead if the accident had not occurred. Yale men were convinced of the superiority of the Cook stroke. Indeed, it would seem the Harvard men shared that opinion. In spite of every effort made by the Yale students and alumni at Saratoga to have the race rowed again, even offering a large purse to be donated to some charity by the winner, Harvard refused.

Yale lost to Harvard in '75, and as I recollect, out of eight or ten crews, came in near the last of the procession. But in '76 Yale won again, and in that same year Cook stroked the four-oared crew which won the International Race at the Centennial Exposition in Philadelphia.

Harvard won from Yale in '78 and '79 (the Yale crews were not one hundred per cent Cook crews); then Yale won in '80 and '81. But there was a rebellion against the English stroke, and in '82 and '83 Yale rowed what was known as the donkey engine stroke, losing both races.

Cook coached in '84 and Yale won. Then there was another rebellion against the English stroke, led by Louis Hull who coached the '85 crew, which lost.

In '86 Cook came back into power and won every race against Harvard up to and including '98, with the exception of '91. There was no race in '96; Yale went to Henley that year.

Briefly, Bob Cook coached fourteen crews that won from Harvard. During the time he coached, Yale was beaten by Harvard only in '75, '78, '79, and '91. Today all American colleges row what is practically the Cook stroke. The beauty of this stroke is that in a four-mile race the men conserve their strength, rowing only about 32 against the American stroke of 40 or more per minute.

My last year at college, 1876, I saw the Yale crew in an eight-oar race at Springfield. On this race I won $25 from my Harvard friend, Ogden Mills, of California. I more than compensated him in later years, however, by making for him many millions of dollars in mining investments.

I have kept up my interest in Yale rowing and have shown my confidence in my Alma Mater by having a small bet on her every year for over fifty years. The net result has been in my favor. Each year for many years I had a bet of $25 with Jack Follensby, a friend from Harvard, and we kept this up even after I went to Africa. Today Samuel Winslow, another Harvard friend, who was one of her crack oarsmen, and I bet a box of cigars on every Yale-Harvard race.

Of all the sports I enjoyed at Yale, boxing probably proved the most useful knowledge for later years. Bill and Lett Dole taught boxing for several years. Bill, the elder, was at times rather brutal and in general rougher than we thought necessary. We planned to play a practical joke on him. Walker Blaine, Chester Dawes, and a few more of us arranged a boxing match for Bill Dole. We secured a professional from New York, hired a hall, and sold tickets. Full of pleasurable anticipation, we conspirators expected to see Dole soundly beaten, but much to our amazement, he gave the professional a good licking. The joke was on us.

Lett Dole, later head of the athletic department at St. Paul's School, was my teacher. He was about my size. The skill I acquired from him stood me in good stead on at least two occasions.

The first affair took place in Nevada. I had been sent to examine a mine, which I soon began to suspect had been salted. Having made an agreement with the owners that I was to have complete charge during the examination, I politely requested the assayer to absent himself while the tests were being made. I then secured another assayer and put up a notice on the door of the office, No One Allowed. I explained to the company assayer that this was no reflection on him, but that, since I alone was responsible for the result of the examination, I must take unusual precautions. He apparently viewed the situation lightly. The next morning, however, I found him waiting at the door, and insisting on going into the assay office.

"You can't go in there," I said.

"The hell I can't!" he retorted.

There was only one way to settle this argument, so we repaired to the back yard. He was considerably taller than I. The patrons of the saloon next door emerged between drinks to watch the fight. They were opposed to engineers as a class, though they had nothing against me personally since they had never seen me before. In the opening round, the odds were heavily in favor of my opponent, who, I soon discovered, knew nothing about boxing. He tried to foul me several times, at which the crowd, with its inherent instinct for fair play, protested. The cheers for him and the boos for me began to shift. As he kept fouling and I kept dodging, there were cries of "Give the little fellow a fair show!" Finally he gave me an opening and I knocked him out.

The other affair also was in the line of duty, but this time in South Africa. In company with a mechanical engineer named Connor, I was driving a horse and buggy to a mine near Johannesburg where I was to make an examination. On the way, I met a heavy-set drunken fellow, also with a horse and buggy. After his erratic course had almost forced me into a ditch, I shouted: "What the hell are you doing?" He reined in his horse, handed the lines to his Kaffir boy, jumped out, and came towards me. I was out of my buggy almost as quickly as he, and met him on the road. Without preliminaries, he closed with me, and with the first blow cut my nose so deeply that I still carry the scar. Connor rushed in to separate us but, so hot was the combat, he was forced out again at once with two black eyes.

My opponent was a bruiser but, because of my thorough training from Dole and, perhaps, because of my tremendous rage, I was able to get in several telling blows. I gave him a black eye for my cut nose, and finally forced him to cry quits.

My face was covered with blood when I reached the house of the manager, Victor Clement. I was busily describing to Mrs. Clement how I had been in an accident, and apparently was getting away with my story, when her husband came in. Victor said he had seen the other fellow.

It seems I had had the temerity to engage in personal combat with Coffee Jacobs, an English Jew and professional prize fighter. When I met him, he was on his way to a wedding and had begun to celebrate in advance. After his fight with me, he met Clement and asked him whether he was presentable enough to attend the wedding. Clement told him to go ahead, his face was really much improved. I had had a lucky escape; if Jacobs had not been drinking, he would undoubtedly have beaten me badly.

The story did not get into the newspapers, although it spread far and wide. A few weeks later, some hundreds of miles away in Rhodesia, Dr. Jameson asked me how my nose had become so damaged. Before I could begin to mumble, "Well, you see, it was this way . . . "

Jameson laughed and said, "You needn't explain, I know all about it."

Curiously enough, the fight made Coffee Jacobs a good friend to me. He kept a bakery in Pretoria, and when I was in prison there after the Jameson Raid, he regularly took bread to my wife to be relayed to me. It was a service that was greatly appreciated. Poor Jacobs did not get off so well with the next Yankee he crossed. About a year after the Raid, while on another spree, he started an argument with an American in a saloon, whereupon the latter in self-defense shot him dead. In contrast to the prevalence of shooting affrays in our West, this and the murder of Woolf Joel are the only two cases of the kind I encountered during my years in South Africa.

In 1899, on one of my many business trips to South Africa, I heard that a certain von Veltheim, a bad character, had threatened the life of Woolf Joel, the nephew of Barney Barnato. I urged Joel to return to London, but he insisted that business would keep him in Johannesburg for a time. At any rate, he said he did not fear von Veltheim's threats as he had Harold Strange for bodyguard. I knew Strange and was not impressed with his ability to protect Joel.

I looked up Strange at once and found that he was not only unaccustomed to guns, but was extremely clumsy in handling his pistol. I warned him that von Veltheim had a reputation as a gunman and that in a crisis, if he could beat von Veltheim on the draw, he should shoot to kill. Like most tenderfeet, Strange was well satisfied with himself and said he was not afraid of von Veltheim.

The next day von Veltheim came to Joel's office and demanded a large sum of money as blackmail. Joel refused. Strange started to draw his pistol, but von Veltheim drew more quickly and killed Joel. At the trial he pleaded self-defense and was acquitted.

During my last year at Yale—I was to graduate in 1876—Daniel C. Easton, the instructor in botany, gave a few students in his class the privilege of accompanying him on botanical excursions. These usually took place on the most beautiful days of the brief New England spring, when some of us, at least, were apt to find other attractions more potent. I, for one, used to make off at the first opportunity for Edgewood and the Mitchells', where with other similarly minded youths I passed the pleasant afternoon hours.

I was quite prepared to flunk my graduating examination in botany. Only a miracle saved me. The day before the examination I was discussing the matter with my classmate, Legrand Smith. I said despondently: "I don't believe I have one chance in a million of getting by botany. Even if I did know anything about it, I can't tell the difference between one flower and another."

"Well," he replied, "botany isn't really so hard. If you do what I tell you for the next two hours you may have a chance yet."

We were going up Hillhouse Avenue. He jumped over a fence and broke a branch from a syringa bush; opening his textbook, he showed me clearly the distinguishing features of that particular plant. Then and there I learned the syringa upside down and inside out.

As this was virtually my entire botanical preparation, it was with considerable inward trepidation that I entered the examination room the next morning. There stood the professor and before him on a table lay a variety of flowers. Each student was to take one to his desk, name it, and classify it according to the manual. When my turn came I had but one hope—if there was a syringa there, and if I could get it, I might still pass. As I approached the table, my eyes searched eagerly through the tangled collection for my one and only friend in the field of botany. Yes! there it was. I was sure I could not be mistaken in its light green leaf and pure white blossom. As nonchalantly as possible I practiced all the legerdemain of which I was capable, extracted the syringa, and took it to my desk. Remembering Smith's analysis of it only a few hours before, I prepared a paper, turned it in the first of all those present, and received a perfect mark for it. Although I am no more able now than I was then to distinguish various flowers, there is one blossom I can always identify, and one delicate fresh fragrance for which I have a special affection.

As the time approached for graduation I had to make a choice of some profession. I realized that an office life would never suit me; I must do something active, preferably something with a dash of adventure. I liked the independent outdoor life with which I had become familiar as a boy in the mining districts of California. Had not gold mining caught and held my imagination then, I might have taken the railroad job that was offered me by my friend, Fred Crocker, of the Central and South Pacific Railway Company. I had studied nothing at Sheff that would lead specifically to mining as a lifework, but now that the time had come for a definite decision, I knew that I wanted to be a mining engineer.

Although my father had already sent me to Yale at considerable financial sacrifice, he concurred in my decision and gave his consent to my entering the famous Royal School of Mines at Freiberg, Saxony, as there were no good mining schools in the United States.

To be perfectly frank, what I really wanted to do at this moment was to continue my athletics and go to Saratoga for the athletic contests. My athletic career at Yale had been sadly interrupted by two illnesses. When I first entered I was in bed for two months with dysentery, and later I had fallen on my head while doing some tumbling stunts in the gymnasium and was laid up ten weeks. However, my father pointed out that it would be necessary for me to be in Freiberg when the semester started, so I set out for Germany.

Since this chapter in my life has been largely concerned with intimate affairs of Yale, perhaps chiefly interesting to Yale men, I should like to close it with a word about the Yale spirit, a feeling about which we-hear much as undergraduates and one which even the least sentimental of us come to realize as the years go on. It is difficult to define. Perhaps only a Yale man knows what it is. Recently, while I was seeking for a definition, Mrs. Arthur Twining Hadley sent me a quotation from an article by Professor Charles Seymour, an article in which he attempts to explain to Yale graduates the purpose of the new College Plan at Yale. He writes:

> The tradition of "good teaching" at Yale is very old. The students, following the natural tendencies of youth, emphasized the social rather than the intellectual aspects of the land, and developed that sentiment of solidarity that came to be called "Yale Spirit." Both aspects have persisted and their vitality may explain the fact that Yale has produced both eminent scholars and distinguished citizens. Four years on the Yale Campus prepared the undergraduate not merely for intellectual power but for a sense of social responsibility.

CHAPTER FOUR

Training an Engineer

MODERN EDUCATION IN A MEDIEVAL SETTING —
STUDENT DAYS AT FREIBERG — I AVERT A DUEL —
THE BIERKÖNIG — THE LURE OF VIENNA — I COMPETE
FOR THE QUEEN'S CUP AND WIN ANOTHER PRIZE

*S*hortly after graduating I set sail for Europe, and during the summer rambled pleasantly through various capitals with my two Yale classmates, Charles D. Hawley and John M. Cunningham. In the fall we three registered at the time-honored Königliche Sächsische Bergakademie founded at Freiberg in 1765. Although the subsequent establishment of great technical schools throughout the world, in which the United States now stands first, has turned later generations of mining engineers to other centers of learning, to the nineteenth century student of mining and metallurgy Freiberg was what Heidelberg and the Sorbonne were to his literary colleague. Freiberg had already produced a long line of leaders in the scientific world.

Among its famous sons were two great American figures: Rossiter W. Raymond and Raphael Pumpelly, pioneers and recognized authorities in mining and mineralogy, not only in America but throughout the world. The former entered Freiberg in 1860 and there prepared himself for a brilliant career of nearly sixty years which was to spread his fame as mining engineer, professor, author, linguist, lawyer, editor, poet, and musician wherever science and literature were esteemed. Raphael Pumpelly, Freiberg '59, has been termed the American von Humboldt. Until his death in 1923 he was pre-eminent in the eyes of the civilized world as author, engineer, and archaeologist.

From the great Werner, father of geology, down to my own time, those eager to extract her secrets and treasures from Mother Earth had turned to Freiberg for instruction; they had sat at the feet of her illustrious Herren Doktoren; under her stimulus they had sallied forth to unlock the hidden places of wealth and bid all nations partake of their abundance. They had learned "to scorn ostentation and live laborious days." Something more than mere intelligence and natural ability drove these pioneers of mineral science to apply their great talents to world-development. Moreover, their rigid training in this old Saxon school bade them prefer the truth and honor of their calling above material considerations.

Germany was a kindly, simple land in those days before *Weltpolitik* became a national cult. Freiberg itself was one of the foremost mining centers of Europe, with a population of some twenty thousand. In every way it was in contrast to the sprawling, ragged mining camps with which I had been familiar in the American West. There were no shanties and no rutted, unpaved streets. There was no raucous crowd of adventurers gathered around saloon bars. Instead, the thrifty, earnest Saxons pursued a quiet and well-ordered existence, conscious perhaps of the great moss-grown bastions and frowning watchtowers of the twelfth century schloss, which brooded above them as a crumbling reminder of their feudal past. In the town below, the dreamy reverberations of the cathedral bell periodically dulled the noisy activities of the quaint old Obermarkt. Beyond the town were the famous lead-silver mines, the concentration mills, and the smelting works in which the ores were treated. Even then these mines had been in operation for six and a half centuries. They had yielded profits for some years, but during my time the profits were small if any; there were even occasional losses. The mines were maintained in large measure for educational purposes.

Hawley, Cunningham, and I agreed to room together, and presently secured pleasant lodgings which tradition said had once been occupied by Alexander von Humboldt. The additional rent, in any case, was an indisputable fact. We took no chances, however, of being deprived of any possible inspiration and promptly installed ourselves in the great man's quarters. We had three plain rooms directly under the roof, up three flights of stairs in an old ramshackle building on a side street, but what did this matter in the "brave days when I was twenty-one"? Nevertheless, if von Humboldt's ghost ever did walk on those moonlit nights in Freiberg, it never sought us, high up in our chambers over the Hornstrasse.

Besides this Yale trio of ours, there were a few other Americans at the Akademie: Albert Seligman, of the banking family of that name; Herman Schlapp, who achieved fame in his profession as a metallurgist, both in this country and in Australia; and Frederick G. Corning.

The regular course at Freiberg, with the degree of mining engineer, covered four years. Most of the Americans at that time studied only three years and were not entitled to the final degree; although the curriculum of the three-year course was comprehensive enough to enable us to practice our profession in America. Corning was the only one of us who completed the full course and obtained a regular degree. He later earned recognition from many engineering associations and schools which showed their appreciation of his ability by conferring honorary degrees upon him. In 1922 he received the title of Ehrenbürger der Bergakademie from the Mining Academy of Freiberg, and in 1928 he was made Ehrensenator of the Freiberg faculty.

Probably no other educational institution in the world had a more cosmopolitan student body: Russians, Englishmen, Americans, Italians, Canadians, South Americans, Mexicans, Japanese, Chinese, Australians, Poles, Austrians, Bohemians—a truly heterogeneous collection of nationalities.

It must be said that a mining engineer is not graduated in the same sense as his medical or theological brother. Because of the very nature of his problems, nothing in the way of instruction can guarantee that he will be able to practice his profession with that well-rounded knowledge of his subject assured to the doctor of medicine or divinity. All that the mining school, or the school of technology, can hope to do is to make him versed in the fundamentals. Other things being equal, however, the mining engineer who engages in his profession with a firm foundation of study and theoretical experiment naturally is immeasurably better equipped than if he had had no academic experience, and is likely to rise far higher than his untrained contemporary—with due respect to the old Forty-niners.

The distinctive feature of Freiberg training—unique at that time but almost universal today—was the division of time between lectures and laboratory work at the university, and field work at the mines. The former covered higher mathematics, descriptive geometry, mechanics, experimental physics, mineralogy, geology, paleontology, mining law, jurisprudence, mining concentration (ore dressing), ore deposits, mine surveying, and mining machinery. Finally, in addition to learning the German mining laws, whoever wanted a degree had to spend five or six months writing a thesis on a given problem or project in practical engineering, the subject being determined by the faculty.

In spite of the extremely difficult and technical nature of the curriculum, there was much frequenting of concerts and biergärten by professors and students. My friend Corning described the picturesque incidents occurring on the trips to the mines in his book, *A Student Reverie*. When day shift relieved night shift, or vice versa, there was usually a prayer service during which the miners sang hymns, to an organ accompaniment. This gave a weird effect, especially when carried on by candlelight.

My friends and I had not been established long in Freiberg before we were waited upon in our sky parlor by one of the officers of a certain fighting corps. He was attired in full dress and carried an invitation for us to join. I, acting as spokesman, refused, saying we had passed through our rollicking days while at college and had come to Freiberg for serious work. "But," he retorted, "suppose you are challenged to a duel, what will you, as self-respecting gentlemen, do?"

To this I replied that it was not our custom to lay ourselves open to affronts nor were we in the habit of picking quarrels; yet, if any German insulted us, we should thrash him on the spot without waiting for the formality of a duel. That, I explained, was the way it was done in America and in England.

ARTHUR TWINING HADLEY (1856-1930)

HAWLEY, CUNNINGHAM, AND MYSELF,
UNDERGROUND AT FREIBERG

I was never again invited to join the corps and was never challenged. Instead of being antagonized by my downright declaration, the corps thereafter showed us many courtesies, especially at
the time of its kneipen. Most of the Americans and Englishmen
at Freiberg in my time felt as I did, choosing rather to belong to
the Anglo-American Club than to the student corps.

The members of the corps did not always fight to avenge an insult. Sometimes the duels were arranged in a friendly spirit; the
participants were selected by the ministers of war of each corps, the
only stipulation being that those chosen should have had equal experience in using the schläger. Meetings were held from time to
time in some quiet beer hall outside of Freiberg and several contests
would take place. The attitude of the law toward dueling was decidedly inconsistent: it prohibited dueling—though no great diligence
was manifested in suppressing it—and at the same time required that
a surgeon be always in attendance.

A duel was not an entirely pleasing spectacle. Although the combatants were protected by a covering over the throat and other vital
parts of the body, the affairs were likely to be gory. The blood was
licked up by the dogs belonging to the corps. It was no dishonor
to be wounded. There was hardly a graduate of a German university who did not carry one or more scars on his face. Indeed, every
effort was made to transform the scars into permanent welts by
keeping them unhealed as long as possible.

On one occasion a young student named Caesar Vicuña y Correa,
brother of the secretary of the Chilean Legation in Paris, was challenged. Vicuña came to me in great concern, and reported that
some impudent German had tried to pick a quarrel with him merely
in order to force him to fight. Although he was not afraid to accept
the challenge, he had promised his brother to have nothing to do
with the corps.

I felt I was involved because Vicuña's brother had asked me to
keep an eye on this newcomer.

"Don't worry," I said grandly. "You just leave the matter in my
hands." Then added, "By the way, you're pretty good with a rapier,
aren't you?"

Vicuña modestly admitted that he had studied in Paris under the best masters. I then sallied forth to meet the challenger's second in the appointed place.

"Vicuña accepts the challenge and has selected the rapier," I announced.

The second seemed surprised, and protested against the use of so dangerous a weapon, which, he insisted, was not justified by the trifling incident that had led to the challenge. I replied that, while the original affront may not have been sufficient to justify the use of the rapier, I could and would add an insult which must necessitate its use.

I then proceeded roundly to declare the contempt Vicuña felt for his cowardly challenger. The second avowed that that opinion and my manner of expressing it made a duel with rapiers practically obligatory, and he retired to consult with his principal. Meanwhile, I was letting the report be spread about that Vicuña was an accomplished swordsman. The net result was that, after some slight further negotiation, I succeeded in getting Vicuña's opponent to make a proper retraction of his challenge before the student body at Freiberg. Needless to say, Vicuña was never interfered with thereafter. He lived long, married, and begot eighteen children, who might have been lost to the world but for my timely intervention.

There was at Freiberg another type of dueling, in which beer instead of blood was spilled. The custom of beer dueling dates back many hundred years. Though entered into in a jocose spirit, it was conducted with great formality. At any slight violation of the etiquette of beer drinking among the students, the offender would be called to account with the challenge, "You are a beer junger." The challenged would reply, "Accepted!" or sometimes "Accepted double!"—the latter meaning that he was willing to tackle two steins of beer. An umpire would then be appointed to see that the steins contained the same amount of beer; in other words, that the opponents were evenly weaponed.

At the word "Los!" the drinking began. The man who first emptied his stein and struck the table with it was pronounced the winner. If either cheated by spilling or leaving a drop in his stein, he was sent to Coventry and tried at a beer court consisting of three judges. Defense and prosecution had the privilege of engaging counsel and calling up witnesses, as in any court. The judges then pronounced sentence—a certain amount of beer to be consumed by the assembly and paid for by the guilty party.

A renowned beer guzzler enjoyed the distinction of being called bierkönig. The capacity of this beer king was incredible: thirty or forty quarts a day could be consumed by an expert. He was such an attraction in the beer halls that it was considered a privilege to be presented to him, to be accorded the honor of drinking a ganzer to his health, and in turn to treat him to a stein of beer. Beer drinking in such large quantities tended to make the imbibers gemütlich, and not disposed to fight, as are the hard liquor addicts. They became comatose rather than combative.

One of my most interesting summer vacations was spent with Count Hahn at his ancestral home, Castle Basedow, in Schleswig-Holstein. It was one of the celebrated estates in that part of Germany. This visit has ever remained in my memory. On my first evening at Basedow, I was given the seat of honor on the right of Countess Hahn, the mother of my friend, young Count Hahn. She was a remarkable woman. When we had finished dinner, I kissed her hand as was the custom and said, "Gesegnete mahlzeit."

I then escorted her to the drawing room for coffee. Cigars were passed. Countess Hahn selected a fat black one and smoked it with deep satisfaction. I also took one, my first attempt at smoking a cigar; the disastrous effect of that, too, has ever remained in my memory.

The elder Count Hahn was harmlessly mad. He spent most of his time collecting stamps to send to China. He believed that each stamp would convert a Chinese and that if he could send enough of them he would save the souls of the whole nation. The Countess Hahn was compelled to assume the management of their great estate, which she was well able to do. She was an enthusiastic sportswoman and kept a large racing stable. The Hahn stables had won races all over Europe, including—I have been told—every English classic except the Derby.

One day she had a very handsome mount brought for me to ride. I surprised her by saying, "I believe he is lame; he favors his off hind leg." She had the horse examined, and the investigation showed that I was right. From this she promptly concluded that I must be an authority on horses. A day or so later a hunt was staged. All the guests posted themselves in wait for the game, which was to be driven in. I must confess that the way they handled their guns made me nervous and I kept conveniently near a large tree. Presently a fox was run up. All fired at him and missed. Then I was lucky enough to bring him down. The countess decided that I must be a great hunter also. She gave me her hearty friendship. Without immodesty I may say that I was an asset to my hostess for the vacation entertainments: I seemed to be something out of the ordinary and I was from fabulous California.

One day in Washington, nearly fifty years later, my friend Baron Ago Maltzan, the German ambassador, asked me whether I had ever been in Schleswig-Holstein. I replied: "Yes, in my twenty-third year, when I was studying mining engineering at Freiberg. I went there during vacation with my young friend, Count Hahn."

Von Maltzan smiled. "Curiously enough my father's estate, where I was born about the time you were at Castle Basedow, adjoins it."

Later the ambassador made a trip to Germany. On his return he told me that while visiting his father, then a very old man, he had mentioned his friendship with me. "And," he added, "my father remembers you very well."

As half a century had passed since my visit to Castle Basedow, and I had no recollection whatever of the elder von Maltzan, I found this statement difficult to credit. I said, "How can that be?"

The ambassador answered: "When my father heard that you were visiting at Castle Basedow, he made a special trip there just to see you. He never had seen anyone from California, and he was very anxious to find out what a young Californian would look like."

During my stay in Freiberg my father's old friend, General E. F. Beale, was American minister to Austria. I visited him several times at his Viennese home. It was he who had carried to Washington, D. C., the first gold nugget found by Marshall. In 1861, Lincoln appointed him surveyor general of California. The early Mexican land grants, heavily encumbered by the easy-going ranchers, were being sold to satisfy creditors and were going begging for buyers.

MY WIFE, NATALIE HARRIS

MYSELF AT FREIBERG

Beale went into the market and acquired league upon league of land. Lincoln heard of his purchases and disapproved; he was himself too honest to relish even a hint of any wrongdoing on the part of one of his appointees. He asked one of the California senators, "Senator, what sort of fellow is this man Beale of California?"

"A pretty good fellow, Mr. President. Why?" came the reply.

"Well, I appointed him surveyor general out there, and I understand that he is 'monarch of all he has surveyed.'"

An investigation quickly cleared General Beale of all suspicion and Lincoln, satisfied that there was no dishonesty, continued him in office.

When Grant became president, Beale was appointed minister to Austria, a post requiring much tact because of the strained relations arising out of the unforgotten Maximilian episode in Mexico. Under these difficult conditions, General Beale scored a brilliant diplomatic success. Part of his personal popularity, perhaps, was due to the princely hospitality he dispensed.

At the Beales' I was treated as one of the family. Mrs. Beale appointed me a committee of one to hunt up and invite deserving American students to her receptions, while General Beale gave me the opportunity to meet many of his colleagues in the diplomatic corps. During my first visit, the Russo-Turkish War was in progress. Speculation of all kinds was rife; gossip and intrigue filled the air; the innermost secrets of the chancelleries were openly whispered everywhere. Naturally I took advantage of every opportunity to absorb inside information about the "sick man of Europe" and the suggested remedies.

The beautiful Empress Elizabeth had not yet withdrawn into retirement, and the court at Schönbrunn was maintained with all the pomp that had always surrounded the Hapsburgs. Although I did not meet Francis Joseph at this time, General Beale managed to smuggle me into some of the minor court functions. I was deeply sensible of the lure of Vienna itself, compounded of bright skies, smiling green parks, crowds of gaily dressed people, gorgeous uniforms, lilting waltz echoes, and incomparable cafés and beer gardens. The *Blue Danube* was new then and Johann Strauss was a popular figure at social functions. To a young man like myself, avid for new experiences, Vienna offered a fascinating introduction to the cosmopolitan European world.

From Freiberg we made occasional visits to Dresden, the Saxon capital, then as now famous for art and music, and popular with Americans. There I met General Nathaniel H. Harris, a Confederate veteran who had brought his young niece, Natalie Harris, to Europe to complete her education in music, and to finish the training of an already beautiful voice. The enchantment of the old town, the common bond of language, and the sense of companionship in exile— all were conducive to romance. I soon realized that Miss Harris meant considerably more to me than a pleasant acquaintance. For some reason which I have never completely understood, she was led to entertain similarly warm sentiments toward me.

At this time it was the custom in Dresden to hold an annual track meet, open to all the students of Germany. At its close, the queen of Saxony would present a cup to the winner of the greatest number of events. While most of those who accepted the invitations to compete were Englishmen, a few Americans and Germans also entered the contest. I enrolled myself in all five events: the hundred yard dash, the hundred and twenty yard hurdle, the quarter mile race, the quarter mile hurdle, and the high jump.

Because of my extreme nervousness at the prospect of appearing before royalty, I felt the need of some special inspiration. Making a jest of a serious matter, I asked Miss Harris what she would give me if I won the queen's prize. She replied, in the same vein, "I will give you my hand." Whether she regarded my victory as a hundred to one shot or not has always been a matter of conjecture, but I had obtained her promise and girded myself for action.

At Yale I had learned something about the value of technique in track events. The technique of hurdling, however, I learned in Germany by watching my English rivals practice. From them I picked up the trick of taking the hurdles in my stride rather than gathering myself together and leaping each hurdle as a horse takes a jump. With this borrowed form I managed in the hundred and twenty yard hurdle to better the record established the previous year in the Oxford-Cambridge meet. I thus became for two years the proud holder of an international record, although I could not have held it for five seconds against a modern hurdler.

In his recollections of those days Fred Corning described me as "not of a long-legged Apollo type of beauty." Nevertheless, I lost only the high jump and I managed to win the four races, and thereby won also the queen's cup. Surely never was prize so thankfully grasped; I am not certain that I did not snatch it from Her Majesty's hand. I do distinctly recall my bow, which, because of its alarming depth, became a legend among Freiberg students.

As I advanced to receive the prize, my long blue cotton stockings modestly covering my knees, I was obliged to walk over wet grass. Even beneath my spiked track shoes the turf was exceedingly slippery and, when the queen handed me the cup I had not only to bow but to retire backwards. Between my original inclination of the body and the first step backwards over the slithery turf, I achieved an obeisance so profound that it brought my forehead almost on a level with my feet. Just in time, I recovered my balance and backed off with comparative dignity, while the German audience, as I was told later, gasped at the astounding grace of the American youth.

Thus, in the quaint old German town, I found the guide to all my better fortunes.

When I wrote the news of my engagement to my father, he replied delightedly that it was none other than General Harris's mother who had entertained Sherman and himself when, as young officers, they had been in Vicksburg on their tour through the South after the Seminole War. It was, therefore, not the first time that a Hammond had bowed to a Harris!—the last welcome was no less cordial than the first. It appeared, too, that one of General Harris's brothers had served in the Louisiana Tigers when commanded by my uncle, General Harry T. Hays, and that the two had been intimate friends.

In this pleasant fashion I brought my three years' stay at Freiberg to a close in 1879. I was in possession not only of my professional education, but also of my future wife. It was now necessary for me to apply my training to practical life—to win my spurs, as my father wrote my fiancée—before I could be married.

Accordingly, I packed my bags and began the long trip home to the Far West.

CHAPTER FIVE

The Bottom of the Ladder

*A*lthough my training at Freiberg had been the best obtainable at that time, I was convinced that I needed additional practical experience particularly in quartz gold mining and the metallurgical treatment of gold ores. Therefore, almost immediately upon my return to California, in the autumn of 1879, I sought and secured introductions to the superintendents of the Idaho and Original Empire mines in the Grass Valley district of California.

Grass Valley is situated in Nevada County some fifty miles north of the great Mother Lode, a mineral-bearing zone which extends for eighty miles along the western foothills of the Sierra Nevada range, but the Grass Valley veins have no resemblance nor geological relation to those of the Mother Lode system. It was in this—the Grass Valley—district that quartz mining had been initiated in 1850 and here its peculiar technique was best developed. After profitably spending several months in the mills and underground workings, I decided to inspect the mining districts of Arizona. My Freiberg classmate, Jack Cunningham, always ready for adventure, joined me on this trip.

Our route necessarily led through Casa Grande, Arizona, then the most important outfitting station for all those headed for southern Arizona or northern Mexico. There we met Major Pauline Cushman, who—with Lotta Crabtree and Modjeska—holds a place of special honor in the hearts of all good Westerners.

Major Cushman had won her commission for secret service work within the enemy's lines during the Civil War; up to that time no woman had attained this rank in the United States Army. Her usefulness to the northern cause was supposed to have been considerably impaired, however, by her having fallen in love with the handsome Confederate raider, "Guerrilla" Mosby, whom she had been sent to spy upon. This incipient romance must have failed to develop as, at the time of our visit, she was married to Jerry Fryer, a one-eighth Cherokee Indian. Fryer was over six feet in height, exceptionally handsome and striking looking. He had also been financially successful. Starting with a tent-structure hotel at Casa Grande, he later built adobe houses, and eventually Jerry Fryer's outfitting place became as well known in the Southwest during the seventies and eighties as Sutter's Fort had been in the days of the gold rush.

I did not neglect to visit the ancient Indian ruins near Fryer's place. These adobe buildings, two or three stories high and rising directly out of the desert, were most impressive. It is thought by archaeologists that their inhabitants were related to the cliff dwellers, but nobody knows exactly who these people were, or when and why they abandoned their city. Although of an extremely primitive civilization, they had built a system of irrigating canals extending thirty or forty miles from the Gila River to Casa Grande, and such good engineers were they that the grade and width of the canal system were carefully regulated to the needs of water development along the course of the river. Today this system has been reopened and utilized.

After outfitting at Casa Grande, Cunningham and I moved on to the Silver King. This mine, which produced eighteen million dollars during its lifetime, played an important part in the development of the struggling Arizona Territory. Our next stop was Globe, the new rush mining camp in the heart of the Apache country. We made an early start across the mountains, taking with us a pack mule to carry our camping equipment and assay outfits. We had been told at Silver King that about halfway to Globe there was a small ranch kept by a woman who would provide us with an exceptionally good meal.

We arrived at the ranch about midday with a good keen appetite, but found it deserted; not a human being was to be seen anywhere around. Disappointed in our hopes for a meal, we proceeded on our way without any suspicion that an Apache raid only a few hours earlier had forced the owner of the ranch to take to the hills. It must have been by some special providence that we reached our destination late in the afternoon without having encountered a single Indian. When we told the stablekeeper at Globe that we had crossed the trail he was amazed. Had we been even a few hours earlier we would have run into an Apache raiding party.

If we had been attacked it would not have been much out of the ordinary, since in the late seventies there were in Arizona numerous bands of roving Apaches who were unreconciled to the invasion of the white men and were, consequently, a serious menace to the lone traveler. Journeys, in stage or on horseback, demanded constant vigilance and considerable boldness.

Nor were the Indians the only dangerous wild men in Arizona. On our arrival in Globe, Cunningham and I went to the principal hotel, a roomy tent-structure run by a lady fully able to cope with any emergency, even of a new mining camp. Jack was lucky enough to get a bunk at once; he was not feeling well, so he turned in immediately. A little later I applied for a bunk, but the landlady said there was none available—all had been taken and paid for in advance. In spite of the woman's hardened appearance, I appealed to her motherly instinct. I told her how weary I was, what a hard trip I had made, and how grateful I would be for a place to spread my blankets. Finally she pointed to a bunk in the corner, saying that a man had engaged it for a week and had paid for it; "but," she added, "he hasn't been here for a couple of nights, and if you're willing to take a chance of him throwing you out if he comes in, you can go on and have it."

I was so dog-tired that I was willing to take the chance and did not much care whether he turned up or not; at least I would try to get some sleep first. About midnight, I was roughly awakened. Somebody was grabbing my shoulder; wanting to know who in hell I was and why in hell I was where I was. *He* had turned up. I tried to explain as patiently—and as soothingly—as a sleep-drugged man could. It made no difference, I'd better get out quick or he'd throw me out—which way did I want it? I saw that he was somewhat the worse for a certain kind of wear, and with what was nothing less than inspiration pointed to my coat hanging on a nail at the bunk head.

"Friend," I said, "have a drink." He reached into the pocket and fetched out a flask. Taking a handsome swig, he passed it to me, and to fan the fire of a feeble friendship, I joined him. After that it was no trouble to get him to say that he wouldn't mind sleeping with me, while I intimated that I would be pleased to bunk with him. Again I rolled up in my traveling blankets and dozed off. About daybreak I awoke, to find him just departing.

Thinking no more of this incident, Cunningham and I spent two days in an outlying mining district. As we were riding back towards Globe we noticed a large crowd of men assembled a little way from the trail under a big cottonwood tree, famous for years as the hanging tree of Globe. This could mean only one thing in the Old West.

"It must be a hanging-bee," I said to Cunningham. "Have you ever seen one?"

At his negative reply, we turned our horses and galloped towards the lynchers. We arrived just as the victim was being cut down, and to my horror I recognized in his distorted features the face of the man with whom I had slept in the disputed bunk.

When we had returned to the tent-hotel I asked the landlady whether she knew what had just been happening.

"Lord, yes!" She knew all about it. "That feller tried to hold up the Wells-Fargo messenger a couple of nights ago, and shot and killed the stage driver." I realized then why the bunk had not been claimed until midnight, and that the lamb had truly invited the lion to lie down with him.

As the lady of the tent concluded her brief and casual relation of this not-unusual western episode, she turned from us into the kitchen, whence issued sounds that to trained ears meant flapjacks for supper.

From Globe we took the stage for Tucson, then a center for mining supplies and the only town of any importance in the territory. With the exception of the adobe huts of the Mexican quarter, it contained only a few brick buildings. Cunningham and I put up at the Palace Hotel on the naïve theory that even in the West this name must somehow mean something. But with a caution also western, I examined the bed before turning in, and found that I was not to be the original user of the bedclothes. I went to the proprietor and remonstrated with him at this secondhand condition. He seemed very much surprised at my complaint, and without the least affectation replied, "Well, your blood much be rich, if you object to sleeping in a bed just occupied by a New York millionaire."

From Tucson our trail of inspection led to Tombstone—already a lively camp—where great strikes had been made less than a year before by the Schieffelin brothers, Edward L. and Albert E.

I listened eagerly while the brothers regaled me with the story of how they had found a rich outcrop in the heart of the great desert, sunk a shaft, and begun its development. While one of them descended into the hole to pick away at the rock, the other remained aboveground to haul up the bucket. Realizing their danger, alone and far from any sort of community, with hostile Apaches near, they agreed that if any Indians should appear while one man was down the shaft, the other would not wait to haul him up but would run for his life. If he escaped, he was to return and erect a tombstone for his brother.

Fortunately, they were unmolested and succeeded in exploring their rich find and establishing their claims. In memory of the risks they had run, they put up a board on which they inscribed TOAMSTON as the name of their mining claim.

Within four years over a thousand claims were being worked in the immediate vicinity. When I saw the town at the end of 1879 it was the richest mining camp in Arizona. In what seemed unending streams, silver came pouring from gaping holes in the very streets. One newspaper had been founded, but since there were already two factions in the town, another journal was manifestly necessary. I suggested to the prospective publisher and editor that he call it the *Tombstone Epitaph*. He immediately accepted the idea and in gratitude sent me free copies of the paper for many years thereafter.

Every old Westerner of the seventies and eighties of the last century will instantly recognize the name of Wyatt Earp, famed as gunman in many an Arizona and Southwest fight. He came to Tombstone in 1879 as deputy sheriff and so great was his proficiency that within two months he became a United States deputy marshal. His successful war with the tough Clanton outfit of cattle rustlers showed that the citizens of Cochise County had not misplaced their confidence. In addition to his duties as a peace officer, he rode shotgun for Wells, Fargo and Company and had an interest in the Oriental saloon, where stakes were high and six-shooters always in evidence.

Earp was not a gunman in the modern sense of gangster. The passing years give different values to words and expressions. The man whom the old frontier termed a gunman was one who fought under a certain code: he never shot even an enemy in the back and an unarmed man was perfectly safe with him. In those days, too, there existed the type now termed gunman or gangster; they were called killers and gun-notchers and were universally despised.

In all mining towns the saloons greatly outnumbered the stores. Every saloon had its green baize tables for faro, roulette, and poker; stacks of variegated chips lay on every table, and a pale gambling overseer in neat black clothes was seated impassively on a raised platform dominating the room.

When the gold rush of 1897 to the Klondike started, Earp went north. A prospector who had also gone to the Klondike told me a story about Earp which not only gives a colorful picture of early days, but is also an example of the stability of English law. The latter is much less concerned with the picturesque than with the enforcement of justice.

A day or so after his arrival, Earp strolled into a Dawson saloon.

It was filled chiefly with Americans, many of them newcomers who in frail boats through hundreds of miles of whirlpools and rapids had followed the drifting, breaking ice of the Yukon. Having finally reached this new and wonderful El Dorado, they felt that a big celebration was indicated. Among these Chee-Chaw-Kas—as new arrivals were termed—was a sprinkling of the old gun-toting bad men. One of them, known as Tumbleweed Todd, was still carrying his six-shooters under his mackinaw. After imbibing freely on one occasion he became suddenly generous and offered to treat the whole house. If any man refused to drink when invited (and this rarely happened), it was a personal insult and often led to a gun fight. Nevertheless, among those who refused to drink in this Dawson "Hell of Joy" were several Englishmen, who resented the compulsory nature of the invitation.

Things had reached a critical and dangerous point when Earp entered the room. He had faced many similar situations and quickly realized the nature of the trouble. Stepping in front of the irate and befuddled Tumbleweed, Earp said in a level tone, "I also refuse to drink with any low-down sagebrush coyote like you." With a mighty oath Tumbleweed started to draw his gun, but found his gun hand locked in a steely grip while his bloodshot eyes looked down the barrel of Earp's gun.

Thereupon a rather small man, in every way Earp's physical inferior, detached himself from the crowd and tapped Earp on the shoulder. He explained pleasantly enough that it was not permitted in Dawson to carry pistols, and furthermore that it would be necessary for Mr. Earp to appear at headquarters within half an hour and hand over his weapon. It would be returned to him whenever he should be ready to leave town.

The audacity of the action took Earp's breath away.

"And who the hell are you?" he asked.

The insignificant-looking man explained casually that he was in command of the Northwest Mounted Police in Dawson. He did not, he said, wish to have a scene in the barroom. Taking out his watch, he added, apparently unconscious of the six-shooter still in Earp's hand, "I shall expect you in thirty minutes—meanwhile there must be no shooting." Then he turned and walked out slowly.

Earp returned his gun to its holster, and still holding the Chee-Chaw-Ka's wrist, said in a voice which carried throughout the room: "Tumbleweed, you long-eared ass of the desert, we're in British territory. You don't seem to savvy what that means. You're up against a game you can't beat any way from the ace. Listen! You'd better go hand over your guns like the little fellow said; I'm going to myself. If you don't, he and some more of his men will round you up. You'll shoot their eyes out—maybe. You're fast on the draw. Then you'll have to get scarce. But every pass out of the country will be blocked—with more of them waiting for you. The militia of Canada will be after you. You'll shoot all of them up too—maybe. The next news you'll get will be that the whole British Army is steaming to Canada to pick you up.

"They'll not shoot you down on sight—it's not their way. They bring their prisoners to jail, these British. You'll get a perfectly fair trial. And the next news about you won't interest you—it'll be a paragraph in the papers reporting that 'Tumbleweed, the gunman, today expiated his crimes on the gallows.'—I tell you this is Canada, and it's also Great Britain—and not the States. Now I'm going to invite the whole house to drink with me and then you are going over with me to turn in your artillery to that little sawed-off officer."

This time there were no refusals.

Lack of law enforcement is a far worse thing than lack of laws. Our metropolitan towns of today and our western wilderness of yesterday combine their annals in recording conclusively this truth. Metropolitan crime statistics and the history of vigilance committees prove it. In the cities feeble enforcement encourages, protects, and multiplies our modern criminal population.

In these days of racketeering and kidnapping there has been much public discussion about the cause and cure of crime and crime waves. The explanation seems to me to be simple. There is no peculiar criminality inherent in the American people: we are not very different from Canadians or Englishmen. Nor does the fault lie in the leniency of our laws: our laws are quite as severe as those in other countries, and there are many more of them. Our error lies in the delay allowed in our judicial procedure, and the loopholes provided by law for the escape of the criminal, aided by unscrupulous lawyers and corrupt politicians. When the criminal is assured that apprehension is certain, and conviction quick and sure, he will be much more reluctant than he now is about venturing into crime. The celerity and sureness of English justice has been the object of my admiration in Africa, and in Canada; and if we in America are more crime-ridden than are people in those countries, it is our own fault. In the wild West there was some excuse for the weakness in the administration of governmental justice. Moreover, it is to the lasting credit of the Westerners that, in the unsettled conditions prevailing in the early days, they set up irregular courts that dealt out punishment swiftly and without impediment of politics.

Some years after meeting Earp in Tombstone I encountered him again at the Tonopah mine, of which I was consulting engineer. Claim jumpers were making a good deal of trouble and he had been installed as "caretaker." I introduced myself as one who had seen him in Arizona in 1879, and told him I was glad to have so capable a man attached to our interests.

"But," I warned, "I'm opposed to gun fighting over mining property. I've seen enough of that sort of thing and believe we are now in a different and better era. Our ownership of this ground will be established by a judicial decision in a trial now pending. Avoid gunplay. I want you to promise me that you will not shoot except in self-defense."

He put out his hand and we shook on it, but in a hesitating way he added, "I'll go through with you on that, Mr. Hammond, but I must be the judge of when the self-defense starts."

I was prettily outplayed and admitted it.

Then Earp added characteristically, "However, Mr. Hammond, I will let my opponent start the draw."

Fortunately we won our case, so that Earp did not have to make that fine distinction between attack and self-defense.

Captain Bill MacDonald was another character who commanded my admiration, though he differed in many particulars from the Earp type. For many years MacDonald was captain of the Texas Rangers. Moreover, he was on several occasions the hunting companion of Theodore Roosevelt and I met him while he was visiting the President at the White House. Subsequently, on Colonel House's recommendation, he became one of the bodyguard of President Wilson.

Bill MacDonald was involved in many shooting scrapes in the discharge of his duty. He seemed to have led a charmed life, and I once commented on this to Colonel House, saying that MacDonald's numerous escapes seemed incredible. Colonel House said he had himself once asked Bill how he accounted for the fact that he was still alive and how he had had the courage to face some of the desperate criminals he had been obliged to arrest. Bill answered: "It's not as difficult as it seems. I always had a psychological advantage: I knew that no fellow in the wrong can stand up against a fellow in the right who shoots and keeps acoming."

It was while Cunningham and I were still in Tombstone that Jack received his western baptism by fire. We were sitting about a table in a saloon one night when shots were heard in the hall. I dropped instantly to the floor. When Jack leaned anxiously over me, thinking I had been wounded, I cried: "Lie down, Jack! I'm all right. If you sit up you'll get hit!" Cunningham flattened himself out. For a few minutes spurts of flame and the whizz and crash of bullets made conversation difficult. Even after the row had quieted down, it was only by exercising my strongest persuasive powers that I could induce Jack to resume his normal upright position and have another glass of beer.

At the end of my two finishing courses in Grass Valley and in Arizona, I returned to San Francisco in an effort to find a paying job as an engineer. My father suggested that I see an old friend of the family who had lived near our house when I was a child. His sons, my brother, and I had been intimate during our childhood, but I had not seen this friend since my boyhood days. Through the promotion of mining properties he had amassed what was considered in those days a large fortune, and he had, of course, a good deal of influence in the mining world.

When I called upon this friend he asked me to dine with him and his family. During dinner he spent much of his time trying to impress upon me that I had made a great mistake in going to Freiberg; he claimed that engineers educated in the theory of mining had not been successful. He himself put more faith in the practical man. In short, I gathered that he would not recommend me.

Bitterly disappointed over my failure to get a job, as well as at this unfriendly attitude, I described the interview to my father. Although he also was surprised and disappointed, he said little.

I learned afterwards that this friend, when a young man, had come from Virginia to California with a letter of introduction to my father. My father and the friend's brother had been at West Point together and both had served in the Mexican War. He was greatly desirous of securing a position which would enable him to bring his fiancée, whom he had left in Virginia, to California. My father, who was collector of the port of San Francisco, gave him an appointment in the Custom House, and this enabled him to marry soon afterwards. My father realized that I was actuated by a similar motive in my desire to find a position. I insisted, however, that I was not discouraged, and that I was determined some day to prove to this friend of the family he was wrong. I was determined to make good. His rebuff was merely an added stimulus. Not long afterwards this man lost his fortune on the advice to invest in properties recommended by his "practical" mining expert.

I next went to Mr. George Hearst—later Senator Hearst, another friend of my father and head of the mining department of the powerful firm of Haggin, Tevis, and Hearst. Hearst and J. B. Haggin were a remarkable pair of enterprising and daring capitalists. In the later seventies and eighties they controlled the greatest mining operations in America, including the Homestake in the Black Hills of South Dakota, the Anaconda Copper in Montana, and the Ontario Silver mine of Utah.

Expecting that family friendship, if nothing else, would procure me a position, I confidently asked Mr. Hearst for a job. To my amazement and chagrin he cheerfully declined even to consider me. When I regained control of my voice I inquired somewhat shakily why I was so firmly repulsed.

He replied frankly: "The fact of the matter is, Jack, you've been to Freiberg and have learned a lot of damn geological theories and big names for little rocks. That don't go in this country."

I asked whether he had any other objections.

"No," he answered, smiling. "Freiberg is enough."

"Well," I said, "I'll make a confession to you if you won't tell my father. I *didn't* learn anything of importance at Freiberg."

"What!" ejaculated Mr. Hearst. "In that case you might come around tomorrow and perhaps I can give you a job."

In this unorthodox fashion I secured a start in my profession. The position itself was no sinecure. Not only did I have to assay ores; I had also to build fires in the furnaces and crush the samples before I could make the actual tests. This took my entire time and energy working at top speed from early in the morning until late in the evening, for all of which I received the munificent compensation of fifty dollars a month. However, it was a beginning. I left no stone —or rather, no ore—unturned to win Mr. Hearst's regard and overcome his scorn of my academic training.

After several months, I went to my employer, and told him what responsible work I had been doing; I reminded him that he was investing large sums of money in purchases of property based on the reliability of my assays. I suggested that I had perhaps been overlooked in the shuffle.

He assured me that, on the contrary, he had not forgotten me and was especially pleased with what I had accomplished. "You've done so well I'm making you mill superintendent at the Homestake." This mill had just been completed and was the largest in the world. I jumped at his offer and was prepared to go within a few days.

Then, quite by accident, on the very evening of my appointment, I saw Gardner F. Williams, one of the leading mining engineers of California, who was later to make a great reputation as the manager of the famous diamond mines at Kimberley. He said he had just received a letter from Clarence King, director of the United States Geological Survey, asking him to recommend two or three young engineers with technical training and some experience, to collect statistics on the mining industry of the West.

He assured me that this was a great opportunity to widen my experience and to become a special expert in gold mining in California, and strongly advised me to accept the offer. I replied regretfully that I had just tied myself up with an engagement to George Hearst. Williams suggested that I explain matters to Hearst; if he was really friendly to me, he would release me from my commitment. I followed his advice and consulted my employer. I was not only advised to accept the government position, but was congratulated on "the opportunity of learning a lot at the expense of the government."

Under the Census Act of 1880, the special experts of the United States Geological Survey were empowered to make detailed examination of such items as cost sheets and profits of the mines. This new position gave me an opportunity to round out my knowledge of mining operations with a study of the economics of mining.

As soon as I received my credentials I went by train to Carson City, Nevada. From there I traveled by stagecoach to Bodie, California. At that time—eighteen years after the death of W. S. Body, who had discovered the first rich gold deposit there—this was a booming mining camp. Body had been frozen to death immediately following his discovery and but little development had been carried on until 1878, when a rich strike of gold and silver brought a rush; thousands of fevered miners poured into the camp with the usual accompaniment of tinhorn gamblers and women of ill repute. A year later Body was dug up and given a formal funeral, complete with newspaper and oratorical eloquence.

When I saw the town in 1880, it had already established its reputation for wickedness. The "Bad Man from Bodie" was not a fictitious character.

Carl P. Russell, of the National Park Service, tells the story—which may be believed or not—of a little girl who, about to leave Truckee for Bodie, prayed, "Good-by, God! I'm going to Bodie." So ran the report in the Truckee newspaper, to which a Bodie paper replied that the punctuation was at fault—what the child had said was, "Good, by God! I'm going to Bodie."

On the morning of my arrival I was walking down the street, when, without warning, the wooden arcades that lined the walks to the hitching rack suddenly blazed with gunfire, and peaceable citizens jumped for cover. In the exchange of shots a bystander was inadvertently killed. A vigilance committee sat at once. The trial was characteristically brief, the greater part of it being devoted to a severe reprimand to the killer for his poor markmanship. Without further formalities they swung him from a tree. The vigilance committee thereupon drew up and affixed at the post office a notice warning a dozen men of bad reputation to be out of town before morning. When the sun rose not one of these was left, but there were plenty of others.

The popular boast of Bodie inhabitants was that they "had a man for breakfast every morning." As a newcomer, I was not inclined to challenge this assertion, for during the first week of my stay there were no less than eight killings. It was possible to shoot down an enemy on the streets at any time in cold blood without interference by the authorities. Most of the slain could be well spared from the community. Rarely was an unoffending citizen a victim; the shootings were usually confined to the "bad men" themselves.

Strange as it may seem, there was at the time probably no other part of the world where refined women were accorded the respect they were shown in the West during these early days. Bodie was no exception. Miners, gamblers, outlaws—all of them discriminated accurately between women of the streets and "real ladies." A respectable woman could travel anywhere at any time without fear and without need of protection, and invariably was treated courteously.

Since saloons were the general meeting places of the men of the town, they were the scenes of a good many gun fights. There was usually present at least one gun-notcher willing to accommodate anyone who wished to try conclusions with him. I was not ambitious to earn the reputation of being a better man than anyone else, so I was never molested. As a matter of fact, I came to know and even formed friendships with some—regarded generally as outside the pale—of the less disreputable citizens of the mining camps.

My youth was often a handicap. This was especially apparent whenever I joined a group of miners of the vintage of Forty-nine gathered around the stove discussing geological theories of ore deposits, or some similar technical problem. I was, of course, anxious to contribute my own ideas, but whenever the weight of the argument seemed to be going in my favor the discussion would drift to the early days of California mining. With ill-concealed superiority, one of the old pioneers would shift his quid and ask me in a patronizing way when I had arrived in California.

I had naturally taken advantage of every previous opportunity to make clear that I was not a newly arrived tenderfoot from the East, but my youthful appearance confirmed the suspicions of unfriendly critics that my mining experience had been brief. When I casually mentioned the year 1855, the obvious skepticism of my hearers, themselves consummate liars, would force me into a feeble admission that the date marked my first arrival anywhere. While it is true that I was not an Argonaut, I have been argonauting ever since. Horace Greeley said, "Go West, young man, and grow up with the country." Since I was born as far west as possible in the United States, I had to go east in pursuance of the activities of my professional career.

In 1880, Bodie was a town of some three thousand inhabitants, with a continuous flow of population in and out, and was the center for forty or more mines. My examination of the mines in this district unfortunately showed that few of them could be worked profitably, and that the majority would have to shut down. The stock market gambling in mining shares was then at its height, and the physical value in the mines themselves certainly did not warrant current prices of stock. As a matter of fact, during the next year the shares crashed and many of the mines were closed.

The Standard and the Bodie remained in operation and continued to be profitable for several years after they were combined in 1887. Interest in this district was revived in 1929 and 1930 by the development work undertaken by the Bunker Hill and Sullivan in the hope of opening up other ore bodies. After the ill-advised expenditure of considerable money this hope was definitely abandoned.

Although my predictions as to the district proved sound, I was so young an engineer that I received little credence. Moreover, under the government's promise, my report on values had to be kept secret. If it could have been made public, the almost immediate proof of the correctness of my valuation would have greatly contributed to my reputation and success as an engineer.

It used to be the saying in the mining camps that when the saloons, gamblers, and disreputable women began to move away, just as rats are said to leave a sinking ship, it was an infallible indication that the camp had seen its best days and prosperity was on the decline. Then individual by individual, group by group, the miners would drift away as the ore bodies became exhausted. The romantic days of the fever left as their only tangible record the empty frame of the town. Transportation was too difficult and costly to make it worth while to carry off the buildings, which remain even today in out-of-the-way corners of mountain and desert—mere shells of houses. Here and there a dump of rusty cans, and empty whisky bottles, and perhaps a dilapidated stamp mill help to carry out the illusion of a naked skeleton.

Bodie is now, for the third time in its history, a ghost town. No one has better explained the feeling of utter desertion than has Don Blanding in the following lines:

> The ghost-town's empty windows stare like
>   wistful eyes
> Down streets where nothing moves save memories
>   and the wind.
> When midnight comes to Sawdust Corner, eerie
>   cries
> Ring out, recalling nights when rowdy sins were
>   sinned,
> Bearded miners, seeking laughter and bright
>   lights
> As well as liquor, flung gold nuggets on
>   the bars
> For brief forgetfulness of lonely mountain
>   nights . . .
> Their cries are only hoot-owls mocking at
>   the stars.

From Bodie, I proceeded to Mono Lake and then south to Mammoth, another center of mining excitement. The mines there also proved of slight value, and I so informed the owners, naturally to their disappointment. They had gone to the extent of erecting a mill in anticipation of ore that existed in imagination only. The worthlessness of the enterprise was apparent to any trained engineer and within a few months speculators and prospectors were moving on to other fields. Today there is at Mammoth a summer camp for trout fishermen, while the crumbling timbers and rusted machinery of the old mill are merely curiosities for the tourist.

In 1880 there were but two practicable passes by which I could return over the Sierra Nevada divide: Sonora Pass, forty or fifty miles north, and Mammoth Pass. Both had been Indian trails to hunting and fishing grounds in the high mountains, but with the development at Mammoth in 1879 the old trail was blazed and monumented and made barely passable for pack animals between Mammoth and Fresno Flats. With guide and pack train I crossed the divide to Red Meadows, then rode down the upper reaches of the San Joaquin River to Little Jackass Meadow, and so came out on the western foothills of the mountains and back to where the mines on the Mother Lode were located. For nearly six months I wound my way northward through the gold districts, on horseback or by buckboard; in the hot months of summer moving in an enveloping column of suffocating red dust; when colder weather came, lurching through mudholes and snowdrifts.

The hardships of early mining trips through New Mexico, Arizona, Nevada, and other parts of the West seem incredible when compared with the trips de luxe made by the present generation of mining engineers. I recall one journey in the summer of 1885 into Death Valley, where there was a mining prospect to be examined. We outfitted at Eureka, Nevada, and after a tedious journey of several days in buckboards we reached the last place where pure drinking water could be found. With four horses and a dead-ax wagon carrying several barrels of water we started over the desert. The desert was an oven, the trails were sandy and rocky, and our progress was consequently slow.

When we finally reached the edge of Death Valley we were shown a vein which had been represented as enormously rich. We found nothing but a "stringer," or worthless vein. A fruitless expedition, which now could easily be made by motor in ten hours, had consumed two weeks of valuable time and considerable money. But I had become accustomed to such disappointments.

Hotel accommodations were so scarce on these trips that I was usually compelled to spend the night on the ground. It was essential, therefore, to keep in good physical condition. I have spent many years of my life traveling on horseback, on skis, and in all sorts of open conveyances. Many a time have I slept in the boot of a stage-coach on the mail pouches, where, being short of stature, I could curl up without discomfort.

One of the strange sights occasionally to be seen on the Arizona desert in the seventies was a herd of genuine Arabian camels. They had been imported just prior to the outbreak of the Civil War in an endeavor, backed by Secretary of War Jefferson Davis, to improve transportation in the desert sections of the Southwest. The undertaking failed and the camels were finally let loose. For many years they roamed the deserts of Arizona, causing as much consternation to horse-drawn vehicles as later the automobile did when first introduced on the roads. The last time I saw them was about 1880. I understand that some time after that the manager of a circus rounded up the survivors and shipped them east.

I soon found that mine was not the only government survey being conducted in the district. One stormy winter's night, after a hard day's work underground, I drove into the livery stable at Jackson. As I was putting up my horses, a young man dressed in the height of English fashion asked somewhat skeptically whether I was Mr. Hammond. I had on my mining clothes and certainly presented a formidable appearance. I was covered with mud from head to foot. After I had assured him that I was Mr. Hammond, he presented, still somewhat doubting my identity, a letter from Clarence King, asking me to render the bearer what assistance I could. This stripling had been appointed to gather statistics on the "social" aspects of mining; that is, to get full information about the living conditions of the miners, and to make notes of their experiences.

S. B—— was a young American of about eighteen, who had spent most of his life in England. I could see at a glance that he was absolutely green in the ways of western life. Since I was going to visit a deserted mining camp the next day where he could get hold of some old prospectors, I said he might go along. Accordingly, the next morning B—— was on hand with detailed questionnaires, naïvely devised by some greenhorn government official in Washington.

This seemed to me an ideal opportunity to play a joke which would be harmless in effect, amusing to me, and above all educational for him. In every not yet completely abandoned gold camp there usually remained a general store with a meager stock of groceries, overalls, miners' picks, and a balance for weighing gold dust. In these almost abandoned mining camps the one remaining saloon was the gathering place for the few prospectors who, yet clinging hopefully to the possibility of a strike, refused to leave the camp.

I explained that a saloon was a species of club for the miners, and that the best approach for B—— was to walk in, go up to the bar, turn, and say, "Gentlemen, the drinks are on me." At the same time I warned him that he would probably find the men diffident at first, but that their tongues might become loosened if he could only persuade them into drinking a little. I tipped off in advance a few of the more responsive of the old-timers, telling of B——'s mission and that he wanted them to "talk quite freely of their experiences."

The first thing my tenderfoot protégé learned was that the miners displayed no hesitation whatsoever in accepting his invitation to liquid refreshment; in fact, they nearly mobbed him in their rush to the bar. In less than a minute the glasses were emptied. B—— then went to work, most conscientiously asking the questions set down in the printed forms supplied by the government.

"What is the most thrilling experience you ever had? What famous mines did you discover?" Each inquiry seemed to offer illimitable opportunities to these habitual romancers. After a few days of hard work B—— returned to Jackson and showed me his report. He had taken down in all seriousness every statement made, and seemed inordinately proud of having collected important historical data. He had a splendid collection of stories about fights with Indians, grizzlies, mountain lions, and claim jumpers; of fortunes made and lost; of fabulously rich finds now being carefully guarded from discovery by anyone else. The only point that seemed to trouble him at all was the great number of men who claimed to have discovered the Comstock Lode and then to have been cheated out of a fair share in their ownership.

After I had gone over the statements with him and pointed out their discrepancies and absurd exaggerations, I told him he had been thoroughly taken in; that all his stuff would have to be destroyed; that he would have to make a fresh start, working from the fundamental principle that any prospector, however picturesque, could shame Ananias himself. Poor B—— was much crestfallen, but went to work. I heard later that he had been given another government position which he filled with credit.

While examining the mines near Coloma, on my journey north, I heard that James Marshall was living in a shack near the scene of the great discovery he had made on Sutter Creek thirty-one years before. Having lost or dissipated whatever fortune he had made in the diggings, he was now leading a miserable existence; he was poor, filthy, and drunken. I hunted him up and promised him a bottle of red-eye if he would stay sober long enough to point out the exact location of his find. He agreed, and the following day took me to the site of the mill race in which, on that famous day of 1849, he had first seen the yellow specks of gold. He did not know whether there was any gold left there, but thought it quite possible as the first miners had possessed little patience and were inclined to abandon their first diggings to rush up or down the stream to any more likely-looking location. Much interested in this opinion, I took my miner's pan and, after prospecting around for about an hour, washed perhaps a quarter of an ounce of gold from the gravel, enough for a certain wedding ring I wanted.

Marshall seemed glad to talk to me about his troubles. He railed at the state legislature which had refused to continue his pension. Merely from sentiment he had been allowed a hundred dollars a month for four years, 1874-1878, and then in a fit of economy the payments had been discontinued. The old man, quite soured in disposition, shiftless, and broken, was living on charity. For him the golden find had not turned out to be a lucky one although a tardy government finally erected a monument to him, many years after his death.

To his employer also, the fine old Sutter, the discovery had brought tragedy. I remember seeing him once on a San Francisco street car. My father pointed him out to me and then introduced me to him. He was a broken man, although in Forty-nine he had owned two Mexican grants of land, comprising six hundred thousand acres of fields and vineyards, together with mills, workshops, stock, and fine horses. Though he himself had had no interest in the gold, he had been kind and generous in his hospitality to the ruthless gold-seekers. They had swept in upon him like swarming locusts laying waste his beautiful estate. He was now without an acre, although the recipient of a pension of three thousand dollars a year from the state. All he wanted, however, was his land; and his land he never recovered.

By pushing my work of mine examination at terrific speed I completed it within six months. There was then little sentiment in favor of surrendering the secrets of mining operations. The western mining man had learned the lesson of self-reliance in a hard school. Although inclined to bristle with suspicion when I began to ask questions, he would usually furnish the information freely when assured that it would be treated as confidential. As a matter of fact, I had the authority to demand the statistics, but I preferred to have them furnished willingly. Much of the required data, of course, I could collect through my own unaided observation.

With few exceptions I examined and reported on all the gold mines—quartz and gravel—from Fresno to Sierra County. I valued greatly the opportunity to keep in touch with mining prospects and to watch their subsequent development. I made a practice of revisiting those which, at the time of my first visit, I considered of potential value. By checking up on my judgment I acquired a certain hunch-sense, known among mining men as "a nose for a mine." This is a practice that I heartily recommend to younger generations of mining engineers.

After a long day in the mines I would set off for my next destination, many times on lonely trails through the mountains and not always certain of the right path. But these lonely rides were not without compensation. At the trail's end, usually at three or four in the morning, I would find a warming brew of coffee, a steaming plate of ham and eggs, and a welcome bunk in the cabin of some hospitable prospector.

CHAPTER SIX

Gold

To write of mines and mining without mentioning the prospector would be like writing a treatise on mathematics without using the multiplication table. A strange and solitary figure, the prospector has been the advance guard of the engineer on every frontier of the world. In the Arctic his dog team was the first to cross the glacier, and he was the first to follow in frail craft the breaking ice to the tundras of the north. In tropical jungles, his machete blazed the first white man's trail. In the far deserts of Australia and Africa his silent-treading camel was first to arrive at the new El Dorado. Prospectors were in the vanguard of the pioneers of civilization. Like other artists, they were born; mining schools seldom produced them. Nor did they come from any single walk of life. Seldom did they have their origin in the big city; ordinarily they were the children of the open spaces.

A great majority of the gold mines in the United States have been discovered not by the mining geologist, but by the "honest" prospector accompanied by his *fidus Achates* and collaborator, the burro. In this category fell that romantic figure "Hopeful" Bill. He started with a scanty food supply of bacon, sow belly, saleratus, flour, a sack of beans, some coffee, and a bottle of red-eye. A mere glance at this provision list will show why Hopeful Bill and his fellow thaumaturgists were usually dyspeptic. To these culinary items were added the essential tools of his art: pick, shovel, gold pan, canteen, and, last but not least, the great horn spoon, which was merely the hollow half-section, carved lengthwise, of a cow's horn. This grubstake Bill secured from some confiding individuals, who, in return, were to have, if and when a mine was discovered, an interest in the property.

Hopeful Bill, with his inseparable and faithful mongrel trotting by his side, was now ready to head his burro on the outtrail to some yet unconquered field. The trip as a rule was long and arduous. Water was scarce, often alkaline, and never enough to satisfy his almost unquenchable thirst, aggravated by the salt sow belly and the dry saleratus bread. Unmindful of hardship, Hopeful Bill toiled on towards the rainbow's end.

He first searched for gold along the countless dry ravines and canyons where he hoped to find float rock, fragments of rock containing gold. If Bill was fortunate enough to discover float rock, he crushed it with his pole pick on a flat stone and carefully shook about half a pound of powdered rock into the spoon. Then pouring water from his canteen into the gold pan, with a dexterous motion of the wrist he stirred the spoon under the water, and by washing away the powdered quartz recovered the particles of gold. An expert prospector could detect a single particle as small as the point of a fine needle. Through long usage the great horn spoon became the acid test for native gold and led to the use of the famous oath, "I swear by the great horn spoon."

Now if Bill found gold in the float rock, he began then to search for its origin in the veins and lodes farther up the ravines. Sometimes this was the labor of months, necessitating countless testing holes and trenches. The mother lode from which the gold had been originally eroded might be miles away. But at last Bill found an outcrop which showed gold. He then took samples of ore to the nearest assayer; if of sufficient value per ton, he was able to induce his grubstake backers to finance him in sinking his shaft to a depth of a hundred feet or more. The ore thus recovered was hoisted to the surface by a windlass and piled on the dump for future treatment.

Should the prospect still look favorable, he would go for more capital with which to erect a small hoisting engine. This would enable him to sink his shaft to a depth of two or three hundred feet and by drifts or levels to ascertain the extent of the ore-bearing vein.

If again he was fortunate enough to find a valuable ore body, he went in search of still more capital. This is where the promoter appeared, and the prospect henceforward was called a mine—a name for the promoter to conjure with. After developing the mine to greater depth and after more extensive drifting, a small mill was erected to crush the ore and to extract the gold. If this again proved profitable, a mining boom began and other prospectors, backed by yet more capital, started energetic prospecting and development upon the extension of the discovery vein or upon other veins in what had by this time become a mining district.

It was now the day of the engineer. Great stamp mills thundered night and day for months or years until at last the ore bodies petered out, the noise and hubbub ceased, and the population moved on to new fields.

But long before this, in the days of the first promotion, Hopeful Bill had sold his interests for a modest sum, and with a new outfit trekked to some distant corner of the earth, obsessed by the desire for new discoveries.

The burro, camel, dog team, and pack horse have been largely superseded today. Planes drone their way over the wildernesses of Canada and the tropical jungles of New Guinea, carrying the descendants of Hopeful Bill, still buoyed up by unending faith and indifference to dangers and privations. So it has always been, from the days of Jason and the Golden Fleece to this hour.

Mark Twain has described a mine as "a hole in the ground owned by a liar." If anyone should attempt to apply this definition to my friend, Hopeful Bill, I would challenge the characterization. Dishonesty usually entered with the promoter after the prospector had passed out of the picture. Hopeful Bill, it is true, was not disposed to minimize the value of the property he sold to the promoter. But his knowledge of mining values was strictly empirical and he should not be blamed for the promoter's overvaluation of the property.

An unscrupulous promoter once asked me to suggest a name for a certain mine not far from Tonopah, Nevada, which he was about to sell to the public. I told him it should be called *Caveat Emptor.*

Much puzzled at this unorthodox title, he asked me what it meant. I explained that it was one of King Solomon's mines, which answer seemed to satisfy him perfectly—for the moment at least.

The following incident, true as well as amusing, illustrates the relations between prospector and promoter. Jeff Clark, recognized for his honesty and unquenchable optimism, was one of the prominent mining promoters of our Northwest and was so liberal in grubstaking that he was regarded by prospectors as an easy mark. On one occasion he was approached and asked for a grubstake by Hopeful Bill, who said, "Jeff, you know I've a great nose for a mine, and . . ."

"How much are you going to strike me for this time?" interrupted Jeff, who was relatively prosperous at the moment.

"Well," said Bill, "I am sinking on a vein near here, and so help me God I'm within three feet of a million dollars. Now, if I had only two hundred and fifty dollars . . ."

The money was immediately forthcoming, and for several weeks Jeff did not see Bill again. Then one day he spied him in the distance on a street in Tonopah. Bill saw Jeff at the same moment and in evident embarrassment started to quicken his pace. Jeff soon overtook him, however, tapped him on the shoulder, and asked, "Bill, how's that mine of ours?"

"Well," replied Bill, "last time I saw you, Jeff, I told you I was within three feet of a million dollars, didn't I?"

"You sure did."

"Now, Jeff, I'm gonna be honest with you and I'm telling the truth. So help me God, I don't think I'm within a million feet of three dollars!"

This story is not only a good illustration of the vicissitudes of miners, it once served equally well as my answer to the question, "Do you believe prosperity is just around the corner?"

It was not always the promoter who got the better of the bargain in dealing with Hopeful Bill. In his peregrinations Bill once landed in London and brought his prospect to Eugene de Crano, a colleague of mine representing the Rothschilds' mining interests there. After waiting several months to get a directors' decision, de Crano

"HOPEFUL" BILL

AT THE BUNKER HILL MINE, IDAHO, IN THE EIGHTIES

finally announced to him, "Bill, we have decided to purchase your property."

"O. K.," replied Bill. "You'll make a good thing out of it. You don't think eight thousand's too much, do you?"

"No," agreed de Crano, "we think it's a good prospect. If you'll wait a few minutes I'll give you a check for it."

De Crano disappeared into an inner office, from which he emerged to hand Bill a slip of paper. Bill's startled eyes descried the words eight thousand pounds instead of the eight thousand dollars he had had in mind. Barely taking time to mumble "Thank you," he hastened in the direction of the nearest bank to convert into actuality this unlooked-for bonanza.

De Crano for his part disappeared again into his inner office, equally pleased with what he considered an advantageous bargain.

Hopeful Bill belongs to all nations and to all times. Driven by this *auri sacra fames,* this thirst for gold, throughout the centuries he has crossed all seas and circled all continents. Many people have tried to account for the overwhelming allure that has tempted him ever farther and farther. They have stressed the beauty of gold, its malleability, the ease with which it is extracted and refined, its non-corrosive qualities, and its rarity. These explanations are not entirely satisfactory. Gold has a human appeal far deeper than any physical quality inherent in it as a metal. The golden ornaments of the ancient world were beautiful and malleable and rare, but above all else they meant wealth. They signified freedom from menial toil, they represented social distinction, power, influence, and prestige. Gold furnished a firm foundation for fortune. In time, in the form of coin it came to symbolize in more convenient shape the possession of wealth. It had become more than a precious metal; it was a medium of exchange between individuals and nations. Now in the great vaults of the treasuries of the world—in New York, Paris, London—gold has been gathered together in fabulous quantities and there lies sequestered as an international commodity to form the monetary basis of currencies. Once more, as in the millennia before Christ, gold is used chiefly in the fine arts.

As a result of the active progress of archaeological exploration in recent years, large quantities of gold ornaments, many of great artistic excellence, have been found among the excavated ruins of ancient civilizations, widely scattered geographically. Gold beads have been recovered which date back as far as 5000 B. C. An edict of Menes (*circa* 3800 B. C.) contains the first written mention of gold: it declares that the ratio between gold and silver should be 2½ to 1. But the mines from which the precious metal for these objects had been obtained have been abandoned for centuries, and even the sites, with rare exceptions, have been lost from the memory of man.

Nevertheless, it has been determined that much of Egypt's gold in the days of the Pharaohs was derived from the Assouan region of Nubia lying between the Nile and the Red Sea. Subsequently these same mines furnished a large portion of the revenue of the Ptolemies. This gold was produced by slave labor working under appalling conditions. The recent discovery of Tutankhamen's tomb, with its fabulous golden sarcophagus and its golden ornaments, indicates, as T. A. Rickard states in his interesting book, *Man and Metals,* that the cumulative efforts of countless thousands were required to produce the funeral equipment of one man.

Other sources of ancient gold were discovered by me in Matabeleland and are discussed in a later chapter.

It is estimated that the total production of gold in the world, since the discovery of America in 1492, is one billion ounces, valued at twenty billion dollars. About half of this has been produced since 1848. The Transvaal, Australia, the United States, Canada, and Russia combined have contributed more than one-half of the total. Since a large part of the gold has been used in the arts or lost, about ten billion dollars remain as the monetary basis of the currency of the world.

If all this gold were melted in one huge lump, it would make a cube of solid gold measuring thirty-eight and a half feet. But to extract this relatively small amount of metal from the auriferous gravels and gold-bearing veins it was necessary to mine, as a conservative estimate, enough earth, gravel, and rock to cover the fourteen thousand acres of Manhattan Island to a depth of three hundred feet.

It was on his second voyage that Columbus carried back to Spain the first gold from the Americas, which he had obtained in the northern part of Santo Domingo. Even today natives occasionally extract nuggets of gold from the same placer deposits.

The date of the first actual discovery of gold in the territory comprising the United States is not positively known. In 1513 Ponce de Leon, while seeking the elusive fountain of youth in what is now Florida, heard rumors of the existence of gold to the north; about fourteen years later Narvaez saw gold in the possession of the Indians, who indicated that it came to them from far in the interior. Over three-quarters of a century later, in 1608, the first Virginians, according to their instructions, looked for gold and discovered a bank of dirt in which were embedded countless yellow particles. Madly abandoning all more practical preparations for the coming winter, the colonists collected a cargo of the rock to send to London. The sad news ultimately came back that the apparently valuable ore was nothing but iron pyrites, or fool's gold. The coop of turkeys, which went by the same boat and were the first to reach Europe, was a far more valuable present to the Old World from the New.

North and South Carolina began to produce gold in small amounts late in the eighteenth century, and gold was discovered in Georgia in 1829. These were very small deposits, however, and the total production of gold in the United States before Marshall's California strike of 1848 was worth only the relatively insignificant sum of twenty million dollars.

Although there still exist gold-bearing veins in many parts of the eastern states, with few exceptions it is not possible to operate them at a profit. Near the city of Washington, for example, shafts have been sunk along the highway to Great Falls on the Potomac. These have reached well-defined quartz veins which occasionally produce fine specimens of gold, but the cost of obtaining the metal is prohibitive.

The West has been the real source of the United States' gold supply. It was fortunate that Marshall's discovery of gold was made after California came into the possession of our country. Had it been discovered earlier, there would have been an inevitable conflict between the United States and other nations for the territory.

The principal gold-mining districts of California extend along the western slope of the great Sierra Nevada Mountains at an altitude above sea level of from a few hundred feet to upwards of eight or ten thousand feet. The auriferous gravels—the placer deposits, as the miners called them—were developed first. The gold-bearing constituents of these gravels had come from the gradual disintegration of gold veins or lodes by atmospheric agencies and by erosion. The resulting debris had been continuously carried downstream and deposited along gulches, bars, and flats. The first mining of these gravel deposits by rockers, long toms, and sluices was of a most primitive character. Gold in gravel deposits occurred usually in fine particles, sometimes so infinitesimal that several hundreds of the gold flakes were worth only one cent. The size of the nuggets in the gravels varies from a fraction of an ounce to several pounds.

Occasionally much larger nuggets have been discovered elsewhere in the world, the most famous of these being the Welcome Stranger from Moliagul, Victoria, Australia, which had a gross weight of 2520 ounces, contained 2284 ounces of gold, and was worth approximately fifty thousand dollars.

In 1854 a mass of gold weighing 2440 troy ounces and valued at forty-five thousand dollars was found near the outcrop of a vein on the Mother Lode at Carson Hill, California. Nuggets with a value of several hundred dollars have frequently been found in California.

It was in pursuit of gravel-mining operations that gold was eventually discovered *in situ,* that is, in the quartz veins or lodes. In the last several decades the bulk of California gold has been obtained from these quartz veins, although an appreciable amount still comes from the operation of gold dredges on the flats and along the river courses where the original Argonauts operated.

From a production of two hundred and forty-five thousand dollars in 1848, the gold output of California rapidly increased until the banner year of 1852 when it reached the enormous figure of eighty-one million dollars. From that time production greatly declined, until by 1913 it had fallen off to about ten million dollars annually. The grand total of gold produced in California from 1848 to 1932 is estimated at one billion eight hundred million dollars.

Following the discovery of gold in California, gold-mining districts were developed in many other parts of the territory west of the Mississippi River. Among the famous gold-mining camps in the

1860s was the Comstock Lode in Nevada, the ore from which carried about forty-five per cent in gold and fifty-five per cent in silver. After attaining a depth of thirty-three hundred feet, the operations ceased to be profitable and were for the time abandoned, having produced roughly nearly four hundred million dollars, almost half of which was gold.

Three years after the California gold rush, a prospector named Hargraves went to New South Wales. Impressed by the similarity of the outcrops there to those he had seen in California, he tested a few specimens and found them rich in gold. Since that date Australia has contributed three and a quarter billion dollars to the world's gold supply. The rate of production declined rapidly, but in recent years, owing to the appreciation of gold, mining activity has been revived and Australia is again becoming an important factor in the world's gold production.

Although gold was discovered in Alaska in 1880, its major output, amounting to nearly four hundred million dollars, did not begin until the Alaska gold rush in 1898. Here, too, the production has recently fallen off considerably.

Russia also has been one of the important gold fields of the world. During the past two hundred years it has yielded about one billion eight hundred million dollars, or almost the same amount as the State of California produced from 1848 to 1932.

The great source of gold in recent years has been the Witwatersrand of the South African Transvaal. Out of the average world production of four hundred million dollars during this period, it has supplied virtually one-half.

Economists have long been concerned about the future gold supply. This is, indeed, of more than academic interest. Whether the present supply is to be maintained, increased, or diminished is of supreme economic importance. Five years ago the Economic Council of the League of Nations, recognizing the grave danger attached to a static or declining gold production, appointed a special committee to investigate this vital question. Late in 1930 this committee reported that, except in the improbable event of new and large gold fields being discovered, "gold production would start to decline about 1934, and would by 1945 be greatly reduced."

My own conclusions are in line generally with this report, although I do not anticipate any such rapid decrease in gold production in the near future. On the contrary, a temporary increase is not improbable as a result of the increased price of gold in terms of dollars. This opinion is based on examinations made under my direction, supplemented by reports of my confreres. These cover nearly every part of the habitable globe, not of course in detail, but in sufficient scope to warrant the opinion that there exist no new potential fields to furnish a supply of gold commensurate with requirements even in the near future.

It is true that the increased price of gold from $20.67 to the present fluctuating price somewhere in the neighborhood of $35.00 will result in the extraction of ore bodies of lower grade than previously could be mined profitably. This will give longer life to many gold mines, but even then the gold output will not amount to the economists' estimate of the annual increase in producion of three per cent required to meet the demands of future expansion in industry and commerce unless the price of gold is enhanced and maintained by governmental decree.

As before mentioned, the mines of the Transvaal now produce about one-half of the world's gold supply. Mining engineers familiar with operations in that field are not only of the opinion that the peak of its capacity has been nearly reached, but they think that in the future there will be a marked decrease in its gold output. More roseate predictions have recently come from the Transvaal based on the possibility of extended ore deposits. Although these may indicate the opening of an important, newly discovered gold-bearing area, as yet there is no substantial basis for assuming that these discoveries indicate that the life of the district is to be long extended.

There is one further source of gold which offers potentialities of tremendous import. It has been estimated that the oceans of the world contain a gold supply equivalent to about fifty million dollars for each person of the two hundred billion population of the world. However, all attempts thus far to extract the gold at a profit have failed.

Analyses of sea water always reveal traces of gold. The largest percentage amounts to only four grains to the ton of water, which was obtained from great depths in the Atlantic. As an exception, however, gold to the extent of eleven milligrams per metric ton, or roughly seven cents per ton, has been found in the waters of the Bay of San Francisco. Sea water from the coast of New South Wales has been estimated to contain from one-half to one grain of gold (two and a half to five cents) per ton.

In the 1890s with Dr. A. von Gernet, a distinguished Russian metallurgist, I conducted a series of investigations off the coast of South Africa, not far from Cape Town, to determine the gold content of sea water at that place. Although we used automatic machinery in so far as possible, the amount of gold we recovered was far below that requisite for economic production.

Sea water contains many minerals in addition to gold. A plant has been erected recently in the mouth of the Cape Fear River in North Carolina for the commercial extraction of bromine from sea water. The chemist of the company owning the plant has stated that "while the gold in sea water is present to the extent of but a few parts per billion" he does not regard it beyond reason to expect the chemists of the next decade to extract gold commercially from sea water. This possibility remains so far distant in the fields of conjecture that it will offer no deterrent to the current development of the world's gold-mining industry or discourage the gold-mining engineer.

CHAPTER SEVEN

Old Mexico

A SHAVE, A HAIRCUT, AND A WEDDING
TRIP — CHANCE TAKES ME TO MEXICO —
BY STAGECOACH, SAILBOAT, HORSEBACK —
''IRISH DIVIDENDS'' — TRAINING MY
BODYGUARD — BESIEGED AT MINAS
NUEVAS — FRANK AND DUTCH JOHN

*A*fter finishing my gold mine examination for the Geological Survey, I went to Virginia City, Nevada, and submitted the report to Dr. George F. Becker, who was Clarence King's western representative and was at that time making a geological examination of the Comstock Lode. Becker complimented me on the fact that I had covered so much territory in such a short time. He well knew the reason for my expeditiousness; the sooner I finished, the sooner I could be married.

Without waste of time I set out for Hancock, Maryland, where my bride-to-be was staying with her married sister. In Chicago, Ned Ryerson and Jim Houghteling, whom I had not seen since the old Yale days, took me in hand and helped select a ready-made dress suit and other necessary apparel. I reached Hancock the evening of December 30, 1880, and immediately went looking for a barber to remove my Forty-niner's beard. The only one I could find was a negro, who, except for the fact that he was just recovering from delirium tremens, was very highly recommended.

The barber was obviously shaky, but I had no alternative. The beard had to be removed. Laying down a five-dollar bill, I put on my fiercest expression and said, "Jim, here's five dollars for you if you'll give me a haircut and a shave without cutting me, but if you so much as scratch me with your razor, I'll . . ." with a significant movement towards my hip. Either the promise or the threat steadied him long enough to perform the operation satisfactorily. When the story came out later in a New York paper Jim was said to have fainted as his fingers closed on the bill, but as to that I cannot say—I was already on my way down the street.

On January 1, 1881, Natalie Harris and I were married. We went at once to Washington, where General Sherman had secured rooms for us at army rates at the best hotel, a delicate attention which I much appreciated. James G. Blaine was also very kind to us, as were many friends of our families then resident in the Capital.

The high point of our stay was a dinner given us at the White House by President Rutherford B. Hayes, who had been entertained in California the year before by my father. Mrs. Hayes was a strict teetotaler and never allowed liquor to be served in the White House —though the President at times was slightly humid. The only relief to her perfectly dry dinners was the appearance of the rum-flavored water ice called Roman punch, which came on about the middle of the meal and contained a generous quantity of the liquor. A hardened old senator once named it "the life-saving station." Mrs. Hayes was kept in ignorance of the wicked properties of her Roman punch, for the butler always served her a specially prepared and innocuous mixture. William M. Evarts, the secretary of state, said that at the White House banquets during the Hayes administration "water flowed like champagne."

My youngest sister, Betty, then at boarding school in New York, visited the White House later and found the presidential family most kind and amiable. Fanny Hayes, about the same age as my sister, blithely accepted her as a companion. Betty was escorted from her school to the President's private car by General Alexander McDowell McCook, military aide to President Hayes. During the journey to Washington a newsboy brought in a copy of *Puck,* which nearly always contained cartoons of the President. This number showed a highly colored cover picture which Betty felt sure must prove absolutely devastating to each and every Hayes, but to her surprise both the President and his wife laughed heartily and seemed actually to enjoy the jokes on themselves.

Life at the White House in those days was extremely simple. Since Garfield was coming into office the next month, the Hayes family were entertaining for the last time a few of their friends from Ohio. The household breakfasted together, President and Mrs. Hayes almost always appearing. After breakfast it seemed the established custom for visitors to stroll sedately through the conservatory until summoned upstairs to the President's study, where he and Mrs. Hayes read prayers and a chapter from the Bible. From then on, entire freedom was the order of the day.

Betty enjoyed herself greatly. She took an artless delight in jogging around Washington in hired "herdics"—those quaint little conveyances named for their designer, Peter Herdic. Another of her favorite sports, in which the youngest of the Hayes boys sometimes deigned to join, was sliding down the banister of one long flight of stairs. On Saturday night everybody played hide and seek—the President and Mrs. Hayes and all the family and guests.

Fanny Hayes was extremely reluctant to leave the White House and my sister recalled very well her remark, delivered with a huge sigh, "Well, soon Molly Garfield will be prancing around here."

My bride and I went from Washington to New York where we were shown gratifying attention by more of our friends. It was at a dinner party for us given by D. O. Mills that he announced the engagement of his charming daughter to Whitelaw Reid. Then I had to go back to California and resume work.

While in New York I had met Alexander W. Stoddard, later one of my good friends. On the recommendation of his nephew, he had invested heavily in a mine and afterwards had become uneasy about it. He commissioned me to make an examination for him on my arrival in California, and considerately offered payment in advance. The commission I accepted eagerly, but the payment, I told him, I would not feel justified in taking. Although I needed the money badly, since wedding trips are expensive, I considered it bad policy to be paid before I had actually earned the money.

Immediately upon reaching San Francisco I went to Grass Valley where the mine was located. I made the examination, wrote my report, and handed a copy to Mr. Stoddard's nephew. He read it carefully and then said: "Your report is not very complimentary to me. You make me out either a damn liar or a damn fool; which is it?"

I replied, "You've read it—you ought to be able to decide for yourself."

When Alexander Stoddard received the report, he paid me the kind of compliment most pleasing to an engineer: "Hammond can be neither bluffed, bamboozled, nor bought."

And so I felt I had earned the promised five hundred dollars, my first fee as a mining expert.

During the first half of 1881, I was kept profitably employed making examinations of mines in California, Nevada, and Arizona. In the fall I succeeded in securing a position with the Vigorite Powder Company for which my brother Harry had just won an important lawsuit. As their consulting engineer I learned much about the use of various kinds of explosives and costs of manufacture. Among other things, I discovered that the majority of mining companies were using powder containing too high a percentage of nitroglycerine, which increased the cost of blasting; also that high-grade explosives were not as efficient in mining certain classes of veins as were those of lower grade. The use of this knowledge later effected a considerable saving in the cost of explosives in mines in which I was interested.

For a beginner I had had great luck so far. Now, the word "luck" may seem a peculiar one to use in connection with a profession relying so largely upon scientific method and exactness. These, of course, are fundamental requisites, but the element of luck—or fate, or whatever it may be called—does play an important part in any individual's life. This same element of chance brought me to Mexico early in my career.

Certain American mining investors had decided to seek out opportunities across the border, disregarding the shifting character of the Mexican governments, which, despite the ability of Benito Juarez and Porfirio Diaz, were on the whole weak and disorderly. This well-known group of mining engineers included Henry and Louis Janin, who had been at Freiberg about ten years ahead of me. They had purchased a mining property known as Minas Nuevas, a few miles from the town of Alamos in the State of Sonora. Through Louis Janin I was offered, in 1882, the managership of this property.

Since reports of the manager of the mine had been most favorable, this seemed a chance for me to make a reputation through the successful handling of a valuable mining property. Furthermore, I should be able to see for myself what opportunities might exist in Mexico. I knew that the country itself was still almost inaccessible, and the political conditions were chaotic. After one term President Diaz had been obliged to give way to Gonzalez: the constitution of the moment forbade consecutive terms. During this interregnum I should inevitably be exposed to real personal danger as well as physical discomfort. I did not mind this half so much as I did the necessity of leaving my family behind, although I knew young engineers had to endure such separations. After considering the proposal from all these angles, the business prospects still remained alluring, and I accepted.

In April, 1882, our son Harris was christened by Bishop Kip, who had also officiated at the wedding of my mother and father. A few hours after the christening I left San Francisco by train for Tucson, my point of departure for Mexico.

From Tucson there stretched before me a trip of several hundred miles to Guaymas, Sonora, the greater part of which had to be made by stagecoach. The first news which greeted me as I stepped from the train at Tucson was that the stages had been obliged temporarily to stop running because of recent activities of the murderous Apache who roamed about Arizona. Soon the route was judged safe—or as safe as it was likely to be for some time to come—and a small party of us set forth for Hermosillo.

Opposite me in the stage sat a wounded Indian—not an Apache. The poor fellow had been a workman in the construction of the railroad which was being carried on from Tucson to Guaymas, and had had his hands badly mutilated by a premature blast. With his hands in splints and fastened across his breast he was absolutely helpless. My fellow travelers and I took turns giving him food and from time to time pouring a little water into his mouth.

During the course of the day an American drummer, who was already intoxicated when we left Tucson, became more and more of a nuisance. He was cheeky and offensive in his language and he enraged me by tormenting the poor Indian. By the time we stopped late in the afternoon to change horses, the limits of my patience had been reached and I made him get out and sit on top of the coach, using a pistol as the most persuasive argument. He took his bottle with him. As we drove along it became increasingly evident that the drummer had found a drinking companion: the coach began to plunge and lurch from side to side, and there was nothing for us to do but trust in Providence.

I was endeavoring to get a little sleep when I was aroused by a violent shock followed by the splash of water in my face. We had finally capsized in the stream bordering the road. It was dark by this time, and we did not know how deep the water might be. Fortunately, the stream was shallow and we were able to wade ashore. When I had collected my wits and we had fished out a lantern and lighted it, I asked what had become of the wounded Indian. After searching for a few minutes we located him under the stage. Although we succeeded in extricating him, he was suffering terribly, probably from internal injuries, and died during the night.

One consoling feature of the accident was the condition of the drummer. When the coach capsized he was thrown some fifteen or twenty feet out into the stream where he lighted on his head. When he emerged, dripping, with several front teeth knocked out, he was sober beyond recognition.

We dared not attract the attention of marauding Indians by building a fire, so we just sat around, wet, cold, and disconsolate, for the rest of the night. To add to our troubles, the drummer dinned into our ears dire threats of what he was going to do in the way of bringing damage suits against the stage company because of injuries and probable loss of pulchritude. We all stated positively, however, that we would give no testimony in his favor. When daylight finally came, we contrived with considerable difficulty to upright the stage and resume our journey. Nothing more was ever heard from the drummer after we dropped him at one of the stations along the road.

At Hermosillo I presented a letter of introduction to Señor Carlos

Ortiz, then governor of Sonora. This call was no mere formality; it was highly necessary for those operating in the country to maintain friendly relations with the ruling political powers. From Hermosillo I went by rail to Guaymas on the Gulf of California and arrived there just in time to secure passage on a small Mexican schooner which was carrying mining machinery and dynamite to one of the ports farther down the coast. My own destination was Agiovampo, which, under a fair wind, would have been reached in two or three days. We were becalmed, however, and for five days floated around helplessly in sight of Guaymas.

Since there was no cabin on our primitive boat, I slept every night on deck under the wonderful glow of a starlit heaven such as those who live to the north of the Rio Grande seldom see. During the day I spent my time swimming, rowing about, or even making occasional trips to the shore to shoot birds. One morning, as I was about to dive off the bow, there came a wild cry of "Tiburón!" from the natives standing near me. Something in their tone made me gather that my prospective dip did not altogether meet with their approval. I looked around inquiringly and one of them pointed to the water. There I saw an enormous shark standing by and fairly licking its chops at the sight of me. I did not swim that morning.

After a voyage which took three times as long as it should have taken, I arrived at Agiovampo and went on horseback to the mine, about eighty miles away. It was good to feel a horse under me again, and to know that I was getting somewhere at last. On arrival I presented my credentials to my predecessor, an irascible old German named Konstantin Heusch, whose temper had not been improved by many years' residence in those lonely parts.

Of course, I was eager to go over the mine at once, but Heusch was obviously reluctant to have me see it. Since I knew the mine was only about a mile up the slope of a mountain from where the mill, smelter, office, and rest of the plant were located, I was irritated and somewhat puzzled by the excuses the man made to delay my examination. Late on the day after my arrival, however, the foreman of the mine came down to the office on business and, without further ado, I accompanied him back.

Upon my return to the mill, Heusch reproached me bitterly, saying that this was a most unethical procedure on my part, and one which placed him in a highly undignified position. Of this there was no doubt, for it had needed but a few hours' examination underground to convince me that the mine had been "gutted." The bonanza, from which some very rich ore had been taken, had been practically worked out and nothing was left but a shell of a mine.

Although not of a suspicious nature except when examining mining properties, I was bound to wonder whether Heusch's disinclination to have me make a prompt examination did not proceed from a plan to commit me first to a favorable impression based on his own accounts of the property. In fact, this was exactly what he had intended, for it subsequently developed that he was making every effort to get rid of the stock he then held in the company before the inevitable exposé.

Indeed, it afterwards came out that on the very day I arrived he actually sent a telegram to the president of the company, informing him that I was enthusiastic over the outlook. At the same time, through an accomplice who also held some of the stock, he was endeavoring to give his associates the rare "opportunity" of buying his own shares, "which he reluctantly had to part with in order to carry out the development of another property" he owned.

I spent several disagreeable days with the slippery old fellow going over his accounts, which consisted mainly of odd scraps of paper kept in a tin cracker box. In the course of my attempt to learn their contents, he made himself so offensive that I was finally obliged to give him twenty-four hours' notice to pack up and leave. He blustered and said he would go when he was good and ready, or words to that effect. But he decided to go at once when he saw that he had to choose between my offer of a mule and a walk of two hundred miles to Guaymas.

As soon as Heusch reached San Francisco he went to the Janin brothers and reported that I was incompetent. In every way possible he endeavored to discredit me, and succeeded to the extent of prevailing on Henry Janin to use his influence to have me dismissed as manager of the mine. But Louis Janin, on whose recommendation I had been selected for the position, was my able defender. With my fighting spirit roused, and counting on Louis Janin's support, I made up my mind not to retire.

A mining engineer named Bartlett was sent from New York to ascertain the true state of affairs. His report commended my work, and I had no further difficulty in establishing myself firmly in the confidence of the dominating faction of shareholders.

At the outset of my first big opportunity I had a gutted mine on my hands. Realizing the seriousness of my position, I went to see the company's agent, Señor Tomas Bours, at Alamos. He told me frankly that, since the company had exhausted its credit, he did not feel justified in advancing money for the next week's payroll. By a happy chance, however, this same agent had known my father in the old California days. On the strength of my father's reputation for absolute integrity—which has often been of service to me in various parts of the world—the agent offered to lend me several thousand dollars to cover the payroll until I could get assistance from headquarters in New York. A fortnight elapsed before this assistance came, since telegrams had to be sent by messenger on horseback to the nearest station, more than two hundred miles away, and thence forwarded to New York.

It required considerable correspondence on my part to convince the outraged directors of the sort of dividends they could expect from their mine in the near future. In the parlance of the day, their returns would be nothing but "Irish dividends," in other words, assessments. I proposed to shut down the mill for a while and to undertake a system of underground prospecting in order to discover new ore bodies. The ore occurred in small lenticular, or lens-shaped, masses, and what there was of it was high grade. With the grudging assent of the owners I went ahead with development work, and after a few months succeeded in opening up new ore.

With the exception of the mine foreman and the metallurgist, the employees were Mexicans and Indians. Consequently, my life for the next few months was decidedly uncongenial, and I managed to endure it only because I was absorbed in the task at hand. I was fortunate at least in having decent quarters in a large two-story hacienda which had been built by the Ortiz brothers before they sold the property to the American company.

One of my first tasks was to learn Spanish, or, properly speaking, Mexican. Fortunately for my purpose, there was in Alamos an old Californian who had married a Mexican woman. Since his señora was somewhat fiery of temperament, he was glad to live with me, and under his tuition I acquired a good working knowledge of the Mexican language. After remaining with me for nearly two years, my poor instructor met a most unfortunate end. On the old man's departure, I had presented him some money, which made him a marked man in Alamos. He was promptly murdered, and it was believed by his friends that his wife, unlike Caesar's was not above suspicion.

One morning soon after my arrival I was stopped on my way to the mines by a young man, patently American, who asked whether I was the manager. He then said he wanted a job. I inquired as to his accomplishments, and he replied that he was an assayer and could speak Spanish fluently. After studying assaying at Los Angeles, he had accompanied a party of mining promoters to the State of Sinaloa. When he had made a number of assays for them they left him with the promise to send him his fee. They had failed to do this and he was now destitute.

I was so favorably impressed with the manner and appearance of this fine-looking fellow—only a few years younger than myself—that, while I could not give him a regular position just then, I offered him seventy-five dollars a month to help me in connection with certain examinations I was making at the mine. Later, when operations should get fully under way, I would pay him on the basis of the value of his services. He accepted my offer, and introduced himself as Victor M. Clement. I was glad of his company, and invited him to stay with me at the hacienda, and thereafter when the day's work was done I taught him geology and metallurgy, the theory and principles of which were still fresh in my mind from Freiberg days.

Clement was ambitious; he bought all the books I recommended and studied assiduously. Minas Nuevas itself was a splendid school in which to acquire a practical knowledge of mining. Since our laborers were entirely ignorant, I was compelled to supervise virtually all mining operations and this gave my young protégé the opportunity to observe them from every angle.

A few months after Clement's arrival I was compelled to discharge the mine foreman. I gave Clement the position and put him in charge of the underground workings. Between us we had the actual direction of the metallurgical operations, which embraced a great many different methods of treatment of ores, and consequently Clement soon gained a well-rounded knowledge of the profession. When I resigned my position, I had him appointed as my successor.

Within a brief period, therefore, Clement found himself, through his own industry and persistence, in a highly responsible situation. I had grown to like him and esteem him so highly that I kept in touch with him, and in subsequent years he went with me on many mine examinations. He served under me at Grass Valley and in 1886, on my recommendation, was appointed manager of the Bunker Hill and Sullivan in the Coeur d'Alene district in Idaho, where he played a leading part in the great labor war of 1892. A year later he accompanied me to South Africa and shared my experiences there. On returning to America he obtained a highly profitable position and continued to rise in his profession until his untimely death in 1903.

I have digressed to outline Clement's career because it so strikingly points a moral and adorns a tale: a young man of intelligence recognized opportunity, and through integrity and application rose to wealth and fame and the achievement of enduring works.

I soon saw that my original hope of making a reputation in Mexico through the handling of a rich property was impossible of attainment. Instead, I was forced to undertake the much less attractive enterprise of so managing a poor property as to keep it from costing the owners too much. My real job was to pull chestnuts out of the fire. However, adversity does have its uses. The isolation of Minas Nuevas, the difficulties of transportation, and the poor returns forced me to use my ingenuity in making the most of primitive and inadequate equipment. Also, I had to solve the problem of labor among a people unaware of the virtue of work, and in a society politically unstable.

A great portion of the Sonora mining district is composed of mountain ranges which even today are largely inaccessible except on horseback. In the early eighties this region swarmed with Indians, revolutionists, and bandits of every sort and description. The revolutionists made up in picturesqueness and local color what they lacked in military discipline. The young gallants in particular considered themselves irresistible in their expensive felt or straw sombreros, richly embroidered with silver braid, and their silver-plated spurs. To a benighted gringo the rest of the attire was somewhat reminiscent of Kipling's *Gunga Din:*

> The uniform 'e wore
> Was nothin' much before,
> An' rather less than 'arf o' that be'ind.

After I had politely but firmly declined to entertain the suggestions of certain of my less desirable neighbors for a share in the product of the mine, frequent threats were made upon my life. In order to take every precaution, I hired fifteen Yaqui Indians and organized them as a bodyguard. First, I supplied them with rifles, and then taught them how to shoot. At that time only the well-to-do classes in Mexico possessed guns, the usual native weapon being a cross between a sword and a meat cleaver which they called a "machete." Clement was an excellent shot, and I had been familiar with the use of firearms from boyhood. After the Indians had had a little practice under our instruction, we began to feel reasonably safe.

It was not long before our army of fifteen Yaqui, two American employees, Clement, and I were put to the test. The revolutionists had withdrawn in high dudgeon after my refusal to reward them by a "consideration" for the privilege of letting me live. When the colonel rode up one morning at the head of his regiment of a hundred or more, and proceeded, after duly deploying his men, to lay siege to our house, we were scarcely taken by surprise.

As soon as his forces were arranged, he sent word that he regretted the necessity of levying a prestamo—forced loan—upon us, but it was essential for him to procure corn for his horses and arms for his troops. In particular, he inquired whether we had a supply of arms. I replied that we were very well armed. The colonel then amiably suggested that we lend him our rifles in order that he might protect us from the Yaqui Indians then in revolt, who had hostile intentions towards us. I hastened to assure him that he need have no concern whatever about us; we felt quite adequate to the task of defending ourselves. His next move was peremptorily to demand our supply of weapons. I declined to give them up, whereupon the colonel sent word that he would come and take them by force. I replied that we were ready for him, and asked who would be the first to step over the dead line which, in this case, was a high adobe wall surrounding the hacienda.

Our appearance was, indeed, formidable. In addition to our barricade, we had mounted several locomotive headlights with which we.were able to sweep the surrounding country after nightfall. Furthermore, we carefully allowed the secret to leak out that, concealed all about the premises, were dynamite caches which could be exploded by an electrical apparatus. This extraordinary preparation for warfare made such a decided impression that, after several days of blood-curdling threats and a few potshots to let us know they were beaten but unbowed, the disconsolate patriots moved off and left us free to continue our labors.

As time went on, one of our chief difficulties was to prevent the rich ore from being stolen. It made so irresistible an appeal to the light-fingered gentry of the vicinity that sometimes sacks would be abstracted on the way from the mine to the mill. A little quiet investigating showed that there were in the neighborhood several small arrastres operating on the ore stolen from our mine. I made haste to establish friendly relations with the jefe politico, or mayor, of the little mining village of Minas Nuevas.

It so happened that he was called Juan, the Spanish equivalent for my name. On the strength of this fortunate coincidence we swore eternal friendship, and general offensive and defensive alliances which were then celebrated convivially, as was the custom, in our observance of San Juan's Day, June 24th. Shortly after, I was honored by an appointment as "special constable" and proceeded to fulfill my duty to the public by raiding the arrastres and recovering the hard-won ore which belonged to the company. The jefe politico then gave the captured thieves the choice of being shot or serving in the army. If the company desired, however, it could have the rascals locked up in the calaboose, on condition that it agree to defray the expense of providing a special guard, food, and necessities for the prisoners. Needless to say, we did not avail ourselves of this privilege.

Even in such an out-of-the-way corner as Minas Nuevas, tramps would occasionally appear looking for work. It is really unfair to call them tramps, since they were usually prospectors out of grub and out of cash. Their sole object was to work their way back to the States where they might get together enough money to enable them once more to set themselves up in their precarious and adventurous business of prospecting.

Two such men presented themselves one afternoon at the mines. It was at once evident that both had footed it for many miles. Dirty ragged shirts and Mexican linen pantaloons were their sole coverings. On their feet they wore garauches, a type of sandal made of stout sole-leather and held on the foot by thongs between the toes. Never did I see two more abject-looking Americans. Moreover, they were suffering from calentura, a fever then prevalent in the lower parts of Mexico.

To their request for employment, I replied that I was familiar with their kind; that I knew they would work only two or three days and would then be off. But they were such sad-looking specimens that I did not have the heart to turn them away: I told them to get some supper at the cookhouse and turn up for work in the morning. These men stayed on the job for several months; they even took a contract in the mine and saved up several hundred dollars before going prospecting again. The family of one of them, I afterwards learned, was one of the most respected in Maryland.

The later story of these two—known as Frank and Dutch John— shows how again and again one crosses the trail of former associates in the mining world.

A few years after I had left Minas Nuevas, and had established my office in New York, a client asked me to see a man who had a bonanza to sell in Arizona. Much to my surprise, the man was Frank. Although he seemed somewhat embarrassed when he saw me, he proceeded to expatiate on the value of the property. So sure of his proposition was he that he offered to put up a thousand dollars as forfeit if, after examination by my client's experts, the mine proved not to be up to his representations. I asked for a few minutes' private conversation with Frank and took him into the next room.

"Now, Frank," I said, "you know me, and you know you can't put up any job on my clients. You'd better save your thousand dollars and sell the mine to somebody else."

"No, Mr. Hammond," he answered, "you're wrong. This is a good mine, and I'm perfectly willing to put my thousand up."

Convinced that he was honest, I recommended the deal subject to my report after examination.

I went first to Colorado to look at some properties, and then continued on to Arizona and to Chloride, where Frank's mine was located. On the stage I rode, as I liked to do, with the driver, because I have found that a stage driver usually knows a great deal about the people and places in his district and is always willing to talk. As we drew near a certain hill he pointed out a dump and two or three buildings near by, which, he said, represented a mine owned by this man Frank and two partners. He further informed me that, while Frank was in the East, his partners had dug out the ore, a rich chloride of silver, and had departed with it for points unknown.

Upon reaching the mine, I found Frank greatly troubled. My examination disclosed a pockety formation of silver chloride, but the stage driver had been right in his assertion that it had been thoroughly gutted. Under the circumstances I felt I could not hold Frank to his agreement about the thousand dollars; I returned it after taking out only enough to pay my actual expenses.

Only a few months later, on my way back from an examination in the Sierra Madre Mountains, I made a side trip to Cusihiurachic to see a new process invented by E. Russell, a Yale collegemate. The process was being successfully used in the treatment of exceptionally "rebellious" ore. On arriving at "Cusi," I went to a little Mexican adobe hotel, which I found quite deserted, the attendants and, in fact, the entire village having gone to a cockfight. From past experience I knew that no hotelkeeper would be forthcoming to give me my much-needed meal and bed until the fights were over.

The manager of the mine was ill but there was a note from him asking me to present myself at the mine shaft at five o'clock the next morning, when his foreman would take me down. To my astonishment, the foreman was none other than Dutch John.

"Well, Dutch," I asked, "how are you? And how do you happen to be in Cusi?"

"I'm fine now, Mr. Hammond," came the reply, "but about a year back, in Tucson, a man tried to get me and I beat him to the draw. They don't like killings in Tucson, so I thought I'd be better off this side the border. Nobody's come after me yet, so I guess it's all blown over."

I then told him what I knew about Frank and asked what he could add to my account.

"Yes," he volunteered sadly, "Frank's dead. You remember those bandits that held up a railroad train in Arizona about a month ago and got away with the Wells-Fargo box? Frank was one of 'em. The sheriff and a posse followed 'em into Mexico, and then the greasers chased 'em."

"But Frank wasn't the kind of fellow to go robbing express cars."

"I know he wasn't. Frank never had the makings for a job like that. I'll bet he just stumbled into the middle of their plans when he was pullin' out o' that mine bust. He always was a great guy fer stumblin' into the wrong places. The yella snakes couldn't let him go because he knew all their water holes. So they yanked him along with 'em."

"How do you know?" I queried.

"Why, the place is just over there aways. Somebody tipped off the greaser posse where they was and they surrounded the shack. The bandits were ready for 'em—plenty of grub and plenty of lead. Like as not they'd be shootin' it out yet if the Mexicans hadn't smoked 'em out by settin' fire to the shack. They all come out with their guns in their hands, but the posse dropped 'em all."

"But how do you know Frank was in the fracas?" I inquired.

"I'm sure, all right," Dutch answered heavily. "I saw his boots. You know Frank was always particular about his boots when he had money. He had 'em made special off east somewheres and the heels was smaller and higher than any man's I ever seen. After the shootin' they brought the bodies in here on the backs of burros. The heads was covered but I saw Frank's boots stickin' out. A man can't make a mistake about his pardner's boots.

"But Frank wouldn't of done no robbin', Mr. Hammond." Dutch

seemed to be gathering his slow wits for a final vindication of his old comrade. "Nor no killin' either. Why, Frank wouldn't even of shot a greaser!"

I was distressed to hear this circumstantial tale, but the matter soon passed out of my mind. Some fifteen years later, after returning from South Africa, I gave a lecture at Johns Hopkins University on King Solomon's mines. After the lecture, President Remsen introduced me to many people as they filed past and shook hands with me. Among them was Frank!

"Why, Frank," I said, "I thought you were dead."

My eyes strayed involuntarily to his boots. "I want to talk with you," I added cordially. "Come to my hotel in the morning. Now be sure to see me!"

He said he would come but he never did. However, he will probably turn up again.

As my experience increased I came to realize more and more that the sympathetic mining engineer often had to serve in a capacity not unlike that of the doctor who is obliged to inform his patient's family that there is no hope of recovery. Somehow one never can become quite calloused to this situation, however often it may occur.

I once made an examination of a mine in the remote district of Jesus Maria in the Sierra Madres. It was hardly more than a prospect, owned by an American, who, with his little family, had been living there a dozen years or more. He had expended his last available dollar on the property and was hoping and believing with all his heart and soul that my examination would result in a favorable report and the payment of enough money to take his family back to the States—to God's country—where they would thereafter live. Unfortunately the poor fellow's wish could not be realized. To my great regret, I was compelled to make an adverse report, and his dreams vanished. He and his wife were heartbroken.

An experience which made a profound impression on me occurred when I went to investigate another mine in the same district, a hundred and fifty miles west of Chihuahua. While there, I was told by Waithman, the young English superintendent, that a famous English engineer was buried near by—a man who had introduced improved

HACIENDA AT MINAS NUEVAS

THE MINE AT MINAS NUEVAS

I START OUT TO INVESTIGATE A MINE IN MEXICO

metallurgical processes into Mexico and who had died in these hills. Out of respect to his memory I hunted up his burial place.

I found his body in a shallow grave hollowed out of the stony ground; the earth and rocks had fallen in and one end of the coffin was broken away. There he lay, his face exposed, gaunt and bearded, upturned to the sky. Though he had been dead some fifteen years, the dry air and soil had so mummified his head that a friend could have recognized his features. It was a gruesome sight, and made me realize what is meant by the term "decent burial."

This reminder of death so affected me that I left some money with Waithman to provide a deeper grave for our fellow laborer. And then, only a few days later and probably before he could carry out our plan, Waithman himself was murdered by Mexicans. The whole circumstance seemed symbolic of the loneliness and the danger that are the lot of the field engineer in the forgotten holes and corners of the world.

CHAPTER EIGHT

Insurrectos and Indians

A RESCUE MAKES A GOVERNOR — MY FAMILY
BRAVES THE JOURNEY SOUTH — THROUGH
HOSTILE COUNTRY — SANCHEZ, THE BANDIT —
LOYAL YAQUI—OUTWITTING THE MEXICAN FIESTA—
THE TIRELESS TARAHUMARES — A BRUSH WITH THE
STATION AGENT—RUNNING THE GAUNTLET WITH
A SILVER TRAIN — I RECOVER OUR STOLEN BAGGAGE

*A*fter seven months at Minas Nuevas I naturally became lonely. Not only was social life nonexistent, but correspondence with my family was as uncertain as Sonora politics could make it. All mail for the mine came by muleback from Guaymas, a distance of more than two hundred miles. Three weeks at least elapsed before letters could pass to or from San Francisco and much could happen to a foreigner in Mexico during that period. The service, moreover, was constantly interrupted, not merely because of un-settled conditions, but because the mail frequently was held at Guaymas until a sufficient amount accumulated to make a mule load.

When my wife wrote that she had made up her mind to join me, I protested, but my objections must have been feeble since they were promptly overruled. Consequently, we arranged to meet at Guaymas. As it turned out, a more inopportune time for her visit could hardly have been chosen. Scarcely had our plans been made and the last possible letter exchanged, before the whole of Sonora was plunged into the uproar of a state election, in which I was unwittingly destined to play a part.

I chartered a small schooner to take me from the little port of Agiovampo up the coast to Guaymas to meet my family. As the vessel was weighing anchor, a man on horseback galloped furiously to the water's edge and shouted wildly in English, "Save me! Take me with you quick!" His tone conveyed such desperation that I felt I could not ignore his appeal. So fearful was he of pursuers that he flung himself off his horse and waded out to meet the boat which I sent for him; then scrambled into it, and crouched down until he was brought aboard the schooner, where he flattened himself out on the deck. I was sympathetic with his distress but could not quite grasp the situation. Then, just as we were getting well under way, a dozen or more horsemen appeared over the brow of a hill, dashed down to the water's edge, and gesticulated frantically at each other while looking in all directions. My uninvited guest, still trembling at his narrow escape, explained that these men would surely kill him if they could get at him. They did not fire at the boat, however, because their quarry took care not to show himself until we were well out of the harbor, and they were apparently not sure he was on board.

After my passenger had recovered from his fright, he told me his name was Felizando Torres. His political enemies had hunted him out from a little town not far away and would have "defeated" him in the usual manner if they could have captured him. In the course of our three days' sail I found he had studied in California, spoke English perfectly, and knew several of my California friends.

When we reached Guaymas, he gave me a letter which he wished me to deliver to the American consul, Alexander Willard, who was also the agent for our company, and who had known my father and my uncle, Colonel Hays, in California. Willard informed me at once that Don Felizando was the outstanding candidate for governor of Sonora. We both realized that neither he, as American consul, nor I, as manager of an American mining company, could risk being embroiled in Mexican political affairs, and therefore must exercise every precaution not to become involved as partisans of the Torres faction.

Willard asked me to convey quietly a message to Torres advising him not to land in Guaymas, where death was certain. He was, instead, to steal our rowboat, escape to the other side of the bay, and make his way to Hermosillo, the capital of the state, where his adherents were awaiting him. This he managed to do and, as the result of a rapid "campaign," became governor of Sonora inside of two days. He held this position until his death, after which he was succeeded by his cousin Señor Luis Torres, who, in turn, held office until 1911 when, as an adherent of Diaz, he was obliged to flee the country.

By helping Don Felizando escape, I was at least partially responsible for the outcome of the election. This incident brought home to me in impressive fashion the nature of political candidacy, particularly in Mexico during the eighties. There politics, like marriage, were not to be entered into lightly; but reverently, discreetly, advisedly, soberly, and with due regard for life and limb. In England they "stand" for Parliament in traditional dignity; in America we "run" for office; but in Mexico, the defeated candidate wisely "ran" —away.

I never shall forget a practical illustration of this in the Sonora state election in 1883. At that time, as I recall it, about a thousand votes were needed by one of the parties to obtain the coveted office. Agiovampo, with a "population" of about a hundred—including men, women, children, burros, dogs, pigs, and chickens—cast the requisite number of votes.

Conditions in Sonora were no worse, however, than elsewhere in Mexico. A story told me by the manager of a silver mine in Chihuahua clearly indicates the qualifications of the electorate there. The managing director of the company had come from the States to visit the mine. After examining the property, he expressed his satisfaction with its administration and told the manager he had nothing but praise for the way it was being run.

"But," he said, "my associates up north cannot understand why you are not more broad-minded in your ideas of Mexican politics. Why don't you put more emphasis on the liberalization of political institutions?"

The manager explained that in his opinion the peons with whom he had come in contact were not qualified to vote.

"You have an entirely wrong conception of the Mexican character," he went on to explain. "They are not at all ready for any liberalization of political institutions. I'll give you a practical demonstration of this. I'll call a meeting and tell my men that on a certain day they will be given the privilege of expressing their personal choice as to who shall be president of the republic."

Accordingly, he issued a proclamation in which he assured the inhabitants that they were entirely at liberty to express their preference secretly and without any prejudice to themselves. The amazing result of this plebiscite was that about a hundred votes were cast for the most popular bullfighter in Mexico, fifty for one of the most notorious bandits in the section in which the mine was located, and a hundred and fifty for the great Mexican patriot, Benito Juarez, who had then been dead more than fifty years. After this example of Mexican political acumen the managing director acknowledged that Mexico did not possess the attributes of an intelligent democracy.

President Wilson once took offense at my telling this story, because he felt it cast an unfavorable light on his and Secretary Bryan's Mexican policies.

While the unsettled political condition in Sonora was most acute, my wife arrived at Guaymas in October, 1882, coming by steamer from San Francisco. Her little domestic expedition consisted of our son Harris, almost a year old, his nurse Theresa, my sister Betty, and my young brother Dick. The revolution started by my friend Don Felizando and his adherents had already had its repercussion in Guaymas, where for several days desultory fighting had been going on. With difficulty I managed to commandeer two rooms in the bare attic of a house owned by an acquaintance who was absent at the time. There we remained in seclusion for two days until the fighting had subsided. Since it was unsafe to leave the house, I could procure food only by foraging at night.

I had intended to take my family from Guaymas to the mine by wagon, but when the far-from-comforting news reached me that a party of foreigners who had been making the trip by land had been massacred by the Apaches a few days before, I decided to return to the mines in the same boat on which I had come north. When we were on the point of sailing, we found that the guns of the fort of Guaymas were trained on our boat to prevent our leaving. Having discovered my connection with Don Felizando, the commanding officers were evidently afraid I might be up to more mischief. However, through the assistance of Willard, we secured the proper papers from the Mexican authorities and sailed.

The boat was loaded to the gunwales with mining supplies, among which was a large quantity of explosives. Below deck the only vacant space was a small hold, badly ventilated and half filled with freight. So far Betty's only traveling had been to and from boarding school. But my wife had described to her the ornate Mississippi River boats with their red plush cabins and, when I told them I had chartered a schooner, they both expected the same sort of luxury. One look, and a whiff of the piles of dried onions in the hold, was enough for my sister; up she went on deck to pick out a bed on some comfortable pile of lumber. We followed her.

One compensation for sleeping on deck was a glorious view of the great comet of 1882, but this was offset by certain disadvantages: we were exposed to the heavy dew and the chill night air. The pathetic wailings of an innumerable family of kittens periodically disturbed our slumbers. We were fed the same kind of stew at every meal; my sister ominously maintained that the stock of kittens dwindled progressively.

It would have been a hard trip even for experienced travelers. Fortunately I had laid in a supply of provisions which included champagne, tins of pâté de foie gras, and ice. This may sound luxurious, but the iced champagne proved to be a veritable lifesaver rather than an indulgence. Harris cut his first tooth, acquired a red bandana when he lost his hat, and developed calentura. Fortunately, he turned out to be an indestructible baby.

Agiovampo was reached on the third day. About ten days earlier, when I had seen it last, there had been a hundred or more natives in the little pueblo, but when we arrived there on the return trip not a living soul was in evidence. Indians had frightened the inhabitants away, and the prospect of the journey into the interior was not cheerful.

Before leaving Guaymas I had sent a messenger by land to the mine with instructions to have a wagon and pack animals meet us on our arrival at Agiovampo. For some reason they were delayed, with the result that we were obliged to wait there for them. Meanwhile we had decided to sleep on shore in a shack, and ordered the captain of the boat to remain anchored near by. He disregarded instructions and sailed off, leaving us with no refuge. We were not molested, however, and finally our wagon put in an appearance.

On the way our driver had encountered an old Mexican whom he engaged as guide. I shall never forget the old fellow's surprise when I gave him a piece of ice. He accepted it calmly enough, but, as soon as his hand touched it, he dropped it, saying it was "too hot." But he was still much interested in it and, at his request, I gave him a large chunk to take home. Carefully wrapping the ice in a blanket, he tied it behind his saddle. I could imagine him later telling his children what a curious present he had for them and his amazement, upon untying the blanket, to find that the treasure had mysteriously disappeared.

Most of the trip from Agiovampo to Alamos was uphill and over sandy roads. I was in constant apprehension of an attack, from either Indians or bandits, since both usually took advantage of disturbed conditions to rob, pillage, and murder. I would ride a mile or so ahead of our caravan, carefully scanning the horizon to make sure the road was clear of hostile parties. If none were in sight, I would wave a handkerchief as a signal to the driver and he would come forward with all the speed he could urge out of his mules.

The trip was naturally one of great nervous tension for the women, but my wife proved to be a heroine—as she did on many subsequent occasions—and did everything possible to reassure my sister and the nurse. By way of encouragement, she frequently declared that in case Dick and I should be killed, she would faithfully promise to shoot: first, the women of the party, then her child, and then herself, rather than have them fall into the hands of the Indians.

Late the first night we reached a little pueblo occupied by peaceful Indians. There we slept, and proceeded early the next day to Alamos. Just before we reached the town we were met by a company of Mexican soldiers, sent by Governor Torres to escort us to the mine. They had been ordered to meet us at Agiovampo, but, evidently knowing the Indians were raiding, concluded that discretion outranked valor. At Alamos we rested a few days under the hospitable roof of the Bours family, and then went on to Minas Nuevas. Once safe behind the barricade I made no effort to stifle a sigh of relief.

The house had been thoroughly cleansed and made ready, but even so life at Minas Nuevas was full of hardships for my little family. It was impossible to obtain any but the crudest kind of peon cooks, and the culinary ingredients themselves were not specially appetizing. Although the climate was hot in summer, it was not unhealthful, and most of our time was spent out of doors on a large veranda.

After a short stay, my brother returned to California. As I was frequently away all day at the mine, I felt that, as a means of self-protection, my wife and sister ought to know how to use a gun. On Sunday afternoons, when the natives were on the streets, we would go out and practice shooting. The ability to shoot straight was in itself a protection against people whose chief weapon was a machete.

In spite of all efforts on the part of the insurrectos, Minas Nuevas continued to operate. My worst difficulty was with a Mexican named Sanchez, whom I had hired as a labor contractor, or mining captain. He had formerly been a notorious bandit, had killed several men, and enjoyed a reputation consonant with such activity. But he had given up the profession of banditry for that of mining, and, as a labor leader, he was first class. When the commander of the revolutionaries threatened to press Sanchez and his men into service, my bandit replied that in that event the first shot he himself fired would be at his officers, while his men would fire into their own ranks. Since he was so evidently a desperado, he and my workers were left undisturbed.

But when comparative peace had been restored in the vicinity, Sanchez began to think himself indispensable, and consequently grew very cocky. When full of tequila—a particularly vicious brand of alcoholic drink, made from the century plant—he would proclaim abroad that I was afraid to discharge him, and boast of what he would do to me if I did.

I knew that if his swaggerings were allowed to go long unrebuked, there would be an end to any discipline in the mines. Accordingly, I determined that the next payday I would make an example of him. When the men were all lined up to draw their weekly wages and Sanchez stepped forward to the desk for his, I said in a loud voice: "Sanchez, I hear you're saying I'm afraid to discharge you. Here's your money. You're fired! Now get out and stay out! If you set foot on this property again or make any move against me I'll shoot the hell out of you!"

Muttering, and with black looks, Sanchez went off, but thereafter made it his business to get me. He carried a gun, and guns were a prized possession among the Mexicans, but he was also expert with a knife, which was better for night work. Since Sanchez continued to lurk in the neighborhood, I had to be incessantly on guard.

I have already referred to my Yaqui bodyguard. They belonged to a remarkable tribe. The late Carl Lumholtz, an acknowledged authority, who spent many years in studying the Indians of Mexico, told me that he regarded the Yaqui as related to the warlike Apaches. But the great majority of Yaqui were not aggressive, though, when drilled, they became the best soldiers in the Mexican Army and in later years have been used as shock troops in battle.

Every week I would send my Yaqui guard with several thousand dollars' worth of silver, in the form of large ingots, to the mint at Alamos for coinage and deposit to the company's credit. Armed and on horseback, it was the duty of the Yaqui to convey the bullion to the mint and then bring back to me a thousand or more pesos in coin, packed in sealed canvas sacks, for the weekly raya, or payroll. The guard would place the sacks upon a table and stand at attention while I counted the money. As soon as I said "Es bueno" they would salute and retire.

Had these Indians ever absconded with the money and fled with it to the mountain fastnesses which were their tribal home and where they sought refuge when pursued by Mexican troops, its recovery would have been impossible. There was, however, not a single defalcation. In a small way they did indulge in the habits of the country.

They would, for example, pilfer a pistol, a knife, or such objects as were regarded by them as legitimate prey. To this local custom their employers were perforce obliged to bow.

It was, in fact, not an uncommon experience for me to buy chickens from my Yaqui employees, have the same fowl stolen by them within a few hours after their delivery, and promptly offered me the following day for repurchase. The Yaqui simply regarded this method of adding to their pin money as a special prerogative. While I was not indisposed to humor them to a reasonable extent, after I had purchased the same chicken several times I would protest and ask them, in the patois at my command, if they did not think they were rubbing it in.

One vexing detail under which we labored at Minas Nuevas was the constant interruption to operations caused by the innumerable holidays. Every saint in the calendar; every patriot, real or fictitious; every battle, fought or contemplated, had his, her, or its day, and, of course, any suggestion that the hero of the occasion might be honored by a stroke of work would have been regarded by the peon as sheer blasphemy. In consequence, fully one-third of each month was simply time lost. With Machiavellian cunning I did, however, manage to establish a triumphant record of having kept our company's smelter running throughout the entire round of the many and various fiestas.

These fiestas always seemed to occur at a time when to close down operations would have been a costly proceeding which we could ill afford. Heretofore, the Indians had been accustomed to leave the mine in a body for several days and repair to their villages for the Easter celebrations. This year I persuaded them to postpone their pious pilgrimage by hiring a circus outfit and arranging for them to celebrate in shifts while keeping operations under way at the same time. Thus, by solemnly mounting the griffins and swans of the merry-go-round between shifts, the Yaqui were enabled to do their duty by the saints and I to fulfill my own by the mine.

In addition to the periodic demands of religion, the observance of Sunday invariably handicapped the work during the early part of the week. Regularly after each Saturday payroll had been distributed, both Mexicans and Indians proceeded to seek consolation in the national beverages of pulque and mescal of which they partook so freely that always on Monday, and generally on Tuesday also, they were incapacitated for work. With Saturday as a half-holiday, Sunday an entire one, Monday and Tuesday set apart for convalescence, and a saint's day or two thrown in for good measure, work at the mines proceeded somewhat spasmodically.

My predecessors had found no solution to the problem and had submitted to what they regarded as the inevitable. My patience gave way at last and I set about seriously to devise some system whereby we might be reasonably sure of at least four days' work a week. Since temperance was obviously impossible, I resolved to outwit the demon rum: first, by setting up a model saloon; second, by purchasing the least injurious brand of mescal; finally, by selling this to the company employees at a lower price than it could be obtained from the village tiendas. In return for this display of public spirit on my part, I entered into an amicable arrangement with the natives. I was to allow them to get freely and gloriously drunk on Saturday night—in fact, I urged them to start early—and to remain intoxicated throughout Sunday. When Sunday evening came, I was privileged to have them all arrested and clapped under lock and key to sober up for Monday morning. The plan worked admirably. All parties were satisfied and the output at the mine was considerably increased.

My method was only less drastic than that of the padre in charge of a California mission in the early days. His church choir was composed of Indians, and to ensure their attendance on Sunday, the padre found it necessary to lock up the choir on Saturday night so that the members might be in proper physical condition for the next day. This confinement tended to inculcate in them the proper Christian spirit.

On my later trips through the northern Sierra Madre region I saw a great deal of the Tarahumare Indians, a most primitive people. Only about twenty-five thousand of them are left today, the remnants of what was a vast population at the time of the Spanish Conquest. Their most striking custom is a curious game in which, like waltzing mice, they indulge from morning until night. The men and women of the tribe drive before them a large ball, ever harder and faster, without any apparent objective. The race goes on indefinitely until the entire community is too exhausted for further pursuit. After pausing for the necessities of food and rest, the game is solemnly resumed. What the contestants see in it, nobody knows; they themselves cannot explain their enthusiasm. They only know that their ancestors for generations found in it a raison d'être; therefore, without further thought, they gird their loins and run with tireless zeal the race that is set before them.

Centuries of playing this tribal game have bred in them such facility in using their legs that they run almost involuntarily, much as a fish dilates its gills or a human being expands his diaphragm.

Consequently, the Tarahumares have phenomenal endurance as runners. A healthy Tarahumare, jogging along with hardly a pause, will run seventy miles a day. There is one well-authenticated instance where one of their messengers covered five hundred miles in five days through an excessively rough and mountainous country.

Rumors of the prowess of these Tarahumares brought an emissary from the managers of the Olympic games with an invitation for the Indians to compete, but, in spite of all inducements, they refused. Although they broke world records every day and thought nothing of it, they preferred their own ball game to athletic laurels.

In making a long journey, the Tarahumare runners live entirely on pinole, a native dish of parched corn ground to a powder and mixed with water. If they crave a more substantial meal, they will stalk a deer, and have been known to follow it through jungles and across mountains for days at a time until the fleet animal itself was exhausted by their tireless pace. Smaller animals, such as rabbits, they kill with boomerangs.

On several occasions I employed Tarahumare guides. I recall one record trip I made from a mine in the Sierra Madres to the railroad at Minaca, Chihuahua. I traveled over the rough trails with the same horse for twenty hours, pausing only occasionally for a brief rest. During the whole journey my guide ran ahead of me with no sign of fatigue.

While I was at Minas Nuevas I had by me constantly day and night and even in the mines my trustworthy friend, a six-shooter. Repeated threats had been made to me, anonymous for the most part, and I had not depended solely on the vigilance of Don Tomas, the night watchman who sat at the foot of the stairway leading to my sleeping apartment at the hacienda. Don Tomas had acquired the reputation of hombre valor some years before, when he had kept watch at the same stairway of the Ortiz family, who lived in the hacienda at the time, to prevent an enemy from approaching. One of the enemies tried to force his way past Don Tomas, and Don Tomas shot him dead.

While as I have said I did not place my safety entirely in the watchfulness and valor of Don Tomas, his presence was something of a comfort, especially to my wife and family when they were with me. Just before leaving Minas Nuevas I passed Don Tomas one day and saw the handle of his six-shooter projecting from the holster. Out of curiosity I pulled it out and tried to shoot it, but I could get no reaction. I pulled at the trigger several times, but without result. Then Don Tomas tried his hand but still nothing happened, much to his mortification. It would have been indeed a slender reed to depend upon.

During the winter of 1882-83, my father-in-law, Judge Harris, come to visit Minas Nuevas. This relieved my wife of some of the great nervous strain under which she had been living. Not only was it almost impossible to obtain proper food for her small baby, but also her own life had frequently been threatened by the same bandits who were trying to ambush me. To be fired at from behind a cactus plant while passing with her baby in her arms made peaceful monotony seem most desirable. By spring, conditions were so alarming that I called a family council to discuss what was best to be done, and it was then decided that my family should accompany Judge Harris back to the States in April.

My wife was so worried by the risks I was constantly running when off the mine property that, before she would consent to leave, she exacted from me a sacred promise never to go out without some of my Yaqui guard.

When the appointed day came, I accompanied my family as far as Guaymas. This time we traveled by wagon, sleeping under it at night, and arrived a week later at Ortiz Station on the railroad between Guaymas and the Mexican frontier at Nogales.

As Ortiz Station was merely a tiny community of about a hundred Mexicans living in adobe huts and boasted no hotel, and as the train was not due until the following morning, I looked around for quarters for the night. The station was in charge of an American agent; the railroad at that time was part of the Santa Fe system. At my request he gave us permission to spread our blankets on the upper floor of the station building. This would at least give the women and the baby an opportunity to rest. Unfortunately, the agent got drunk. He then amused himself by firing his pistols at anything within range. As the day wore on, this performance grew more and more annoying, yet there seemed to be no way of stopping our inebriated host, who was enjoying himself immensely.

About dusk we went to a near-by Mexican hut where I had arranged for frijoles and tortillas. During the supper our spirits were lowered still further when we learned there were several cases of "black" smallpox in the village. After supper, my wife and sister went upstairs again while I sat below on the station platform to have a smoke. I had been there only a few minutes when the agent rounded into view, very unsteadily, and asked me between hiccoughs if I liked music. I responded in the affirmative; whereupon, he said, "Do you see that greaser over there trying to play a fiddle? Now, you go over and get that fiddle and I'll show you what real music is."

I replied that I did not believe I cared enough for music to do that, and then asked, "Why don't you go yourself?"

Like a flash he pulled out a pistol and, leveling it at me, shouted, "You go get that fiddle, if you know what's good for your health."

The pistol was fully primed and his finger on the trigger was alarmingly shaky. Meanwhile, my wife had overheard the row; she rushed to the window and pleaded with him not to shoot. Without taking my eyes off the agent, I called up to her not to worry, and then proceeded to revile him in all the fluent, vivid phrases of the Forty-niners, among other things calling him a dirty coward and daring him to shoot.

This so astonished the agent that he actually paused to listen to my eloquence. Taking advantage of his hesitation, I suddenly wrested the pistol from his hand. Nevertheless, it was a close call. A knowledge of the psychology of a drunken man, gained during observations of many rough scenes in the mining camps, had taught me that nothing could be more disconcerting to one in the agent's state than a sudden bold verbal attack.

However, this was not quite the end of the adventure, for the man, having gone to his room, came back in a few minutes with his right hand behind his back, walked menacingly to within a few feet of me, and demanded, "Now give me back my gun!"

But I had him covered. "Move that hand an inch and I'll shoot you full of lead!"

He saw I meant business and sheepishly admitted he was only bluffing. Nevertheless, I kept my finger on the trigger as I walked slowly around him to make sure he was unarmed.

The rest of the night passed peacefully, albeit uncomfortably. I am sure, however, that my wife and sister were glad to see the train come down the track the next morning. They reached Guaymas safely and from there went east, having had enough of Mexico for the time being.

I returned to the mines, although I had decided to resign as soon as the company could conveniently spare me. Any expectation I might have had of gaining reflected glory as manager of a famous mine had come to naught. I realized that there was neither wealth nor fame to be had at Minas Nuevas. Because of the difficult situation there, I waited several months before taking formal leave; the revolutionists were making things exceedingly trying. The political faction which then had charge of the mint at Alamos was making unfair returns on the weight and fineness of the metal we sent to be coined. To evade this imposition, I decided to hold the silver at the mines until I was ready to leave, and then take it with me to Guaymas for shipment to the States.

Immediately upon my wife's departure, my loneliness began to return. One evening, about a month later, I rode off to visit a German who was running a mine some five miles away. I enjoyed his company, and when he asked me to stay to supper, I accepted the invitation. As we were sitting before a grated window, I saw a dim figure pass. I recognized Sanchez. If I had told my host that Sanchez was probably planning to waylay me on my homeward journey, he would have given me an escort, but with some false pride at confessing alarm, I said nothing.   Soon afterwards I set off in the moonlight over the trail.   I rode an active and sure-footed cow pony in whose speed and quickness I had great confidence.   Indeed, there had been times when I was safer alone on my mount than if attended by guards on slower horses.

Except for one steep, sloping outcrop of rock, twenty-five or thirty feet long, the trail furnished good footing.   As we started gingerly across this bad stretch, I caught sight of the shadow of a man rising from the bushes.   I clapped spurs to my pony's flanks.   The little beast covered the slippery rock in two noble jumps, and I was away down the trail.   I confess the bandit gave me a turn, but what was most disturbing was the thought that if I had been murdered my wife would thereby have discovered that I had broken my sacred promise to her.   Conscience doth make cowards of us all.

Sanchez continued to stalk me, his last attempt on my life taking place the day before my departure.   As Clement and I were sitting on the broad veranda in the upper story of our building, two rifle shots were fired, one very narrowly missing me.   Both Clement and I immediately dropped to the floor and crawled off to the stairs.   Mounting our horses, which were always standing in the yard saddled, we started off in quest of the desperado.   We might have spared ourselves the trouble because, as usual, the wily fellow had gone to cover.   This was his parting shot.

Preparations were carefully made for the departure of the silver train which I was to take to Guaymas.   Ordinarily the mules used to transport the silver carried a load of three hundred pounds each.   But since this time we were convoying a ton of pure silver bullion worth many thousand dollars, which I knew would bring the Mexicans hot on our trail, we loaded the mules with only half the usual amount—a seventy-five pound ingot in each saddlebag.   In order to make even greater speed, I had fresh mules relayed about fifty miles away on the road to Guaymas.

Late one afternoon, during a heavy thunderstorm, I called ten of my Yaqui guards together and had them saddle and load up the mules with the silver bars, blankets, food, and other equipment necessary for the trip.   Off we started.   The first few miles were over a mountain trail, which we were able to follow only with the help of occasional flashes of lightning. All that night and late into the next afternoon we kept going in order to reach our relay station. There we snatched a few hours' sleep, spreading our blankets over the bars of silver and using them as mattresses. This, I need hardly say, was to ensure their protection, and not because of their comfort or resiliency.

When we resumed our journey, I was very glad to change from horseback to buckboard—the week before I had slipped in the mine and hurt my back. Sitting astride a horse was decidedly uncomfortable. My team was made up of a horse and a mule. Although we had only a few hours' start on the Mexicans we never saw them, but it may have been only because we never took time to look back. I led the way in the buckboard, while the pack mules were driven from behind by the Yaqui guard. In record time we reached the Yaqui River.

In attempting to cross, I found that the recent heavy rains in the mountains had so increased the depth that it was impossible to ford the river. I made several attempts to cross with the buckboard where the river seemed most shallow, but each time the mule, in spite of much whip cracking and urging, declined to go on when the water came up to his belly, although the horse, who had less "horse" sense, was perfectly willing to do so.

I was still trying to make the crossing when a voice hailed me from the bank. Turning, I saw a man on horseback, who yelled to me in Spanish that the ford was impassable. When I replied in the same language he gathered from my accent that I was an American, and rode down to speak to me. The water in the middle of the river, he said, was well over the animals' heads and the only available ford was two or three miles farther upstream. The mule's obstinacy was fortunate for me as well as for the pack animals as they would certainly have sunk with their heavy loads if they had attempted to follow my team into the river.

I asked my new acquaintance whether he knew an American named Williams who lived on the other side of the river. He replied that he was Williams but had recently moved to this side. I then told him that I was seeking his hospitality; that because I had a large cargo of silver and a small bodyguard I did not dare proceed after dark; and that the Mexicans knew I was traveling en bonanza. He said cordially that he would be very glad to put me up for the night.

During the course of our conversation that evening it developed that Williams, a man of about sixty, had originally come from Texas, where in his early days he had conceived an ardent admiration for Colonel Jack Hays. When he discovered that I was none other than the old Ranger chief's nephew and namesake, he at once brought out the red-eye. The next day Williams and his three powerful sons took me up the river and escorted me safely to the other side. I offered to pay them for their trouble but they refused to take any money; they did, however, ask me to send them some tobacco and coffee from Guaymas. Naturally, I was glad to do this.

Shortly after crossing the Yaqui River we received word that American troops had driven the Apaches from Arizona into Mexico, and that the Indians were massacring people in wholesale fashion as they came south. We already knew that the Yaqui Indians were marauding. There was what might be called a twilight zone of about thirty miles between the warring Yaqui on our left and the renegade Apaches on our right. Then, too, we had pursuing Mexicans at our rear. If the Apaches should close in, we planned to edge over into Yaqui territory, because even "bad" Yaqui were preferable to the murderous Apaches. I drove my caravan unremittingly and after three days more of hard riding we reached Guaymas, worn out but with the silver intact.

After I had delivered the metal to Willard, I told of my meeting with the Williams family. Willard congratulated me on having escaped from them alive. When I displayed evident amusement, he went on to explain that the senior Williams had once been considered one of the most desperate characters in Texas. After committing a number of crimes there he had escaped with his family to Mexico, and no one had since had the courage to cross the border and arrest him. I suggested that perhaps Williams had dealt gently with me because I was the nephew of his old hero, Colonel Jack. "Ah," Mr. Willard remarked at once, "that explains everything."

From the reports of Indian depredations that reached Guaymas I realized even more strongly than at the time how narrow had been our escape, and my appreciation of the loyalty of my Yaqui guards was considerably enhanced. These Indians could easily have done away with me or allowed some "fatal accident" to happen and then could have taken the silver up into their mountains. As a matter of fact, until within recent years no military expedition has been able to expel the Indians from their mountain retreats. The loyalty of the Yaqui to their employers, however, is well recognized by all Americans in Mexico and, indeed, even by their hereditary enemies, the Mexicans.

This question of stealing was the ever-present problem of every mining engineer and manager operating in Mexico.

In 1885, accompanied by George W. Starr, manager of the Empire mine of which I was consulting engineer, I made a trip to examine some mines in the State of Oaxaca, about three hundred miles south of Pueblo, Mexico. The journey was made alternately by stage, horseback, muleback, and litera. The litera is a sort of palanquin, generally in the form of a narrow, coffin-like structure with long poles at either end, which serve as shafts. It is harnessed to mules in front and behind, the animal in front being led by an Indian on horseback. Our litera was the height of luxury, with a canopy to protect the traveler from rain and sun. It was not uncomfortable, though the movements of the two mules did not always synchronize.

We made about four miles an hour traveling continuously night and day over the rough mountain trails. After leaving the city of Oaxaca, where the great Mexican presidents, Juarez and Diaz, were born, we passed the ruins of the Maya Indians at Malta, which are now celebrated because of their archaeological interest.

We also saw the famous tree at Tule, a gigantic cypress, measuring about a hundred and fifty feet in height, a hundred in girth, and with a colossal branch spread of a hundred and forty feet. It is supposed to have been standing a thousand years before Columbus discovered America, and to have sheltered Cortez and his soldiers when they invaded Mexico. The great naturalist and traveler, von Humboldt, had carved his name on the trunk and it could still be seen.

When we arrived at the mines we found that the machinery was of the most primitive type and practically useless. Every morning before the mill started, the miners held divine service asking for heavenly intervention to improve the grade of ore. At the time of our visit, at least, these prayers were of no avail, for the mine was a losing proposition. After about ten days of sampling the mine, Starr and I started on our return trip on horseback to Oaxaca, where we hired a wagon and a team of four mules to take us to the point where we could secure literas to carry us across the mountains. Starr occupied a seat within the wagon, I did the driving, and the driver himself devoted his energy to securing little rocks to throw at the lead mules, which he could not reach with the whip—he called it feeding the mules maize.

We had proceeded about fifteen miles when Starr called my attention to the fact that our baggage, which had been stowed in the rear of the wagon, had disappeared. Upon examination we found that the straps and ropes that had securely fastened the baggage had been cut with a knife. We were not greatly concerned about the clothing we had lost, but with it were all the samples of ore we had so laboriously collected to bring back to the States to be assayed. Unless we recovered these samples we would have to return to the mine and resample it, involving a delay of several weeks.

Accordingly we started to retrace our steps. A light rain had just fallen and we had gone no more than a mile when we saw clearly marked footprints along the road. This was at a point directly opposite a lane which ran through a patch of sugar cane. The tracks of the bandits led into this lane and as we stood at its entrance an Indian came hesitantly toward us. When he reached us at the junction of the main road he sidled off and started away at a rapid pace. His manner was definitely suspicious. I unslung my sawed-off shotgun loaded with buckshot (a Wells-Fargo "messenger" gun), covered him, and ordered him to come up to our wagon. After I threatened him with all kinds of dire punishment, he confessed that he knew where the baggage was hidden. He pointed to a place about three hundred yards from where we had stopped and said that there were six half-breeds hiding there in the sugar cane. I left Starr to watch the Indian and the driver, in whom I did not have much confidence, and went to recover the baggage, first cautioning Starr to keep guard and not to leave the wagon unless he heard the report of my gun.

I went stealthily along the lane until I came to the point where the footprints led into a dense sugar cane patch and there, not more than twenty feet from the lane, were six men sitting on their haunches, ripping open the sacks containing our baggage. At my unexpected appearance they started to scramble to their feet but I had my gun on them and ordered them to stay as they were. One fellow made a break and struck at me with his machete, narrowly missing me, and skipped off. I forced the remaining five to repack the ore samples and precede me in single file to the wagon. Few things proved to be missing from the baggage, so we dismissed the men with divers threats and warnings and proceeded to Mexico City, with no more unpleasant adventures.

Fifteen months in Minas Nuevas had temporarily ruined my health. I was in a seriously run-down condition, due not only to the incessant nervous strain I had been under, but also to the lack of proper nourishment and bodily comforts. I was little better off in worldly goods, after all my hopes of discovering treasure, but I had gained much in the way of practical experience. Aside from learning how to deal with the Mexican natives and with labor in general, I had been compelled, in the absence of technical assistance, to familiarize myself with many methods and processes of mining and metallurgy which thereafter were to make me more or less independent of scientific equipment. Finally, I had managed to pick up a good working knowledge of Spanish, which enabled me to keep abreast of the many mining projects all over Mexico. Thus my sojourn there gave me, early in my career, a glimpse of the tremendous possibilities concealed in that little-explored country.

CHAPTER NINE

In Far Places

HEALTH RESTORED—BOSTON AND NEW YORK—THE
"PRACTICAL" VERSUS THE TRAINED ENGINEER—
THE STRANGE STORY OF AN AMBIGUOUS REPORT—THE
GOLD THAT WAS ALWAYS OVER THE HILL—HEAD-
WATERS OF THE ORINOCO AND AMAZON—THE PRAC-
TICE OF COUVADE—LIVING ON THE COUNTRY—THE
GOLDEN FISHHOOKS—GUATEMALA—HURRICANE AND FEVER

*A*fter nearly two years in the wilds of Sonora I was happy to feel about me once more the stir and bustle of San Francisco. Within a week after my return in June, 1883, I was offered the position of consulting expert to the public administrator of San Francisco, Philip A. Roach, in connection with the examination of the Blythe estate. The fact that Blythe had died intestate made it necessary to have a public appraisal of his property, much of which consisted of mines, partly in Trinity County, California, and partly in Nevada. I was glad to accept this offer as I had saved up little from my salary in Minas Nuevas, and the generous fee was much needed by my family.

At this time my wife was in the East, visiting her sister, Mrs. J. P. Broiderick, at Jamaica Plain, a suburb of Boston. One day, as she was about to go into the city with our son Harris and his nurse, she received a check from me. She stopped in to cash it at one of the Boston banks. As the cashier did not know her, he was naturally reluctant to honor it and asked whether she knew anyone who could identify her. Unfortunately, her entire acquaintanceship was in Jamaica Plain.

The nurse, Mary Lynch, quick-witted and of course Irish, overheard the conversation, and stepping up to the window said, "And ye don't know that this is Mrs. Hammond?" The cashier replied that he did not.

Mary then picked up Harris, turned him upside down, and exhibiting him back-to at the cashier's window, exclaimed belligerently, "Well, look at this now!" On the inside of Harris's baby drawers was printed the name Hammond. The cashier honored the check, but admitted it was the first time that kind of identification had been made.

My new job gave me the welcome opportunity of leading a wholesome outdoor life without serving as a target for someone lurking behind a cactus plant. While I was examining the mines in Trinity County, I was invited to stay at the ranch of Mr. John Carr, who was in charge of the property. On the strength of good milk and butter, chicken and eggs, the bracing California air, and the motherly care of Mrs. Carr, I rapidly threw off the ill effects of Mexico and regained my health. After a month of this pleasant existence I made a brief excursion into Nevada to inspect a copper mine belonging to the Blythe estate. Then, anxious for a reunion with my family, I hastened east to join my wife and small son.

A few weeks' visit was all the vacation I felt I could afford at this time. I had long been considering an office in New York. I fully realized this would cause me great financial inconvenience, since the cost of living in the East was considerably greater than in San Francisco; that I would be losing the advantage of my business connections, those I had inherited and also those I had built up during my early engineering career in the West. There were serious risks involved, but I recognized the advantage of being near abundant capital, and I also realized that, if I were fortunate enough to succeed, it would be on a larger scale than I could hope for in California. Furthermore, if I were successful in New York, I could thereby establish a national reputation.

In this situation, in which risk and profit were evenly balanced, I called to mind the quotation from Browning's *Paracelsus:*

> "Are there not, Festus, are there not, dear Michal,
> Two points in the adventure of a diver,
> One—when, a beggar, he prepares to plunge,
> One—when, a prince, he rises with his pearl?
> Festus—I plunge!"

Thus I plunged, and took an office in the Mills Building. This building, the most impressive skyscraper of its day, had just been completed by D. O. Mills.

Mr. Mills, whom I had known as a boy in San Francisco, was one of the most prominent of the old-time bankers of California. His large fortune had been made in mining, railroading, and the development of many important industries in California, Nevada, and elsewhere in the Far West. Highly respected for both integrity and ability, he did more than anyone else in that period to make mining recognized by eastern investors as a legitimate industry. He was always one of my strongest backers, even promising his friends that if they could "get a favorable report from John Hays Hammond" he would put money of his own into the enterprise.

Not long after launching myself on my professional career, I called to see my old friend Senator George Hearst at the Hoffman House, then a famous hostelry, as I knew he would be interested in what I had been doing. The senator greeted me cordially by asking, "Well, my young friend, how've you been getting along?"

I replied in what must have seemed a self-satisfied tone, that I was getting along very well and that I had made no mistakes up to that time. Then the senator said, "Well, that is splendid as far as it goes, but have you made any successes?"

Crestfallen, I had to admit that I had not, whereupon he said, "Now go ahead and make some mistakes, and follow through by making some successes."

I did not realize the value of this advice until later in life when I was thrown professionally in contact with a certain type of engineer whose highest ambition was to attain the reputation of conservatism. Men of that type were conspicuous by not having made any mistakes, but lacked the daring spirit essential to making a few successes.

After an engineer has made large investments which have turned out profitably for his clientele, he may advise longer shots for that clientele and take chances that as a younger man he would not have been justified in doing.

There may be a happy middle of the road which the engineer should follow between ultraconservatism and too much daring, but to attain signal success in big enterprises the words of the first Marquis of Montrose are worth keeping in mind:

> He either fears his fate too much,
>   Or his desires are small,
> That dares not put it to the touch,
>   To gain or lose it all.

In the East I found less prejudice against an educated engineer than was indicated by Mr. Hearst's earlier attitude when I applied for a position.

Looking back now, I recognize that there was much justice in what Mr. Hearst had said about men with a Freiberg degree.

Unfortunately in the preceding generation the educated engineer was disposed to affect a certain superiority which naturally aroused the hostility of the so-called practical miner. In my case I was fortunate in having been brought up in a western community that judged a man solely by his achievement. For that reason I succeeded in getting along well with the practical miner, but I soon realized the immense advantage of technical training as I observed that a trained engineer could in a short time qualify as "practical" in the operation of mines.

It did not take the educated engineer long to become more proficient in the handling of pumps and other mining machinery, in timbering the mines, in the use of explosives, and in the extraction of ore bodies, than the practical miner himself. And, of course, in the metallurgical treatment of ores he was immeasurably superior by reason of his technical knowledge.

It is a commentary on the "practical" miner that he is far more of a theorist than the "theoretical" mining engineer when he attempts to explain geological phenomena, for he is not restricted by scientific considerations from giving free play to a glamorous imagination.

I was not long in learning that the financial backing I established through my eastern clientele greatly enhanced my reputation in my native state, and enabled me to demand and obtain much higher fees than would have been the case had I confined my professional activities to California.

Believing that the "laborer is worthy of his hire," I exacted from my clients in the way of fees all that the traffic would bear, or almost the limit. The technical man, as well as the laboring man, often has been forced to battle for his rights in this connection.

That this attitude was not unconscionable may be shown by the relation of the engineer to his employer. It is on the strength of the recognized integrity, ability, and successful experience of the engineer that capital is invested in mining enterprises. The success or failure of such enterprise determines the career and future value of the engineer. He risks his reputation when he submits a report to his client.

The engineer is not privileged to urge extenuating circumstances in case of failure. The lawyer may ascribe the loss of his case to an incompetent judge or to a corrupt jury; the doctor, the loss of his patient to the will of God; but the engineer must escape the odium of failure. *He must make good.*

That the engineer should be fully requited for the professional service which has contributed large profits to his employer and the investing public should not be regarded as grasping or unfair on his part. The engineer is entitled to a larger part of the profits of the mining industry than the mere promoter, and the lawyer who organizes the company. This is not advocating professional racketeering.

Why should a man who assumes the initial responsibility be deprived of a reasonable profit after the enterprise proves successful? Why should a promoter pocket all the money, because he gets up a prospectus and gets the people to come in on the strength of the engineer's reputation? The investor is entitled to his share of the profits, but the technical man should stand up for his own rights and be paid well. I have also always maintained that the engineer has the right to invest in the stock of the company and announce the fact in the prospectus, provided he will hold on to his stock until the mine has proved a success.

There are many types of risks which mining engineers must run. One of the most curious of these hazardous experiences was told me by Professor W. P. Blake, who, although considered by practical miners as belonging to the theoretical class of engineers, yet stood high in the ranks of the profession. Blake was a man a little over sixty years old, at this time. He was singularly handsome with a courtly manner of a gentleman of the old school. I had known him socially for some years past.

One of my clients, the manager of the Wells, Fargo Express Company in New York, brought me a report made by Professor Blake on a copper mine located on an island in the Gulf of California not far from Guaymas. I read over the report quite thoroughly. At first, I was somewhat perplexed because of its ambiguity. After reading it more carefully, I told my client it was long-winded and noncommittal, and consequently he would not be justified in sending me to make an examination of the property.

A few days later I was honored with a visit from Blake, his first since I had established my office. I surmised why he had called and braced myself for his indignation. After a few words about our many mutual friends, he said, "Well, Mr. Hammond, you made a pretty hard criticism of my report."

All I could say was that I had made my criticism conscientiously and did not see how I could have done differently under the circumstances.

He looked at me steadily for a moment. "I wonder what you would have done in the same situation."

"I'm afraid I don't know the situation," I replied, a little nonplused.

There was a pause. Then Blake said;

"I'd like to tell you, if you don't mind.

"A Mr. and Mrs. Williams engaged me to make an examination of a copper mine. On a certain day I met them, as agreed, in Guaymas. They were to take me with them in their small schooner to the island on which the property was located, several days' sail away. An acquaintance of mine who saw me about to board the Williams boat, called me aside and asked whether I intended to accompany these people. On my replying in the affirmative, he inquired, 'Do you know what you'll be up against—going with this man and woman?' I admitted I didn't know anything about them.

"Then he explained. 'She's a notorious murderess. She was tried for murder, and was accused of dissolving the man's body in nitric acid. She got off, and later married this Welshman, Williams.'

"I was disturbed over the news, but as the boat was not only about to sail, but also had all my belongings aboard, and I had accepted half my fee in advance, there was little else left for me to do. At the outset of my examination I saw that the property was no good, but I was in mortal terror that, if I should make an unsatisfactory report, I would never see my home again. Williams said he expected to sell it on the strength of my good report but I was convinced, nevertheless, that he knew it was utterly worthless.

"At the conclusion of the day's work, I was evidently expected not only to express some kind of opinion but to put it in writing. I tried to get them to let me take home the data I had gathered and later submit them a written detailed report. But they evidently could see the way my mind was working and insisted that it be completed before we leave the island. We were entirely alone, with the exception of a few Mexicans, and there was absolutely no communication with the outside world except by their schooner.

"There was only one thing I could do. I wrote a report which conveyed practically nothing in as many words as possible. I described at great length the geology of the mine, entering into many mineralogical technicalities. Then I described the Indians and their ancestry, paid a glowing tribute to the climate, and finally added pen sketches of the scenery. I hoped the noncommittal part of the report might be overlooked if I magnified the good features, but I tried to include sufficient qualifications to prevent readers from being misled. I think it worked.

"I was in the position of Scheherazade in the *Thousand and One Nights,* whose life depended on keeping the sovereign interested and amused. My hosts were entertained as I had planned and at the same time you were not deceived."

I congratulated him on his shrewdness in getting out of a decidedly delicate situation.

One of the most important of my early commissions came in 1884 when I was employed by New York clients to make an examination of a reputedly valuable deposit of gold in Colombia. Victor Cerruti, promoter of the proposed mining deal, went with me on this three months' trip. Our route took us first to Aspinwall and thence by rail across the Isthmus of Panama, where we waited a few days for a steamer bound down the west coast of Colombia. The region now called the Canal Zone and also the Republic of Panama at that time belonged, of course, to Colombia.

At the time of my arrival there, French engineers and their swarms of laborers were dredging a channel through the fever swamps and digging through the low hills. Yellow fever and malaria were killing hundreds and taking the heart out of the great de Lesseps enterprise. Not lack of courage but fever, imperfect engineering, and corruption defeated the French, and turned their project into disaster. The canal had to wait for Theodore Roosevelt, Gorgas, and Goethals.

I was fortunate enough to secure from the French officials a contract for a dredge to be made by the Union Iron Works of San Francisco, of which I was then consulting engineer. This dredge was of such excellent workmanship that it was the only one in good enough condition to be used when the American government took over the construction of the canal.

The original engineering plans of de Lesseps had been to cut a sea-level canal. When he finally realized, however, that the cost would be vastly increased and the time required would be much greater, he adopted the system of locks identical with the plan of the American engineers when our government took over the completion of the project. From a military point of view a sea-level canal would still be desirable, and it is probable that some time in the future our government will construct a canal through the right of way already acquired in Nicaragua.

At Buenaventura I was greatly shocked to learn of the death of my dear friend and classmate, David Root Alden, who had died about a year earlier from the Chagres fever while constructing a railroad from Buenaventura to Cali. This made me realize keenly the dangerous nature of this disease which was again epidemic and hastened my departure for the high lands of the interior. After two days' travel on horseback, we reached Cali where I stopped with the Cerruti family.

Cerruti himself was one of the wealthiest and most important merchants in that part of Colombia. His wife, a descendant of Bolivar, was a highly cultured and charming woman, who had been educated abroad and spoke several languages fluently. They had three small children, to whom the mother taught music by means of a piano which had been brought over the trails from Buenaventura by pack mules. It was a great surprise to find a home like this so remote from civilization.

A few years after my parting with Cerruti he was one of the principals in an international incident. He had been arrested as an alleged political conspirator against the Colombian government. As an Italian citizen, he naturally appealed at once to his own government for help. Warships were immediately sent to make a demonstration along the coast of Colombia. Direct negotiations failing, the Colombian and Italian governments submitted the matter to President Grover Cleveland as arbitrator, and he decided in favor of Cerruti. Soon afterwards he and his family returned to Italy.

Leaving Cerruti in Cali, I secured equipment and guides for the trip into the country between the headwaters of the Orinoco and the Amazon. I spent several weeks searching for quartz veins and placers containing gold, but found no precious metal in quantities warranting development. Everywhere I went, however, the natives assured me through my negro guide, who acted as a kind of interpreter, that just over the next rise was a hill of gold. There were, then, no maps of the country, and often no trails; sometimes I had to wade for hours waist-deep in the streams to avoid the jungle.

Though I found no gold, my wanderings were interesting in other respects: I had been where no white man up to that time had ventured; I had stood on top of the continental divide; I had seen streams flowing to three great rivers, one of which emptied into the South Atlantic, one into the Caribbean, and one into the Pacific.

It was in Colombia that I first heard of couvade. I had employed negro girls, in charge of an elderly negress named Maria, to help in prospecting work. One day Maria did not report for duty. I readily understood the reason, as it had been evident that she was an expectant mother. Within a few days, however, she returned to her duties.

Coincident with her reappearance came the disappearance of her husband, a lazy negro who looked after the camp and whose principal duty was to see that our beds were free from scorpions and other dangerous insects. After searching inquiry I ascertained that he had gone to take charge of the baby in his wife's place and was lying in bed with the child, receiving calls and congratulations from the old wives of the village.

Many years later I related my Colombian experiences at a luncheon given me by Colonel House, at which were Balfour, Lloyd George, Austen Chamberlain and several other important Englishmen. Couvade was a custom entirely unknown to these eminent statesmen. Indeed, I have met few men who had heard of the custom, though the subject is extensively treated in the Encyclopaedia Britannica. Strangely enough, this practice is known to modern anthropologists, and Marco Polo in medieval times came across it in Chinese Turkestan.

Accompanied by two native guides I penetrated some distance into the cannibal country of Colombia. The tribe was stated to be truly cannibalistic; that is, human flesh was used as food and not merely in the observance of ritual practices. At one time our supply train failed to meet us as arranged, and for two days we had to live as best we could. All we had to eat was a kind of coffee bean toasted in a miner's gold pan. On my return to camp I rode through a native village from which all the men had departed; there were left only women, children, and chickens. I tried to buy some of the chickens, throwing down a silver dollar and expressing my wishes in a sign language invented for the occasion. As the women refused to sell, I shot a chicken and picked it up. A terrible racket ensued. There came cries of "white devil" from the women. Not satisfied with terrific howls and shrieks, these inhospitable females began to pelt us with stones. We stood not upon the order of our going, but went.

One of the dishes often prepared for me in the wilds was a very tasty stew. Not inquiring too closely into its ingredients, I found it excellent and ate it with great gusto until the day I fished up a small skull—a monkey's skull. The revulsion was acute; I lost my taste for stew.

The most unpleasant experience I had on this trip was when I started alone with two half-breeds as guides from Cali to Buenaventura. In order to avoid a longer stay than was absolutely necessary in Buenaventura to await the arrival of the steamer I was to take for Panama, I delayed my departure from Cali. I had given myself but little spare time in which to make the trip. After we left Cali the mozos (guides) began to indulge in too much liquor and became lazy, stubborn, and even impertinent. At times both of them, against my earnest protest, would jump on the pack mule carrying my baggage. I was compelled to apply the whip to them to enforce obedience. Fortunately they carried no gun, their sole weapon being the machete. If they had dared they would have killed me; but they were afraid to attempt this, knowing that I was armed. I spent three sleepless nights in fear of an attack, but I succeeded in reaching Buenaventura with barely an hour to spare before the departure of the steamer.

I returned to New York, richer in experience, and with a good fee, but with no gold discoveries. However, the natives must have been right in their belief that at one time there had been gold somewhere in the vicinity. Years later I sent an engineer back to this same section to examine some of the alluvials with the intent to start dredging operations. The alluvials were disappointing, not carrying sufficient gold to warrant commercial exploitation. But in boring test holes in the bed of a long dried-up stream, the engineer dug up some gold fishhooks from a depth of about forty feet. Exceedingly thin and curiously wrought without barbs, these relics of a forgotten civilization must have lain hidden for centuries. But no one could make a fortune out of a few gold fishhooks.

In January of the next year, 1885, I made another prospecting expedition southward. Some clients of mine, hearing of extensive auriferous gravels in the northeastern part of Guatemala, had engaged me to examine them.

When I arrived at New Orleans, I found that the regular steamer from there to Guatemala had been wrecked off Yucatan two weeks before, and a small one had been put into temporary use. The moment we reached the Gulf of Mexico we encountered heavy seas, and by the end of the first day our little craft was obliged to stop frequently for engine repairs. The second day out the storm greatly increased in violence.

Besides myself and my assistant, Garthwaite, the only passenger was a man who was on his way to Guatemala to give exhibitions of landing by parachute from a balloon. The captain of the steamer, calling the three of us together, told us quite frankly that we were in a dangerous position, close off the rugged shore of Yucatan. In fact, we were near enough to see the wreck of the other steamer. He intimated that, if our engine trouble became more acute, there might be some doubt of our being able to survive the storm.

At this the balloonist said, enthusiastically: "Cap, I've got an idea. My balloon's here on board, and I can gas her up in a few minutes. With the wind blowing the way it is inshore, it'd be a cinch to take a half dozen of us off."

I could not see exactly how this was to be accomplished in so brief an interval, particularly as the ship was rolling and pitching at such a rate that even the cook could not function in the galley. However, I was not called upon to put the problem into words because the captain replied hastily to this interesting offer: "Not on your life. My crew, especially the niggers, are so frightened already that your idea would finish them. I'd have a dead crew on my hands and we'd land in hell."

This was not cheering news but, since there was nothing to be done about it, I went to my cabin and wrote a short will and farewell letter to my family. This I carefully placed in a bottle and sealed it with a cork, ready to throw overboard in the final emergency. Then

I uncorked another bottle and settled down to read Prescott's *Conquest of Mexico,* a book I have found so diverting on other occasions as to take my mind off imminent danger and which proved equally efficacious in this emergency.

Though the steamer was so long overdue that it had been given up as lost in the storm, we finally arrived safely at Belize in British Honduras. From there the voyage to Guatemala was uneventful.

My acquaintance with the balloonist naturally ripened during the voyage. He told me he had been giving exhibitions in New Orleans, which culminated on Thanksgiving Day with a descent in his parachute. The wind had taken him off his course so that he involuntarily landed on the roof of a little negro shack. The last thing he remembered was breaking through the roof and falling on the table, around which the dusky inhabitants were enjoying their Thanksgiving meal. So surprised and frightened were they that they jumped up and left him there unconscious for some hours. He was laid up for several weeks in the hospital and had only just recovered before starting for Guatemala.

Two years afterwards I met him again, giving an exhibition in San Francisco. This time he was carried out into the bay in his parachute, but was fortunately picked up. At Honolulu, some time later, his luck deserted him; he was blown far out to sea and was eaten by sharks before rescuers could reach him.

In order to reach the Guatemalan mines I had been sent to examine, I had to descend a river in a dugout made from a mahogany log. As my four natives paddled along, I noted that some of the wood of the country sank in the water. I was even more interested to find that the pieces of rock which I broke off floated. They were pumice stone!

After a long tedious day the monotony of which I relieved by shooting at alligators, darkness stopped our advance. As our dugout approached the shore the natives shouted, and I fired my gun repeatedly so that the noise might drive off the alligators on the bank of the river. Then we camped for the night. As it was too dark and rainy to collect wood and build a fire, we had to be content with digging into our supply of canned food. Notwithstanding my fatigue, I could not get to sleep. The monkeys in the trees kept up a continuous chatter. Occasionally they became bold enough to drop twigs on us; fortunately there were no coconut palms handy. The next day we arrived at the place where the promised horses were waiting, and after two days' ride over marshy ground reached the gravel deposits.

While there was obviously some gold present, there was at that time no process known which would warrant working the gravel for such a small recovery; gold dredging was a subsequent development in the treatment of auriferous gravels.

After a few days' work, I was prepared to make my report to my clients. Garthwaite returned via Guatemala City and the Pacific coast to San Francisco, while I headed for New Orleans. Before I started I made a side trip to the wonderful Mayan ruins at Quirigua, not far from where I was examining the gravels. Although the ruins were so overgrown by jungle that it was difficult to get much of a view, what I did see of them overwhelmed me by its grandeur. My impressions are not so clear as they might have been had I not fallen ill of a bad case of malaria, and found, to my consternation, that Garthwaite had carried our medicine kit with him to San Francisco. My temperature was so high that it was impossible for me to travel and I was consequently obliged to accept shelter in a little two-room hut occupied by an entire family of half a dozen negroes. They gave me a place to sleep on the floor, the only space available. Although their resources were limited, no one could have exceeded their kind hospitality, not even in our own South.

In this hovel I remained for two or three days until I had somewhat recovered, and then started out on horseback for Lake Isabel. Although I was so weak that I could not ride more than a mile or so at a time before dismounting for a rest, I finally reached the lake, where I was fortunate enough to find a dear old Californian couple who kept a store. The kindly old lady took me in hand and dosed me with calomel, quinine, and other medicines and after a few days I was well enough to resume my trip back to the States.

It was months before I was entirely recovered, and I had to turn down many opportunities for mine examinations which would have greatly increased my bank account and, perhaps, my reputation. Some years later I discussed malaria with Henry M. Stanley, who headed the expedition sent by the New York *Herald* to Central Africa to search for Livingstone. Stanley was exposed to all kinds of malaria during his life, but he told me that the worst case he ever had was contracted in the State of Arkansas.

Be that as it may, I am quite content with the memory of the severity of my own Central American brand!

CHAPTER TEN

All in the Day's Work

*I*n 1890 the Mulatos mines in Sonora, Mexico, were purchased from the Aguayo brothers by a syndicate composed of American and English investors. The price agreed upon was $1,500,000 United States currency, of which $750,000 was paid over immediately and the remainder left in escrow to be remitted at regular intervals.

No sooner had the property been taken over by the syndicate headed by the successful California mining firm of Hayward and Hobart, than it began to appear that some deception had been practiced. For example, the mill run at once showed ore of little value. There could be no doubt as to the integrity of Dan Gillet and Alexis Janin, the San Francisco mining engineers who had made the examination on behalf of the purchasers; they would seem to have taken the usual precautions to verify their tests. Nevertheless, the mill runs indicated that the sale was a swindle.

The mystery was soon solved. After the original payment had been made to the Aguayos, one of their Mexican agents in the transaction became dissatisfied with the amount of his commission. Upon being refused further compensation by his employers, he let the cat out of the bag and confessed that the mine had been salted by its former owners.

Now, there are many ways in which ore can be salted, some of which are very ingenious. In this case it was done either by inserting a fine tube through the mesh of the sacks in which the expert's samples had been placed and blowing additional metal dust into the sacks, or by a solution of the metal injected by a hypodermic needle. Gold added in this way obviously increased the gold content in these ore samples upon which the value of the property was estimated.

At this time General John Eagan, who subsequently figured during the Spanish-American War in connection with the "embalmed beef" scandal, was stationed at San Francisco. When he heard of the Mulatos fiasco he immediately communicated with the firm of Hayward and Hobart. He informed them that he was a close personal friend of President Diaz and said he felt sure that if it could be proved to the president's satisfaction that the deal had been an out-and-out swindle on the part of the Mexicans, Diaz would order a cancellation of the sale and insist that the money be refunded.

Accordingly, General Eagan was sent to Mexico City to discuss the matter with Diaz. He explained to the president how carefully the examination had been made, and that the American firm involved was not only reputable but among the most important in the United States; that they were in no sense gamblers in mining stock, but bona fide scientific developers of mining properties. In spite of having taken the usual precautions, they had been shamelessly swindled, and the general pointed out that if the injustice were allowed to go unrebuked and unpunished, the logical consequence would be to keep American money out of Mexico, and perhaps English as well, for English investors were associated with the Hayward and Hobart firm.

This touched Diaz's cardinal policy. He told Eagan that if it could be clearly shown that the Mulatos ore was of such inferior grade that it could not be worked profitably, and was far below the grade indicated by the syndicate's own experts, he would compel the Aguayos to refund the money already advanced and would order a legal cancellation of the sale. The fact that the Aguayo brothers belonged to the anti-Diaz political faction in Sonora accounted perhaps for this responsiveness to General Eagan's appeal.

When Eagan returned with this assurance, the syndicate naturally made haste to follow it up. To prove the honesty of its intentions, the syndicate offered to defray the cost of examination by a disinterested expert whom Diaz was asked to name. To my gratification, Señor Romero Rubio, the Mexican minister at Washington, presently notified me that I had been selected, and formally invited me to undertake the mission.

As I had not met Diaz, I could not imagine how I had come to be chosen. Eventually I learned that Señor Rubio, who in addition to being Mexican minister at Washington was also Diaz's father-in-law, had applied to James G. Blaine, then our secretary of state, for advice on the matter, and Blaine's recommendation of me had been accepted by Diaz.

The affair was given much publicity, not only because of the fraud, but also on account of the appeal to the president of Mexico. In Sonora the excitement was intense, for the Aguayo brothers through subsidized newspapers and circular letters had spread the report that they were being victimized by unscrupulous gringos who, with characteristic Yankee cunning, were endeavoring to impose upon the trusting minds of the poor Mexicans.

I realized that the trip would be attended by considerable personal danger, for the Aguayos would certainly not be disposed to let me stand between them and their fraudulently secured gains. Nevertheless, I lost no time in accepting the offer. By chance, I talked over the expedition with General Alexander McDowell McCook, one of the famous fighting McCooks, who was stationed in California at that time. General McCook was not only a friend of mine but he was also a close friend of Governor Luis Torres of Sonora, and he offered to secure an escort of Mexican soldiers to accompany me to the mines. I thanked the general for his suggestion but declined the offer, recalling Juvenal's question, *"Quis custodiet ipsos custodes?"* One might well ask who would guard the guards themselves when one had to do with the military arm of Mexico.

I still felt that it would be unwise to make the trip into Mexico alone; therefore, through Dominick Broden, a cowboy I had known in Arizona, I secured a bodyguard of American cowboys. Although only eight in number, they constituted an army. Each in himself was sufficiently bold and adventurous to storm Chapultepec, while the notches on the pistols typified their standing in the matter of expert use of firearms. From the governor of California I obtained leave of absence for the state mineralogist, William Irelan. This man was noted far and wide through the West for his integrity, his great skill as an assayer, and his vast, irrepressible good-nature.

Having finally made up a party which seemed formidable enough to brave even the wrath of the Aguayos, and having completed careful preparations, we set forth.

Even before leaving American territory there occurred a humorous prelude to the more startling adventures that were to follow across the border. When, at the time appointed for the start, we met in the little town of Benson, Arizona, we discovered that we should be obliged to pass the night there; no train left for Ortiz Station before morning. I immediately hastened to the one and only hotel, where a supercilious young clerk flatly informed me that he could give none of the party accommodations. The cowboys, of course, did not matter; they would not have known what to do with a hotel bedroom if they had had one. But I knew that Irelan, of Falstaffian figure and unused to roughing it, would not take kindly to the idea of passing the night on the floor.

Since soft persuasion did not affect the clerk's obduracy, I had to resort to guile. Accordingly, I assured him that, so far as I was concerned, I did not care what happened, but I did hope that he would "be able to find comfortable quarters for General Irelan."

The clerk swallowed the bait completely.

"What?" said he, no longer indifferent. "You don't mean the *famous* General Irelan!"

I replied that, as I knew of no other individual by that name, it must be the same.

"And who are you?" asked the clerk.

Willing by that time to go to any length, I promptly said I was the general's private secretary.

The clerk thereupon disappeared and presently returned with the proprietor, who demanded visible proofs of my association with greatness. Together we went out to the general, who was placidly sunning himself. He gazed upon us benevolently while the delighted proprietor introduced himself and hastened to assure his honored guest that, if he would consent to wait for a few hours, he and his secretary would be well provided for. The general acquiesced with entire complacence, and when we returned from a stroll we found ourselves ensconced in no less a spot than the proprietor's own room, with a delicious meal awaiting us.

Seldom, if ever, had I realized what possibilities lie in titles, while that of "general" was particularly one to conjure with in the Indian-fighting West of those days. At any rate, I had conjured well. As a matter of fact, so successfully had I wrought that my friend was known far and wide as General Irelan until the day of his death.

Just across the border at Nogales, I was met by a Mexican who had been a classmate of mine at Freiberg, Baudelio Salazar. He begged me earnestly not to make the trip to Mulatos because he was well acquainted with the Aguayo brothers and knew that they were desperate. He told me, although I was already fully aware of it, that they had succeeded in inflaming public sentiment against the syndicate, and that for me to proceed with the examination under such circumstances would be suicidal. He was so determined that I should not go on that he threatened to wire my wife, telling her the true nature of the risks I was running.

I reasoned with Salazar that it was now too late to alter my plans; that to turn back at this point would be a confession of rank cowardice; and that, finally, an immense amount of money was involved in the result of the examination, to say nothing of my own reputation. No matter what happened, I must proceed.

First, I went alone to Guaymas to see my old friend Alexander Willard with whom I desired to discuss plans, and whose help I needed in outfitting the expedition. He, too, warned me of the dangers attending the trip, and urged me especially to take every precaution against the chance of my wild cowboys becoming embroiled with Mexican soldiers. They were such a mad crowd that at any moment the eight of them might take it into their heads to declare war on all Mexico. Furthermore, if they did too much drinking and got into a brawl with the soldiery, it might give the Mexican government cause to interfere.

Since it had been stipulated that the examination must take place within a limited period, now almost expired, we had no time to lose. To hasten matters, it was arranged that Willard was to telegraph the result of the examination to Diaz as soon as I returned to Guaymas with my report. The following day I found myself once more at the all-too-familiar Ortiz Station, whose agent was considerably more sober than his predecessor had been.

Although constantly on guard to keep the cowboys from getting into trouble with any of the Mexicans, I knew they were fairly itching for a chance to start something. One night we camped near a place where tequila was manufactured. The cowboys had a very sociable evening and it was with difficulty that I got them together next morning for an early start. In fact, I had to go around and kick them out of their blankets, one by one. Just as the outfit was ready to break camp, I noticed a large demijohn strapped on top of the baggage on one of the mules. I asked the cowboys what was in it.

They answered cheekily, "We'll give you two guesses."

"One's enough!" I said. I pulled out my pistol and the demijohn disappeared in a shower of glass.

To the accompaniment of indignant shouts, the tequila ran to the ground. Before the boys had had time to work themselves up into any concerted action, I read them the riot act and gave them to understand that I was running the party and would have no nonsense.

Shortly after leaving the railroad we learned that a regiment of Mexican troops had been sent down to the border of the Yaqui country to suppress a new Indian uprising. Since our route lay near the scene of trouble, I decided to spend the second night after we left Ortiz Station as near as possible to the Mexican encampment. Recalling the magical effect of the title of "general," I sought out the colonel in command, introduced myself to him, and asked him whether he would have any objection to General Irelan and his party spending the night at his headquarters.

With great animation he replied: "On the contrary, I shall be delighted to meet General Irelan. I have often heard of him and will do whatever I can to make his stay here comfortable."

In due time, therefore, I presented the general himself, having prepared him for the cordial reception he might expect. It was not necessary for me to impress upon him the official dignity and martial air he should exhibit. Indeed, before the evening was over I suspected that after the many toasts he had drunk to the prosperity of our sister republic, Irelan would have looked patronizingly upon George Washington himself.

It was long after midnight when we adjourned to the tent provided for our sleeping accommodations. Between Irelan's snoring and the near-by military band which indefatigably played in our honor, I had but little sleep. When we left in the morning the colonel gave his military colleague an open letter to all Mexicans, bespeaking their cordial hospitality for "the great American General Irelan, a sincere friend and admirer of Mexico."

Things went well the first day out; the country proved level and the general was being conveyed in a comfortable buckboard. But on the following day we reached a more rugged country where the only routes were by mountain mule trails. There we found awaiting us a huge mule, especially selected because of his strength, on which the general was to be transported over the dangerous trails. In spite of Irelan's many attainments, he had never learned to ride. Consequently, we were confronted with the serious problem of how to get him upon a mule, since his unwieldy bulk was hardly suited to the ordinary ways of mounting.

We finally evolved the following method: We selected a large boulder which we assisted the general to climb, and finally located the mule as close underneath as possible. The plan then was for the great man to descend into the saddle from this point of vantage. The mule, with characteristic perversity, had his own ideas, however. At the critical moment he was inspired to move out of reach of the general's right leg—the general was handicapped by unusually short legs. We had many rehearsals, and it was necessary to try four or five different boulders and to push the mule within reach by main force applied from the off side before ultimate success was attained. The total force of cowboys was eager, of course, to lend their assistance to this noble endeavor until finally, all of us working shoulder to shoulder, we mounted the general.

To dismount—or rather, to be dismounted—was an even more dangerous experience for him, as when riding he could retain his equilibrium by holding on to the pommel of the saddle. He would finally come to earth in a huge tottering mass; then, his fatigue overcoming him, he would sink to the ground and there lie expressing his exhaustion in pitiful groans. It was always a considerable time before he felt able once more to resume an upright position.

After watching this exhibition of horsemanship, the Mexicans we had employed as mozos came to me and asked if an American general could not usually ride better than that. I was afraid they might discover that Irelan was only a make-believe, but I succeeded in banishing all suspicion by explaining that he was a general in the navy, belonging to the Marine Corps. Under the circumstances, I, of course, did not mention the horse marines.

When we arrived at Mulatos we were given an unfriendly reception by the inhabitants of the little village clustered about the mine. Consequently my examination, which was chiefly confined to the large vein on the outcrop, had to be made under an armed guard of cowboys.

Here, as in the majority of Mexican mines, there were no ladders; one had to climb notched poles made from trees six or eight inches in diameter, into which grooves had been cut to give the miner a foothold. These poles were tilted slightly and supported in the shaft by scaffoldings made from light timber. The Mexican miners preferred these chicken ladders, as we called them, to American ladders. Since they went barefoot, or wore flexible garauches, the rungs of our type of ladders were difficult and painful for them to negotiate, particularly when carrying heavy loads on their heads. In time the notches became smooth from constant wear, and were consequently ill adapted to American boots.

After ten days of working from early morning until dusk, I completed my survey, and Irelan was ready with his assays on the value of the ore. The results of our examination confirmed the fears of the syndicate. We found that the large ore bodies which had been represented as carrying gold to the extent of several dollars per ton in reality contained but a few cents per ton. The sale had undoubtedly been a complete swindle.

Owing to the threats made against us, on the night preceding our departure we slept in the company's office, well barricaded. Many drunken Mexicans passed shouting, "Mata los gringos!" which we all understood was no idle gesture. The next morning I called the cowboys together and told them we would leave immediately after lunch. They protested at this, pointing out that the trails were very slippery, which was undoubtedly true since it had been raining for days. To strengthen this argument, they insisted it would be foolhardy to attempt to travel after dark. In effect, they flatly refused to leave that day. I was well aware of the reason behind their actions: each and every one of them had a generous-hearted señorita who had promised him the evening.

As time was a serious consideration, I informed the cowboys, equally flatly, that the expedition would start at two o'clock, and that those who were not at hand would have to foot it back, since I would be taking all the saddle animals with me.

Realizing I meant exactly what I said, but breathing all sorts of threats and in an ugly mood, the cowboys reported on time.

Our return trip began in a heavy tropical rain. We kept on throughout the first night with the help of our guide, Jimmy Owen, a little Virginian who had been in that country many years and who knew every cow path in the region. Instead of taking the usual mule road, we followed the devious cow trails. These were often used to smuggle gold out of the country to avoid its being stolen by revolutionists.

At intervals I could hear some of the cowboys damn me for a fool tenderfoot in attempting to get over the mountain under such adverse conditions. When in the dark a projecting limb of a tree nearly dismounted some rider, there was an especial outburst of profanity. It was as much as I could do to restrain myself from replying to some of their taunts, but I decided that, in such a situation, silence was golden. About four o'clock in the morning we stopped for a cup of coffee, and then pushed on until noon when we rested and had a substantial meal. By feeding the cowboys well I kept them from becoming mutinous.

When we arrived at Guaymas after a fast "record" trip of four and a half days, I handed my report to Willard, who immediately transmitted it to President Diaz. It amply confirmed the statement of the American and English syndicate that the property had been salted, and in due course Diaz compelled the Aguayo brothers to take back the property and restore the payments already made on account.

It was such instances of justice and fair-mindedness that made the Diaz government respected by the world at large as no other Mexican government had ever been.

Salting mines was by no means confined to Mexico; in our own country the practice was equally prevalent. The methods employed were often exceedingly clumsy, but occasionally were remarkably clever.

One primitive means of salting was to load a shotgun with gold dust and then shoot it into the quartz where the face of the vein was exposed. The expectation was that the engineer would break off samples from some of these salted faces and use them for assaying. In other cases, where the face of the ore was wet and muddy, the practice was to gouge out the original quartz and replace it with ore showing a much richer gold content. Then the whole face of the vein was mucked over so that the counterfeit section would not show. More difficult to detect was the method by which gold was dissolved in acids and the mixture sprayed not only on the quartz, but also on the dump containing recently mined ore.

Other attempts, even more intricately devised, have been made to salt mines. For example, a small core of gold has been inserted in the pestle to be used by the assayer, or gold dust has been placed in the cigarettes smoked by the helper who then purposely allowed the ash to drop into the samples.

Although punishment for salting is now provided by law, in the old days there was no penalty involved beyond the loss of the gold used in the deception. Under any conditions, salting resembles counterfeiting. The engineer, like the government expert, must, in self-defense, by his own scientific methods detect any attempt at fraud. He has now developed means of protection more efficient than any method of salting can surmount; in fact, any prominent engineering firm which today allowed itself to be taken in by a salted mine would be the laughingstock of the profession.

I recall one case of salting in a California mine I was sent to examine. Before reaching the mine a friend living in the community had informed me that its Italian owner had an unenviable reputation, and warned me that he would probably make an attempt to salt my samples.

I was received cordially enough on my arrival and given a delicious Italian dinner.

There was a broken-down old wreck of a mill operating on the property and the owner was suspiciously insistent on having the test for the value of the ore made by a mill run, which, if honestly conducted, would have been admittedly more satisfactory than the ordinary method of sampling and assaying. Ostensibly to guard against fraud, I placed my own millman in charge, and posted notices that no one would be allowed inside the building. I then selected sections in the mine from which I had the ore extracted by the workmen and sent to the mill. The owner, evidently assuming that I was a novice in my profession, dropped gold in the cars which carried the ore to the mill. Meanwhile, I was personally getting another set of samples which I carefully sealed in sacks and sent by Wells-Fargo to an assay office in San Francisco.

The owner asked me pertinently why I needed the extra samples, which in the aggregate amounted to only a few hundred pounds. He said the tests of the hundred tons of ore then going through his mill would give a much better idea of the value than the small samples I had selected. To this I assented but astutely pointed out that his rattletrap mill might not be able to effect the proper extraction of the gold, and, in case the returns should fall below his statements as to the value of the ore, my samples would prove useful.

When I had finished my sampling and had run about a hundred tons of ore through the mill, the mill returns were exceedingly high. The salting had been most effective. I had made what is called a cleanup in the mill, and carried away the amalgam; that is, the gold included in the quicksilver used to extract gold from ore. In San Francisco I had the amalgam retorted, and obtained therefrom a large ingot of gold. A computation showed that the ore, judged by the mill returns, amounted to the unusually high figure of twenty dollars a ton, while the assays I had made showed the value to be slightly over one dollar a ton. I presented the ingot to my clients, who were happy to find that its value covered not only my fee but also all other costs involved in the examination of the mine and left a dividend to provide a banquet for the prospective victims. I then wrote my report, showing exactly how the salting had been conducted, and exposing the owner's dishonesty. According to previous arrangements, this report was forwarded to him by my clients.

The mine owner was furious and threatened to bring suit for recovery of the value of the gold bar. I wrote him that the less he said about the nature of the examination and of my report, the better chance he would have to swindle some less suspicious victim. He evidently agreed with me in this, since he made no further attempts to recover the gold bar in dispute. This was a good case of the salter salted.

The only mining swindle comparable to that of the Mulatos mine was the great diamond hoax in 1872. Two rascally mining prospectors had bought in England several thousand diamonds in the rough, all of them small, and had planted them in an almost inaccessible part of Wyoming. They succeeded in having a company formed in San Francisco, on the directorate of which were many of the most prominent business men of California.

The examination and favorable report on the diamond area by Henry Janin caused the greatest excitement, and there was a rush to acquire shares in the company. Clarence King had been over this ground a short while before for the United States Geological Survey and had found no diamondiferous formation. If he missed it, he had committed a serious error. Since his reputation as a geologist was at stake, he went back to make a re-examination. It took him little time to discover what had occurred. He proved conclusively that everyone connected with the affair had been duped. Taking with them the hundred thousand dollars they had deftly gathered from the public, the prospectors had disappeared. The shrewd business men of California were so abashed over the way they had been fooled that they judged it unwise to advertise their shame by making too great an effort at pursuit.

The ordinary difficulties experienced by engineers in examining mines are greatly increased when exploring abandoned workings. For example, there is always danger because of the possible caving in of earth, the falling of loosened timbers, or the breaking of rotting ladders. Another unpleasant feature is the omnipresent animal life. Engineers have often found a dead coyote, occasionally even a live one, that had fallen into old mine workings, and the pits are almost always crawling with reptiles, frequently rattlesnakes or scorpions.

On one occasion an assistant of mine in Johannesburg, J. A. Chalmers, English geologist, whom I had taken with me to Rhodesia, was lowered to the bottom of a mine shaft about thirty feet deep by two Matabele workers. When he reached bottom he saw an adder ready to strike. Chalmers signaled to the men above, yelling to hoist him up. After he had been raised about ten feet or so, his foot slipped out of the noose and he fell back to the bottom of the shaft. The two natives were greatly alarmed and hastened for help to a neighboring prospect of white men, who came as quickly as possible. One of the white men was lowered to the bottom of the shaft to see what was the trouble. He found Chalmers unconscious. With difficulty they hauled Chalmers to the surface and he was taken immediately to the nearest mining hospital where it was found that several of his ribs were broken. It was some time before he recovered consciousness, and he then told those about him of his seeing an adder in the shaft. The serpent did not hit him when it struck. The white man who had gone to his rescue saw nothing of the adder, and was greatly surprised to hear the story. Since Chalmers was a total abstainer, he could not have seen snakes through excessive drinking. Now the question is, what became of the adder? The most plausible explanation is that the snake was as much alarmed as Chalmers and sought refuge in some crack of the shaft.

In 1886 I went to an abandoned district, a long day's drive from the town of Magdalena on the Nogales-Guaymas railroad. My only companion was the prospective seller, an American mine promoter. When we reached the mine at dusk we found that the provisions and water that were to have been supplied had not been left for us.

The promoter at once started back to the nearest village to get food while I was left alone for the night, about thirty miles from any habitation.

The mine was located in a limestone district full of great caverns, alive with bats, which made it extremely difficult for me to sample the ore bodies. The bats swooped against my candles, sometimes putting them out and always spattering me with hot grease. For hours I worked away in the passages and caves with no company but these objectionable squeaking, fluttering creatures.

Frequently during the night I climbed to the surface of the mine for relief from the fetid air. I took particular pains not to venture far from the shaft, because Indians had recently been active in the neighborhood. The stark solitude of the desert spread for miles about me under the starlit heavens, and the silence was unbroken save for the occasional sharp bark of a coyote. In my loneliness the night seemed unending.

The mine promoter returned with food in the morning, and in two days more I finished my work and went back to Magdalena. There I was paid two hundred and fifty Mexican pesos in coin to cover traveling expenses. The peso, then worth fifty cents, is larger than our silver dollar, and I had to carry this great weight of money with me out of Mexico.

The night I took the train for Nogales a fiesta was being held at the border and the coaches were filled with drunken Mexicans. There were no Pullman cars, and I had to sit in a day coach. Loaded down with the silver coins, and in constant dread lest their jingle betray the fact that I had this treasure on my person and so make me a good prospect for abduction, I sat like a statue through the whole night but, with my usual luck, escaped notice and reached Nogales in safety.

Mexican mines are not the only ones which have afforded me exciting moments. One of my most hazardous experiences occurred in the examination of the Pioche mine in eastern Nevada. In former days the Pioche had been a well-known silver-mining camp, but water from underground springs seeped into the mine in such quantities as to make pumping expensive. The rising level of the water and the dropping price of silver caused a cessation of work. The mine had been closed for twelve years prior to my visit in 1890.

Accompanied by my assistant, E. A. Wiltsee, I made a trip to the mine in the dead of winter to ascertain for my clients if any mining possibilities remained.

The Pioche district was about a hundred miles from Milford, Utah, then the nearest station. From there Wiltsee and I drove into Pioche in an open buckboard on which runners had been substituted for wheels because of the deep snow. It was a bitterly cold trip and, in spite of my huge buffalo overcoat, I was nearly frozen. We were frequently obliged to slow up the horses so that one or the other of us might get out and run alongside to keep our blood in circulation.

When we finally reached our destination, I found that preparations had been made for my examination; the old engine had been rigged up so that we could descend to the bottom of the shaft in an iron bucket.

About daylight Wiltsee and the foreman, who had formerly been in charge of the mine, and I were carefully lowered in the shaft. The hoisting engineer, fortunately, was competent to exercise the requisite care to prevent the rope's swinging too far from side to side in the shaft and possibly knocking loose rocks or timbers on us. After considerable difficulty, we reached the twelfth or water level, and managed to get out the eight-foot collapsible canvas boat which we had in the bucket with us. By the light of our candles, we opened and floated the boat; then we climbed in and started for the interior of the mine.

Before getting into the boat, however, I found that the water was about six feet deep. Wiltsee was six feet four and could walk safely with the water only up to his neck, while it would be over my head and swimming would be out of the question. I told him, therefore, that if the boat sank I would depend upon him to keep cool and let me put my hand on his shoulder until I could work along the level to a place of safety. This prospect appeared to perturb him exceedingly; his face loomed white and distressed out of the darkness. I added that, if in an emergency he showed any signs of seeking his own safety without reference to mine, I should have no compunction in grabbing him firmly around the neck.

Luckily, our maps of the underground workings were accurate and with their aid we reached our objective. Since we had to navigate about half a mile through water which at the beginning reached almost to the top of the level, we were obliged to crouch down and propel the boat by pushing on the roof of the tunnel, while at the same time trying to keep it from bumping into any jagged rocks along the sides. There was additional danger that buckled rails might puncture the canvas. Wiltsee was greatly relieved when after a half mile he discovered that the water was so shallow that it would not come above my shoulders.

By such slow method of locomotion we came to the end of the level, where we found an upraise: a little shaft which connected the twelve hundred with the eleven hundred foot level. After fastening our boat and climbing up this raise, we were able to gain access to the old workings of the mine.

We had estimated that it would take about two days to finish the examination and had taken with us only our lunch, intending to return to the surface in the late afternoon, and then to make a final trip the following day. By the time we had reached the eleventh level, however, we realized that the difficulties and dangers were too great to warrant a second trip. We decided to work right through until the examination had been completed. For a long time we were obliged to crawl through narrow drifts and crosscuts, and in this fashion covered several thousand feet of underground investigation.

About midnight we completed the examination and started back for the main shaft in our boat. Proceeding with the greatest caution, we reached the bottom of the shaft from which we had disembarked in the early morning. There we abandoned the boat, hauled ourselves into the bucket, and, after much shaking of the rope, attracted the attention of the engineer on the surface. Several loose rocks fell about us as we ascended very slowly but, by standing on the rim of the bucket, and each using one hand to keep it from touching the sides of the shaft, we prevented it from catching on any of the protruding timbers. We had had enough of the water below and certainly would have been averse to being dumped into it from any great height.

At last we reached the surface, to find a cold, sparkling, starlit night. As we stepped into the icy air, we were met by a dozen or more people assembled from neighboring farms. After waiting for many hours beyond the time of our expected return, they had about given us up for lost. Although our courage had held out all through the dangerous experience, it was a great relief to find ourselves again on the earth's surface. It required several stiff drinks to produce the necessary favorable reaction.

While recovering my spirits, I was alarmed afresh by the news of a messenger's having been sent to the nearest telegraph station to wire the newspapers that I had met with disaster in the mine. I immediately despatched another messenger with a telegram to my wife advising her that I was well and would be at home in a few days. I gave this rider instructions to break all records for speed, and so well did he accomplish his task that my wife received my message before the newspapers published their harrowing story.

CHAPTER ELEVEN

Grass Valley and the Coeur d'Alene

GRASS VALLEY — FINDING A LOST VEIN AND
DEVELOPING A FAMOUS MINE — A SMALL FEE
AND A LARGE ONE — THE BUNKER HILL AND
SULLIVAN — THE APEX RULE — I TACKLE YELLOW
DOG SMITH — BLACKMAIL LITIGATION — THE
TEST OF A WONDERFUL MEMORY — KELLOGG'S
BURRO — WEALTH OF THE COEUR D'ALENE —
STRIKES AND MARTIAL LAW — THE AMAZING STRAT-
EGY AND COURAGE OF A PINKERTON DETECTIVE

*I*n 1884 I became consulting engineer to the mining department of the Union Iron Works of San Francisco, the largest on the Pacific coast. I retained this connection for nine years—until I went to South Africa—and it offered me the opportunity to make a thorough study of the production costs of mining machinery. Later, when my duties included the ordering of equipment worth millions of dollars, this knowledge was of great economic value. One of my problems was the devising of methods by which machinery could be delivered to mills and smelters in the mountain regions of Mexico and South America, where the only means of transportation was by mule. We overcame this difficulty by planning the packing of the machinery into sections, each of which weighed no more than three hundred pounds, in other words, the loading capacity of the average mule. Airplanes have developed this idea still further and have carried great dredges, piece by piece, to the most inaccessible parts of New Guinea where they have been reassembled and are now operating.

Among other services I rendered to this company was assistance in securing for them the contract to build the battleship *Oregon,* famous in the naval battle during the war with Spain. It was through my collegemate, Walker Blaine, that Irving M. Scott, general manager of the Union Iron Works, was presented to James G. Blaine, at that time secretary of state. Secretary Blaine appreciated the importance of having a battleship constructed on the Pacific coast, and of establishing shipyards at San Francisco. It was a wise decision on the part of the government to award the Union Iron Works the contract, though their bid was not the lowest one received.

The last time I saw Walker Blaine was when I visited his home in Augusta, Maine, in the middle eighties, after my return from Colombia. I was on my way to examine some gold mines in Nova Scotia and Walker met me in Boston and accompanied me as far as Augusta. He asked me to visit him on my return from Nova Scotia and I accepted his invitation.

A few hours before my train reached Augusta on my return trip I was handed a telegram from James G. Blaine telling me that Walker had been called away for a day or two to visit a friend who was seriously ill, but that he would endeavor to entertain me until his son returned. Mr. Blaine met me at the railway station in Augusta in a one-horse buggy and after showing me the interesting sights of the town drove me to his home.

At this time there was considerable tension between the United States and Canada over fishing rights. I had got all the information I could on this subject, hoping to impress Mr. Blaine with my knowledge. A favorable opportunity came one evening at dinner when there were present several men prominent in Republican politics in Maine. I was very impatient lest the conversation would not turn to the fishing controversy, but finally it did and I gave quite a discourse embodying extensive statistics. The guests seemed interested in what I had to say. Mr. Blaine then took up the subject and was very considerate in exposing my superficial knowledge.

I felt greatly embarrassed, but I am sure I profited by the unpleasant experience.

I had thought that at least on the subject of the western silver-mining industry I could tell Mr. Blaine a thing or two, but during the next few days I discovered to my surprise that he had intimate knowledge of that subject also. This was my first meeting with Mr. Blaine, and we became friends. He afterwards showed his friendly interest in my professional career as evidenced by the help he gave me when I was consulting engineer of the Union Iron Works.

Up to 1884 I had been called in as a mining expert by many mine owners for whom I had examined and reported on properties in different parts of this country, as well as in Mexico and South America. In addition, I had been in charge of actual operations at Minas Nuevas.

My first position as a consulting mining engineer came in 1885. I was much pleased that it was for the Original Empire mine in the same Grass Valley district of California where I had made my first notes on mining practice after returning from Freiberg.

In addition to the Union Iron Works and the Original Empire mine, I soon had engagements of the same character for the North Star mine, the California Mining Bureau, and the Central Pacific and Southern Pacific railroads. Since these varied activities required that I spend much time in California, I decided to move my family back to San Francisco. It was there that my second son, John Hays Hammond, Jr., was born in 1888. I still retained my office in New York, and made frequent trips there to keep in touch with eastern clients.

My work in connection with the North Star was both interesting and profitable. This mine had once been highly productive, but the vein had been lost at a depth of a thousand feet, and thereafter for ten years the mine had been abandoned as dead. My friend, William B. Bourn, of San Francisco, owner of the first successful quartz mine in Grass Valley—the Original Empire, had been offered an option on the neighboring North Star. Not caring to take all the risk himself, he had asked my first client, Alexander Stoddard, to co-operate with him in the endeavor to reopen the property. I, as the representative of Mr. Stoddard, accordingly made an examination of the deepest accessible levels, which convinced me that the faulted vein could easily be found and in all likelihood would develop valuable ore shoots. Basing their action in reopening the mine on my favorable report, Bourn and Stoddard engaged me as manager.

My judgment of the mine's potentialities proved accurate. After we had installed pumping and hoisting machinery, sunk the old incline shaft deeper, and run levels, we easily picked up the lost vein. Then we leased an old ten-stamp mill in the neighborhood, to which we hauled the ore. Within two years we had made enough profit to begin operations on a large scale and to warrant the erection of a modern thirty-stamp mill, the first one I built. The North Star proved a great success and produced many millions of dollars in dividends for its lucky shareholders. It was recently consolidated with the Original Empire and is still being profitably operated.

Shortly after the mill was completed, the property was sold to James D. Hague, a distinguished engineer, and his eastern clients. I resigned as manager, but continued as consulting engineer for the North Star, and the Original Empire as well.

From the beginning of our association Hague, Bourn, and I proved congenial spirits. We spent our time, as Hague expressed it, "with quartz by day and pints by night." The new owner, however, although most cultivated and delightful and an accomplished engineer of wide experience, did not have "a nose for a mine." This is well illustrated by what happened when Mr. and Mrs. Bourn, my wife, and I went on a vacation to the Yosemite Valley to enjoy some of the profits made in the sale of the North Star. We had not been gone long when I was overtaken by a frantic telegram from the unhappy Hague.

PIPELINE SUPPLYING POWER BURST. MILL SHUT DOWN. WHAT DO YOU ADVISE?

After deep consultation Bourn and I despatched the following wire to Hague:

ADVISE MENDING PIPELINE AND RESTARTING MILL.

With all seriousness Hague followed this sage, though obvious, counsel. Although endowed with brilliant qualities, Hague is a typical example of panic in the face of responsibility, a characteristic often to be observed in men otherwise rational and balanced.

Shortly after this episode, Hague was compelled to go east and offered me the job of supervising the mine during his absence. I accepted without mentioning any compensation, leaving the matter entirely to his judgment of values, and on his return some months later I was considerably taken aback at his low estimate of my worth. But since I had made no stipulations before taking the job, I felt I could offer no objections then.

Presently, however, a chance presented itself to square matters. A telegram came from Hague's resident manager saying that Hague was away and that the quartz vein had once more been lost. Immediately following this came a wire from Hague asking me to make a professional inspection of the property, and to direct the manager how to find the vein and how to continue the shaft.

I kept the manager waiting for a reply until both he and Hague had had time to become thoroughly worried. Then I went to the property, descended into the mine, and after a few minutes at the bottom, ordered the car to be hauled to the surface. As I arose from the depths, the surprised manager confronted me and inquired whether I proposed to make my report after so brief an inspection. I replied loftily that a mere glance at the situation had convinced me that the only thing necessary was to incline the shaft at such and such a different angle and the vein would again be picked up. "This," I continued, "should be obvious to any practical miner; therefore I shall appreciate your check for five hundred dollars."

The manager, aghast, stammered, "Why—I could have advised Mr. Hague to do that myself."

"But, unfortunately, you didn't!" I pointed out.

I then went on to show him that my services were analogous to those of a diagnostician, who often receives the same compensation for advising against an operation as for it. "So," I wound up, "the company's check for five hundred dollars, please." It was forthcoming. I went away with my professional honor vindicated and the feeling that Hague had received no more than was due him for his earlier parsimony.

Hague certainly had his troubles. At one time he and Clarence King owned a small gold mine in California. After several stagecoach holdups in which the bullion was stolen, they had a fake gold brick made which looked exactly like a real one. This gold brick was given to the driver of the stagecoach to be surrendered in case of a holdup, and the real gold was carefully hidden in the coach. The camp cook was Chinese and this great wealth left lying about carelessly proved too great a strain on his honesty. One day he stole the fake gold brick and started for the mountains. He was pursued for some distance by the employees of the mine who believed that he had escaped with the real gold. Finally he was overtaken. When he began shooting, his pursuers returned the fire and killed him.

There was a saying in the western mining camps that "no mine has established its value until large sums have been expended in the litigation of its title." Title litigation, for example, cost the Bunker Hill and Sullivan mine more than half a million dollars. Although the legal expenses were very high, such charges were not uncommon.

Litigation often arises from the ambiguity and unscientific nature of the United States mining laws relating to ownership of ore bodies below the surface of the ground. In this country, it is necessary to possess only the rectangular surface area in which occurs the apex of the veins carrying the ore bodies. The owner may then follow the vein downward in its "dips, spurs, and angles," and extract all the ore found, even when the veins lead under adjoining claims. In this respect the laws of Mexico and the Transvaal are much more satisfactory. In both these cases the owner of a surface right is entitled only to the ore lying within an area defined by the vertical extension of the property boundaries in depth; that is, he enjoys no extralateral rights.

In these great mining lawsuits of the past lawyers, of course, have received the lion's share of the fees. Experts in the geology of ore-bearing formations have also been handsomely remunerated for their investigations. After the geological findings of one of these experts was reported to the lawyers who employed him, he was retained as a witness if he could conscientiously give testimony that would further the case of his employers. There have been instances in which his conscience proved too flexible a guide.

In the early fifties there were few qualified mining engineers, and the soi-disant experts were often rule-of-thumb Cornish miners, a class of surveyors whose code of morals was frequently as primitive in its conception of right and wrong as their technical knowledge was rudimentary.

The late William M. Stewart, one of Nevada's first United States senators and greatest lawyers, was once engaged to represent one of the groups involved in a mining case which hinged ultimately on the exact location of the ore bodies in dispute. Not anticipating that the verdict would depend on the correct survey of the underground workings, Stewart was unprepared in that phase of the litigation, and was perturbed by the very positive evidence given by the so-called surveying expert, on the other side.

The case seemed to be going against Stewart, when he had an inspiration. Just as the witness was about to leave the stand, Stewart asked him how many degrees there are in a circle. The Cornish expert cast a supercilious glance at the jury and directed his answer to them: "Why, a schoolboy would know that depends upon the size of the circle." The audience burst into laughter, the judge smiled, and even the nontechnical jury perceived that the expert was an unscrupulous faker. Stewart won the decision.

In 1886, Simeon G. Reed of Portland, Oregon, asked me to manage the Bunker Hill and Sullivan mine, a silver-lead property he had recently acquired in the Coeur d'Alene mining district of northern Idaho. Though the salary offered was attractive, I felt it unwise either to give up the management of the North Star and Empire mines or to discontinue my work as a mining expert. Consequently, I declined his offer but recommended Victor Clement, and he was accordingly placed in charge of the mine.

A few months later Mr. Reed employed me to make a geological survey of this property so that I might give expert testimony in a lawsuit involving the title. I spent several weeks in a thorough examination which included many of the newly developed mining properties in the Coeur d'Alene. The results convinced me of the great potential value of the ore deposits and enabled me to boost this district when interviewed.

One of the chief witnesses for the group fighting Reed's title in the Coeur d'Alene was a widely known character known as Jack Smith, or, more colloquially, as Yellow Dog Smith. The reason for this nickname was the jaundiced-looking cur that always attended him. Surly by nature, Smith had no friends, not even among those associated with him in the lawsuits against the company. He held an undivided one-sixth interest in the outcome of the suit instituted by his associates. For legal reasons, it would have been of great advantage to the company to secure Smith's interest and deprive him of any conceivable or legitimate concern in the matter, minimizing the possibility of what they regarded as an outright blackmailing suit.

I decided to have a personal interview with the unfriendly recluse, although Clement tried to dissuade me because of the man's uncertain temper. Confident that I should have no trouble with the man, I was determined to go to his cabin, located in one of the gulches near Wardner, the local town serving the mine. As a precaution, I did tell Clement that if I had not returned at the end of an hour he might bring along the coffin.

About supper time I approached the little log cabin set off by itself in the loneliest part of the gulch. My knocking brought savage growls from the dog within. Smith pulled the door half open and peered out in obvious surprise at the presence of a visitor. While he was hesitating, unable to make up his mind whether to let me in or set the dog on me, I said suggestively, "That coffee smells pretty good, Jack." Slowly and reluctantly he kicked the dog aside and allowed me to enter.

When I had the cup of steaming coffee before me I lost no time in introducing the object of my visit.

"Jack, you'll regret it all your life if you don't accept the proposition I'm going to make you. The Bunker Hill and Sullivan is going to win this lawsuit regardless of what it costs them. They have to win if they're going to establish a reputation in this country for fighting all blackmail suits. If necessary, they'll take the case to the

United States Supreme Court. You won't gain anything in the long run. I happen to know you put up most of the money for your associates and I'm sure your confidence in them is no greater than mine. I've been told on good authority that you've said that even if you did win, you'd have trouble getting your share. Isn't that so? How much do you expect to get out of it?"

"About twenty thousand dollars," he replied.

"I'll buy it," I promptly interjected. "That's all you can get even if you do win the suit, and there certainly won't be much of that left if you have to put up money for the others."

"Maybe," he allowed, "but I wouldn't be safe here twenty-four hours if I sold out my interest."

"Well, what is there to keep you here?" I queried.

"I have some town lots in Wardner," came the reply.

"How much are they valued at?"

"Probably four or five thousand dollars."

"I'll take those lots off your hands, too," I promised.

He was somewhat bewildered by the speed of this conversation, but followed it up by inquiring, "Then what would I do?"

"You're a good prospector and I'll send you down to Arizona," I answered. "All your expenses will be paid, and I'll give you a fair interest in any property we get through you."

Without any further hesitation he stated firmly: "Mr. Hammond, I never in my life sold out a partner, and I won't do it now."

Since he was undoubtedly right and I was wrong, I said the only thing there was for me to say: "Jack, give me your hand. I think a great deal better of you even in this questionable affair" (an outright reference to the blackmail suit!), "even though it's a set of rascals you're being loyal to; and if I hadn't known that, I should not have made the offer."

The suit was tried at Murray, the county seat. The jury, the lawyers, and the witnesses were domiciled in a ramshackle wooden hotel near the courthouse. Though our official relations were none too friendly, after each court session we went back to the hotel and had drinks together. It was the custom of the day for the bars to invite their habitués to a morning cocktail "on the bar." Many of us took advantage of this hospitality in order to create an appetite for the poor food provided at breakfast.

Jack Smith was the most important witness against us. The trial had its colorful moments. At all times the courtroom was filled with violent partisans of both sides, and we were fortunate that the judge was upright and courageous in standing for equity in the face of intense local feeling.

Each side retained the most brilliant counsel available. W. B. Heyburn, afterwards senator from Idaho, and later a valued friend of mine, represented the Smith crowd, while on our side was Judge Ganahl, who enjoyed a splendid reputation as a mining lawyer, and William Claggett, who bore and deserved the title of "the silver-tongued orator of the Northwest."

Our group had the foresight to hire a Pinkerton detective who, posing as a prospector, soon ingratiated himself with the Smith crowd. They considered him such a good fellow that they revealed to him many facts injurious to their case. When he went on the stand to testify on our side, they became so enraged that his life was in danger. As soon as he had given his testimony I drove him secretly to Missoula and put him safely on an eastbound train.

The principal difficulty with Yellow Dog Smith's evidence in this trial was its overperfection. Although he was on the stand for two days under severe cross-examination by the shrewdest lawyers in Idaho, his memory proved extraordinary. For example, one of the critical points in the case involved the priority of the location made several years before. Smith remembered every minute detail that had occurred in connection with it, throughout the five or six hours intervening between the time of starting out to locate the claims to the posting of notices. Exhibiting a truly amazing system of mnemonics, he professed to remember where the locators of our side had been, explaining this by claiming to have kept tabs on their movements. His testimony, given quietly and without truculence, was as unshakable as the Rock of Gibraltar. Had I not been certain that he was a consummate liar, I should have accepted his testimony *in toto*.

Fortunately for us, the court adjourned from Friday afternoon until Monday morning. The judge had issued an order that during this period neither side was to have any of its representatives even approach the claims in question. The object of the court's injunction was to make sure that certain stakes marking the locations were not interfered with.

Since we suspected that Jack Smith was not so honest as his testimony in court seemed to indicate, we had him shadowed. Sure enough, late Sunday afternoon Smith was seen examining the notices on ground where he had been forbidden to trespass. During his cross-examination resumed on Monday, Smith was asked where he had been at five o'clock Sunday afternoon. His wonderful memory collapsed; he had not the slightest recollection of ever having been near the claims. He did admit he might have been "somewhere" at that time, but had no idea where. Impressed by this amazing vagueness, so much in contrast with his previously infallible memory, the jury brought in a unanimous verdict in our favor.

Some years after the Bunker Hill and Sullivan had won this suit, the company became involved in another legal action. Although Jack had no personal interest on this occasion, he possessed important and honest evidence in favor of our company's contention, which he volunteered to give. In dilatory judicial fashion, the case was adjourned time after time. Before it was finally called, the Klondike discovery exercised a lure impossible for Smith to resist. Before departing he promised that he would come back from the Klondike and give his testimony whenever the case should be tried. And this he actually did, refusing to take any compensation beyond expenses.

After Mr. Reed had won his suit over the Bunker Hill and Sullivan title, he felt unable, because of his failing health, to continue the development of the property. There was particular need of extensive new equipment, since all we had was an antiquated mill, which had been running intermittently during the litigation period.

Mr. Reed offered one large block of stock figured on the basis of a million dollars for the property, and gave me an option on the rest at about a million and a half dollars for his entire holdings. I said I was satisfied with the price and would undertake to raise the necessary funds for its purchase.

First, I wired James L. Houghteling and Edward L. Ryerson, and also Cyrus H. McCormick, of Chicago, son of the inventor, for whom

I had made several mining examinations, telling them briefly about the property. Then I hurried to Chicago. After a brief conference, these men purchased the portion of the stock I had reserved for them. From Chicago I went to New York and sold to D. O. Mills the remainder of the first block of stock. A few months later I exercised my option on the remaining shares of the company with money provided by William H. Crocker, of San Francisco, and other friends.

In July, 1891, I was elected president of the company and retained that position until I went to South Africa in June, 1893. I was succeeded by my wife's uncle, General N. H. Harris, who held the office for four years. The property has proved immensely valuable. The annual report of the company showed that up to the end of December, 1931, $48,444,488.84 had been paid in dividends. The gross value of the ore was $167,163,780.42, recovered from 13,925,786 tons of ore mined. The depth of the "dip" of the vein from which the ore was mined is 5250 feet (practically one mile) and the mining developments (crosscuts, drifts, "raises," and shafts) were sixty miles.

The Bunker Hill and Sullivan was discovered by Noah S. Kellogg, Phil O'Rourke, and Jacob Goetz, known as Dutch Jake. Later Dutch Jake and O'Rourke came into full possession of the properties and sold them to Reed for six hundred and fifty thousand dollars.

Kellogg always maintained that they had not been the real finders of this famous mine. According to his story, they had gone on a prospecting trip, and one night at the mouth of Milo Creek their burro had strayed. As Kellogg tells the story:

"The next morning we started out to find him. His tracks was clear and we found wads of his hair where he had climbed over the down-timber and scraped his sides. How the little son-of-a-gun managed to get through that place, I can't tell, but after we got into the canyon his trail was easy. Pretty soon we saw him on the side of the hill with his one good eye slanted across the canyon. He sure was looking hard at something.

"Now you know a jack. They'll stand like a rock till you get almost up to them, and then, just when you put out your hand—easy-like—you get a bunch of gravel in the eye or a kick in the belly. Then they go stand somewheres else.

"But this one didn't act like that. He let us come right up to him and just kept right on standing. Now if there's anything can shake up a ornery cuss like a jack—you bet I'm gonna look too.

"I'll be doggoned if he didn't have his feet planted on an outcrop—and his ears was pointed at another over the gulch!"

The burro became a celebrated character, his fame being perpetuated in the following jingle:

> When you talk about the Coeur d'Alene,
> And all the wealth untold,
> Don't fail to mention Kellogg's Jack,
> Who did the wealth unfold.

Whether or not this account is apocryphal I am not prepared to say—I tell the story as 'twas told to me. At least it is a legend of the Coeur d'Alene.

·At the time we took over the Bunker Hill and Sullivan, the Coeur d'Alene territory was filled with the usual rough crowd that followed the opening up of all new mining districts. On one of my extended visits to the mine, I found there existed a good deal of prejudice against the company, while feeling was particularly unfriendly towards its officers. My headquarters were at the mine about a mile up the canyon from Wardner, and since I was much occupied in underground development, my visits to the town were rare; in fact, I went there only on matters of business.

Some of the company's enemies began to spread the report that I was afraid to come into the town. Unwilling to let this pass, I sent word that I would appear on a certain day, and at a certain hour I would walk the full length of the street, down one side and up the other. If anyone desired to attack me, he would then have his chance. No attack was made; I had called their bluff. I did not do this in a spirit of bravado, but because I realized that evidence of personal cowardice was prejudicial not only to the interests one represented, but to one's own safety as well.

In addition to our legal difficulties, we soon had a labor war on our hands in the Coeur d'Alene. The labor union of Montana had been giving trouble to the mine owners in the section around Butte. In order to relieve the tension in their immediate neighborhood, the exasperated mine operators had diverted the attention of the agitators to the Coeur d'Alene district. Thus, in 1891, Moyer, Harry Orchard and Mozer, and later Bill Haywood, arrived from Butte in the endeavor to unionize the Coeur d'Alene mines.

There was not the slightest discontent among the miners at the Bunker Hill and Sullivan. Shortly after the union organizers' arrival, a delegation of our miners called on me to ask whether the company would insist on their joining the union; they were satisfied with things as they were and had no desire to pay the required fee.

Their particular objection was to being treated by a certain ignorant and incompetent union doctor. I replied that it was a matter of entire indifference to us whether they joined the union or not, but that under no circumstances would our mine become a closed shop.

The company at this time was preparing to extend operations. We had a new mill and we needed more men to operate it. We had ascertained that there were no objections on the part of those already working at the mill or in the mines to our bringing in additional outside labor. Although labor was scarce in the Idaho section, there were many miners out of employment in California. I went to San Francisco, where the company's main office was located, and advertised for the necessary complement of miners to join the Bunker Hill and Sullivan. Large numbers of miners appeared in answer to the advertisement.

Meanwhile serious trouble was brewing throughout the Coeur d'Alene district and this fact was widely reported in the California papers. A great majority of the newly hired miners, even after having expressed their satisfaction with the terms of employment, refused to go to Idaho lest they become embroiled in these labor disputes. Nevertheless, I succeeded in collecting a carload of first-class miners who stated that as American citizens they did not propose to be denied their right to work for any company which offered them satisfactory terms. I explained fully the situation in the Coeur d'Alene and a few days afterwards I left with them in a private car. My wife insisted on accompanying me; and although I had hoped to induce her to stop off at Portland, she would not do so. Newspaper accounts of trouble in the Coeur d'Alene were most alarming and, if I was to be near danger, she insisted on being with me.

Before we started, I sent a telegram to our manager, Clement. Since I was well aware that wires were being tapped by the agitators, this message was designed to act as a blind; Clement had already received other instructions and knew what to expect. My fake telegram informed him that I was taking the miners through to Spokane and would reach Wardner the next day by the regular train.

The main line of the railroad went on to Spokane, but at Tekoa Junction there was a spur running to Wardner and then on up the Coeur d'Alene Valley to Wallace, and other stations in the mining district. The headquarters of the agitators were at Wallace, about twelve miles beyond Wardner which was my real objective.

I made private arrangements with the railroad to have an engine ready at Tekoa Junction so that our special car might be hauled direct to the mine via the spur line. They were, of course, glad to co-operate with us on their own account because they were anxious to have mining operations resumed.

My message to Clement was duly intercepted by the strikers, as I had hoped and believed it would be. When our car reached Tekoa Junction there were at hand apparently only a few spies who had been sent by the agitators to keep in touch with the progress of our train. Our car was hastily switched and I took charge of the special. Meanwhile, one of the spies rushed to the telegraph operator, scribbling frantically:

HAMMOND AND HIS SCABS HAVE STARTED FOR WARDNER.

As I mounted to the cab, the engineer said: "I suppose you're Mr. Hammond. Shall I pull her wide open?"

"We've got to beat the union miners from Wallace. Let her go!" I replied.

There were forty miles between us and our destination, while the men from Wallace had only twelve to go. We raced at hair-raising speed around the tortuous curves of the Coeur d'Alene River. On the bridges we had to take our chances as there was always the possibility that our plot to divert the agitators had miscarried and they had had time to blow them up. Mile after mile of track was reeled off; bridge after bridge was safely crossed on our way to Wardner. But, instead of pulling into the Wardner station, we stopped the train about a mile short, unloaded the men, and started them on a run for the mill, a few hundred yards distant.

When I turned to help my wife descend, I found that she had been clutching the seat with such a vise-like grip, to keep from being thrown, that her muscles had stiffened. It was with difficulty that I got her safely to the ground.

It was indeed fortunate that we did not go on into Wardner. As soon as the union miners at Wallace received the wire from Tekoa Junction, they tried to intercept us. Unable to procure an engine on such short notice, they jumped on flat cars and coasted down the long grade. About a hundred of them were at the station awaiting the arrival of our train. Nevertheless, before they discovered what we were doing, we had all our miners behind breastworks at the mill, and, since the strikers knew we had already smuggled in guns and were well armed, they committed no overt act. No strike was declared at the Bunker Hill and Sullivan; not a man walked out. The responsibility for the trouble in the district lay solely on the shoulders of the union agitators from Butte.

I remained in Wardner until everything was apparently quiet, and then went to Nevada on professional work. During my absence there was a general uprising, culminating on July 11, 1892, with the dynamiting of the Frisco mill by union men. After a number of murders had been committed, martial law was declared, and federal troops called in. To protect ourselves as well as we could during these disturbances, the Mine Owners' Association hired detectives whose job it was to find out the plans of the agitators.

In my experience, the most interesting, resourceful, and courageous of these Pinkerton detectives was Charles A. Siringo who worked for us throughout the semiwarfare in the Coeur d'Alene, 1891-92. In his youth he had been cowboy and scout in Texas, Kansas, Indian Territory, and New Mexico. When he came into our employ he was a dark, slender, wiry fellow with a small mustache, easily identifiable by pockmarks. Some of the services performed by Siringo, and some of the personal hazards he coolly met during this trouble, are set down in his own notes and the records of the Mine Owners' Association.

On arriving in the district, he secured a job in a mine at Gem where he worked for four weeks. At the end of his second week he joined the union, and two months later was elected its recording secretary. Meanwhile, he purposely had himself discharged from the mine on a genuine charge of dereliction of duty. As a result, he could devote all his attention to the union miners, ostensibly supported by his position as recording secretary. His reports of union plottings he sent secretly by mail to the Mine Owners' Association. The postmaster at Gem being a rabid union man of the anarchistic type, the detective used to walk four miles to Wallace to post his letters.

Siringo secretly bought a small building in which he established a widow and her daughter to run a store and rooming house. In this way he could appear to the town as a mere lodger while using the building as a vantage point. He witnessed and reported many murderous beatings of our miners who had strayed from our fortified properties into the town seeking pleasure. The house stood on stilts two or three feet off the ground, level with the board walk which was raised above the road to avoid dust and mud. Siringo sawed a hole in the floor of his bedroom through which to escape if necessary. Directly under his window ran the river.

Siringo had been a union sympathizer before coming in contact with the cutthroat Coeur d'Alene crew, but he was now thoroughly out of sympathy with their views, as evidenced by his letters which described the leaders of the union as a vicious, heartless gang, many of them "rocked in the cradle of anarchy at Butte"; many were escaped outlaws from other states.

Siringo steadily relayed to us plots for beating up and killing scab miners whenever they should be brought in from other places for resumption of operations. He reported in advance the plans made for a "bloody revolution" on the Fourth of July, when, as a matter of fact, the American flag was riddled with bullets, trampled, and spat upon.

He cut from the minutes one page of particular interest to me. It not only recorded the union's decision to have its members creep up in the night on two of the mines and flood them by pulling the pumps, but also on this same page was written the decision of the unionists to "do away with" Clement and me. This page Siringo mailed to our lawyers.

While it was being extracted, he had been careful to have two union members handling the book at almost the same time, so as to be sure of witnesses to his innocence if the theft was discovered. The book had then been put in a safe place to which he had not since had access. Such was the accuracy of our foreknowledge of their plans that the unions finally began to suspect the presence of a spy at their councils. It was intimated to Siringo that he had been "making too many trips to Wallace to mail letters." At a secret meeting, held at night, the book was exhibited with the page missing. Pandemonium followed. Although Siringo had his forty-five in a holster under his left arm, he did not think it would be possible to escape from the hall with his life.

That the detective was ordinarily devoid of personal fear is proved by many accounts of his bravery in books dealing with that period and place and his many other thrilling experiences, but he admitted to me that he was badly frightened at this meeting. His fear was not so much for himself, he said, but because of the suspicion he had cast on the two innocent men who were with him when the page was taken out.

At the height of the excitement the president locked the door and, raising his hand, demanded silence.

"Someone has been betraying union secrets! Only three men had access to the minutes-book. These three men are all in this room at this very moment. One of them must be guilty. I propose that we determine which one it is and punish him as he deserves, here and now!" This meant death. Siringo had not only to extricate himself from his perilous position, but also to remove suspicion from the two innocent men whose lives he had jeopardized.

He rose to speak. First of all, he qualified some of his previous statements reflecting on the loyalty of these men by admitting he might have been mistaken. He said it was too serious a matter for him to implicate them without being absolutely positive of their guilt. By means of amazing nerve and a complicated fabric of lies, Siringo finally succeeded in getting the meeting to disperse without taking action.

Knowing it would be not only futile, but also certainly fatal for him to attend further meetings of the union, he remained away from the next one, where, as secretary, he was due at eight in the evening. When at eight-thirty a union committee came to his room to ask why he was late, he told them to go back and he would be there in ten minutes. They went away muttering. Siringo at once wrote a letter, full of indignation, which explained he had been tipped off that the union had foolishly concluded he was a detective spy. In view of this unjust suspicion he felt he must resign both his secretaryship and his membership in the union. This letter he sent to the hall.

During the dance which followed the adjournment of the meeting, Siringo scouted around outside union headquarters, and learned from miners who had not yet heard of his resignation that a violent demonstration against mine owners and strikebreakers was scheduled to occur within a few days.

On the morning the Frisco mill was blown up, in which a number of men were killed, shooting began simultaneously in the town. Siringo was spotted on the street. Realizing the game was up, and followed by the maddened crowd, he fled for the near-by shelter of his house. Then, to divert pursuit, he threw a large, previously prepared parcel into the Coeur d'Alene River. This achieved its object; the strikers thought he had jumped from the window. During this momentary respite, he coolly moved a trunk which had been placed over the hole in the floor, lowered himself into the space beneath the building, and from there crept under the wooden sidewalk.

As he crawled along he identified a number of the men responsible for the shooting and dynamiting, partly by their voices and partly by glancing upward through the wide cracks between the boards. Watch in hand to note the exact time, he jotted down this evidence in his notebook for later use at their trial.

United States troops, delayed by the blowing up of train bridges by the union agitators, finally arrived on the scene. Siringo distinguished himself further by discovering the cellar where most of the strike leaders were hiding and informing General Carlin. These and others arrested during succeeding days were crowded into the celebrated bull pen.

Just before the trial of the union agitators, I had some matters to discuss with Siringo, who was hidden in the mountains not far from

Wallace. I endeavored to induce him to leave the country and not return until time for the trial, telling him he was too valuable a witness to take any chances. Indignantly repudiating my suggestion, he said "no damned foreigners," such as composed the leadership of the union, could scare him, an American, out of the country. Although he concealed himself in the mountains during the night, he appeared frequently in the mining town in the daytime.

On the occasion to which I have just referred, he insisted on accompanying me back to the railway station, which required traversing the length of the town's only thoroughfare. We walked together down the middle of the road, each of us carrying two pistols in our side coat pockets. There was a running fire of comment from miners on the sidewalk as they expressed their hatred for Siringo in no uncertain language. As he walked Siringo kept his hands in his pockets. The outline of his guns could clearly be seen as he swayed ominously from side to side.

Every man knew that the guns were cocked, and our fingers were on the triggers. Although from time to time he challenged them with the term "coward," a fighting word in the West, no one dared take the offensive. It is easier to talk than to be the first man to die.

In spite of the threats against his life should he take the witness stand, Siringo boldly testified in the federal court at Coeur d'Alene against the strike leaders. We had not only the page from the union minutes-book proving their sabotage plans, but also his identifying information gleaned from under the sidewalk. As a direct result, several of the strike leaders were convicted and sent to the penitentiary. Siringo concluded his final report to the Mine Owners' Association with the words: "Such damnable outrages as have gone on here could not happen in any country but my own."

Some years later, after my return from Africa, Siringo came again into my employ. With David H. Moffat, president of one of the banks in Denver, and Harry Payne Whitney, with whom I was associated in many other mining enterprises, I was interested in buying a mining property not far from Leadville. We were anxious to ascertain whether the samples from a bore hole that we had put down on the property had been salted. As the assays were suspiciously high, Moffat got into communication with the Pinkerton Detective

Agency and my old friend Siringo was sent to take charge of the investigation.

This time he appeared in the role of a man from the Middle West —"not in very good health"—who was a victim of asthma. It took him only a few weeks' sojourn in the mining community where the property was located to establish most cordial and intimate relations with the people suspected of attempting fraud. In this case as before, the reports we received from Siringo showed his remarkable knowledge of human nature, as well as an extraordinary ability to adapt his character to any situation.

After fighting in many other strikes, and performing detective work in various western cities, Siringo settled down in Hollywood where he wrote several books, the most prominent of which are *History of "Billy the Kid"* and *A Cowboy Detective*.

One of the problems connected with the operation of the Bunker Hill and Sullivan was the smelting of lead concentrates produced at the mine. As president of the company, after tentatively securing attractive railroad rates for hauling the ore to San Francisco, I was endeavoring to purchase the Selby Smelting Company's near-by plant. Negotiations were proceeding satisfactorily when I was called away on a mine examination trip to Mexico.

On my return, I learned that a Freiberg collegemate, Alfred von der Ropp, had happened to visit the Selby plant on his way to Australia, where he was to take charge of large smelting operations under the management of another Freiberg man, Herman Schlapp. Ropp's visit to the Selby plant convinced him that the metallurgical operations in effect there were not scientific. He convinced the directors that he could make money for the company, which at that time was in the red. This resulted in his giving up his engagement in Australia and taking charge of the Selby Smelting Company.

It is extraordinary how seemingly unimportant events may exercise a vital influence on one's career. Had I purchased the Selby plant, my responsibility to the capital necessarily invested therein, and the vastly increased burden of operating the joint properties, would have so involved me that I should not have been able to go to South Africa and consequently my whole career would have been changed—for the better, quién sabe?

CHAPTER TWELVE

The Call to Africa

THE LAND OF ADVENTURE — MAGIC BLUE CLAY —
BARNEY BARNATO AND THE DEPRESSION SEND ME
TO AFRICA — I TIE UP WITH BARNEY — ROMANTIC
STORY OF BARNATO'S RISE — COSMOPOLITAN JOHAN-
NESBURG — NATIVE SERVANTS — WASTED ADVICE —
BARNATO'S WHITE ELEPHANT — I RESIGN — A THOU-
SAND MILES TO MEET RHODES — I BECOME CONSULT-
ING ENGINEER OF THE CONSOLIDATED GOLD FIELDS
OF SOUTH AFRICA AND THE BRITISH SOUTH AFRICA
(CHARTERED) COMPANY — BARNEY'S TRAGIC DEATH

As a boy, I always thought of Africa as the land of mystery. My mind conjured up endless deserts and snow-capped mountains and impenetrable jungles. I knew there were cataracts that dwarfed Niagara. In the zoo I saw elephants, lions, camels, and other strange animals of the Dark Continent.

As I grew older, I read books and talked with travelers about Africa. Those few who had been to its diamond mines had stories to tell of the strange negro tribes with their still stranger customs. Rumors of the great ruins at Zimbabwe came to my ears.

Even after I went into business, I found it impossible to avoid being influenced by these early impressions. Yet I knew that Africa, for the mining engineer and the entrepreneur, offered unlimited opportunities for wealth, however proportionate the risk might be.

In Africa the world's natural resources were still to be found in profusion. To me, already practical and experienced in the world, Africa remained the land of adventure. Diamonds, copper, coal, rubber, ivory, palm oil, and spices—all were there for the taking. For hundreds of years these remained unexploited. Out of Africa came only ivory, slaves, and a small amount of gold.

Then suddenly a new vista of wealth opened. A Boer child brought to her home, near what is now Kimberley, some pretty stones to play with. A chance traveler suspected that they were diamonds. When further search proved the existence of these precious stones on a colossal scale, there was a rush to the diamond fields. Kimberley, almost overnight, became the mecca for adventurous prospectors.

The greatest of all diamond fields are still those in the neighborhood of Kimberley, and even there the average yield in the profitable mines is only about a grain and a half per ton. The stones are found in the necks of extinct volcanoes, called pipes, which have eroded down to the general level of the country. After the indurated mud of bluish color has been excavated from the shafts and hoisted to the surface, sometimes from a depth of several thousand feet, it is spread out on the "floors" and allowed to remain untouched for two or three years, until it oxidizes or disintegrates from exposure to sun and rain.

After the material has been broken up in the mills it is run over inclined tables. Beside these stand the native "boys" deftly picking out the resinous-looking stones as the slow current of water carries them past. The *modus operandi* has now been simplified. Purely through the carelessness of a white overseer, it is said, some greasy material was once spilled on one of the tables. It was found that the diamonds adhered to this substance while the extraneous minerals were washed off, regardless of their specific gravity. This accidental discovery forms the basis of the new process of recovering diamonds.

To avoid all opportunity for peculation, the boys are confined to compounds during the customary three years of employment. At the end of that time they are penned for a few days in narrow quarters where every precaution is taken to thwart their frequent attempts at smuggling. They will even endure the pain of making deep cuts in their bodies in which to conceal the diamonds, and not infrequently they will swallow the gems. This latter type of smuggling is provided against by the administering of strong and thorough-"searching" aperients before the boys are released.

However arduous diamond mining may be, in the past it has been highly remunerative. It is still an extremely condensed form of wealth. Moreover, it is a geological wonder that the greatest known deposits of gold and diamonds should both occur in Africa within three hundred miles of each other. From the profits of the diamond industry at Kimberley abundant capital was available for the subsequent exploitation of the greatest of the world's gold fields—the Witwatersrand, the White Water Ridge.

Naturally, my interest lay in the huge gold camp worked by its vast black army of Kaffirs digging endlessly underground. During the early nineties, very attractive offers came to me from Barney Barnato and other British financiers who wanted me to go to South Africa to take charge of their mining properties. All these I refused, expressing regret and offering to recommend in my place competent American experts in gold mining. At the time, I was busy with the development of silver and lead mines in the Coeur d'Alene district of Idaho.

After the election of Grover Cleveland in 1892, however, I realized that the tariff policy of the Democratic party would result in a period of industrial depression in the United States. I felt that this would be a good time to go to South Africa for a few months to look over the possibilities of the new gold-mining field then rapidly developing on the Rand. Although I had already answered Barnato's proposals in the negative, he was not satisfied. He renewed his offer opportunely at this time, with an invitation to a conference in London. He not only suggested recompensing me for the time I should lose from my professional work in America by coming to London, but also expressed his belief that he would be able to offer terms so attractive that I should be justified in accepting the managership of his mining interests.

By a coincidence, I received at the same time a cablegram from Scotland asking me to make a report in person to the board of directors of the Arizona Copper Company, whose property I had recently examined. This request, coupled with Barnato's offer, induced me to go to England, and I cabled Barnato accordingly.

I arrived at Southampton on a Saturday morning in April, 1893, and from there wired Barnato that I should be at his office the following Monday at noon. Although I had heard that he was careless about keeping appointments on time, I found him ready for me on the dot of twelve. It was hard for me to believe that this short, thick-set, little fellow, blond and rosy as a Cupid, was that same Barnato whose reputation for shrewdness had spread throughout the business world. His brother Henry was also present, although he took little part in the conference beyond nodding confirmation to his brother's remarks.

After shaking hands, Barnato inquired politely whether I had had a pleasant trip. Then, going straight to the point, he asked as to my immediate plans. I informed him that I had booked my return passage for the latter part of the week. He expressed the fear that this would not allow us sufficient time in which to settle our affairs. This, in turn, gave me the opportunity to explain at once the foundation upon which any business connection between us would have to be based. Having heard rumors that Barnato was a keen trader, I wanted to make certain that I, as an engineer, would not be involved in any extraprofessional activities. I began by saying, therefore, that if we could not agree on the fundamentals of our relationship in half an hour, there would be no point in continuing the discussion.

"I've been told you've often engineered the market for your stocks," I said. "That's not my kind of engineering. Before we discuss any terms it must be clearly understood that my professional reputation is not to be used for the purpose of rigging the stock market for your mining securities."

Without hesitation came Barnato's reply: "I'm glad to hear you say that, Mr. Hammond. If you'd do whatever I told you to, what use would you be to me? Why, you'd be just as likely to do the same for someone else to my loss if he could make it worth your while."

Then looking at his brother, he continued: "Henry and I have been talking over this proposition and have decided to offer you twenty-five thousand dollars a year. You know, Mr. Hammond, that's the biggest salary any American engineer gets in South Africa."

Having already determined for myself the minimum for which I should be willing to leave my established American practice, I at once said: "I'm sorry, Mr. Barnato, but I'm not interested at that figure. I've been doing much better than that at home."

"How much *do* you want then?" came his question.

"Double it," I said.

He looked inquiringly at Henry, who nodded approval. Barnato then agreed. "All right, that's satisfactory to us."

But, since I desired to leave no loophole for misunderstanding, I continued: "Inasmuch as you are to spend many millions of dollars in the development of your properties, and, believing as I do, that I can increase the operating efficiency of your mines and introduce economies that will amount yearly to many times my salary, I shall accept your offer of fifty thousand *only* until such time as I have been able to convince you, as a good businessman, that my services are worth a great deal more to you. Therefore," I concluded, "when that time comes you must be prepared to expect from me a request for a much higher salary."

"All right," he agreed. "If you can do what you claim, you'll be earning it. All the other engineers have a three years' contract. I suppose you'll want the same?"

"No," I replied, "you'll be able to determine in six months just how valuable my services are to you. If I should enter into an agreement for a longer period, and then fall out of favor with you, you could make it so uncomfortable for me that out of self-respect I should have to tender my resignation and you would consequently be relieved of your contract. On the other hand, if I were tied up for three years with you, I should not be permitted to resign even if the position became distasteful to me. In other words, Mr. Barnato, I should regard such a contract as one-sided and to my disadvantage."

Rather to my surprise, Barnato accepted all my terms, and the agreement was drawn up and signed the following day.

The next day I spent in Edinburgh and presented my report to the directors of the Arizona Copper Company. While at their mine in Arizona, I had assumed the responsibility of discharging the manager of the property whom I found incompetent and more than wasteful of the company's funds. I had temporarily installed James Colquhoun, their chief chemist.

The directors approved my report of the changes I had suggested for the development of the mines and the treatment of the ores, but when it came to adopting my recommendation that Colquhoun be made permanent manager they demurred, saying they doubted whether he had the ability for such a position. I reassured them as to this. Then the question of salary came up. They said they had known him for many years and he had never been the recipient of such a large salary as was paid to the manager of their mines. I told them that was really a small matter, and I sympathized with Colquhoun in that they had evidently undervalued his services in the past and had not given him the compensation to which he was entitled.

The subsequent history of the great success of the Arizona Copper Company under Colquhoun's able management justified my recommendation; he remained there many years, until the property was sold by the Arizona company to the well-known firm of Phelps-Dodge. Thirty years later I had the pleasure of renewing my acquaintance with Colquhoun, at Del Monte, California. In the meantime, as manager of large copper interests in Russia he had had most thrilling experiences after the Soviets had taken over the country. With great difficulty he finally escaped and went back to England, where he now resides.

By the end of the week I had completed my business with the Arizona Copper Company and with Barnato. I returned at once to the United States to settle up my affairs before taking my family to South Africa. Barnato, meanwhile, went to Cape Town.

It was due to the Brothers Struben that the Johannesburg gold fields developed so rapidly, although gold was first discovered there by a man named Arnold in 1885. In 1886 Johannesburg began rapidly to grow through the activity of the new discovery.

Whether one regarded him with admiration or distaste, Barney

TABLE MOUNTAIN, CAPE TOWN

BARNEY BARNATO (1852-1897)

Barnato was an extraordinary character. He was born in London in 1852, the son of a Jewish shopkeeper in Whitechapel. The name "Barney" Barnato, by which he was generally known, was not his own. He had assumed it in place of the original Barnett Isaacs when he set up a small store in Kimberley, the raw new town in the diamond fields.

His parents had been unable to make much headway financially. Barney, however, had inherited not only their tenacity but had in himself tremendous resourcefulness and energy. Although self-educated, he had a brilliant mind and possessed a remarkable appreciation of intellectual achievement in others. As is generally true of his race, he was fond of his family and loyal to his friends.

As a companion he was interesting; as an entertainer, inimitable. Amateur theatricals had been his chief relaxation as a boy in London. He could quote more extensively and accurately from Shakespeare than anyone else I have ever known. Frankly proud of his dramatic talents, he seized every opportunity to display them. To the great advantage of charity, he staged many benefits in Johannesburg, not only engaging the theater and supporting cast but assuming all other expenses. His performance in *The Bells*—that famous play which the great Henry Irving had made his own—was quite untouched by amateur failings.

I was once seated next to Barney at a large stag dinner in London. According to the English custom of hiring a music hall artist to entertain their guests, Marshall P. Wilder, an American, was the one selected for that evening. He was so successful in keeping his audience in gales of laughter that I, who knew Barney well, could see that Wilder's quips had quickened in my friend those inexhaustible springs of anecdotes that were always ready to bubble over.

I wrote hastily on a card "Try Barney" and sent it to our host. At an appropriate moment this suggestion was acted upon. Barney, nothing loath, accepted the invitation and, like a conjurer, began to produce from his prodigious memory such varied examples of humor that the guests sat enthralled. Although at first Wilder was somewhat piqued at losing his audience, he also was caught under the magic spell of Barney's flow of reminiscence and anecdote. When the party finally broke up in the small hours of the morning he approached Barney and thanked him with the true artist's ungrudging appreciation for a master of his own craft.

In Barney's frequent voyages back and forth from London to the Cape he was always accompanied by his wife, his children, and two pets. The first of these pets was an English pugdog named Blue Rock, who received as much attention from the friends of the Barnato family as one of the children. The other was a green parrot who possessed a luxurious gilded cage. After his success in the gold fields Barney had initiated the custom of giving occasional breakfasts to friends of his on the stock exchange. The parrot had been taught to greet the guests with, "Barney, what price Primrose today?" Primrose was one of Barney's gold mines, the stock of which was rising perceptibly in price at this time, due perhaps in part to the parrot's advertising.

Barney was a master of financial wizardry in any field. Jacob Schiff and other Jewish banker friends of mine once asked me what I thought of his ability as a financier. I told them that if he were alive today and penniless, I would grubstake him to a few hundred dollars and a push-cart, and that, launched with this small capital, he would soon be taking their money away from them in Wall Street. They did not particularly like this characterization of Barney; nevertheless, I do believe his equal would have been hard to find.

Barney was the sort of man who never let his pride stand in the way of his making "an honest penny." One day, I said, "Barney, I will get some people from the 'Corner House'"—meaning the Eckstein Company, local representatives of Wernher, Beit and Company—"to come over and have a talk with you about a project Eckstein discussed with me today."

Barney inquired, "Do you think there is anything to it?"

"Yes," I replied. "It looks pretty good!"

"Well," said Barney, "I will not waste any time. I will go right over and see him. I'm a busy man, but I have always found that if I go to the other fellow's office, I can get away better. I will not be detained too long, and if things are not going as I want them to, but are against me, I can always *say* that I have an important engagement and leave."

Barnato bought his first claim in the Kimberley diamond fields in 1876 with money saved from his shop. Only five years later he floated his first company. From the hundreds of small claims then operating in the pits came a flood of jewels that was disrupting the diamond market. Barnato was one of the first to see that the great opportunities for profits lay in amalgamating the smaller companies into larger organizations, which could then control output and keep supply commensurate with demand. In a few years the diamond companies were mainly aligned in two groups: the De Beers with Barnato at its head, and the Kimberley controlled by Cecil Rhodes. Finally, in 1888, the two competing groups were joined into the great De Beers Consolidated Mines, Ltd., which still controls the major part of the world's diamond output.

In the autumn of 1893 my family—consisting of myself and wife, my sister Betty, and my two sons Harris and Jack—came to Africa. Still distinct in my mind is the memory of that first view of Table Mountain as it stood out clear and stark in the golden sunrise. Often since then I have seen it covered by clouds as by a tablecloth. From the deck of the steamer *Scot,* Cape Town seemed a part of the white surf breaking on the shore.

"Mr. Barnato came down to meet us in high good spirits, and from my cabin," wrote my wife in describing our arrival, "where I was searching for small boys' caps and coats, I could overhear his hearty welcome, and his breezy excuses for not being conventionally dressed to meet us.

" 'I had time only to put on my ulster over my pajamas, I was so anxious to be down at the wharf in time to receive you,' he said, 'but I don't suppose Mrs. Hammond will mind.' The heart of 'Mrs. Hammond' in the cabin dropped at these significant words; and it seemed to her that crossing the equator had subverted other laws than those of climate."

After we had passed through the Custom House, Barnato himself took one of my handbags and we mounted into a waiting Cape cart. In this peculiar high-wheeled contrivance we drove to the Queens Hotel in near-by Sea Point where a suite had been reserved for us through Barnato's forethought. The peak of the morning's excitement for the children was Barnato's parrot which he had brought along to entertain them.

There was some difference of opinion between the landlady and my wife as to which rooms were more suitable for the children. The landlady thought it a great mistake for the children to have the best rooms in the suite. Indeed, she objected to their being with us at all. My wife explained that it was now too late for us to rid ourselves of these encumbrances, but that we should guarantee good behavior on their part. I admit, we were assuming considerable liability.

There was further difficulty when I asked for a bedroom fire. for Jack, who was not well. I was told that the chimney smoked and a fire was out of the question, and in any case it was better for the boy to get up and exercise to keep warm. "Fires are not considered healthy in South Africa," the landlady volunteered. In spite of these minor differences of opinion, there was about the place a fraternal spirit to which we quickly accustomed ourselves.

As there was little to amuse the children at Sea Point, Barnato kindly took them to his office where they could be entertained by looking at his great collection of diamonds. When he brought the boys back, full of excitement over the shining playthings, Barnato told us how chance had just played him a scurvy trick. It was customary for the De Beers Diamond Company once a year to sell the entire annual output of the mines to the highest bidder based on the price per carat, irrespective of the size of the diamonds. Barnato had held the contract which had just expired. Within an hour after the new syndicate had assumed control a lucky blast had uncovered a pocket which contained many diamonds of large size. This was hard luck for Barnato, as the value of the find ran into several hundred thousand dollars. When these diamonds were retailed, the price per carat mounted greatly with the increased weight of the stone.

I did not stay in Cape Town any longer than was necessary, but started almost immediately on the thousand-mile rail journey north to Johannesburg. The city was located on the high veldt which stretched far and wide in every direction. The houses were in no way pretentious, being merely one-story structures, each with its broad veranda.

Those who had seen something of the western mining camps in the United States, supposed we suffered similar privations in Johannesburg. Though the town was comparatively new, it was not a mining camp in the western sense of the word, but had already attained a cosmopolitan atmosphere. As a matter of fact, living conditions in Johannesburg were quite equal to those in large cities elsewhere in the world. Everything was very expensive, but salaries were high, and markets were plentiful.

The population, of course, was extremely heterogeneous. The small percentage of Boers was almost drowned out by the foreign inhabitants, who had built up the city after the gold discovery. The majority of the Uitlanders—as we foreigners were called—were law-abiding substantial citizens by temperament, and most of us were accompanied by our families.

My wife was keenly observant of the social customs of this new environment. She found the elaborate and costly balls rather dull because the husbands always retired to the smoking room to discuss mining problems and local politics. Because of ever-increasing interference from the Boer government at Pretoria, these subjects, truly interrelated as will be shown later, occupied the men for the entire evening. The women devoted this prolonged interval to talking about their own feminine concerns. What little gossip there was had neither malice nor unfriendliness in it.

Although Johannesburg was largely an English community, not much time was devoted to sports; the men were too hard at work all day. An occasional polo match, gymkhana, and now and then a horse race were held at the Wanderers' Club. These social functions were usually made disagreeable by the constant dust from the bleak dry veldt and the "tailing" piles of the mills.

Because the town was so prosperous at this time, servants were hard to procure no matter what inducements might be held out to them. On one occasion my wife advertised for a housemaid and a delicate little woman applied. When asked about her experience, she admitted that she had had none beyond keeping a tearoom in town; she had once been in the asylum, and now that she felt her mental ills coming on again from overwork, she thought she would like to be in domestic service.

On another occasion we advertised for a coachman. As my wife described it, a dapper-looking individual with curly banged hair and golden mustache applied. Genial and communicative, he said he had never been a private coachman, but was a first-rate driver of oxen. He wanted a position as Mr. Hammond's servant because it would give him a standing among his fellows.

Our native servants were quite different from the Chinese to whom we had been accustomed in California. One of our houseboys was docile, but very forgetful. When reproved for remissness he invariably went to his cabin, arrayed himself in a straw hat and a sweater violently striped red and yellow, and sang *Lead, Kindly Light* with the voice of an angel. Another houseboy was a six-foot Zulu named Jim, who had to be treated as though he were a child of six.

I remember giving a dinner to Baron Ferdinand Rothschild on one occasion when he visited Johannesburg. There was everything in the food line that one could find anywhere else: fruit and vegetables came from Cape Town; we had the choicest wines that the best cellars of Europe could provide.

At this time we had a fine, but expensive, chef whom my wife had hired in Paris and brought to Johannesburg; not with the idea of ostentation, but because she wanted to be sure of my having the proper and most palatable food. This chef had been employed by one of the Rothschilds of Vienna. He was an excellent cook; one of the best. My wife wondered how the Rothschilds could afford to let such a man leave their service. Some weeks later when my wife came to me in dismay over the bills run up by the chef, I said, "Well, maybe the answer is, the Rothschilds couldn't afford to keep him."

Some time later, I planned to give a dinner to Alfred Beit. The afternoon of the dinner, the chef started getting drunk, and wound up by chasing one of the maids around the house with a butcher's cleaver. It was necessary to overpower him and lock him up. The dinner had to be called off at the eleventh hour. When the man sobered up I gave him a good scolding, but tolerated him for a while longer. Then he began drinking again, and finally it was necessary for me to give him a good thrashing and discharge him. He immediately started in business for himself, as a caterer, and made twice as much money as he had been receiving. I discovered that he had deliberately got drunk so that I would fire him and he could open his own business. I sometimes found it embarrassing when dining with friends, to discover that the food was supplied by the caterer whom I had discharged as my chef.

A man's wife—and this applies particularly to the engineering profession—can exert an unusual or peculiar influence on his success. A woman of this kind, who has sympathy and understanding, can do much to ensure the co-operation of her husband's staff. My wife learned first aid when she was a young woman, and many times she applied that knowledge and afforded great relief to the suffering when physicians were not available.

In Johannesburg our Sunday luncheons were given up to entertaining young engineers, or engineers away from their homes and families, to give them a share in a domestic atmosphere. This had naturally, though it was not intended for that purpose, a great moral influence.

My wife always believed that men ought not to talk shop away from shop, and for that reason she established a rule of fining anyone who attempted to discuss technical mining matters. If "pump," "gear," "shaft," or any other such term was used at our home, she would fine the person using it, the money to be given to charity. Because it was difficult at first to teach the men not to refer to the subject of mining, she collected quite a sum.

Immediately on my arrival in Johannesburg, I looked up my old friend, and classmate at Freiberg, Edgar Rathbone. (He was the father of Basil Rathbone, the well-known English actor.) Rathbone had been employed for a year or more as mining reporter on one of the Johannesburg papers. He had an intimate knowledge of the relations of the mining groups, of which there were several strongly competing ones on the Rand.

I spent the greater part of two or three days quietly apart with

Rathbone, and from him I got a good knowledge of the dramatis personae of the mining industry. This information was of great value to me, and undoubtedly prevented my making mistakes in my dealings with these men. Otherwise, I would have required several months of actual experience to find my way about in my business dealings with the various groups engaged in mining.

Rathbone was most eager to be of help to me, not only because of our friendship during Freiberg days in '76-'79, but because I had been able to render him an important service.

Before I left the United States I received a cablegram from Rathbone, saying that his firm in England was very much embarrassed. It had agreed to send an engineer to examine a mining property in Nevada, but unforeseen circumstances made it impossible for an engineer from London to make the examination before the expiration of the option held on the property by their clients.

At no little inconvenience, and with a good deal of hardship to reach the mine in winter, I made the examination for Rathbone's firm and sent a cable report on the property. This relieved his firm of the financial liability which would have been imposed in default of the report they had agreed to make. Rathbone was naturally grateful for my help in this matter.

Ernest Wiltsee had preceded me to the Transvaal and had written glowing accounts of its future. Victor Clement accompanied me to South Africa, while shortly afterwards Pope Yeatman, George Starr, E. M. Garthwaite, Hal Tilghman, Robert Catlin, and S. B. Connor were included in my staff of American engineers. I soon added several brilliant young English geologists: S. J. Truscott, now professor of mining at the Imperial College of Science and Technology in London, Dr. F. H. Hatch, and J. A. Chalmers. This was an exceptionally able staff whose services contributed greatly to the successful development of the mining properties of Barnato, and subsequently of Rhodes.

Part of my arrangement with Barnato was that I should be free to accept other engagements as a consulting engineer so long as they did not conflict with his interests. This had always been my custom.

Soon after my arrival in Africa, I was employed on the recom-

THE MARKET PLACE, JOHANNESBURG

DR. MURRAY AND JACKIE IN MY CAPE CART

mendation of Eugene de Crano to examine for some of his English
clients a mining property near Johannesburg in which a great deal
of money was involved. My examination did not take long as it
was a type of geological formation with which I was familiar.
In due time I sent in the bill for my services.

De Crano wrote me in a friendly but frank tone that his clients
were rather surprised at the amount of my bill. They had previously consulted another engineer on the Rand who would have
made the examination in question for much less money, "if he
had known that type of mining."

I replied that I did not consider the fee excessive. I said the
arguments of his clients reminded me of the sea captain who was
in a great hurry to get his clearance papers at a port in Maine. By
employing the lawyer most familiar with the necessary procedure
he obtained them without delay.

On the way to his boat the captain met one of his friends who
said, "Well, Cap, you're getting out quick."

"Sure thing," replied the captain, with a smirk of satisfaction.

"How much did it cost you?"

"Twenty-five dollars," admitted the captain.

"Gosh Almighty! Why, ole lawyer Smith would of done it for
five dollars—if he'd a-known how."

De Crano saw the point.

My first task in Johannesburg was to inspect Barnato's mining
properties and to advise him about them. I soon called his attention
to the East Rand gold-mining section, at that time undeveloped,
and urged him to acquire an interest there. But Barney was
occupied with other matters, principally social, and did not adopt
my recommendation. He spent too much time listening to stockbrokers who were trying to interest him in various speculative
schemes. Barney was always a speculator at heart; he employed
his tremendous courage on the long chance rather than on the sure
thing. This does not mean, however, that he had vision or foresight as to future developments in mining.

This was well brought out by his reaction when I urged upon
him the possibilities in deep-level mining; that is, the working of
ore bodies at several thousand feet below the mining operations at

that time. Although surface claims above the deep-level areas had not been taken up and could have been obtained cheaply, yet since the majority of mining experts still thought such a scheme chimerical, Barney would not listen to me.

Naturally I was much disappointed that my recommendations on these two important propositions had been ignored. The first project, the development of the East Rand, was subsequently taken up by others and proved enormously remunerative. Hundreds of millions of dollars were extracted from the very properties I had once recommended to Barnato. The second scheme, the opening of the deep levels, will be referred to later.

Barnato's repeated failure to act on my recommendations decided me to resign at the end of six months' engagement. He also made things difficult for me by failing to keep appointment after appointment which I made for him with the owners of valuable mining claims. When I suggested leaving his employ, Barney seemed both surprised and disappointed. He asked me to wait until he should arrive at Madeira, en route to London whither he was sailing within a few days. He advanced as his reason for the delay that he would have no opportunity before he departed to discuss with Woolf Joel, his nephew and business associate, the renewal of my engagement on the basis of my contract, but that on the steamer between Cape Town and Madeira he would take up the matter with Joel and would cable me from there a proposition to renew my services. I replied that unless I could accept his proposal without further negotiations, *ipso facto* my engagement with him would terminate.

I saw in the newspaper that Barney's ship had arrived at Madeira, but the promised cable did not materialize. As soon as I knew the steamer must have left for London, I presented my resignation to Solly Joel, the nephew in charge of Barnato's Johannesburg office. He endeavored to prevail upon me to wait until I heard from Barney on his arrival in London, but this I declined to do. I told him that it was not a question of compensation alone; that my coming to South Africa had been heralded as the arrival of "Barnato's White Elephant," and that I felt it was doing myself an injustice to let pass opportunities of making a professional reputation, because of

Barnato's failure to avail himself of the counsel I had given him. Accordingly, I insisted on definitely resigning.

Although I had given him timely notice, Barney was taken aback by my leaving his company. We always remained good friends, however, and for some time after joining Rhodes I continued to manage Barnato's mines.

The news of my resignation spread rapidly. Almost immediately came a telegram from Cecil Rhodes, who had recently been made prime minister of Cape Colony, asking me to come to see him at Cape Town. I had already met Rhodes on a train, having been introduced to him by Robert Williams. He knew that I was then under contract with the Barnatos for a fixed period and had not approached me during that time. I had already received offers from several powerful syndicates contingent upon leaving Barnato. They had even proposed to finance independent companies in which I was to have an interest. None of these offers, however, proved sufficient inducement. Rhodes was the big man of Africa, and it was with him that I preferred to become identified, and I lost no time in accepting his invitation and starting for Groote Schuur, his famous residence not far from Cape Town.

Early on a beautiful South African spring morning in 1894, Rhodes and I retired to a stone bench a few hundred yards from the house, on a little path leading up to Table Mountain. From this point our glances ranged over the glorious harbor.

As we sat there I studied Rhodes. He presented a striking figure, typically Augustan, I thought, with his heavy forehead, his strong mouth, and square cleft chin. This impression of his origin was strengthened by the curly blond hair, always in confusion. His gray-blue eyes could be cold as ice, but when he smiled, as he frequently did, they were no longer cold. Although slender when young, as he grew older his big-boned frame filled out until he seemed to tower rocklike over most of his companions. His hands were blunt and powerful, expressive of himself. He rarely moved them to gesticulate.

Rhodes came to the point quickly. "Mr. Hammond," he begun, "I take it you are not in South Africa for your health?"

"No, Mr. Rhodes," I replied; "with due appreciation for the climate of South Africa, I prefer that of California."

"Well," he continued, "how would the idea appeal to you of taking charge of all my mining interests on the Rand?" And he added, "Name your own salary!"

"Seventy-five thousand dollars a year and a participation in the profits would suit me."

"All right," he promptly agreed.

"But," I added, "I want to deal directly with you without interference from your local board of directors. Unless this can be arranged, I can't accept."

I told him frankly that I had a very poor opinion of his properties, but I felt that with his backing I could acquire some other mining interests to level up his investments. Rhodes picked up a scrap of paper only a few inches long, and wrote on it:

> Mr. Hammond is authorized to make any purchases for going ahead, and has full authority, provided he informs me of it and gets no protest.

In this brief manner I was made chief consulting engineer of the Consolidated Gold Fields of South Africa, and soon afterwards of the British South Africa Company (Chartered), which controlled the mining rights of the country then known as Mashonaland and Matabeleland. On the sole strength of this little scrap of paper, I spent many hundred thousand pounds.

There was naturally considerable friction when I took over this position, owing to the jealousy felt by some of the English engineers towards their American colleagues. But Rhodes gave me his unqualified support and agreed to accept any recommendation I should make on one condition: the acquiescence of his brother, Captain Ernest Rhodes, former engineer in the British Army, who was at that time resident managing director of his companies. As I had formed a high opinion of Captain Rhodes and he had expressed confidence in my judgment, I felt sure he would accept my recommendations without hesitation.

Ernest was entirely different from Rhodes in temperament. He was a soldier, fine and high-principled, but he knew little about mining or finance. Rhodes would say, "If Ernest agrees, and you don't hear to the contrary, go ahead." Ernest always agreed and I never heard to the contrary. We made rapid progress.

Thus fairly early in 1894 I had the Rhodes mines well organized, with the help of my mining staff who had followed me from the Barnatos. I secured additional engineers from America.

Barney chose to consider that Rhodes had played him a mean trick. He went to see Rhodes and, thumping the table angrily, said: "Suppose you had a first-rate chef and after dining with you I hired him away from you. You'd think me a cad, wouldn't you?—and you'd be right, too. But you've done the same sort of thing in getting Hammond away from me."

My explanation here will show that this was wholly unjust.

Later at a banquet given to the leaders of the Reform Committee after their release from Pretoria Gaol, Barney was kind enough to say that he regarded me as the best investment he had ever made and was sorry he had not followed my advice. Although I had not been connected with him for several years prior to his death, I still had a genuine affection for him, for which there was good reason.

Barney Barnato stood bail for me when the Boer government permitted me to go to Cape Town because I was ill of Zambesi dysentery. In fact, he remained in Pretoria for six months, doing everything in his power to help me. On my return from Cape Town to Pretoria to stand trial, Barney vehemently criticized my foolhardiness in coming back.

I said, "Barney, didn't you feel a little worried that I might skip out and you'd have to forfeit $100,000?"

He replied hotly. "I thought you had more sense than to come back when you might have skipped out altogether. The $100,000 bail is nothing to me. You and I could make that in London in a few days. Now you're in for God knows how long."

Barnato's end was tragic and lamentable. A few months before his death in 1897 he formed a corporation called the Barnato Bank to take over all his mining interests. On his advice many friends in England purchased shares in this new company. There was every reason to suppose Barney's representations as to the value of the stock would be realized; but unfortunately a financial depression set in in London and the Barnato Bank stock, with all other South African shares listed on the market, sharply declined.

Barney, who was in Johannesburg at the time, became seriously depressed. The prospect of hurrying to London to meet his disappointed shareholders weighed so heavily on his mind that he threatened to commit suicide. His nephew, Solly, and some of his friends made it their business to keep constant watch over him on the voyage.

So carefully did they guard him that he did not succeed in carrying out his intention until the day before the steamer touched Madeira. While pacing the deck arm in arm with Joel, Barney said, with disarming casualness, "Solly, what time is it?" Solly released his grip for a moment to get out his watch, whereupon Barney rushed to the rail and jumped overboard. It is said that the fourth officer of the *Scot* almost lost his life in a vain attempt to save poor Barnato. When the body was recovered he was dead.

As I happened to be in London when Barnato's body was brought to Southampton, I was able to render some slight service to his family by taking charge of his remains.

The tragic irony of Barney's suicide lay in the fact that it was so unnecessary. Had he lived to reach Madeira, where he would have been in touch with London by cable, he would have learned that the market had taken a turn upward; that the shares he had sold to his friends were actually standing at a premium, and that he would not have had to suffer the ignominy of facing a disappointed group of shareholders; on the contrary, he would have been the recipient of hearty congratulations.

Under the management of Solly Joel the Barnato firm eventually became the greatest financial power in England, surpassing even the Rothschilds.

CHAPTER THIRTEEN

The Empire Builder

RHODES'S EARLY LIFE—THE FIRST DIAMONDS
AT KIMBERLEY—OXFORD—THE HIGHEST OBJECT—
RHODES'S "NORTH"—HIS LAST WILL—THE AMAL-
GAMATION AT KIMBERLEY—THE RAND CONSOLIDA-
TION—"I DO LIKE POWER"—GENEROSITY—"FOUR
THOUSAND YEARS"—GROOTE SCHUUR—PICKER-
ING AND JAMESON—UNCONVENTIONALITY—"SO
LITTLE DONE"—MATABELE DEATH CEREMONIAL

Cecil Rhodes has been considered a mysterious figure by many historians. At the time I was with him in South Africa, he was greatly misunderstood by the world at large but never·disparaged by those associated with him in the development of South Africa. More is known about him, however, as time goes on, and his true worth becomes less difficult to discern. He looms higher with each succeeding year.

His career was intense and magical, so crowded with action and event that it was impossible for most of his contemporaries to see the man with any clarity of perspective. There were those who argued that he was a proud and greedy hypocrite; there were others who considered him a great humanitarian whose ideals were irreproachable. The South African natives are said to have thought him mad. If so, it was the kind of madness that appealed to them and made them trust and follow him. It is certain that he was possessed of an energy so inexhaustible that to the ordinary man he must have seemed almost a demon. Coupled with this energy was a driving desire for power—whether for himself first and for his country afterwards, or vice versa, was a question at one time debated by his friends and admirers who knew him, as well as by his political enemies and those who had had no contact with him— but not now. History has settled this in favor of Rhodes's protagonists. Whatever his motives, whatever the complex psychological sides of his character, the effect of his deeds has been indisputably great, as he was the greatest personality I have ever known.

I have known many statesmen, industrialists, and scientists in my life, and have been associated with some of them in politics and business. I have talked with explorers, philosophers, writers, scholars, and military leaders who have achieved distinction, but no one of them stands out so vividly in my memory as typifying greatness as does this man who lies buried in the Matoppo Hills of British South Africa.

I had the good fortune to be intimately associated with Rhodes for seven years. He was my close friend. I was engaged with him in the active management of large mining enterprises. Most important of all, we were coconspirators in a political revolution.

For these reasons I may claim a special knowledge of him. In my estimate of his career and character I do not believe that I am moved by blind hero worship. I have tried to be impartial. In some respects my relations with Rhodes were more detached than were those of others. In the first place, he was not quite two years older than I, and the disparity of age was not sufficient to induce in me reverence for one whom I admired. In our business dealings events had so shaped themselves that I was more necessary to him and he was less indispensable to me. That gave me a sense of independence the importance of which Rhodes fully appreciated. For these reasons, and because of the fact that I am an American and not overcome by the patriotism that inspires Englishmen, I feel better qualified to judge Rhodes than might otherwise have been the case. He had decided faults and irritating ones; but they were chiefly faults that accompany greatness. The faults of a man among whose heroes was Napoleon Bonaparte.

Cecil John Rhodes was born in the quiet vicarage of Bishop's Stortford, in Hertfordshire, England, on July 5, 1853. He was the fifth son of the Reverend F. W. Rhodes, a well-to-do clergyman of liberal tendencies, who held this living for twenty-seven years. Cecil was educated at the grammar school of Bishop's Stortford with the intention of preparing him for the church. It was only at home, however, that he was addressed by his Christian name. At school and thereafter he was known as Rhodes, and only as Rhodes. His older brothers were called Captain Ernest and Colonel Frank, or Herbert, or whatever their names were, but his patronymic, like that of Caesar, formed his only title.

This boy, whose nickname was "Empire Builder," who thought in continents and eons, had started life with the serious handicap of a frail constitution. At the age of sixteen his health broke down. The English climate was not good for anyone threatened with tuberculosis; hence, in the latter part of 1870, he joined his eldest brother, Herbert, who was cotton-farming in Natal, South Africa. He did not remain long in an agricultural environment; shortly after he arrived, diamonds were discovered at Kimberley and by the end of 1871 Rhodes and his brother were busy digging.

Kimberley in those early days was neither inviting nor healthful. It lacked sanitation and was a fever breeder, yet the out-of-door life and dry air of the interior seemed to benefit young Rhodes.

The illimitable spaces of the veldt invited an expansion of Rhodes's mental horizon far beyond that possible within the circumscribed limits of an English country village. Yet England called him home. Oxford was a part of his tradition, and he could not break with it.

Digging in the diamond pits did not at first bring him riches, but he did succeed in making enough to permit him to matriculate at Oriel College, Oxford, when he was twenty. On account of interruptions through ill health and the necessity of looking after his interests in Kimberley, he was obliged to keep his terms intermittently; and did not receive his degree until December, 1881. Although he did not read with particular diligence at Oxford and was more than once reprimanded for nonattendance at lectures during his earlier terms, he passed all his examinations. The study of prescribed courses did not interest him; he was no student in the academic sense. The books he liked he absorbed thoroughly. Biography, political economy, Gibbon, and certain of the classics, particularly Marcus Aurelius and Aristotle, he read enthusiastically to the end of his life. Above all, he was a student of his fellow men.

> Know then thyself, presume not God to scan;
> The proper study of mankind is Man.

He seemed to be following the precept of Phillips Brooks, who said, "No man has come to true greatness who has not felt in some degree that his life belongs to his race, and that what God gives him he gives him for mankind."

Rhodes's long vacations were spent in South Africa where his financial interests were daily increasing in importance.

There were then two important influences acting on his young mind: the first was Oxford, and the encouragement of his ideas that he had obtained there; the second was South Africa.

When he was only nineteen, the year before he entered Oxford, he spent eight months in journeying with his brother Herbert, who was on his way to the Tati gold fields, through the little known regions lying to the north of the Orange and Vaal rivers. He carried with him as his chief equipment his well-worn volumes of Greek and Latin classics. His route lay through Bechuanaland to Mafeking, from there to Pretoria, and through Pilgrim's Rest in the Drakensberg Mountains to the borders of Matabeleland. He returned through the Transvaal to Kimberley, passing at the rate of some fifteen to twenty miles a day through vast spaces of rolling veldt.

This expedition had a profound effect upon him. He became convinced that this country, so full of potentialities yet so sparsely populated, should and could be secured for occupation by Great Britain. This was directly in line with his fondness for Aristotle, whom he had now accepted as a guide and whose precept he followed in seeking the "highest object" on which to exercise the "highest activity of the soul." During this trip he found that "highest object" to which he proposed to devote his future life—the domination of the world by the British people.

The political theory on which his career was patterned is set forth in the first of his six wills, written on the long vacation at Kimberley when he was only twenty-two. The preamble states his reasons for accepting the aggrandizement of the British Empire as his ultimate aim of practical achievement. It ends with a single bequest—everything of which he might die possessed was to be used to further this great purpose.

Rhodes's plan was to form a secret society whose aim would be to extend British rule throughout the world by perfecting a system of emigration from the British Isles to any and all lands that could be colonized successfully by energy, labor, and enterprise. He specifically enumerated those parts of the world which he considered suitable for this purpose: the whole of Africa, Palestine, the Euphrates Valley, Cyprus and Crete, all of South America, whatever Pacific islands were not already possessed by Great Britain, the Malay Archipelago, the Chinese and Japanese seaboard, and, lastly, the recovery of the United States as an integral part of the British Empire.

He proposed to have these colonies represented in an imperial parliament which would weld them together. The resultant power would "render wars impossible and would promote the best interests of humanity." This, in its initial form, was the grandiose political theory of this amazing young man. Present-day psychiatrists would designate this a Messianic complex. Modified by circumstances, it served as a model throughout his life. Again and again in Rhodes's utterances we find expression of his love of peace and of humanity.

Only a year after he had made this first will, Rhodes and four other young men addressed a long letter to a fellow imperialist, Disraeli, then prime minister of Great Britain, in which they told him how the Empire should be run. Not long before Rhodes died, he said to me, "I have never deviated from the policy I laid down in that letter."

His theory was in many respects practical—in others visionary—

but in his mind it was based on logical premises which led inevitably to one end: the hegemony of the Anglo-Saxon race, which he considered not only the most civilized, but also the most capable of all the races in the world. Long ahead of other Englishmen he recognized that the future greatness of England lay in a federal arrangement with her dominions.

He insisted that British statesmen should be imperial-minded; he had no use for Gladstonian Little Englanders. "What should they know of England who only England know?" says Kipling in *The English Flag.*

He wanted coadjutors who would agree with him that Great Britain should acquire new territories, to serve, on the one hand, as sources of raw materials and, on the other, as markets for the manufactured products of the mother country. This, he felt, was the only way to prevent foreign countries from securing an economic grip on world trade and erecting prohibitive tariff walls against England. Although the men of his time regarded such a change in British colonial policy as revolutionary, his plans disregarded utterly the static influence of time and custom. His conception is now a recognized fact as evidenced by the Ottawa agreement.

It was natural that the practical application of his plan should be confined to Africa. He was passionately convinced that Africa must be kept open for British occupation and commercial exploitation. In this lies the key to his political policy.

Rhodes never made any secret of his aims and ambitions. He loved to get out a big atlas and study it. Perhaps the best known story about him is that in which, sweeping his hand over the map of Africa from the Cape to the Mediterranean, he exclaimed, "I want to see that all British red!" It was in line with this ideal of building an empire for Great Britain that he relentlessly pushed the British boundaries always farther and farther towards his "North."

He also enjoyed speculating as to the future of China and Mexico and other backward countries, trying to look far into the future to envisage their interrelations.

Rhodes was a sincere admirer of America and Americans. Once, in a reflective mood, he remarked to me that "the English-speaking race, by its virtues of courage and justice, and in spite of much muddling, holds the keys of the world. You Americans and we Britishers both prefer peace to war, and right to wrong. With all our faults, we are the peacemakers."

Then, after a long pause, he burst forth again and exclaimed with great vehemence, "Unless we English-speaking peoples stand together, all that we hold dear and all the ideals we represent will be lost."

On another occasion he roundly denounced George III for the loss of America, and stated that but for the King's stupidity there would now be one great country with two capitals—one in London, the other at Washington. In a lighter vein I pointed out that it might have started with that arrangement of capitals, but that ultimately the American would have absorbed the British. Rhodes never liked to have his dreams taken lightly. He smiled politely but he was not amused.

At another time, after listening attentively to my description of our American system of government, with its separation of authority into executive, legislative, and judicial branches, he repeated what he had said on other occasions:

"Don't you think your triple division of authority, however well knit, too rigid for so vast a country as yours, which contains a population so divergent in racial origin and economic interest? Aren't you unconsciously trying to fit all these individuals into your frame of government? I wonder whether you haven't put your cart before your horse. In my opinion, the government should fit the people: moreover, it should be flexible. What is just for a man in Florida may be rank injustice for a man in Maine. People are not meant to be ground through a machine and made into political sausages, all of equal length and weight. That, it seems to me, is what you Americans are trying to do. You have stubbed your toe on the rock of equality. All men are not equal. Democracy is greater than equality; it should mean justice for all!" Rhodes was eminently an individualist.

He meditated for a moment. As I made no reply, he continued in effect: "Lawmakers are useful; we have to have them; but all the legislators in the world cannot build molds in which the human spirit or even human actions can be rigidly confined. The church tried that for centuries, and failed; and now it seems as if we were to be circumscribed by legislation which may be as galling as any tyranny of the Dark Ages."

Rhodes's sixth and final will was, in many ways, an admission that his earlier ideals were not to be accomplished in his lifetime. In this last testament the bulk of his vast wealth went to found scholarships at Oxford for students from every important British colony and from every state and territory of the United States. The idea back of this was that young colonists would obtain breadth of view, training in savoir-faire, and the realization of the advantage of a united empire. The inclusion of American students was intended to instill in them an affection and a sympathy for the mother country and thus foster the union of English-speaking peoples. Rhodes and Hawksley, solicitor of the Chartered Company, who drew up the will, believed, as Sarah Gertrude Millin says in her biography, *Rhodes,* that "there were still only the original thirteen states in the Union of America." So, having provided for a representative from each state, she says, "there are, accordingly, rather more Rhodes scholars from America than from all the British Dominions put together."

Rhodes drew up a list of qualities and accomplishments on the basis of which these scholars should be chosen. These are as follows: literary and scholastic ability and attainments; qualities of manhood, truth, courage, devotion to duty, sympathy for and protection of the weak, kindliness, unselfishness, and fellowship; exhibition during schooldays of moral force of character and of instincts to lead and to take an interest in schoolmates; and fondness of sports.

I have always doubted that Rhodes himself could have qualified for one of his own scholarships. He certainly would have failed under "literary and scholastic attainments," while, if judged by success in manly outdoor sports such as cricket, football, and the like, he would have been immediately eliminated on grounds of ill health. Yet, without ever having been a participant in college sports, he recognized their value.

Rhodes had been turning this scholarship project over in his mind for a long time before he actually put it into definite form.

During a discussion concerning the benefits to be conferred upon the recipients, I ventured to point out that the average American university student was better informed on the subject of British history and traditions than the English undergraduate was on American institutions and customs. "Would it not," I suggested, "be well to provide for sending English students to America as well as American students to England?" My views did not prevail, however, and Rhodes adhered to his original plan.

Rhodes realized that the command of large wealth was requisite to the accomplishment of his great ambition. In the first instance, he had to create an independent fortune for himself. With the power thus obtained he could arrange for the financial assistance of others when needed.

Before the end of his Oxford days, Rhodes was already rising to wealth, and was establishing his position as a practical financier by his part in the gradual amalgamation of the Kimberley diamond mines. This was finally completed March 13, 1888, when, with Barney Barnato and Alfred Beit, he formed the De Beers Consolidated Mines mentioned in the previous chapter. At thirty-three Rhodes was the actual head of one of the largest corporations in the world, which not only produced, but regulated and fixed the prices of practically the entire world's supply of diamonds. Up to this time the cutthroat competition in the diamond markets had been so severe that the price of the stones had actually been below cost of production. The industry was on the verge of financial collapse when the amalgamation went through.

The effects of the combination of the rival diamond interests spread far beyond Kimberley. At that time Cape Colony itself was dependent upon the diamond industry for a considerable part of its revenue, and almost entirely for its maintenance.

When the amalgamation agreement had been drawn up, a certain number of founders' shares were set aside for Rhodes, Barnato, and Beit. Whereas the regular shares in the company were legally entitled to only a fixed return, all the residuum of profits—which far exceeded their expectation—was divided among these three men.

Rhodes next devoted his attention to the organization of an important consolidation of gold mines on the Rand, which he called the Consolidated Gold Fields of South Africa.

The wealth necessary to carry on the development of the territory now known as Rhodesia was obtained at first largely from those associated with him in the diamond fields of Kimberley and the gold mines on the Rand. With this he formed the Chartered Company.

In order to make Rhodesia fit into his scheme, he had to find there, first, gold, and then other minerals. If he could locate this mineral wealth, the railway would naturally follow, and in its wake would come the agricultural population to feed the industrial development. His dreams thus far completed, beyond would lie new and greater territories waiting for the English touch to develop into new colonies.

As I have said, money *per se* did not interest him. "I do like power," he admitted to me more than once. He loved this game of empire building.

Besides the wealth required for the industrial development of his projects, Rhodes was well aware that the command of political influence was essential. Accordingly, as early as 1881, when he was twenty-eight, Rhodes entered the Cape Parliament. Rather than be elected from Kimberley, where his financial interests would have made his political success certain, and have been a pocket borough, he chose to stand for the rural constituency of Barkly West, which, although largely Dutch in composition, remained faithful to him throughout his life. Rhodes never for a moment doubted that he would in time become premier of Cape Colony. This, too, was included in the career he had laid out for himself, and the ambition was realized in July, 1890.

His interest in the betterment of conditions was not confined to Rhodesia but embraced all South Africa as well. He was in a similar way interested in the Dutch farmers of Cape Colony. It gave him peculiar pleasure in being of assistance to the Dutch farmers who were frequent visitors to Groote Schuur.

He would ask an old Dutch farmer what kind of sheep he was raising. After the farmer told him, Rhodes would say "Well, let's get a better breed!" and then went ahead and got them. In this way he imported superior breeds of sheep, goats, donkeys, and other do-

CECIL RHODES (1853-1902)

KIMBERLEY DIAMOND FIELDS

(*Letting the clay disintegrate by sunlight before washing for diamonds*)

mestic animals which seemed best adapted to rocky kopje or grassy veldt. He used to relate with pleasure that his ancestors, too, had been men of the soil.

His generous gifts in many ways improved the agricultural methods of Cape Colony. On one occasion he asked me about the physical and climatic conditions of California. He then said: "We have good soil and good climate. Quite as good as California from what you tell me, but we don't seem to get proper efficiency out of our horticultural industry." He asked if I knew some experts in that line in California. After inquiry I recommended two brothers. He sent to California for them and started scientific development of horticulture in Cape Colony which has added materially to the success of that industry in South Africa. That is why the Dutch continued to love Rhodes, in spite of the Jameson Raid and President Kruger's personal hatred of him.

Although Rhodes's income in time reached many millions of dollars a year, he spent little on himself. Most of his spare cash he gave away privately and with boundless generosity. His personal bank account was overdrawn most of the time; sometimes he did not have sixpence about him. His securities were often tucked away in pockets of disused coats or in obscure pigeonholes of his desk. When, as a matter of precaution, his secretary hid his checkbook, Rhodes would issue gift checks on half-sheets of note paper or backs of envelopes, sometimes signing them in pencil. They were invariably honored by the banks.

When he had money in his pockets he handled it as though he were a child who did not understand its value. In London, he was often forced to apply to his secretary for money to pay cab fares; when it was given him, it was amusing to see him close his hand clumsily on as much gold or silver as he could hold and drop it uncounted into one of his pockets. When he paid his cabby, he would take out a coin, hand it over, without looking at it, and walk away. More than once it turned out to be a sovereign.

When I came back to the United States after my South African experiences, I was disgusted with our American financiers who repeatedly asked me how much money Rhodes had left in his will. I told them the sum was probably from twenty-five to forty millions

—but in this case that amounted to nothing. He could have made many times that much if he had wanted money for himself. Actually he never knew how much he had.

Biographers have tried to find something in the physical appearance of Rhodes to explain his extraordinary attraction for and power over human beings, black and white. There is really no salient characteristic for them to fix upon. Yet every man who met Rhodes was conscious of being in the presence of greatness. He gave that strange, almost hypnotic impression of a man convinced of the grandeur of his own destiny.

When Rhodes's political career was in effect terminated by the Jameson Raid fiasco, an eminently reputable periodical informed South Africa that the problem of how to treat him was perfectly simple. "Just go ahead and ignore him."

Edmund Garrett, the journalist, replied curtly, "As well ignore Table Mountain."

Many people have tried to apply a general yardstick to human greatness, but with little success. Each genius must be measured according to the nature of his aims and the degree to which he actually achieved them. No Roman emperor ever won more territory than Rhodes brought under his native British flag. When the Chartered Company was incorporated in 1889, he added territory equal to the combined areas of the British Isles, France, Prussia, Austria, and Spain. He made possible the federation of the South African states, and carried halfway to fruition the Cape-to-Cairo Railroad before his untimely death. Few men have accomplished so much; but Rhodes knew that his time was limited. And since there was no son to inherit his ambitions, he was often forced to pound things through by driving the men who had committed themselves to his cause. From these men he expected efficiency, but he never expected perfection. Rhodes was noted as a great compromiser, and in effecting important political and economic negotiations realized that perfection was not attainable. But he had no patience with a stupid subordinate and would be scathing in his denunciation.

I do not believe that Rhodes was the type of man who ordinarily attempted to crush personalities. He often lost his temper, but he was not vicious. I have seen him speak very harshly to some of his subordinates, particularly in the case of Dr. Rutherfoord Harris. But I believe it was because of his feeling that there was no time to lose in the accomplishment of his purpose and that he could not afford to be patient in the face of what seemed to him either inefficiency or delay. He most certainly did not suffer fools gladly.

Although in advancing his cause he did not go so far as to adopt the Jesuitical maxim that the end justifies the means, yet he felt that he must be the sole judge of what was good for mankind.

Rhodes had many queer ways and often expressed himself in terms that might be construed as the insanity of egotism. It was not meant so. He was merely viewing himself and his work impersonally as from some Olympian height. In this connection Dr. Jameson told Percy Fitzpatrick the following story, which has often been repeated but is so indicative of his character that it must be included here.

Rhodes's trusted friend, Dr. Leander Starr Jameson, once asked his leader how long he thought he would be remembered. Without pause or smile, Rhodes answered, "I give myself four thousand years."

"It was not a boast," said Jameson. "He would not have said it at all, if I hadn't asked him, and he stated it as a fact—like a fact in history. It did not seem to have any personal bearing."

His impersonal belief in his own star was in marked contrast to his personal simplicity and democracy. He never accepted a title, although he could have had a peerage. I asked him once why he did not allow himself to appear on the honors list. "The only title I should like is an honorary degree from Oxford," he told me. This honor came to him, unsolicited, not long afterwards.

There was no pretense of democracy in his nature; simplicity was an integral part of it. I have often seen him decline invitations to be present with those prominent in society and in business, preferring to chat informally with his own simpler comrades.

He could never tolerate circumlocution in any form. Nor did he have a memory for details; and would quote statistics "in globular figures." He would form a conception and his trusted subordinates would carry it out. There is no doubt that at times Rhodes was dictatorial. This was partly due to the great burdens he carried under the shadow of death, partly to that quality in his nature which refused to let any barrier, great or small, keep him from his goal.   His resourcefulness was a matter of constant amazement to his associates.

Enemies of Rhodes have often declared that he was selfish and ruthless.   This was emphatically not true; fairness and justice were guiding principles from the observance of which he never intentionally swerved.   I heard him say more than once: "Always be sure to satisfy the other fellow.   Any trade that is not satisfactory to him is not satisfactory to me."   And again, "I have never in my life met anybody with whom it wasn't just as easy to deal as to fight."   In fact, Rhodes fought only when he was driven to it.

Long before American corporations took up welfare work, Rhodes had built comfortable homes which he rented to his workmen at low rates.   He had erected clubhouses, churches, and recreation grounds for them.   He instructed me to spare no expense in looking after the health and happiness of all his workers under me, both white and black.   One of his maxims was "The only employee worth having is a contented employee."   This was borne out by my own experience. Just before Christmas the second year I was with him, I explained to Rhodes that it was customary for mining companies to give bonuses to their employees at this season, and that my staff of American engineers deserved something substantial, especially as we had made a large profit during the past year.

"That is quite right," replied Rhodes.   These were his favorite words of affirmation.

I then handed him a sheet of paper on which I had figured out the amount each man should receive.   Without even glancing at it, he picked up his pencil and scribbled across the face of it.   "We have had a remarkably successful two years under Hays Hammond's management, due, as he says, to the ability, untiring energy, and self-sacrifice of his American staff.   They are entitled to the sums he recommends."

"But you've not even looked to see how much I've suggested," I protested.   "This is going to the board of directors, and you should at least know how much money is involved."

"You wouldn't recommend it if it weren't all right, would you?"

With this remark he dismissed a matter which amounted to nearly $250,000 participation in the shares of his companies at cost.

One of the things that caused me considerable embarrassment at the time was the arrival of numerous young Englishmen, many of whom were Eton and Oxford graduates, seeking a billet in South Africa. Rhodes was under certain obligations to friends in England for political favors, past—and to come. He was importuned by many of his influential friends who wanted positions for these young men who came to South Africa. Rhodes would give them letters of introduction to me, requesting that I do what I could for them.

Few were qualified for any technical position at the mines, and I could use them in no other capacity. I would always give these young fellows a chance, however. Most of them professed their willingness to work at any kind of job, but they were invariably unsuited to the work and after a few days at the mine would return and admit that there was nothing for them to do. It was a waste of time and money for them to go to the mines even to look for a job.

The only other hope for these young men, it seemed to me, was in Rhodesia, so I would give them a letter to Jameson, who was just as much embarrassed as I was in trying to assist the "bearer." Finally I complained to Rhodes about this and suggested that the best way to repay his obligations was to form some kind of polo, golf, or cricket club at Kimberley, where they could spend their time until something better turned up. I told him it would cost him only about fifty thousand dollars a year. I sincerely sympathized with these fine fellows and felt it my duty to find employment for them in preference to those of any other nationality since the mines were under English ownership. But obviously, as I explained to Rhodes, it would demoralize my staff of engineers, who were specially qualified by education and training, if I should displace them in favor of incompetents. Rhodes accepted this view of the situation and with good-humor, I believe, although at considerable expense, provided gracefully for his young friends.

Much of the affection which, given other conditions, would have centered elsewhere, was lavished on his home at Groote Schuur (the big barn). Rhodes purchased it in 1890 from one of the old Dutch families and rebuilt it in keeping with the Dutch architectural traditions: two stories, thatched gables, and large many-paned windows. It was beautifully located in a grove of pine and oak on the slope of

Devil's Peak, the outlying shoulder of Table Mountain. Looking from one of his bedroom windows he could see Table Mountain; from another he could view Cape Town harbor.

This home was filled with old colonial furniture and the best examples of domestic handicrafts. Even General Smuts—who had never met him and who long was bitter against him for his part in the Jameson Raid—admitted that Rhodes had helped to conserve what was precious in South Africa's past, and highly commended this spirit.

Dear as Groote Schuur was to him, his friends were dearer still. There were men such as W. T. Stead, Alfred Beit, and myself. To us he gave his confidence. There were two men in the course of his life whom he truly loved: first, Neville Pickering, secretary to the De Beers Company; and afterwards Dr. Jameson, familiarly known as Dr. Jim.

Rhodes never entirely recovered from the death of Neville Pickering some years before. Like himself, Pickering was threatened with tuberculosis. During one of the latter's attacks of illness, Rhodes had been obliged to go to Johannesburg to conduct important and delicate negotiations on behalf of the Consolidated Gold Fields. In the midst of these a telegram came saying Pickering was worse. He glanced at the message and then exclaimed to Dr. Hans Sauer, his companion in the transactions: "Get me a seat on tonight's coach! Quick! I must get back to Pickering. He's dying!"

"But, Rhodes, you can't go now. Everything depends on your being here."

Rhodes exclaimed impatiently: "What do I care? You know I have to go. Get me a seat!"

Sauer departed, but returned almost immediately and announced cheerfully: "You can't go. All seats are booked."

The choleric temper of Rhodes flared up. "I must go! Buy a seat from someone who has already booked. Hire a coach! Buy a coach! Do something! I'm going!"

And that night he went. For many days he kept his hopeless vigil at Pickering's bedside, letting his countless business affairs go unheeded until there was no further need to watch. Something went out of his life which, unlike Groote Schuur, could not be restored.

Dr. Jameson, brilliant young surgeon at the Kimberley mines, had attended Pickering in his last illness. It is possible that Jameson's habitual air of amused tolerance and cynical indifference dropped from him in this crisis, and it may have been this less known side of him that appealed to Rhodes. However it happened, from this time forward Dr. Jim succeeded Pickering in Rhodes's life; no one ever replaced him.

The enemies of Rhodes have denounced him as cold-blooded and heartless and quite willing to sacrifice his best friends should the cause warrant. Like so many other attacks upon him, this was not true. For example, when Groote Schuur burned, the news came first to Lord Grey, then acting administrator of Rhodesia, who had come to see Rhodes at Bulawayo. He hated the duty that had devolved upon him, of adding the tale of another misfortune to those which had already been heaped upon Rhodes. As they rode along that morning to visit the site Rhodes had selected for his tomb, they talked over the misadventures of the past year which had culminated in Jameson's surrender. Grey had waited for a suitable opportunity. Now he told Rhodes he had more bad news for him. At this Rhodes pulled in his horse and, his face drawn with agony, cried, "Good God! Out with it, man! What's happened?"

When informed that Groote Schuur had burned, he heaved a sigh and, as Stead relates, exclaimed: "Oh, thank God! Thank God! I thought you were going to tell me that Dr. Jim was dead. The house is burnt down. Well, what does that matter? We can always rebuild the house, but if Dr. Jim had died I should never have got over it."

Even after the Raid he loved Jameson none the less dearly, though during their separation at this time Jameson was apprehensive that Rhodes would hold him responsible and that their old-time friendship might be impaired. Rhodes had commented on the failure, "Jameson has upset my applecart."

Although Rhodes had but few intimate friends, there were many to whom he gave freely of his time, energy, and money. There was one man whom, it was jokingly said, he had picked out of the Milky Way and elevated to the status of a fixed star of magnitude. Again and again Rhodes had to refix him—financially and politically. Nevertheless, this man became obsessed with the idea that Rhodes owed everything to him; that he was the original maker of Rhodes, who was jealous of him. Finally he assailed Rhodes viciously in a political campaign, which resulted in his own inglorious defeat.

A few months later, sitting around a table in a hotel in Kimberley, several of Rhodes's friends were joking about this man's attacks. One of them said, "Now, Mr. Rhodes, I suppose it is time for you once again to set this star in the heavens."

With a whimsical smile, he replied: "I suppose so. You know the poor devil is stony broke again!"

Many anecdotes might be cited as illustrative of this quality of mercy. For example, Sir Lewis Mitchell tells of an old Rhodesian pioneer who once sought help from Rhodes. Out of work, out at elbows, and reduced to a pitiable condition, he was about to state his case when, to his delight, he was hailed by name. The chief had recognized him.

Putting his hand on the man's shoulder, Rhodes said, "Not a word; a good square meal first!" He took him to the kitchen and told him to get what money he needed from his secretary, adding, "Come back tomorrow." When the man returned he found Rhodes in a temper. "You took only ten shillings." The old fellow had so obviously been ashamed to ask the secretary for more that Rhodes at once took him into town in his own carriage—went with him to the outfitters—completely clothed him—and gave him money to get back to Rhodesia.

Such a man as Rhodes could not fail to create in the hearts of many men a devotion so absolute that they not only were willing to risk their lives for him, but actually did so. Women, however, had little place in his life. It was not that he hated them: he was not a misogynist, though he might have been regarded as a misogamist. His excuse for not having married was that he had not the time to give a wife the attention she was entitled to receive. It may be, as Colley Cibber says, "Ambition is the only power that combats love." Yet it was significant that, at the time I visited him, in all the thirty rooms of Groote Schuur there was only one picture, a painting of a young woman by Sir Joshua Reynolds. It hung in the dining room above the fireplace, where Rhodes could easily see it. He often told how as a boy he had observed it in the home of a relative, how he had been won by its beauty, how his love for it had increased with manhood, how finally he had been able to buy it. The story always ended with "Now I have my lady, and I am happy."

Rhodes was especially fond of my wife. One evening that I remember with particular pleasure we were visiting at Groote Schuur. During the conversation my wife sustained her argument by a quotation from Marcus Aurelius. He at once took us to his bedroom and pointed to two books lying on his night table. One was the Bible, the other Marcus Aurelius. He said he never went to sleep without reading something from both books. He was surprised and delighted that anybody, especially a woman, should be familiar with his favorite authority. He went on to mention a quotation which he was very proud to have written in Queen Victoria's guest book at Windsor. *"Coelum non animum mutant qui trans mare currant"* (They change the sky, but not the soul, who cross the sea). I told Rhodes that I should have written *"Oderint dum metuant,"* since what did it matter that politicians in England and South Africa hated him so long as they feared him. Rhodes replied, "Your quotation is too much like playing to the gallery."

Following this discovery of their mutual fondness for Marcus Aurelius, Rhodes formed a great admiration for my wife's intellect. And here I wish to quote the following, which my wife had hurriedly scribbled with pencil in her notebook, describing Cecil Rhodes:

He has the superb head of a Roman Emperor. He is a man, and the most impersonal man I have ever known —strong, broad and splendid. He is not fine, nor keen, nor sensitive. The world is his omelet and the men the eggs which compose it. I can believe that he would lap human bodies like sandbags to build his fort, but the enemy should have equal vantage. He can crush and cut, but never pinch. Money is his steed; instinct his spur, and a generous power his aim. His weaknesses are but the outer fringe to his imperial nature.

And later as she began to know him better, she wrote this about Rhodes:

No book and scarcely a pamphlet written about South Africa is without a description of Mr. Rhodes. I can only give my personal impression and entirely from a woman's point of view. Mr. Rhodes is a great man. His brain is great, and as level as Table Mountain. There are no spiritual pinnacles to his nature, and he is not lacking in imagination and massive, forceful magnetism, in its accepted meaning. He gives one a sense of confidence in him and in oneself. You feel that he understands himself and that he understands you. He lives entirely beyond the pale of everyday life. The tender, gentle things of human intercourses are not for his consideration. His life is speeding at too great an impetus for him to be seen in detail, or to feel in detail. He is exceedingly generous, and tries to be just and noble. His affection gives place to his ambition, which is not a personal ambition. The man is the most impersonal personality—for he is a personality in spite of being impersonal—that I have ever met. His sympathies are for the human race, and not for the individuals. In this respect, he is unlike Mr. Beit and Mr. Barnato. Mr. Rhodes can be as bloodless as fate when people are not of use to him. They drop out of his life, as leaves from trees by a new growth or the spring budding. He simply has no place for a disused member. It is not that he means to forget or ignore them, but in his busy life, has no place for them. They are as out of place in his life as a bit of broken machinery would be in a steam engine.

One of the main reasons why Rhodes never married was as he said, he felt that a wife and family deserved much more time than he could ever give them. It is also true that he feared the intrusion of the fussy type of woman in his life, the type a friend of mine has

characterized as "hen-brained." His life was not without the influence and the pleasure of women's companionship, but he refused
to allow any woman to gain sufficient hold on him to complicate
or slow up the pursuit of his dreams. He enjoyed the society of
intelligent women and he had many such friends in his social circle
at the Cape.

Olive Schreiner pursued him before she turned against him and
became one of his bitterest enemies. In her teens she had written that
classic tale of the veldt, *The Story of an African Farm*. In spite of the
fact that her family were Rhodes's great friends and that she always
insisted she admired him, she later wrote a book called *Trooper Peter
Halket of Mashonaland,* a venomous attack on the actions of Rhodes
in Matabeleland. She told how this monster, Rhodes, had crushed
the noble savage, how the poor natives had been staked to anthills
and otherwise tortured, and how this land-grabber had defeated the
will of God. Rhodes paid no attention; nor did he utter one word
in refutation. She had overplayed her hand. The public for whom
she wrote knew better.

A tragic episode of the last years of his life was the Princess Radzi-
will incident. This middle-aged Polish woman attempted to force
her attentions on him, although he never was more than merely polite to her. Finally, she forged his name for £29,000. Rhodes was
in England at the time. He was so infuriated that, in spite of warnings from his doctors, he made the long trip to Cape Town to testify,
and on his deathbed gave evidence against her. She was convicted
of forgery and sentenced to a year and a half in prison, but after
several months in Cape Town jail, was released on grounds of ill
health.

Rhodes's voice, like that of Theodore Roosevelt, broke into a fal-
setto whenever he became excited. This was particularly noticeable
when he was talking of his life goal. His voice would climb higher
and higher until at the climactic phrase "my North" it would be an
octave above where he had begun. Contrary to the general impression, he was not a silent man; he would talk incessantly and in rolling
periods on whatever ideas interested him at the moment. In a crisis
he thought quickly, and acted with equal rapidity.

In spite of the fact that he usually acted with complete control, he nevertheless was thoroughly human. On one occasion, when we were returning from our trip to Rhodesia, the large wagon carrying our luggage capsized crossing a spruit. I sat on the banks of the spruit smoking until I became impatient at the futile attempts of the natives to upright the wagon. I went over and made some suggestions, then returned and sat down by Rhodes. He smiled and said: "Hammond, the trouble with all you Americans is your desire to complete everything immediately. You have no patience. It took me ten years to effect the consolidation of the diamond mines at Kimberley. Your countrymen would have attempted to put it through in as many months, but I doubt whether they would have succeeded in creating any permanent trust." We sat there a while longer watching the natives. I knew Rhodes was very anxious to get back to Pretoria to have a talk with Kruger, but I simply waited, enjoying his nervousness as time went on.

He did not know I was aware of this until finally he got up and went over to undertake the supervision of the matter. I walked over to the scene with him to let him see that I appreciated the fact that even the imperturbable Englishmen possessed the same restless spirit as their American cousins.

In his personal habits Rhodes was inclined to be unconventional. Surroundings meant nothing to him. At Kimberley he lived under the most primitive conditions, even when comparatively wealthy; at Groote Schuur there was every luxury. He recognized no difference. Nor did he care anything about being well dressed. On his way to an audience with the sultan of Turkey he stopped to see the British ambassador, who was shocked to see him attired for his meeting in a shabby tweed suit. Fearing the consequences of this breach of sartorial etiquette, the ambassador told Rhodes he must wear the indispensable frock coat.

"I can't," replied Rhodes, "for I don't possess one."

With great presence of mind, the ambassador at once put his own overcoat over the offending garments, buttoned it, and warned Rhodes not to undo it if he valued his life.

So far as his clothes were concerned, or, in fact as regarded most of the details of his private life, Heaven knows what would have become of Rhodes if it had not been for Tony, a Cape boy—his cook when on the veldt, his valet, and his purse bearer. Tony was a most remarkable man. His position was no sinecure. He was indispensable to Rhodes on his trips to London, for Rhodes rarely arrived there with the proper clothes—in the winters not heavy enough to keep him warm. Rhodes hated to buy clothes, but Tony would arrange to have the tailors waylay him and provide the wardrobe necessary for that visit.

Rhodes had never enjoyed robust health, but this did not really prove a handicap as it undoubtedly taught him the value of time and the necessity to conserve his strength for undertakings of prime importance.

On his wrist there was a small aneurism which by its throbbing indicated to him that he had reached the danger point of overexertion. His heart had never been equal to his spirit; as he grew older it fell steadily behind. As his forty-eighth year drew towards its close it was apparent to him that he had but little time left. He was not afraid of death; he had never known what it was to fear any person, much less any thing. He regretted with deep bitterness and sorrow that he was not to see the completion of what he had dreamed in far-off Oxford and in the darkness of the veldt.

"The great fault of life is its shortness," he exclaimed towards the last. "Just as one is beginning to know the game, one has to stop."
Kipling caught this:

Dreamer devout, by vision led
Beyond our guess or reach,
The travail of his spirit bred
Cities in place of speech.
So huge the all-mastering thought that drove—
So brief the term allowed—
Nations, not words, he linked to prove
His faith before the crowd.

And as Rhodes lay dying in his beloved Africa, his words were: "So little done, so much to do."
For three days, thousands of warrior Matabele, his former foes and later allies, congregated to perform over his grave the cere-

monial of 'Mzlikazi, their chief and founder. They were honoring the man whom they regarded as their great white chief and friend. Each day the stately ceremonial continued; each night the sky was red with fires. Thousands of feet beat the ground in unison. War drums throbbed dolefully. The warriors' mournful songs ended in the darkness. Dressed in full war panoply, these chosen representatives of the proudest of the black natives with outthrust spears gave the bayete, the royal salute to their adopted chieftain. For the first and last time, such a tribute was paid to a white man in Africa.

CHAPTER FOURTEEN

The Winning of Rhodesia

DRAFTING THE MINING LAWS OF SOUTHERN
RHODESIA — THE KINGDOM OF THE MATABELE —
SLAGTER'S NEK — THE GREAT TREK — THE PLACE
OF SLAUGHTER — JAMESON'S BARGAIN WITH
LOBENGULA—THE WAY IS OPEN TO MASHONALAND—
THE PIONEERS ADVANCE—THE UNCLEAN ONES —
FORTY WHITES ATTACK TWO THOUSAND NA-
TIVES — DESPERATE INVASION OF MATABELELAND—
WILSON'S LAST STAND IN THE JUNGLES OF THE
SHANGANI — THE SECOND MATABELE WAR — KILL-
ING THE MOUTHPIECE OF GOD—"IT IS PEACE"

*7*he latitude given me by
Rhodes in Johannesburg
made my work for him far more congenial than had been my previous association with Barnato. I soon felt that I had gained my
new employer's complete confidence so far as the management of
the Consolidated Gold Fields of South Africa was concerned. In
addition to supervising the mining interests of the Gold Fields, I
spent considerable time in drafting the mining laws for the British
South Africa Company (Chartered) in Rhodesia. The Company
had already adopted the mistaken principle of the American mining
law regarding the right of the owner of an apex of veins to follow
the vein under the property of adjoining owners. As discussed in

Chapter XI, I should have much preferred the simpler mining laws of the Transvaal and Mexico, but it was too late to make the change.

I anticipated much difficulty and litigation from the inclusion of this provision, but H. U. Moffat, premier of Southern Rhodesia, in a recent letter assured me that the mining laws have proved suitable to the local needs and requirements of Rhodesia. As a matter of fact, with one exception, no disputes of importance have arisen. The idea of Rhodes in including this extralateral rights provision had been to attract capital into the country, and to accomplish this he had been willing to make concessions.

Rhodes's economic interests were never more than a means to the end of reaching his "North." Yet they were an essential part of his scheme: in order to make manifest destiny possible, he had to find mineral wealth.

The ancient mines of Mashonaland had been rediscovered in 1868 and brought to the notice of Europe by the American explorer and hunter, Adam Renders. A few years later Dr. Karl Mauch made an even more careful investigation. The reports of these explorers convinced Rhodes of the existence of gold in the North.

Therefore, in the fall of 1894, just after the First Matabele War, Rhodes and Dr. Jameson, the administrator of the district, and I went to Matabeleland and Mashonaland on a trip that was to have important and dramatic consequences. In order that the reader may have a clear picture of this country—later known as Rhodesia—I deem it essential to describe certain characteristics of it and its people, the many wars waged by the native tribes, and the ultimate winning of it by the white man.

Rhodesia embraces an area of 440,000 square miles; exceeding the combined areas of our New England, Middle Atlantic, and East North Central states. It includes all of the region extending from the Transvaal north to the borders of the Congo State and German East Africa. On the east it is bounded by Portuguese East Africa, Nyasaland, and German East Africa, and on the west by the Congo State, Portuguese West Africa, and Bechuanaland.

For the most part the interior of Rhodesia is a high plateau varying in altitude from 3000 to 5000 feet. It is fairly well watered—abundantly so in the rainy season, and in much of its topography

LOBENGULA

MATABELE

and vegetation strongly resembles parts of the western section of the United States, particularly Wyoming and New Mexico.

Rhodes's problems would have been simpler had Africa been left free of outside interference, but in the last decade of the nineteenth century the attention of Europe was suddenly focused upon it. The necessary annexations of native territory, which in prior decades had gone on as a matter of course, now became subjects for international discussion. To understand the whys and wherefores of the dramatic events related in the subsequent chapters, it is necessary also to grasp the historical background of the struggle now about to take place for the great regions north of the Boer republics.

South Africa has been known to the European world since Vasco da Gama rounded the Cape of Storms in 1497 and found the ocean route to the Indies. The Portuguese never attempted settlement, although occasionally their ships had to take refuge in Table Bay. When the Dutch supplanted the Portuguese as the great Eastern trading power, an outfitting station was set up in Cape Town in 1652.

The Dutch found nobody but roving Hottentots in the vicinity of the Cape. As the invaders gradually encroached on the Hottentot lands a series of wars began. For nearly a hundred and fifty years the Dutch pioneers, never numerous, led a pastoral existence and expanded slowly into the hinterland. In 1795, through no fault of theirs they found themselves under the British flag, due to the fact that Holland was France's involuntary ally in Europe and the British were mopping up enemy territory throughout the world. During the temporary truce with Napoleon between 1802 and 1804, Cape Colony was handed back to the Batavian Republic, as Holland was then termed. War broke out again, and the English recaptured the Cape in 1806. In 1814 the Dutch definitely ceded Cape Colony to England, and it remained a British colony until 1910 when it took its place in the newly formed Union of South Africa.

After 1814 English customs and laws were introduced into a population of only 42,000 white settlers, predominantly Dutch. From 1820 on, however, the English began to pour in and their language quickly spread throughout the colony.

In addition to an alien population, the British almost immediately found themselves faced with a native problem of great magnitude.

While in their early years the Dutch had had to face only the Hottentots, the British were now confronted with a major movement of peoples. The tribes of the great Bantu race were pushing down from the thickly inhabited regions of the North into the less populated districts of the South, thrusting before them the weaker peoples. Inevitably the Boer-English and Bantu fronts collided. These wars continued for many years.

Of all the Bantu tribes the fiercest and most warlike were the Zulu, the "Children of the Heavens." They fought in regiments, or impis, a thousand strong. They asked no quarter and gave none. Sheltered behind their long oval shields of oxhide, instead of hurling light assegais they used short-handled spears in the Roman thrusting fashion. The other native races melted away before them. Under their great chief Chaka they reached the zenith of their power. Fierce, intelligent, ruthless, he proved a superb military leader. He organized the Zulu for war and, like Attila the Hun, he annihilated his enemies, slaughtered their men, took their women. When Chaka entrusted a military undertaking to one of his chieftains he demanded not only its successful accomplishment but also that the entire booty be returned to his kraal.

Second only to him in ferocity was his great induna, 'Mzlikazi, the "Pathway of Blood." On one occasion, having conquered a tribe, 'Mzlikazi failed to send the spoils to Chaka, and the latter, in accordance with his custom, sent an army to exterminate his untrustworthy induna. 'Mzlikazi, hearing of the approach of the main army and knowing that he and his men would be clubbed to death with knobkerries if captured, led his army to conquer a kingdom for themselves. He went into the northern part of what is now the Transvaal, with probably no more than ten thousand warriors at the start, leaving a trail of desolation and destruction. Recruiting his numbers from the most warlike of the young men of the conquered tribes, he formed what was called the Matabele nation, the "Children of the Stars." Meanwhile Chaka had died and his equally bloodthirsty successor, Dingaan, ruled over the Zulu nation. By 1830 their incessant wars had depopulated a vast stretch of land.

There had always been friction between Boer and Englishman as to the treatment of the blacks. The former regarded them as slaves; the latter, under the influence of the humanitarian spirit of Wilberforce, then sweeping England, regarded them as fellow men. This movement culminated in 1833 in the abolition of slavery throughout the British Empire. Thus the agricultural Boers found themselves at one stroke deprived of what they regarded as their most essential private property.

About twenty years before, in 1816, there had already been serious difficulty over the Boer treatment of natives. The outstanding example of this was the so-called Rebellion of Slagter's Nek. A Boer farmer named Frederik Bezuidenhout was accused of maltreating a native servant. Gathering a band of friends around him in the pass of the Winterberg Mountains, he resisted arrest and fired on the government forces. After a short conflict he was killed and the "rebellion" put down. Six of his comrades were tried for high treason by the British government; five of them were executed on the scaffold. The Boers, who considered the blacks as their property to do with as they wished, felt that this was not only a harsh but also an unjust penalty. It would have been quickly forgotten, however, had there been no other causes for bitterness between Boer and Englishman. Instead, it became a rallying cry for every anti-English demonstration.

The most reactionary of the Boers decided to move beyond the frontier; with this end in view they set out on the Great Trek. One party went into what is now Natal—although its members well knew that the Zulu power would have to be conciliated or otherwise dealt with.

In 1837 a delegation was sent to Dingaan, who received them in friendly fashion and gave them land. Then, at a farewell feast, he massacred them at the Hill of Slaughter; and fell on the main body of immigrants and slew three hundred at Weenen, the "Place of Weeping."

In vengeance for this slaughter, the Boer leader Pretorius took out against Dingaan a punitive commando of four hundred white men and a few natives. Ten impis of Zulu fell upon the Dutch laager; the river by which this fight took place was called the Blood

River, and the victory which the Boers won is still celebrated among them as Dingaan's Day.

But the Boers were destined to be disappointed in their hope of setting up a republic in Natal. The English were already at Durban and had no intention of having a Boer hinterland. After a brief conflict, the Boers again set off on trek in 1844, and this time in the valleys of the Orange, the Vaal, and the Limpopo formed the Transvaal Republic. This district had been depopulated of the Bechuana and other native tribes by the Matabele forays.

Meanwhile another branch of the Dutch voortrekkers had come up against the warriors of 'Mzlikazi. Every spruit was a battleground, because in such arid country life and water were synonymous terms, and every kopje, or hillock, which commanded these small streams was an outpost, costing blood. For two years the fighting went on. The Matabele, in spite of reckless bravery, were cut down in hundreds by the Boer rifles. The eventual outcome of the struggle was the retirement of 'Mzlikazi to the north of the Limpopo River, where he fell upon the unfortunate Mashona, who lived in that district, as earlier he had butchered the Bechuana. He established a capital, a huge kraal, at Bulawayo, the "Place of Slaughter" and there his son, Lobengula, "he who drives like the wind," held the throne.

Lobengula was a huge man; in later life he became so enormously fat and unwieldy that he had to be carried about in an oxcart. Too sluggish himself to lead his impis, he preferred diplomacy. He lived in his goat kraal, surrounded by his eighty women. Majesty was simulated by a band of leather serving for a crown and blue monkey fur arranged at his waist like a Scotch sporran. Otherwise he was naked. It was a custom of his to exact propitiatory gifts of champagne from concession seekers. He was not only extremely fond of it, but was a connoisseur and insisted that the wine be of superior and expensive vintage.

The Matabele had carefully treasured many of the warlike traditions of their Zulu forefathers. Among these was the annual ceremony at the end of which the king, stepping into the midst of the kraal, lifted his great assegai and hurled it from him. As it struck, still quivering in the ground, the warriors bounded forward to see whither it pointed, for in that direction the impis were to make relentless war during the ensuing year.

Of course, as time went on, it became harder and harder to find humans available for slaughter within easy reach of Bulawayo. The British had assumed the care of the peaceful Bechuana; they were not to be touched.

The next misfortune for Lobengula was the formation of the Chartered Company which intended to enter the Mashona country to the north of the Matabele. There was only one road by which Rhodes could penetrate Mashona territory. He could not go to the east because of the Portuguese. He could not go straight north because of the Boer republics. He had to go around the western end of the Republics through Bechuanaland and then cross the country of the Matabele north of the Limpopo into Mashonaland, there to establish his settlements and to develop the mineral wealth reputed to exist.

In 1890, in addition to being head of the Chartered Company, Rhodes had become premier of the Cape. He had, therefore, both political and economic power. Cape Colony could not develop the North but the Company could, while Rhodes and his associates would furnish the money. Rhodes was desperately afraid some power, Boer or German or Portuguese, would forestall him. He knew that other concession hunters were with Lobengula; there were at least eleven. He tried to get Sir Hercules Robinson, high commissioner of Cape Colony, to do something about Matabeleland, and by persistent endeavor he had it arranged to send the Reverend J. S. Moffat to Lobengula. The former secured an agreement that Lobengula would not alienate any of his lands without the consent of the high commissioner. This effectually blocked Kruger's designs.

Rhodes now prepared a mission of his own to obtain what he wanted from Lobengula. To protect his interests he sent to Bulawayo his most trusted partner, C. D. Rudd, his Oxford friend, Rochfort Maguire, and F. R. Thompson, known as Matabele Thompson because of his knowledge of the natives. In addition to a pension of a hundred pounds a month, Lobengula was to have a steamboat on the Zambesi and one thousand Martini-Henry breech-loading rifles and with them one hundred thousand rounds of ball cartridges. In return, Lobengula promised that Rhodes's company should have complete control of all metals and minerals in his kingdom and full power to collect the revenues; also, Rhodes could exclude all other concession hunters. This agreement gave no rights to grant land titles. Rhodes went through the form of obtaining this by buying up a previous concession which Lobengula had granted to one Eduard Lippert in 1891, upon which the Chartered Company later issued land patents.

Many people in South Africa were alarmed at the Rudd Concession. They thought in particular that the Martini rifles would lead inevitably to a breach of the peace. Rhodes in his customary way quieted discontent, arguing that rifles were more humane than assegais. He not only had to square the Cape Parliament but the English Parliament as well, and this, in diplomatically judicious but effective fashion, he succeeded in doing.

He had to go to England to get the Company's charter confirmed. He also knew that one of his rival concessionaires had taken two of Lobengula's indunas to London to see the Queen, and he feared the effect of this. Therefore, off to London he went. He knew Lobengula was not entirely satisfied with his bargain. Rudd had been forced to conceal the concession in an ant's nest. Rhodes, who had great confidence in Dr. Jameson, asked him to go to Bulawayo to keep Lobengula in good-humor. The story of what occurred is not entirely certain beyond the fact that Lobengula's gout, to which he was becoming increasingly subject, was relieved by Jameson, with subsequent gratitude on the part of the monarch. Furthermore, Jameson, knowing the savage's childish delight in pageantry, composed a letter purporting to come from the great White Queen herself and had it delivered in a gorgeously decorated coach accompanied by three officers clad in the uniform of the Royal Horse Guards.

Meanwhile Rhodes had been in England, had seen the Queen and won her esteem, had seen Salisbury and conciliated him, had seen his enemies and satisfied their scruples. He returned with the promised charter.

His next move was to get settlers into Mashonaland. He consulted the commander of the Bechuanaland police but could not come to terms. He then hired Frank Johnston, trader, merchant, and mining man, for ninety-seven thousand pounds to recruit a force for the conquest.

The result was the famous Pioneers, two hundred in number, carefully selected from all trades and classes, partially drilled and disciplined in military fashion. With them went five hundred mounted police equipped and paid by the Chartered Company. Their guide was Frederick Selous, one of the great elephant hunters of Africa, whose name is still a household word there. Selous died in the World War, fighting the Germans in German East Africa. There was also Maurice Gifford, who was with me on my later Matabele trip. He was a younger son of an old English family with a fighting record in every war. To interpret for them went Johann Colenbrander, half Dutch, half English, frontier-born, whose knowledge of the Matabele tongue and other native dialects was of inestimable value. All these were young men, "infaans," as the Matabele called them, full of hope and enthusiasm. No river was too wide nor forest too dense for them to cross or penetrate.

Although Jameson had extracted from Lobengula a half-hearted promise "to give the road," the Pioneers decided to avoid Bulawayo so that the impis might not be tempted to make a surprise attack. Nevertheless, every precaution was taken. Each night when they outspanned their fifty ox-wagons they formed them in a square laager, front to end, with Maxims guarding the corners.

Founding Fort Victoria on the way, they finally reached the site of Salisbury in Mashonaland, September, 1890, and set to work at once to build the town. They had to contend with many difficulties. The rainy season began; the long road south was impassable with mud, a railway was started from Beira on the east coast but had to be abandoned, the police force cost two hundred fifty thousand pounds a year, food had to be carted seventeen hundred miles from the Cape.

It was a well-planned stroke of genius when Rhodes appointed Dr. Jameson administrator for the Chartered Company in Mashonaland in 1892. It was never openly expressed between these two Englishmen that favors had been given or received, though the feeling of gratitude and esteem was mutual. Although Jameson was neither soldier nor statesman, yet he was able to accomplish what was little short of miraculous both in warfare with the natives and in statecraft. Furthermore, this gambler by nature saved the Chartered shareholders from great losses by his economical management of the Company's affairs. For example, the expensive police were replaced by the unpaid volunteer Mashonaland Horse. But to the great distress of Jameson and Rhodes and the stockholders of the Chartered Company, no profitable gold deposits had been developed as yet.

Just at this moment, when the stock of the Company was steadily sinking, the young warriors of the Matabele began the war which everyone on the frontier had always regarded as inevitable. Jameson himself thought it would come; Rhodes publicly professed his belief in peace, although he had told people privately that as soon as the Matabele interfered with his rights he "would end their game." This was a reluctant confession that the peaceful amalgamation which both had been aiming at was in reality a forlorn hope.

Lobengula undoubtedly had had no intention when he granted the Rudd Concession of giving up his feudal rights over the Mashona, the Zulu term for "Unclean Ones." Among these rights was that of pasturing his cattle on the Mashona farms. In May, 1893, a few Mashona at Victoria stole some lengths of wire from the telegraph line Rhodes had built to the Cape. They were detected by the English and a fine of cattle imposed on them. This they paid with Lobengula's cattle. Lobengula thereupon sent an impi under Manyao to punish the Mashona. These young warriors remained about Victoria for a week murdering and burning and plundering the Mashona, although little was done to the whites beyond making threats.

Jameson, who was at Salisbury, the capital of Mashonaland, one hundred miles away, hastened to Victoria. He summoned the native leaders to an immediate indaba. He absolutely refused to give up any Mashona. He delivered an ultimatum to Manyao telling him to be beyond the border within an hour. Although an appeal for help had been sent to all the Mashonaland Horse, only about forty had assembled when Jameson gave the order to attack the Matabele who, instead of carrying out his orders, had made camp a short distance away.

What the Matabele thought when the little line deployed before their hundreds can only be conjectured. Jameson said Matabele fired on him first, though the evidence on this point is conflicting. Some thirty-seven natives fell in this sortie; no attack was made on the whites.

Jameson at once telegraphed the news to Rhodes. He urged sending a punitive force of a thousand men against the Matabele immediately. The war spirit of the settlers was high. Furthermore, everyone realized that Lobengula would not be able to hold his fighters in check. Rhodes paid out of his own pocket the cost of the equipment of the expedition which nearly every white in Mashonaland joined.

The very boldness and swiftness of the contemplated invasion offered the only chance in its favor. The grim determination of the white man, when stripped of the veneer of civilization, is more relentless, more persistent, and more terrible than the ferocity of the most formidable black warrior who ever trod the African continent. Apart from this consideration, it seemed from a military point of view a hopeless venture. What chance would a handful of settlers have against the impis of well-armed Matabele?

The fact that this raid was successful and that Jameson's later raid of 1895 was unsuccessful does not detract from an inevitable comparison. Here, as in the later raid, Jameson betrayed a lack of judgment. In this instance, however, Fortune smiled upon him. None the less, he had tempted Fate. The defeat of the advance guard would have meant the massacre of every white man, woman, and child north of the Limpopo River.

The total effective force, about a thousand all told, white and native, advanced into Matabeleland in two columns which united at Iron Mine Hill, so called because prehistoric workers in Rhodesia had dug there for iron ore. Then they crossed the frontier of Matabeleland and marched on Bulawayo.

The little army's method of defense was adopted from old-time Boer tactics. Twenty-two commissary wagons, each drawn by sixteen oxen, were driven in double column, protected on all sides by mounted men and artillery. Within three minutes of the time an alarm was sounded it was possible to form the wagons into a laager and place a piece of artillery at each angle. It was decided that the horsemen, if defeated, should retreat within the square, and that the final stand to oppose the onrush of the Matabele should be made with the wagons as a barricade.

By continuous fighting and marching the punitive column came close to Bulawayo. Lobengula then set fire to his huge kraal of twenty thousand native huts, loaded his treasure on seven wagons, drove fifty thousand cattle over his trail to obliterate it, and fled north to the impenetrable jungles of the Shangani River. Dr. Jameson, who was directing the expedition in a nonmilitary capacity, sent a letter to the Matabele monarch promising him safe-conduct if he would return for an indaba. Lobengula replied that he would come back but, when a few days had elapsed without his arrival at the English camp, Colonel Patrick Forbes, military commander of the column, called for volunteers to trace and, if necessary, capture Lobengula. One hundred and sixty went to the Shangani, but only thirty-seven were selected to follow Major Alan Wilson on the dash across the river after the king.

The Wilson Patrol proceeded about four miles and then made another camp. It was noticed that the Matabele were showing themselves in ever-increasing number. Wilson could still have retraced his path, but he was awaiting word from Colonel Forbes who was to send him reinforcements. The forces of the Matabele, augmenting hourly, finally made an attack at daybreak. After hours of fighting Wilson realized that his situation was desperate; there was still no sign of Forbes. He then called upon his most able scout, Frederick Russell Burnham, to perform the almost impossible task of breaking through the ring of savages to reach Forbes.

Burnham selected Ingram, an American, and Gooding, an Australian, to accompany him. Using every precaution which the danger prescribed and every art he had learned from years of Indian fighting in the American West and scouting in South Africa, Burnham succeeded in leading his companions through the encircling impis and by a miracle reached the banks of the Shangani River.

The drift, or ford, over the river by which they had crossed shortly before had vanished. A red muddy torrent confronted them. The scouts had been sixteen hours in the saddle and the horses were nearly exhausted, yet they succeeded in crossing and reaching Forbes. As Burnham swung himself from the saddle, he said heavily, "We are all that are left."

When Rhodes and I visited this part of the country the following year, we learned from natives who had been engaged in the Wilson massacre that it had cost Lobengula eighty men of the blood royal and five hundred warriors to kill Wilson and his thirty-four men. It was said that Wilson was among the last to fall, and that the wounded men loaded their rifles and passed them to him during the final stages of the defense. But when both his arms were broken and he could no longer shoot, he stepped from behind the barricade of dead horses and walked toward the Matabele, who were firing. Then it was that a young warrior advanced toward him and stabbed him with a spear. In spite of his mortal wound, Wilson still continued to approach. In fear, the warrior shouted, "This man is bewitched; he cannot be killed," and threw away his spear just as Wilson pitched forward on his face, dead.

We were also told by the natives that in a lull of the firing, the heroic Englishmen sang a song that the natives often heard them sing in the church at Victoria. It was the National Anthem, *God Save the Queen*. The natives were appalled when they found that the men they had massacred were infaans. They clapped their hands to their mouths and exclaimed, "If infaans can fight like this, what will we do when the bearded men come to avenge them?" Later, the bones of the Wilson Patrol were gathered up, and now rest beside the grave of their great chief, Rhodes, in the Matoppo Hills.

Wilson's Last Stand was produced on the stage, as a patriotic play, and ran in London for two years to crowded houses.

One thing that helped to save the settlers was that Lobengula's warriors had got the idea that their newly acquired rifles must be more effective than their native spears; and most of them persisted in using their guns in the fighting that followed, firing wildly instead of making their charges with the stabbing weapons they could handle so dexterously.

Also they imagined that by raising the sight of the rifle to the highest elevation they could make it shoot straighter and harder. Had they thrown away their rifles and rushed the white men while on the march, or caught them at night when the skill of the white marksmen would have availed them little, they could have annihilated the column.

Lobengula was not captured. He had no part in the Matabele surrender, and died of smallpox in the jungles of the Shangani a few months later. All the head chiefs under command of Manyao marched to Bulawayo and surrendered. On Christmas Day, 1893, peace was made with the Matabele, and the whole of Matabeleland and Mashonaland was thrown open to settlement.

In January, 1895, Rhodes was at the height of his power and popularity. He had been made a member of the Privy Council and was further rewarded by the renaming of Matabeleland and Mashonaland as "Rhodesia." On many occasions Rhodes expressed his gratification that the country had been named for him and declared that he would devote the rest of his life to earning the honor bestowed upon him. As he had rescued this large territory from savagery practically single-handed, he undoubtedly was entitled to the tribute. For a much lighter consideration, a certain Italian peddler of pickles was honored—one Amerigo Vespucci, who accompanied an expedition to Venezuela, wrote a book about that country, and without having visited any other portion of the two great continents, had his name given to North and South America.

The result of the war was to turn over to the Chartered Company all the lands Lobengula had claimed as his own. Dr. Jameson was to be administrator of the conquered territory, as well as of Mashonaland. Two land reserves were set up for the natives, but outside of this comparatively limited space, all lands could be granted by the Company as it pleased. The stock of the Chartered Company went booming and within a few months the old goat kraal of Lobengula became the town of Bulawayo, the capital of Southern Rhodesia.

Although life was always much simpler at Bulawayo than at Cape

Town or even Johannesburg, the inevitable dinners and amateur theatricals typical of all English settlements were soon being given where but a short time before the Matabele impis had drilled. Social ethics were not exceptionally strict; "slightly married" couples mingled freely with those more legally bound together. In fact, almost anyone, however tainted socially in the Old World, could find recognition on the frontier of South Africa.

For three years the peace continued, but the Matabele were by no means ready to admit that they had been definitely conquered. Furthermore, there were undoubtedly native grievances against the whites. This dissatisfaction was kept alive by the witch doctors who, after Lobengula's death, were in control. These priests preached to the natives that Lobengula's defeat was due to his failure to follow their counsels and "make medicine" as his father 'Mzlikazi had done.

After the Jameson Raid, when the Matabele learned that Dr. Jameson was a prisoner in the hands of the Boers and that "his medicine had gone weak" and his troops had been captured, they realized that their opportunity had come. They began to plan an uprising.

The Second Matabele War owed its inspiration chiefly to the head high priest, who was called the 'Mlimo and claimed to be the "mouthpiece of God." He declared that he would make the native warriors invulnerable to the white men's bullets, and gave orders that on a certain night they should attack simultaneously over the whole of Rhodesia. Part of the plan was that on the designated night, when the moon would be full, every native servant should kill his master, and that no woman or child should be spared in the general massacre to follow.

One day a native woman was seen entering the town of Bulawayo pretending that she was carrying a load of firewood. The guard stopped her and questioned her. It seemed to him that her load was unreasonably heavy. On examination it was found to contain a number of assegais, with which every servant in the town was to be armed.

Now, no white community can be safely trusted with a military secret, but untutored black savages will keep one in a silence as of the grave. It is likely that the 'Mlimo's program, involving the murder of every white person in Rhodesia, undoubtedly would have matured had it not been for the impatience of a group of young native warriors on the Inhembesi River, forty-five miles from Bulawayo. They began killing the colonists three days before the time agreed upon.

Thus suddenly awakened to the peril, the whites at Bulawayo at once organized military units and called in assistance from the countryside. Nevertheless, many were massacred, and for a while the situation was desperate. Bulawayo was so closely besieged that its defenders had actually planned the killing of their own women and children when the first relief column reached them.

At this juncture there arrived in Bulawayo a young man named Armstrong, commissioner for a neighboring district, who had an important communication to make. It related to a Matabele youth, who had suggested to him a means whereby the 'Mlimo, who directed all the operations of the foe, might be killed. All of his own family had been killed by the 'Mlimo, and he thirsted for revenge. Furthermore, he had a shrewd notion that the whites would win the war in the end, their "medicine" being probably more powerful. The Matabele youth explained that the 'Mlimo dwelt in a cave in a certain place in the Matoppo Hills, where it might be possible to take him by surprise and slay him.

Of course, the story might be a trap; there was no telling. But desperate emergencies demand the taking of desperate risks, and the upshot of the matter was that the duty of stalking the 'Mlimo and catching him in his mountain lair was assigned to Frederick R. Burnham and young Armstrong. The latter, though a mere boy, was keen-witted and fearless as his leader. Major Burnham tells the story fully and interestingly in his book, *Scouting on Two Continents*.

The two men started for the mountains and found their way at length to the neighborhood of the cave, which, it appears, was not the 'Mlimo's habitation but, so to speak, his church. It was a sacred place, which none but he dared enter. When he spoke in a loud voice at the cave's mouth, an echo was heard, and this was supposed to be the utterance of the Great Spirit. He translated that utterance as he chose, and the true believers bowed in recognition of supernatural power.

Not far from the cave was a village of about a hundred straw-thatched native huts. And when Burnham and Armstrong arrived on the scene there was a whole impi of warriors assembled out in front. They were there to be rendered immune to injury by white men's bullets, a feature of the ceremonial being the skinning of a live ox and the eating of it raw.

Notwithstanding the difficulty of eluding observation, Burnham and Armstrong succeeded in getting into the cave undetected. For a considerable distance they had crawled on their bellies, screening their slow and cautious movements with branches of mimosa held before them. Their horses had been tethered in a thicket.

Once inside the cave, they had only to wait until the 'Mlimo should enter; and after a while he came. He was a man about sixty years of age, very black, sharp-featured, and with a cruel, crafty cast of countenance.

"This is your job," whispered Burnham to his companion.

"No," replied Armstrong, "you do it."

Burnham, who already had the 'Mlimo covered with his rifle, said to him, "You claim to be immune to the white man's bullets—stop this one," and fired. He shot him through the body, just below the heart. The "mouthpiece of God" fell dead.

There was not a moment to be lost. Burnham and Armstrong leaped over the body and down the trail in the direction of their horses. Immediately, of course, there was tremendous excitement. Hundreds of natives encamped near by picked up their guns which were scattered on the ground and started in pursuit of the fugitives. In order to distract them, Burnham and Armstrong paused in their flight long enough to set fire to the village. Burnham's first match ignited slowly, flickered, and went out. The second gave a quick flame, and the straw thatch began to burn. It was all that was necessary; the fire spread, and the Matabele stopped to put it out.

Burnham and Armstrong soon reached their horses and made their escape. When they felt that they were safe, they looked back and saw a great cloud of black smoke rolling over the granite hill above the cave.

Although the killing of the 'Mlimo destroyed the myth that centered about him and brought despair to the hearts of the Matabele, most of whom surrendered, there was still a small group of irreconcilables led by a chief named Babyaan. From his lair in the Matoppo Hills he carried on constant guerilla warfare against near-by Bulawayo. The situation was still dangerous when Rhodes stepped in.

Nothing better illustrates the character of Rhodes than this oft-told story of how he ended the Second Matabele War. It is fortunate that he was in Rhodesia at this time. Through the failure of the Jameson Raid, Rhodes was stripped of his great political power. No help could be expected from England; she had enough international complications to straighten out at the moment. On the one hand, Rhodes's great fortune was not sufficient to support a war indefinitely prolonged; on the other, so long as the blacks remained unconquered no settlers would come to Rhodesia.

Rhodes proposed to go alone and unarmed into the Matoppo Hills, there to meet the indunas of the Matabele and endeavor to pacify them. He knew that the warriors desired his life beyond that of any other white man. All his friends and companions urged him not to go, adding entreaty to entreaty in a cumulative effort to prevent what they regarded as a useless sacrifice. Rhodes resolutely refused to listen to them. Instead, he summoned Johann Colenbrander and asked him to get in touch with one of the late 'Mzlikazi's wives and through her to make arrangements for an indaba with the Matabele indunas.

It was through the offices of this old Kaffir woman that the conference between Rhodes and the indunas was finally effected. Sarah Gertrude Millin, in her book *Rhodes,* says: "This is the old woman with the bunched-together face, and the rheumy slits of eyes, and the arms like sapless branches and the hands like dead twigs and the empty sacks of breasts, whose portrait hangs in Rhodes's bedroom—the only portrait of a woman in Rhodes's house today, the only one he ever did have except a painting by Reynolds he had coveted in his youth and bought out of his wealth."

VOORTREKKERS

OXCARTS CROSSING A STREAM

It took a long time before the wary Matabele would agree to a meeting. They suspected treachery. Finally consent was obtained and Rhodes selected three men to accompany him. Colenbrander, of course, had to go as interpreter. Dr. Hans Sauer, who had been associated with Rhodes more or less closely since Kimberley days and who was a Reform prisoner after the Jameson Raid, insisted on being of the party. Vere Stent, the representative of a Cape Town newspaper, insisted on going because he was sure his youth would protèct him and he thought the world ought to have an accurate account of how the others died.

On the appointed day Rhodes and his companions went up into the Matoppos. They found the indunas in a vlei; Babyaan was seated on a rock, the others were standing. I have heard Rhodes tell the story of how he looked Babyaan sternly in the eye and ordered: "Get up!"

Babyaan rose sullenly, and Rhodes took his seat. Then a crowd of impetuous young warriors came thrusting forward, brandishing their assegais menacingly and shouting: "Stab! Stab! Let him roast like a pheasant on the fire."

Without a sign of perturbation, Rhodes spoke quietly to Babyaan. "Tell your men to sit down." The older and calmer indunas once more brought the crowd to silence.

Rhodes's action was a remarkable illustration of the force of a dominating personality. The instant he took the seat from the chief, Babyaan was on the defensive and his attitude was that of an accused criminal before a judge.

When all was quiet Rhodes spoke, Colenbrander interpreting rapidly. "You have killed my white people. Why have you done this?" was his first question. The long indaba went on while the issue hung in the balance. A single misstep on the part of Rhodes and his life would have answered for it. But Rhodes listened encouragingly as induna after induna came forward to pour out his wrongs.

He was no longer the arrogant empire builder; he was the father listening to his children with infinite patience. But at last he demanded of the chiefs: "Now, for the future, is it peace? Or is it war?" And the indunas, each laying a small stick at his feet in sign of surrender, declared "It is peace."

No one believed that Rhodes would come back alive out of the Matoppos. He was greeted as one returned from the dead. He told his friends that not only had he made peace but that many indunas were coming to Bulawayo for a great series of indabas to arrange matters definitely for the future.

At these meetings Colenbrander again interpreted. On the last day of the conferences Rhodes spoke in praise of Colenbrander, giving him credit for the peaceful understanding that had so fortunately been reached. Then Samabulane, an old induna, rose and spoke in the pure liquid Zulu.

"We the Matabele all know the great Johann. We knew him as a promising youth. We remember his daring deeds as a young man. We know he was the voice of great men sent to our King Lobengula. But as compared to the Great White Chief whose words I am now answering, the Great Johann is only the tick bird that picks the ticks off the rhinoceros."

So it was that Rhodes came to be called Lamula 'Mkunzi—"he who separates fighting bulls."

CHAPTER FIFTEEN

Trekking Through Matabeleland

WITH RHODES INTO THE HINTERLAND — THE
YANKEE SPIDER VERSUS THE CAPE CART — MY
FIRST MEETING WITH DR. JAMESON—BLUE BEADS
AT A DISCOUNT—SPEAKING OF LIONS—VARIED
DISCUSSIONS—ASCERTAINING THE MINERAL WEALTH
OF RHODESIA —BURNHAM'S WELL SHOWS THE WAY
TO THE GREAT COPPER DEPOSITS—PREHISTORIC
MINES OF EAST AFRICA—I ADVISE RHODES TO REOPEN
THE ANCIENT WORKINGS—A TENABLE THEORY—THE
GOLD OF OPHIR—KING SOLOMON AND HIRAM OF TYRE
FORM THE FIRST MINING CORPORATION—RIDER HAG-
GARD HAS A WORD TO SAY—''ROUND THE CAMP-FIRE''

*I*n 1891 Lord Randolph Churchill
was in Mashonaland collecting
material for a series of articles on South Africa for the London *Daily
Mail*. One of these articles dealt with mines. Since the most important feature of the new country was the possible occurrence of
gold in profitable quantities, he had employed two American mining experts to examine and report on the abandoned workings.
These experts had without qualification condemned the entire country on the theory that the veins, or reefs, were only gash-veins without persistence in depth. Churchill accepted this evaluation as final,
and published it not only in his articles, but also in the resulting

book, *Men, Mines, and Animals in South Africa,* which was presented to the public the following year. Coming from a man of Churchill's standing, the report that the country held out no inducement to mining investors was a serious blow to Rhodes's aspirations.

Rhodes, however, was never a man lightly to abandon his cherished plans. In spite of this adverse report he still believed that the country possessed a potential gold-mining field. In 1894, therefore, he asked me to conduct a personal investigation to determine whether the veins on these abandoned workings had really pinched out, or whether the American experts had been mistaken. Rhodes also suggested to me that the country might contain other minerals which could be exploited profitably.

I had now been long enough on the Rand to be satisfied that the Rhodes properties could get along without my supervision for a few months. Accordingly, it was arranged that during August and September of this year Rhodes and I should make a trip through Mashonaland, Matabeleland, and Manicaland in company with Dr. Jameson, Sir John Willoughby, Maurice Gifford, Robert Williams, and Jefferson Clark. I took with me also two of my assistants from Johannesburg, J. A. Chalmers and Dr. F. H. Hatch.

I had hired a private stagecoach to transport my engineers and myself five hundred miles from Pretoria to Bulawayo, where Rhodes and Jameson were to meet us. Loaded to the gunwales as we were, we were frequently compelled to leap out when the stage threatened to capsize on the rough trail. In fact, sometimes it actually did capsize without warning, although fortunately no one of us was injured in these accidents.

There had to be numerous readjustments of luggage, following the frequent capsizings of the stage. Whenever we stopped an irrepressible suitcase marked "W. K." kept appearing. I ordered it chucked out several times, but it was always there at the next rearrangement of luggage. Finally I said: "I wonder who W. K. is. There's no one with those initials here." Chalmers, one of the most faithful, reticent, and efficient of my staff, replied that the suitcase was his.

I said, "But those are not your initials."

"No," he admitted. "I borrowed the suitcase."

"Didn't you notice," I replied, "that we've been chucking it out?"

"Yes, I know," he smiled, "I've managed to retrieve it each time."

The laugh was on me and the rest of our party who, in spite of my orders to travel light, had indulged ourselves as to the amount of baggage we carried. Chalmers, being a conscientious and thrifty Scotchman, was the only one of the party who had literally obeyed my injunction.

From Bulawayo on, Rhodes and the other members of the party traveled in a Cape cart, a high top-heavy, two-wheeled vehicle, uncomfortable and predisposed to tip on the slightest provocation. Jeff Clark and I, being Americans, were given a "Yankee spider," as the English contemptuously called our vehicle. It was a light buggy, which seemed to Rhodes altogether too frail for such a rough trip as we were making. More than once I invited him to ride with me, but he always declined. After several days, however, I induced him to try this new method of locomotion; he was soon convinced that the buggy was not only much more comfortable, but was safer than the Cape cart. After this trip, many of the Yankee spiders made by the Studebaker Company of America were introduced into Rhodesia.

At Bulawayo I met for the first time the famous Dr. Leander Starr Jameson, whom I had not seen before as he had been busy with his duties as administrator of what was coming to be known as Rhodesia. Jameson was small of stature, slightly built. His brown eyes, alert and brilliant, were set far apart. His personality was forceful with a magnetism which led his men to follow him in whatever enterprise he might recommend, however desperate.

Jameson had abandoned the safe and sure position of a resident medical officer in a London hospital to seek his fortune in Africa. As a brilliant physician and surgeon in the De Beers Company hospital at Kimberley he was credited with saving the lives of many who were later to be his enemies.

Jameson's presence in Africa at this time was the result of pure chance. The Kimberley position he came to fill had previously been offered to Dr. Henry A. Wolff, an American graduate of the Harvard Medical School. Dr. Wolff arrived in Kimberley only to find that his letter of acceptance had never been received, and Dr. Jameson already on duty.

This episode shows how momentous issues often hang on trivialities. Had Wolff's letter reached its destination, Dr. Jameson would not have gone to Africa and the Conquest of Rhodesia would probably have been postponed, since there was no one with ability comparable to that of Jameson to whom Rhodes could have entrusted that difficult enterprise.

Jameson was a most engaging companion; there was in him a spirit of daring, and a willingness to risk all on the throw of the die, that at times was regarded by less adventurous souls as foolhardy. As administrator of the Chartered Company in Mashonaland he had held in his hand the scales of peace and war and had done an excellent job.

His health, like that of Rhodes, was far from robust. Both men labored always under the strain of fighting against time. No sooner was one problem out of the way than two new ones presented themselves. The solution of every one required immediate decision and positive action. Jameson loved the excitement of this adventurous existence. He cajoled the Matabele chiefs when he could; when he could not, he fought and conquered them.

Hour after hour and evening after evening he would listen to Rhodes talking about his "North," would smile at him tolerantly and doubtfully. Yet, in spite of the fact that he considered these ideas as "dreams," when called on he would go out and risk his life to realize them for Rhodes.

They were an extraordinary pair: both had the pioneer instinct. As I have said before, one of the traits I admired especially in Rhodes was his high regard for the pioneer. At many a Chartered Company meeting, I have seen him pace the floor, advocating vehemently that preference in mining concessions be given to the pioneer instead of to influential syndicates.

He would say: "I don't like to turn capital down; we need it for the development of South Africa. But the old pioneer who has been up in the country for years, who has endured every kind of hardship and carried on alone so long, represents a spirit even more important to the future of the country than money. I'm in favor of letting him have the concession."

Among these Rhodesian pioneers was an aged Boer hunter named Piet, whom Rhodes had known in the early Kimberley days. Rhodes, Dr. Hans Sauer, and I once made a side trip on horseback especially to see the old fellow. Rhodes characteristically insisted on riding for hours through a blinding storm of locusts to reach the goal he had determined on.

The old hunter, living in a little two-room hut with his wife and three children, was amazed and delighted to see his patron. As there were no chairs available, Rhodes sat down on the bed and they chatted for some time. The family was obviously in considerable want. With his usual generosity, Rhodes wished to relieve their necessity. When they refused his offer of money, he had a happy inspiration: he said he needed some wild animals with which to start a menagerie at Groote Schuur, and finally persuaded Piet to accept the money as advance payment for whatever animals he might capture. Rhodes did actually form a menagerie, and his first specimen was a lion sent by this Boer hunter.

As we were about to leave, Piet pointed to a ragged, none-too-clean, little urchin and said: "Mr. Rhodes, my boy here is your namesake. I've taken the liberty of calling him after you." The little boy, pushed by his father, came forward to shake hands. Rhodes was as embarrassed as the boy and slipped a five-pound note into the little fellow's hand. I whispered to Rhodes that he should take the child on his lap and kiss him. He picked him up gingerly, as one unaccustomed to showing affection, held him for a moment, and then rose to go. Once outside, I glanced slyly at Rhodes; "You've performed a noble deed today!" I remarked facetiously. His dignified silence indicated that he did not think this funny.

I have often noticed that men who are possessed by their ideas do not as a rule have a sense of humor. It was certainly so with Rhodes. Whenever he was obliged to listen to humorous stories, he would do so politely, but always seemed relieved when the ordeal was over.

On this trip we carried with us a large number of blue beads with which to trade with the natives. However, we found that some "damned Yankee" had been ahead of us and had created such a craze for pink beads that our blue ones were accepted only at a considerable discount. The natives were evidently not so far advanced in currency stabilization as we who boast of a "superior" civilization.

Every evening after supper we sat about our campfire and discussed trivialities as well as world affairs. Lions roared close at hand, and against this menace we kept up a wall of flame, and even occasionally fired off our guns. The conversation naturally returned again and again to lions. Almost every one of the party had personal experiences to relate. One anecdote, that I have often told, I consider better than any told around the campfire.

I once had with me on a trip to Rhodesia a valet named Joseph, fresh from London. At Bulawayo I told my man I should have to leave him there because if I took him farther into the hinterland he would be an encumbrance rather than a help. I said that I should be back on the evening of the fifth day and instructed him to have my bath ready and my dinner clothes laid out, as I was dining at Government House that evening. At the appointed time I returned, and while changing, conversationally asked Joseph what he had been doing during my absence. He informed me that he had been lion hunting.

"The devil you have," I said. "Where did you go?"

"About fifteen miles south of Bulawayo," he answered.

This was a place really infested with lions—and Joseph had never been beyond the sound of Bow Bells.

I asked who had gone with him, and was told that a friend of his, who was valet to one of the officers stationed there, had accompanied him.

"Had your friend ever been lion hunting before?" He had not.

Needless to say, I became extremely interested. "Joseph, you certainly went to the right place. I've been there and it's good lion country. What kind of gun did you use?"

Joseph seemed hesitant but replied honestly, "I didn't think you'd mind, sir," pointing to a shotgun in the corner of the room, "so I took your gun."

"How many lions did you get, Joseph?" I asked immediately.

"We had pretty hard luck, sir. We didn't kill any. We didn't even see a lion."

"Well," I said, "that was hard luck. You didn't even see one?"

"No," replied Joseph.

"What kind of shot were you going to use?"

He showed me some number six bird shot. I could hardly believe my eyes.

"Joseph," I asked, "how'd you ever expect to kill a lion with bird shot?"

"Oh," he replied innocently, "we thought we'd blind the lion with the first barrel, and kill him with the second one."

I decided that Joseph's luck had not deserted him.

Another lion story with an equally happy ending was told me by Major Burnham's brother-in-law, John Blick, who gained fame as an African mining prospector and hunter, and became even more renowned later for his paleontological discoveries in the western part of the United States.

Blick was out hunting one day near Bulawayo. He was on horseback and his two dogs were running beside him. Abruptly, as he rode over the brow of a kopje, he found himself confronted by a lioness. She advanced slowly towards him. There was no possibility of retreating, and Blick shot her.

As he rode on, he heard his dogs making a frightful clamor on the hillside above the trail. They came rolling down, struggling with what looked like two balls of yellow fluff, which he recognized finally as two young lion cubs. In this scuffle they were about evenly matched with his small hunting dogs. With their mother dead, he knew they would starve if he left them. He also knew that their father could not be far away and he was not anxious to meet him. Hurriedly dismounting, he managed to separate the cubs from the dogs; he carried them back to his camp, holding them over his saddle horn.

Blick's cabin was an isolated and lonely place. He fed the cubs assiduously, at first from a baby's bottle. He housebroke them and trained them to his rough, celibate domesticity. As the days passed, the lions became his constant companions and they were invaluable in frightening off hostile natives. The male cub, of which he was particularly fond, he named "Lobengula"—"Loben" for short.

They accepted Blick as their close friend and for the most part they were as tame as lap dogs. Occasionally when reading by his fire in the evening, he would be startled to see one of them leap clear over his lamp, the entire length of the room, to play with the other. Once when Loben bridged the hunter's knees as he sat in his chair, the man was surprised to see that all four of the lion's paws were on the ground, that the beast stood well over three feet. But Blick kept up his end of the adjustment and the trust continued a mutual one.

Blick began to develop what he thought was rheumatism, and couldn't discover what was giving him such dreadful cramps in the legs. One night he woke to find Loben occupying the entire lower part of his bed, while he had been maneuvered to the head and was lying with his knees drawn up to his chin. He got up and angrily commanded Loben to get off his bed and to lie on the floor. Reluctantly the huge lion obeyed and Blick went back to sleep; but when he woke on the morning, Loben was once more curled on the bottom half of his bed. The gigantic pet had crawled up so quietly and gently that his master hadn't even stirred in his sleep.

One year several friends sent word to Blick that they were trekking up to spend the Christmas holidays with him. Since the party included two ladies, Blick realized he would have to remove his lions from the house. Accordingly he staked them down in the yard and for several weeks before his guests' arrival accustomed them to this new and circumscribed way of life.

His friends were eager to see the domesticated lions. After their initial fright, the women were enchanted. Loben allowed one of them to stroke his great black mane. He and his sister were behaving very nicely and the show was a considerable success. Suddenly one of the ladies deliberately opened a parasol in Loben's face. So quickly came the lion's retaliation that the movements appeared simultaneous. He struck out with one of his powerful paws and it was only the sheerest of good fortune that the woman was not disemboweled. She stood rooted to the spot, shrieking, completely naked from the waist down. Loben tore the parasol to shreds.

When the woman had been taken into the house out of danger and Loben had been calmed down, the two male visitors came out and insisted that the lion be shot at once. A heated argument followed. Blick was adamant in his defense of Loben. If his guests didn't like his lions, they could get out. The visitors packed up and left immediately and spent a bleak Christmas traveling on the veldt.

A short time afterwards, Blick was called away on imperative business. Since he couldn't very well take his lions along with him and couldn't entrust them to the care of his black boys, who were terrified by them, he was faced with the painful task of disposing of them. Fortunately a friend stopped in on his way to an encampment farther west. This man kindly offered to take them with him. At first Blick couldn't bring himself to relinquish them; only after repeated assurances that they would be given the fondest of care did he give them up. He was genuinely bereaved.

John Blick never lost his interest and love for animals. After he returned to his home in Los Angeles, several years later, he frequently visited the zoo and he saw every circus that came to town. He would walk out to the menagerie early in the morning before anyone else was around and look at the lions, always the lions first.

One day he strolled into the animal tent of a small traveling circus. In a cage marked "MAN-EATING LION FROM AFRICA" a huge, black-maned lion was raging furiously. The keeper turned as Blick approached. "I don't know what's the matter with him," he said. "He's the unhappiest lion I've ever seen. He roars and storms, whenever anybody goes near him."

"I think I can tell you," Blick answered. Before the guard could stop him, he jumped over the ropes and went up to the cage. "Hello, Loben!" The lion turned, tensed his ears, and became still. Blick put his hand through the bars. "Hello, Loben," he called again. The lion ambled over, amiably shook his mane, and stretched comfortably while Blick stroked him. Loben was happy. The friend who he thought had deserted him was here again.

Our campfire conversation often took a serious turn. One evening the tariff was under discussion between Rhodes, Jameson, and myself. Rhodes had been criticizing America for having levied a heavy duty on diamonds the previous year. His particular grievance was that the De Beers Company had gone to considerable expense in sending an interesting diamond exhibit to the World's Fair at Chicago, and immediately afterwards the Americans had imposed a heavy duty on diamonds. I explained that the United States was not discriminating against the De Beers Company but that the powerful American silver interests had blamed the decline in silver on the English bankers headed by the Rothschilds. Knowing that the Rothschilds were largely interested in the De Beers diamond mines, the silver producers successfully exerted their influence in Congress to have a tariff placed on the De Beers diamonds in reprisal against the Rothschilds.

This led to a discussion of tariffs as an economic policy. Although Rhodes sometimes took the opposite side of an argument to test the soundness of his own views, on this occasion he was in earnest and criticized our American tariff, I thought, intemperately. Provoked by this, I told him that he might be a master of South African politics, but there was apparently much he did not know about the American tariff.

I continued, in what proved to be a prophetic vein: "The tariff is a business proposition entirely. If Great Britain were wise, she would establish a protective tariff. Then she could grant concessions to her colonies and to other nations and in return secure favorable treatment from them through reciprocal tariff arrangements. Indeed, Great Britain could in this way establish an economic empire, binding her dominions, colonies, and dependencies to her by enlightened self-interest, as well as by considerations of sentiment."

Rhodes, who had been brought up under free trade principles, became much excited and lost his temper. I, therefore, ended the discussion by stating firmly: "When you can discuss this matter as one gentleman with another, I shall resume my argument. Your attitude is childish!"

Without saying a word, Rhodes picked up his blankets and moved off about fifty feet from where he, Dr. Jameson, and I had already spread our blankets for the night. Jameson, who, with all his fondness for Rhodes, knew his temperamental weaknesses, smiled at me and said, "He'll get over it."

Awaking early the next morning, I saw Rhodes stretching himself and rubbing his joints ruefully as he rolled out of his blankets. After remarking to Jameson, "He must have had a pretty hard night of it," I strolled over. His stiffness was readily explicable. He had been so preoccupied with his peevishness, that in the darkness he had carelessly spread his blankets over some stones. I tried to re-establish an entente cordiale by sympathizing with him on his uncomfortable bed, but he had very little to say. His ill-humor continued during breakfast. I finally became tired of his dour looks, and when the meal was over, I rose and said: "Since you aren't in a very amiable frame of mind, I'm going out for a ride and a shot at some big game. I'll meet you at the next outspan about lunch time."

On the horse with which Jameson had provided me I spent three or four pleasurable hours riding over the grassy upland. Here and there were herds of animals, sometimes grazing, sometimes running about aimlessly. There were antelope of various kinds in abundance. Swift-footed zebras fled pell-mell at my approach. I found these so interesting that I lost track of the time.

It was nearly noon when I realized that I had wandered far and must be a great distance from the rest of the party. However, I finally succeeded in picking the trail, and after several hours of hard riding reached the place where Rhodes and Jameson were outspanned for the day.

In his anxiety over my prolonged absence Rhodes had completely forgotten his splenetic behavior of the morning. He laid his arm affectionately across my shoulder and said: "Hammond, we've been worried about you. You must know how dangerous it is to go wandering off like that alone on the veldt."

"Oh, well, I had a gun," I replied deprecatingly.

"Yes, but it's very easy to get lost unless you're an expert tracker in this particular kind of country. It's not enough to have a gun with you. Your horse might have broken a leg, and you would have been left alone on foot. You had no food, water, or blankets.

"Let me tell you what happened to me once in my early days, before I was used to the ways of the country. I had a glimpse of what it might be to be lost on this same veldt. I had strolled away from camp, lured by great herds of game, and found myself miles away with all sense of direction gone. I was lost, completely lost, and overcome by that terror that grips you when you turn, first in one direction, then in another, and finally in a circle and realize that all directions have suddenly become alike. For hours I was hopelessly bewildered. Finally, from sheer exhaustion I sat down and wept. That seemed to clear my brain and, slowly, I began to be able to discern certain remembered landmarks. I might have been lost for good and all. It was only by the rarest good luck that the adventure ended otherwise."

For the rest of the trip we proceeded in amity. We devoted our evening causeries to the subject in hand: the mineral potentialities of the country we were exploring, and their bearing on the working out of various of Rhodes's plans.

Rhodes's greatest dream was always the Cape-to-Cairo Railroad. He knew it was essential for the railroad that coal be located not too far from the proposed line and hoped coal fields might be discovered in Mashonaland. Coal actually was found there not long after. Through the Company, grants of land of one hundred square miles each had been given to Burnham, Ingram, and Colonel Maurice Gifford for exceptional services in the First Matabele War. These could be pegged anywhere north of the Zambesi River, and were to include all minerals.

Realizing the importance of the discovery of coal fields before this idea had dawned on other prospectors, these three men began a search. Burnham received a geological tip from natives, who told him that in their country there were "black rocks" that burned. He rushed Ingram and John and Judd Blick, with a quick-moving outfit, off to the north. This resulted in their pegging ten square miles of land containing enormous coal reserves. Afterwards, this property was consolidated with the Mashonaland Agency. The Wankie Coal Fields, as they are now called, are indispensable to the industrial life of Rhodesia.

On our trip we kept constantly in mind, too, the possible occurrence of other metals, such as iron, copper, and lead. Although we did not find them then, the explorations by Burnham led indirectly to the development of the great Congo copper fields and shortly afterwards to the exploration and discovery of the copper deposits in Northern Rhodesia, which is rapidly becoming an important factor in the world's copper production.

The discovery of these copper deposits resulted from a remarkable bit of detective work.

Burnham had started to sink a well back of his cabin in Bulawayo. Among the diggers was one of Lobengula's former warriors, whose girl-wife belonged to the Matokas, as indicated by the fact that, according to a tribal custom, her two upper incisors had been removed. The Matokas lived hundreds of miles to the north. Burnham, whose eyes missed few things, noticed that the girl wore a bracelet of "native," or pure, copper. Trade copper, or brass, an alloy of copper and zinc, was common as an ornament, but native copper was extremely rare. Upon being questioned, the warrior said the girl had been captured in a raid into Barotseland undertaken by King Lobengula's men just before the fatal war with the whites, and that he himself had been in the raiding party.

Burnham began to suspect he was on the trail of something important, but unfortunately he could not understand the slave girl's dialect—probably her entire vocabulary did not exceed three hundred words. Interpreters were secured, as a result of which her dialect was translated into Barotse, and that into Mungwate (Basuto), and that again into Matabele (Zulu), and from Zulu finally into English.

Messages repeated back and forth from interpreter to interpreter through four languages brought out these facts: her country was the same number of days' march beyond the Great River (the Zambesi) as it was from Bulawayo to the Zambesi; that once, when very small, she had seen men in white robes and wearing white cloth on their heads—undoubtedly Arabs—come into her country and trade for the red metal of which her bracelet was made; that this metal came from ingudines, holes in the earth. There were no words in her language, however, to express the size or depth of these holes. Judicious gifts to the warrior and his friends led to many indabas, which brought out a complete history of the great raid made by six thousand of Lobengula's warriors. The girl related how they were defeated and killed by hundreds, not by the spears of the Barotse, but by smallpox.

Since hoisting equipment was practically unobtainable, Burnham had decided to sink his well native fashion by passing up the broken rock from man to man to the surface. All the while this talk went on the well was slowly deepening. He had the girl and the interpreters brought to the well, and asked her if this well was like the ingudines in her own country where they found the red metal. She said emphatically, "Yes, some one-man deep; some three, like this."

Burnham began at once to prepare for the long trek to find the red metal. An expedition was financed in London and started from Bulawayo in May, 1895, under his command. Howard U. Moffat, at that time local manager of the already existing Bechuanaland Exploration Company, did everything possible to help. Burnham wisely decided to consolidate his grant with those of Ingram and Gifford and, upon the advice of Rhodes, turned over the whole three hundred square miles to the Bechuanaland Exploration Company.

This company was later consolidated with Northern Coppers, and, finally, with the extensive concessions given by the government of Rhodesia and the Congo Free State to Robert Williams and associates.

On its return Burnham's expedition met that of George Grey, brother of the late Viscount Grey, at the Zambesi River; Grey was going north to peg out claims for Robert Williams, then head of the Zambesia Exploring Company. Credit is due Williams for the development of the Katanga district in the Belgian Congo, just north of Rhodesia, under the auspices of the Union Minière du Haut Katanga, of which he is vice-president. Through his perseverance, vision, and courage, this property has become the source from which a large part of the world's future copper supply is being derived. In 1928, Williams was made a baronet in recognition of his services in the development of Central Africa.

Rhodes himself once came near to controlling the copper output of the world. The story has never been told before. The plan of campaign had been tentatively formulated around our campfire,

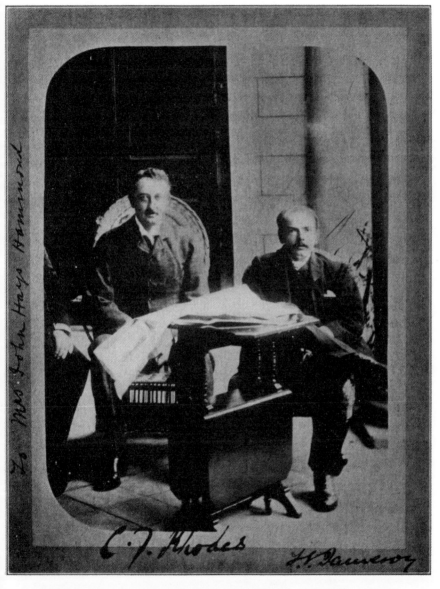

RHODES AND JAMESON ON THE GARDEN PORCH AT GROOTE SCHUUR

IN FRONT OF THE ZIMBABWE RUINS

and the near-coup scheduled for 1895. At that time both the De Beers diamond mines at Kimberley and the new gold fields on the Rand were producing large dividends. In addition, through Rhodes's association with important investors in England, we could have raised the large capital for our project.

The memorable Secrétan Copper Syndicate, which had aimed at buying up the bulk of the world's stock of copper, cornering the market, and boosting the price, had collapsed ignominiously a few years before. The brilliant but erratic Frenchman, Secrétan, had given me much useful information which I passed on to Rhodes and his associates.

Since these men had established control of the international diamond business through ownership of the diamond mines, this copper project made a strong appeal to them. The Rothschilds, who controlled the Rio Tinto copper mines in Spain and an important copper mine in Mexico, would have entered the syndicate.

My plan was to leave for the United States towards the end of 1895, in the hope of acquiring control of several of the great copper properties there. Unfortunately, the Jameson Raid diverted my attention; after that Rhodes went to Rhodesia to quell the native uprising, and the whole gigantic plan fell through.

To return to the story of our expedition. Scattered throughout the country we were covering we found thousands of excavations made upon gold-bearing quartz veins, aggregating several hundred miles in length. Also, there were the ruins of hundreds of ancient temples and fortresses which stood as the sole monuments of the forgotten people who had worked these mines.

The land was more or less undulating, the general altitude of thirty-four hundred feet making it fairly healthful for white people in its higher parts. Towards the eastern side the mountains tower to a height of ten thousand feet. The development of the country at that time was handicapped by the prevalence of the tsetse fly, the bite of which was fatal to domesticated animals, but not to man. Through the bite of the fly the animal develops a disease known as nagana. We were fortunate, however, in being able to keep away from the district infested by the tsetse fly. We would ask an old prospector or native how far away the fly was and if told it was only a mile or two we would change our course, and thus avoid it.

It was of supreme importance to Rhodes that my report on the mining prospects of this country be favorable—on my findings would hinge the investment or the noninvestment of enormous sums of British capital for the development of the country. Yet never once during the many days that we rode and drove together did Rhodes embarrass me by asking me to indicate the tenor of my report. After I had examined the nature of the ore deposits, however, I did inform him that Lord Randolph Churchill's engineers had been greatly mistaken in their geological conclusion.

The geology of the country is similar to that of many of the gold-mining sections of the United States; therefore, the gold was chiefly in quartz veins. That is, I found broad bands and patches of metamorphic schists, from five to twenty miles wide, which contained gold veins. At the date of my examination nearly two thousand miles of quartz reefs had been actually pegged out, of which about four hundred miles were estimated to cover ancient workings. The origins of these ancient workings and their history have always seemed to me one of the most exciting things to speculate upon in the whole story of mining. As we traveled through the country, I was reaching my conclusions about this as well as the more technical aspects of the situation.

These excavations were generally several hundred yards in extent and more or less continuous on the surface. The depth attained rarely exceeded a hundred feet; on the average it was about sixty. In order to extract the ore from a vein a large amount of barren rock had to be taken out and piled on either side of the excavation as the vein was followed deeper into the ground. So far as my examination extended, the ancient workings showed no evidence of the use of scientific methods in their exploitation. Indeed, as regards both the mining of the ores and the extraction of the gold from the ore, the methods employed were very crude.

Since the ancient inhabitants of Rhodesia had no knowledge of explosives, their ingenious method of extracting the ore was to build open fires against the face of the veins. When the rock was well heated, they dashed water against it, which caused cracking and disintegration. The broken fragments of ore were crushed upon a surface of hard rock in much the same way as the Mexican Indians have always ground their corn upon metates. Then followed the washing of the powdered quartz with water; the lighter particles separated and floated off, and the heavy residual gold was collected and melted.

The molten gold was poured finally into soapstone molds and so converted into bricks or ingots for exportation.

Many of their furnaces, sunk in the solid rock, still remain, some even contain cakes of gold.

As previously stated, the object of my examination was to determine whether it would be worth while to reopen those mines and work them by modern methods. I drew up a complete but naturally conservative report on the mines of the country. After describing the general geology, I referred in particular to the character of the reefs, stating that they belonged to the class of ore deposits known as true fissure veins, and that veins of this character are universally noted for their persistence in depth; but I called attention to the fact that this attribute does not imply the occurrence of pay shoots or bodies of commercial value in their veins. I emphasized this point because I did not wish the investing public to be misled into believing that the reefs of Rhodesia resembled those of the Rand in the remarkable continuity of pay ore; the reefs of the Rand are unique among the ore deposits of the world in this respect.

I furthermore expressed my belief that the abandonment of these mines was not due to the impoverishment of the reefs in depth; as is characteristic of this type of gold reefs in America and elsewhere, such impoverishment in depth does occur far more frequently than on the Rand.

I stated that it would be an anomaly in the history of gold mining if upon the hundreds of miles of mineralized reefs valuable ore shoots should not be uncovered as the result of future work, and that there was substantial grounds to believe that an important mining industry would ultimately be developed.

I concluded my report by stating:

> I consider it my professional duty to urge on the investing public the exercise of due discrimination in the

selection of the properties on which money is to be expended in development; and, furthermore, to impress upon mining companies the necessity of establishing the commercial value of the properties before undertaking the erection of plants for the reduction of ores. The majority of disappointments in quartz mining all the world over are attributed to disregard of these preparations. With proper discrimination in the selection of the properties upon which extensive developments are to be carried out, and with due regard to the determination of the appropriate time for the erection of the reduction plant, the mining risks should be no greater than in other quartz mining countries. With these admonitions I confidently commend the country to the attention of mining capitalists. . . .

Upon our return from Rhodesia I submitted my report in my Johannesburg office to Rhodes, Dr. Jameson, and the secretary of the Chartered Company, Dr. Rutherfoord Harris. After hearing my report, Dr. Harris said, "Well, if we have to depend on Hammond's geological report to raise money for this country, I don't think the outlook is encouraging."

To his criticism Rhodes replied emphatically: "Hammond is absolutely right. He's said everything he's justified in saying and the public will see that it's the report of a conscientious engineer, and give full credit to every word he says. If you don't like his report, you'd better go ahead and sell your Chartered shares."

Shortly afterwards, Rhodes went to London. At a meeting of the shareholders of the British South Africa Company he read my report. There was again some disappointment because the report did not depict a sufficiently roseate future for speculators, and I had not pulled another Witwatersrand out of my hat. Rhodes supported me by saying, "That is the report of a cautious man who visited the country and reported on what he saw."

Moreover, in discussing the report later, Rhodes was scrupulously careful not to exaggerate its favorable features, though others, including Jameson, were less reticent. To judge from the remarks of

JOHN HAYS
HAMMOND'S
trip to
MATABELELAND
with
RHODES
and
JAMESON

the various mining promoters, I must have visited every mine and claim in Rhodesia and reported glowingly on them all. This was a source of unending annoyance to me, however profitable it may have been for the speculators.

On the strength of my report interest was revived in the energetic development of Rhodesia. Eventually sufficient money began to flow in through British syndicates to carry on the work, and with gratifying results.

All through Southern Rhodesia shafts were subsequently sunk upon and through the old workings and some of these mines are now being worked more than a thousand feet below the deepest excavations made by the ancient miners, proving conclusively that it was not because of the pinching out of the veins or the petering out of the ore that the mines had been abandoned.

How, then, is one to explain the cessation of mining on the ancient workings? The explanation may be that insuperable physical difficulties were encountered: the rock became excessively hard as the excavations deepened; seepage of water flooded the workings; or the ore became too rebellious or refractory for treatment by the primitive metallurgy known to the ancients.

It has been suggested that warlike tribes from the North invaded the country and dispersed the gold workers. This might have occurred at a time when political trouble in the mother country withdrew from the industry the necessary protection. In many localities there is considerable evidence that the mines were abandoned suddenly, lending plausibility to this theory. There is, however, unmistakable evidence that the reefs were worked at different periods after their original abandonment: at times by the Arabs, the Portuguese, and even the Mashona, but the attempts were desultory and the operations were merely superficial and conducted on a small scale.

It has been estimated that over one hundred million dollars' worth of gold had been taken from these ancient workings when the white men reopened them. The question that has fascinated me ever since I first saw the Great Zimbabwe is, Who built these massive structures and where did the gold go that these workers extracted?

The walls of the Temple of Zimbabwe are some thirty-five feet high, of roughly finished blocks of granite laid in even courses without mortar. Separate towers, which must originally have been about the same height as the wall, although the tops are now broken off, were built of solid masonry. Decorative patterns of geometrical design extended around the outer side of the main wall.

In the valley below the temple was an Acropolis, almost impregnably located; it was further fortified by masonry walls and buttresses, and with labyrinthine approaches.

Although no mine workings are found at Zimbabwe, it was undoubtedly the center of the industry, serving as a residence for the directors of mining operations, and also as a collecting place for the gold, which was there smelted and cast into ingots. A great number of gold ornaments, bands, and bangles have been found there.

There are also other ruins, each occupying a central position surrounded by abandoned mine workings. At the ruins of Dhlo-dhlo pottery and ornaments have been found. These outlying forts were probably built to protect the mines from native attack, as it is noticeable that the positions are carefully chosen with a view to defense. At the Mundie ruins there are abandoned iron, as well as gold, workings. Here we found crucibles with cakes of gold still in them.

With the exception of Zimbabwe, there are no temple ruins. Apparently Zimbabwe was also the religious capital.

Hall and Neal, recognized authorities, have divided the ruins into four types: the first and best, then one of an inferior but still sound architecture, a third decadent type, and finally a local native attempt to continue the Zimbabwe style of architecture.

There are two distinct theories as to the builders of this temple. Dr. David Randall-MacIver, in *Mediaeval Rhodesia,* states that the ruins of Zimbabwe date no farther back than the fourteenth or fifteenth century A. D. In this theory he is followed by Miss Caton-Thompson. Both archaeologists assert that the ruins and the abandoned workings are of Bantu origin, the Bantu being one of the numerous negroid tribes of Central and Southern Africa.

The Mashona, who inhabited this region at the time of my visit, are said to have been a militant people. But the conquest of the country by the Matabele not only absolutely shattered their power but also made slaves of them, and they became a degraded race. Although largely of Bantu blood, the Mashona have a distinctly Semitic cast of countenance. It is an interesting fact that neither the Mashona nor the Matabele have any knowledge of the builders of the forts and temples; they have not even any legends or traditions regarding them. Neither do they inhabit these ruins; they use them as sepulchers for their chiefs.

It seems incredible that any Bantu negro ever reached a point of civilization high enough to warrant assumption that he was the architect and the engineer of Zimbabwe.

With the sole exception of Dr. Randall-MacIver and Miss Caton-Thompson, all authorities on the origin of the ruins in Rhodesia oppose the Bantu theory. Sir H. H. Johnston, who stands first in the knowledge of Bantu ethnology, is firmly convinced that no race of Bantu negroes could have created Zimbabwe without Semitic teachers. Not long ago I wrote to Mr. Howard U. Moffat on this question and received the following reply:

"I too, agree with you, in spite of Miss Caton-Thompson's theory, that the ancient work done in this country and the old ruins which must be connected with the old mines and date from the same period, cannot have been the work of the Bantu people alone. No doubt the mass of labor required for these works was supplied by local natives, probably, almost certainly slaves, but it must have been done under some foreign and superior direction."

This is also the opinion of Theodore Bent, who is recognized *facile princeps* among the authorities who have investigated the subject. His evidence is set forth in *The Ruined Cities of Mashonaland,* which ascribes the Zimbabwe civilization to Sabaean or Phoenician origin.

A. H. Keane, eminent anthropologist, agrees that the ruins are Semitic.

Hall and Neal likewise agree with Bent.

There is naturally wide divergence of opinion as to the period during which these mines were worked. There are no inscriptions to serve as definite, unimpeachable evidence. One of the more recent investigators, Professor Raymond Dart, puts the earliest workings as from 4000 to 3000 B. C. From this extreme period, estimates range down to comparatively modern times.

Professor J. W. Gregory, of the University of Glasgow, thinks some of the gold recently excavated at Ur came from these mines. The archaeological and religious evidence in favor of dating these ruins far back in antiquity is well summed up by him in his lecture on Ur.

There are signs [he says] of pre-medieval mining in Rhodesia, such as a Roman coin found in a shaft seventy feet deep near Umtali; beads referred to Ptolemaic Egypt and pre-medieval India; the use of ingot moulds of the x-shaped pattern used by the Phoenicians in Cornwall; soapstone birds similar to those used in Assyria and in the gold and turquoise mines of Egypt; a knobbed cylinder compared by Hogarth to one from Cyprus; the Groote Schuur platter with the signs of the zodiac; inscriptions that have been identified as proto-Arabic and Semitic characters.

Innumerable evidences of phallic worship have been found in these ruins. The great number of soapstone birds, pronounced by authorities to be similar to the images of birds found in Arabia, Egypt, Phoenicia and Assyria—birds sacred to the Assyrian Astarte or Venus, and emblems symbolic of the female element in creation, further attest the practice of a cult characteristic of those countries.

There seems to be a substantial basis for the theory that Rhodesian mines were worked by King Solomon, and that it is from this source that he derived his fabulous wealth. The proof necessarily remains circumstantial. To refresh the memory of Bible students I insert the following quotations:

I Kings ix: 26. And king Solomon made a navy of ships in Ezion-geber, which is beside Eloth, on the shore of the Red Sea, in the land of Edom.

I Kings ix: 27. And Hiram sent in the navy his servants, shipmen that had knowledge of the sea, with the servants of Solomon.

I Kings ix: 28. And they came to Ophir, and fetched
from thence gold, four hundred and twenty talents,
and brought it to king Solomon.

I Kings x: 22. For the king had at sea a navy of
Tharshish with the navy of Hiram: once in three
years came the navy of Tharshish, bringing gold, and
silver, ivory, and apes, and peacocks.

The Rhodesian mines lie inland about two hundred miles from
Sofala, famous as a gold-exporting seaport in the days of King
Solomon. From Sofala there is well-marked evidence of an ancient
road to the interior through Portuguese East Africa. The forts along
this road, of which there are still extensive remains, were almost
certainly built to protect the gold carriers on their way in and out.
This ancient town of Sofala lies a short distance south of the present
important Portuguese port of Beira. Sofala is about twenty-five
hundred miles from the lower end of the Red Sea. That distance
was not too great to be covered by the Arabian and Phoenician navi-
gators. They carried on trade with many parts of the Mediterranean;
developed mines in Spain and reached as far as Cornwall, England,
where they mined tin. The voyages along the eastern coast of Africa
were facilitated by the monsoons—the trade winds of the Indian
Ocean.

From a study of the map it seems obvious that the ships fitted out
at Ezion-geber, near the head of the Red Sea, were to be used for
trading with India or down the African coast. Asia Minor, Persia,
Arabia, Egypt, and even Southern Siberia could have been reached
far more conveniently by land.

While there are many gold deposits in Siberia, and some perhaps
as yet undeveloped in Mongolia, I saw no evidence of ancient workings when I visited those regions in 1898 to study their mineral
resources.

As to Egypt, ancient gold mines did exist, but so far as known
they are of insignificant extent compared with those of Rhodesia.
Arabia was formerly regarded by many authorities as the site of
King Solomon's mines, but there are in that country no gold mines
of sufficient size to warrant this assumption, and the building of the

Red Sea fleet would not have been required for trade with Egypt or Arabia as both were more accessible by caravan.

The fact that ships were built by Hiram at Ezion-geber at the head of the Red Sea to transport his gold precludes any suggestion that the source of gold was in the countries bordering the Mediterranean.

The wealth of Croesus was drawn from gold mines near Smyrna; that of Darius came from western Asia Minor. Midas found his gold in the mines of Phrygia south of the Hellespont. The Argonauts' legendary land of the Golden Fleece was probably the alluvial deposits along the rivers of Armenia.

India and the east coast of Africa, then, where ancient workings are known to exist, remain as the only possible sources of the enormous amount of gold brought to the land of the Jews in the reign of Solomon.

The Mysore mines of India were undoubtedly worked in ancient times. There were some mines in Behar, and gold is found in the Himalayas and in Tibet, but in none of those fields is there evidence of extensive ancient workings, certainly none comparable to those of Rhodesia. It is well known that highways across the desert bounding Assyria and Babylon connected these countries with what is now Palestine, and thus with the Mediterranean Sea and Egypt, while the overland routes to India lay across Central Asia. All this tends to prove that the ships at Ezion-geber could not have been used in bringing gold from India or thereabouts.

King Hiram of Tyre brought back from the land of Ophir slaves whom he used in building King Solomon's temple, and, according to the sculpture of the period, those slaves had unmistakably negroid features. For that reason the slaves could not have come from Southern India or from that part of the world where the racial physiognomy was of a very different type.

The conclusive proof, to my mind, is the fact that the culture of the miners of India was of a type entirely distinct from that of the Phoenicians, which is characteristic of the culture of the Rhodesian miners.

My personal research has been confirmed by the works of more competent authorities who have investigated this problem. I have concluded that these mines are actually the famous mines of King Solomon. As stated before, the proof must necessarily remain circumstantial. My line of reasoning is, in the first place, that there was no other source known at that time where such quantities of gold could have been obtained, and, in the second place, the objects found at Zimbabwe were similar to Phoenician objects used for the same purpose.

The date of the first Phoenician expedition to the land of Ophir was made in the reign of Solomon, about 1000 B.C. From this time to the destruction of the Phoenician and Israelitish fleets at Eziongeber was about a hundred years. With this defeat, so far as we know, the Phoenician control of the Indian Ocean ended.

When I regarded it as strongly probable that Southern Rhodesia was the land of Ophir of the Bible, I wrote to Rider Haggard and asked him why, in his book, he had located King Solomon's mines within a few miles of where I believed I had seen them. He replied that he had placed the mines in Southern Rhodesia because he felt that its almost inaccessible character would prevent any Yankee mining engineer from penetrating there, and reporting that Haggard's King Solomon mines did not exist. "And thus," he said, "imagination precedes reality."

It may interest the reader to see what has been accomplished by the re-establishment of the mining industry in Rhodesia.

For a long period prior to the advent of the British South Africa Company, Rhodesia was known as a land of constant and murderous tribal warfare. Within a few years the country underwent an extraordinary transformation. Even when I visited it last in 1899, I saw every evidence of the rapid progress that had been made towards civilization.

Rhodesia is now a well-governed country, with a population of fifty thousand whites, four thousand Asiatics, and a native population of over a million. Bulawayo (the Place of Slaughter)—the old kraal of Lobengula—has now a population of twelve thousand Europeans.

In education, the country has also made remarkable strides. There are a hundred and sixty-three schools for Europeans, in which nine thousand European children are provided with education. There are fifteen hundred schools for native pupils, with a total enrollment of one hundred and ten thousand pupils.

There is a high court composed of a chief justice and two judges, having both criminal and civil jurisdiction. Natives are subject in the main to the same laws as Europeans, though there are special restrictions relating to arms, ammunition, and liquor; and there are laws particularly applicable to natives, such as those dealing with marriage, taxation, and registration. Native commissioners have jurisdiction in civil and criminal matters in which natives only are concerned.

In 1923 the British South Africa Company relinquished to the British government all rights and interests in lands in Southern Rhodesia. The Crown recognizes the Company, however, as the owner of the mineral rights throughout both Southern and Northern Rhodesia.

The country is well adapted for agriculture. The cattle industry is carried on extensively. In 1930 nearly four hundred thousand acres were planted in maize, tobacco, and fodders. Large fruit orchards have been planted and nearly all varieties of fruit thrive. The cultivation of oranges and lemons constitutes a rapidly expanding industry, and much of the citrus fruit is exported to Europe. A thriving business is done in dairy products and poultry. A land and agricultural bank makes loans to settlers on easy terms for repayment for the purpose of improving and developing their agricultural holdings.

Since the reopening of the country, the total output of all minerals is valued at about five hundred million dollars, of which the gold amounted to about three hundred and fifty million. In 1931 the gold output was about twelve million, and the total mineral output, including coal, chrome ore, and asbestos, was over twenty million dollars.

There are a number of minor industries now established in the colony. These include brick and tile works, cigarette and tobacco factories, cold storage and ice-making installations. At the time of my first visit in 1894, there were no facilities for making ice. It was my privilege to donate the first ice-making machine to Bulawayo, and this proved a blessing, especially for use in the hospital. There are also iron and brass foundries, mineral water factories, electric light and power plants.

The British South Africa Company has a controlling interest in the Rhodesian Railway system, with a total mileage of twenty-seven hundred miles. In connection with the railways of the Union of South Africa, it provides through communications from Cape Town to the Congo border, 2149 miles. In addition to these, a line stretches three hundred miles from Bulawayo via Salisbury to the port of Beira.

A system of road motor services has been organized with a total mileage of sixteen hundred miles. There are two hundred and twelve post offices, forty-seven of which are money order and savings bank offices. The operation of mines, farms, and other industries furnishes employment to a large part of the million natives of Southern Rhodesia.

The transformation of this country is indeed marvelous and a blessing, not only for the whites, but for the natives as well. Here, as elsewhere, British colonizers have faithfully assumed the White Man's Burden.

In his *Life of Jameson,* under the chapter "Round the Camp-fire," Ian Colvin makes the obstetrical observation that "There are many events in the womb of time which will be delivered." He says:

> Mr. Hammond came, a messenger of fate laden with the heavy destinies of these two men. He brought portentous news, ominous messages. But neither the messenger who bore them nor the two friends who received them could have felt the burden of fatality as they took their tranquil and leisurely way over the high spacious plains up there as it were on the roof of Africa. There with their wagons on the open veld, with game to shoot and with Tony to cook, under the sun, under the stars, in that up-lifting air, in that new, clean and boundless country, there was laughter, there was keen talk, there were the exhilaration of past success and the inspiration of great projects but no shadow of the impending disaster.

Mr. Hammond furnished Mitchell, the biographer of Rhodes, with an account of this visit, how they rode together and drove together for weeks on end, how his opinion on the minerals of the country was "of the greatest moment to Rhodes, both for political and financial reasons," yet how "during the many days that we rode and drove together there was not the slightest attempt on his part to obtain from me any premature expression as to the value of the country." Such was Rhodes's delicacy of mind; but Mr. Hammond also has his reticence, for he does not mention the one great subject upon which these three certainly *did* talk.

[This is an implication of *suppressio veri* on my part.]

We hear of it, however, from Jameson, who said, long afterwards, to a certain Select Committee: "At the end of 1893, shortly after the conclusion of the Matabele War, I had many conversations with Mr. Rhodes on the subject of the Federation of South Africa, and the obstacles presented to this by the attitude of the South African Republic." And Jameson adds that while they were still discussing this problem, "about the middle of 1894," John Hays Hammond came up to Matabeleland with a very important contribution to the debate. "Unless a radical change was made," Mr. Hammond told them, "there would be a rising of the people of Johannesburg." As a fact he came up to them because by this time it was obvious that there were only two men who mattered.

Here, again, we might almost reconstruct the talk not between two this time but between three. The scene, of course, is different, no longer the tin bungalow in Kimberley, but the velvety sky with the Southern Cross hung like a jewel above, a roaring camp-fire, throwing dramatic gleams and shadows strange as their own fates on and around the three figures before it, behind them Tony, the mules, and the wagons, and the stillness beyond broken now and then by the nightmare laugh of a hyena or the roar of a prowling lion, mockeries and threats from the darkness.

So far as concerns the "portentous news, ominous messages" that I had brought posthaste to Rhodes and Jameson, it certainly would have been presumptuous for me, who had been in Africa not quite a year, to have undertaken to give a true picture of the political conditions in Johannesburg to Rhodes and Jameson, who had been in the country for many years. Moreover, it would have been an unwarranted assumption of authority on my part to speak for the mining investors of the Rand, with whom I had no affiliation except as an engineer and manager of the Consolidated Gold Fields of South Africa—a company controlled by Rhodes.

The implication in Colvin's account of my trip with Rhodes and Jameson to Mashonaland is that the prime object, if not the ulterior motive, of the journey was to discuss with them the political conditions on the Rand. As a matter of fact, Rhodes was at the time far more concerned with the kind of report I was to make as to the potential mining value of that region, and I was there solely for that purpose. It is quite true that I spoke of grievances of the Uitlander population, and admittedly must have said that had the mining population of the Rand been of the more turbulent character of the western mining districts of America, there would long since have been a serious outbreak against the Boer government. This was undoubtedly true, and I very likely did make the statement attributed to me: "Unless a radical change was made there would be a rising of the people of Johannesburg." This was my opinion at the time and there was no reason why I should have hesitated to express it. I, of course, intimated that my sympathy lay with the Uitlanders. This I subsequently showed by my participation as one of the leaders of the Reform Movement which was doomed to defeat by Jameson's Caesarean operation "upon the womb of time." Yet to assign to me the function of accoucheur in the birth of the movement, for reform, as represented by Colvin, is obviously absurd.

I have discussed "Round the Camp-fire" at length because other authors have, without further substantiation, assumed the correctness of Colvin's theory of the origin of the Jameson Raid.

A SOUTH AFRICAN MINE

KAFFIR MINERS

CHAPTER SIXTEEN

Deep-level Mining

A REVOLUTIONARY DECISION—TWO CABLES TAKE
A MONTH—OPEN SELLING AND SECRET BUYING—
ACQUIRING THE DEEP-LEVEL AREAS ON THE
RAND—PARABOLIC CURVES VERSUS THE METHOD OF
TRIANGULATION—THE PROJECT IS REGARDED WITH
SKEPTICISM—CONVINCING THE BROKERS AND THE
PUBLIC—THE ROBINSON DEEP ARRIVES ON SCHED-
ULE—ADVANTAGES AND OBSTACLES OF DEEP-LEVEL
MINING — ASSURING AN ADEQUATE SUPPLY OF KAF-
FIRS—KRUGER STANDS IN THE PATH OF EMPIRE

*D*ays of traveling together, with its pleasant companionship, brought about a close bond of friendship between Rhodes and myself. This inevitably gave me many opportunities to discuss subjects of communal interest. As the result of this intimate association my admiration for Rhodes was greatly increased, as was his confidence in me.

As we sat around our campfire one starlit evening on our trip through Mashonaland, interrupted only by the roar of distant lions, Rhodes asked me my opinion as to the future of the Rand. He wanted to know what would be the life of the mines.

I told him that geologically there was no reason why the Rand should not last many years; that from an engineering point of view mining could be successfully carried on to a depth of several thousand feet, surely upwards of five thousand feet vertically. The lowest workings of the outcrop companies at that time had reached only five hundred feet vertically. I made some drawings explaining the geology of the Rand formation and the reasons determining my views as to the continuity in depth of the ore-bearing formation. I gave him some figures on the yield per acre of the outcrop companies and the resulting profits from operations. I told him that I believed properties on the dip up to several thousand feet in vertical depth could be operated at a cost but little exceeding that of the outcrop areas; and I satisfied him that large profits could be made by acquiring the land (which subsequently became known as the deep-level areas), sinking the vertical shafts to strike the ore-bearing formation and mining and milling according to the methods of the outcrop companies but upon a larger scale of operations.

"Why would it not be good business," Rhodes asked, "to sell our holdings in the outcrop companies; buy all the available deep-level areas for several miles along the strike of the outcrop reefs and start deep-level mining, using the money we get from the sale of our outcrop companies holdings for that purpose?"

"That's exactly my idea. In fact," I added, "I had recommended it to Barnato, but he was too much engaged in other affairs to give it serious consideration and that is one of the reasons why I severed my connection with the Barnato firm."

"You are sure, are you, Hammond, that your geology is sound on this deep-level theory of yours?"

Without a moment's hesitation I replied, "I'll stake my reputation on it."

"Let's send a cablegram to London at once!" Rhodes exclaimed. Together we composed a cablegram to the Consolidated Gold Fields Directors in London, of which Rhodes was the controlling factor. And about two o'clock in the morning, my secretary—the Honorable Eustace Fiennes—a fearless adventurer, a D.S.O. man, who in later years became governor-general of the Leeward Islands—started with two natives on a five hundred mile ride across dangerous country to the nearest telegraph station at Mafeking with the cable, signed by Rhodes, which was in substance as follows:

HAVE DECIDED BEST POLICY FOR COMPANY WOULD BE SELL
OUT OUR ENTIRE HOLDINGS IN OUTCROP COMPANIES DO THIS
AT ONCE HAMMOND APPROVES CABLE REPLY

It took a month for our messenger to cover the journey, receive the reply, and rejoin us near the Zambesi, a total ride of over a thousand miles. And this was the directors' reply:

WE DO NOT UNDERSTAND YOUR CABLEGRAM DO YOU WISH
US TO LIQUIDATE COMPANY THIS CANNOT BE DONE WITH-
OUT FULL EXPLANATION TO DIRECTORS

Rhodes was furious. He was not in the habit of having his explicit instructions disobeyed. He sent another cablegram:

DO EXACTLY AS I INSTRUCTED YOU TO DO AT ONCE WITH-
OUT ASKING QUESTIONS I TAKE FULL RESPONSIBILITY C.J.R.

This time the London directors obeyed. When we got back to Johannesburg several million dollars' worth of shares had been turned into cash at high prices, the Kaffir market then being at the peak of a boom.

Just as Rhodes was ready to leave Johannesburg for London to submit my report on Mashonaland and Matabeleland to the British South Africa Company shareholders, he asked, "Hammond, what are you going to do about acquiring the ground for our new deep-level enterprise?" I replied that I had certain plans which, of course, would have to be kept secret. We then discussed them; he approved and told me to go ahead.

Rhodes's notes to me were often pithy. In the little black notebook that I always carried with me I find the following. It refers, of course, to the deep-level mines and, although it may seem cryptic to the average reader, I quote it because it illustrates a certain dryness in his humor and a liking for epigrammatic philosophies undoubtedly springing from his admiration for Marcus Aurelius.

"Do not buy deeps with poor parents. Drunkards' children are no good. Go always into good things, not doubtful ones unless they cost you nothing. Remember poor ground costs just as much to work as rich ground, the only difference is the first cost. My idea is you should gradually as you can get out of your doubtful holdings and companies you do not control, and consolidate in those of which you have the control, or see a chance to work by getting the control. My idea of B—— is that he is an honest man but no head or judgment. If he wants to go throw no obstacle in his way. The same article in America worth perhaps 20 shillings per diem."

Rhodes's reference to "buy deeps with good parents" was to purchase ground underlying or adjacent to areas of proved value. This shows his excellent judgment in the advice he gave to me.

Some of the London financial papers criticized my not having been present when Rhodes submitted my report. They did not know I had remained in Johannesburg to attend to the details of the deep-level project. My plan was to secure large tracts of land adjoining those of the producing outcrop companies. Much of this deep-level area was regarded as of no prospective value for mining; nor was it of much use for agriculture. Some small farms had, however, been purchased at a low price by the outcrop companies and by individuals and syndicates. These were being held for possible development in the remote future, as it would not pay to sink deep shafts as pure speculation.

The owners of these properties did not realize there was an immediate possibility of their being worked as mines, and it was part of my task to see that secrecy was maintained. Had even a whisper of our intentions been spread abroad, the price would have gone rocketing. Working independently through several brokers pledged to silence, I was able to secure most of the desirable land on favorable terms. There remained, however, certain properties essential for carrying out the proposed scheme which could not be secured by purchase.

As soon as the individuals and syndicates mentioned above ascertained that Rhodes was behind the project, they insisted on having stock in the new enterprise instead of cash. To meet their demands I held a meeting of all persons concerned. I proposed that each be allocated a certain interest in the consolidated plan according to a percentage I had previously worked out with my engineers. The appraisal was based on, first, the distance of the properties from the outcrops of the gold-bearing reefs, second, the depth of the reefs below ground, and third, special technical considerations.

The appraisal was fair, even generous. Although I knew I would have little difficulty in securing the consent of most of the property holders in their respective allotments, I apprehended some delay in settling with H. J. King for his quota. King was a prominent mining investor who had acquired considerable reputation as a "mining man" in the early days of the Rand because of a trip he had made some years before through the western mining districts of America. There he had acquired a fluent though superficial familiarity with mining terminology. King rather prided himself on his knowledge of mining, and the mere fact that he was an American favored his pretensions. Everyone else at the meeting had agreed to the terms, but, as a matter of business habit, King objected to the amount of stock I had allocated to him.

"I suppose you've figured out the relative importance of the holdings in the Consolidated Company by the usual process of triangulation," said King.

I replied: "No, Mr. King, as a matter of fact I did not. I'm glad, however, you asked the question. The triangulation process is obsolete. I've worked it out by parabolic curves, which, as you know, is too technical to be understood by anyone not thoroughly familiar with mining." Then I added, "Of course, Mr. King, as a mining man you must admit that the accuracy of the parabolic curve method cannot be disputed."

Admitting that results computed by this new formula must be beyond cavil, he attached his signature to the agreement without further argument.

A few days later, I encountered King. When we were alone, he asked me somewhat diffidently, "By the way, Hammond, since everything is closed up now, what is that system of parabolic curves?"

"As a matter of fact, King," I said, "that is just something I invented to overcome the unjustifiable objections of a recalcitrant negotiator!"

Twenty years later King was my dinner host in London and told this story on himself. By that time he had become a mining magnate and had outgrown his reputation as a mining expert.

After this large area had been acquired, it was subdivided for deep-level companies, based on economic and engineering considerations. After the acquisition of the deep-level properties large sums were required for shaft sinking and development of the mines and erection of mills to treat the ore, amounting to several million dollars for each property. Therefore, it was necessary to take immediate steps to get the large capital required. The financial groups operating the outcrop companies not unnaturally objected to the large sums of money being diverted from speculation in their shares. Also, the majority of them quite honestly believed that the deep-level project was not feasible. With the exception of my own engineers and a very few others, the Rand in general regarded the whole plan as visionary.

I was not only disappointed in the failure of the mining groups to co-operate, but was hindered by their direct opposition to the project. Immediately on Rhodes's return from London, I went to Cape Town to see him. I told him I had expected positive co-operation from the Eckstein group, representatives of Wernher, Beit and Company, but instead, their engineers were expressing much adverse criticism of our plans. Rhodes thought opposition from this quarter so serious that he advised me to take the first steamer to London to see Alfred Beit, who was one of the controlling factors in Wernher, Beit and Company. This I did.

Alfred Beit was the same age as Rhodes and, like him, unmarried. He had been Rhodes's devoted and intimate friend since the time when, with Barnato, they had formed the De Beers diamond trust. His imaginative and daring nature had often been fired to tangible response by Rhodes's glowing enthusiasm for the advancement of Africa. For example, Beit had been prodigal in support of the Chartered Company. Courageous as he was, however, his actions were usually tempered with forethought and wisdom. Jameson died a poor man; Sir Alfred Beit, as he later became for his philanthropies, amassed one of the great fortunes of the world.

Almost my first action on reaching London was to call on Beit. It was late in the morning and he suggested that we drive to the Savoy for luncheon. I plunged into the subject immediately and asked Beit outright just what his objections were to the deep-level scheme. He repeated the arguments of his engineers in Johannesburg. I had a conclusive answer ready for each. Just before we arrived at the Savoy, which took us about twenty minutes, I asked whether he still considered his objections valid.

He frankly replied, "I am now inclined to agree with your views."

Before the luncheon was over he was not only entirely converted, but committed financially to the enterprise as well.

While I was in London, I followed out Rhodes's request to call on Lord Rothschild, whom I had met several years before. I reminded him that at our first meeting he had asked me to let him know when I should acquire any good mining property. I now told him about the deep-level scheme, which I said certainly ought to interest him.

Lord Rothschild seemed more or less surprised, and remarked: "You know, Mr. Hammond, that's a coincidence. Curiously enough, on the recommendation of my chief mining expert, Hamilton Smith, I've just sold out my interest in that project."

"Yes, of course," I replied. "I know that. As a matter of fact, Mr. Rhodes's syndicate has purchased your interest. He'd like, however, to give you a chance to come in again and I've come here to see whether or not you care to change your mind about it."

I went over one by one the arguments I had used on Beit until Lord Rothschild was convinced he had made a mistake in selling and, much to my satisfaction, agreed to buy in again.

As I look back, it seems almost inconceivable that there should have been such a lack of faith in the deep-level enterprise. The particular objection which seemed insuperable to both engineers and investors was their belief that it was impossible to sink shafts and mine ore profitably at the great depths contemplated in many of the deep-level projects.

The history of the great Comstock Lode in Nevada was cited as a case in point. My opponents stated that the heat encountered at a depth of thirty-five hundred feet had compelled the abandonment of the mine. Again and again I had to explain the fact that the Comstock was situated in a district of recent solfataric action; that many hot springs had been tapped long before any real depth was reached, and that consequently at only a short distance below the surface the heat became intense. On the other hand, I believed that this geothermal gradient, as it is called, would be found exceptionally low on the Rand. This eventually proved to be true. The increase in temperature has not been more than five degrees for every thousand feet of depth.

I knew that if I was to convince hardened skeptics I must have concrete facts with which to back up my theory. Therefore, I made a special trip to Příbram, one of the famous silver-lead mining districts in Bohemia (now Czechoslovakia) which had been worked for several hundred years. I returned from Příbram to London just in time to deliver an address in Cannon Street Hall on deep-level mining, to a group of moneyed men interested in mining. In order to get a dramatic effect, I said: "Will someone please open a window! I find it very stuffy here compared with the cool temperature I found at the bottom of the mine in Příbram, thirty-six hundred feet down." I said further that, while it was true it had taken a hundred years or more to sink the shafts at Příbram, I felt sure that by using modern methods of shaft sinking, we could reach as great a depth in South Africa in not more than five years.

It was essential to secure the support of the stockholders dealing in the Kaffir market. After many meetings with the heads of these firms I devised a plan which helped materially to convince mining investors of the attractiveness of deep-level shares. I made diagrams which indicated clearly the number of claims being mined on the outcrop areas. I showed that the yield per claim averaged two hundred and fifty thousand dollars, with a profit of about ninety thousand dollars.

On the same diagrams, immediately below the skeleton drawings of outcrop companies, I outlined on a proportionate scale the deep-level companies. In size the latter were eight or ten times as large as the former. The diagram not only included the estimates I had made of the cost to sink shafts to reach the reefs, but also showed the time required and the comparatively enhanced costs of mining upon the deep-level areas. These diagrams were then hung with my compliments in the offices of stockbrokers dealing in South African shares.

In fact, I developed into what would now be regarded a high-pressure salesman and as my confidence—perhaps I ought to say temerity—increased I was emboldened to assert that within a few years the cost of deep-level mining would not exceed that of the out-crop companies owing to better equipment, more efficient methods, and cheaper dynamite, coal, and other mining supplies. These pre-dictions have been fully realized; at present mining is actually carried on at a depth of eighty-five hundred feet at a cost less than that of the outcrop properties in 1894.

During 1897 I spent considerable time in Paris trying to secure the financial co-operation of French capital for the further development of the South African deep-level mines. South African mining shares were then extensively dealt in on the Paris Bourse. I frankly told the French financiers that they were making the mistake of being followers, instead of leaders, in mining enterprises. I showed them how they had been taking a lot of skimmed milk from British mine promoters after the cream of the profits had already been removed. I pointed out to them that they now had an unusual opportunity to get some cream. By dint of hard work I finally established an important clientele in Paris, who invested in the deep levels.

Twenty-five years later one of the secretaries of the American Embassy in Paris started to introduce me to President Doumergue, when the president interrupted. "Why, Mr. Hammond doesn't need any introduction to me." He then informed me that he was present when I delivered one of my addresses in Paris in 1897. Acting on my recommendation, he had made money by investing in the deep-level mines of the Rand.

As soon as sufficient capital was available, we started sinking shafts in the deep-level areas. To prevent loss of time, we decided to start at once the erection of the stamp mills and appurtenant plants where the ore was to be treated. Each of these mills, the largest of their type at the time, cost several hundred thousand dollars. We had to incur the expenditure of many millions of dollars in the develop-ment of the deep-level properties before we recovered an ounce of gold. It was, therefore, most important to sink our shafts with the greatest possible speed so that the stockholders could have quicker returns on their investments, and the time element obviously was the "essence of the contract."

When we started sinking shafts, we found we could get down

only about seventy or eighty feet a month. This was not fast enough. I sent one of my assistants to the United States to bring back the best shaft sinkers he could find, regardless of wages. He combed the Comstock district of Nevada, where shafts had been sunk to a depth of thirty-four hundred feet, and also the Lake Superior district, where an even greater depth had been attained. He proudly returned with a hand-picked crew.

Although these expert shaft sinkers did speed up operations considerably and were making records, their achievement fell short of my desire.

When I had exhausted the capacity of the practical shaft sinkers, I sent for Leslie Simpson, a young man on my staff who had recently graduated from the University of California. I told him that I intended to put him in charge of the sinking of our deep shafts. Modestly he said, "I have never had any experience in shaft sinking."

"It is for that very reason I want you," I replied, "as you have no preconceived ideas. You are not bound by traditions or established rules. My paramount object is speed regardless of cost. I want you to spend a month or more in ascertaining the amount of time consumed in the different operations of shaft sinking and to eliminate every possible loss of time."

It was a question of combining clear thinking with hard work. Fortunately Simpson possessed a good supply of brains and unbounded willingness to work. He started and soon established world records. We offered a monthly monetary prize to the crew that would set a new goal and this spurred them to extraordinary efforts.

One of the first of these mines we developed was the Robinson Deep. I had estimated that we would strike the reef on a certain date at about eighteen hundred feet. We did strike it within a few feet of that depth and within a few days of the time I had set.

Deep-level mining received a great impetus from this "remarkable" guess while I gained an unearned reputation as a prophet, which caused me considerable embarrassment in meeting my confreres. I had to disclaim any responsibility for the extravagant statements of those who were not so careful in promoting my reputation as they were overzealous in disposing of deep-level mining shares.

As a matter of fact, the record does justify my prophecy as to deep-level mining. In reviewing the yield of gold obtained from the Robinson Deep during the past thirty-two years, I find that about eight million fine ounces have been produced, valued at about a hundred and sixty million dollars, from which dividends of approximately a million dollars a year have been paid. The incentive to deep-level mining which was furnished by the success of the Robinson Deep is obvious. Other deep-level mines of the Rand have likewise produced many millions of dollars in gold. If it had not been for this type of mining, the gold output of the Rand would have already fallen off greatly.

A large part of the world's gold production in recent years has come from the deep-level mines. The Robinson Deep is now operating profitably at a vertical depth of about a mile and a half (8500 feet) or a distance of three miles following the dip of the ore bodies. It is probably the deepest mine on record, though both the Morro Velho gold mine of Brazil, which has been worked for a century, and the Champion Reef Mine at Mysore, India, have reached almost an equal depth.

Operations at such a depth are becoming costly. How much deeper mining will ultimately be carried is a matter of conjecture; it will depend chiefly on whether the grade of ore justifies the inevitable increase in cost. At present certain factors are decisive in determining how deep mining shafts may be driven.

One important obstacle is the tremendous pressure of the superincumbent ground. Just as in the case of fluids, the tendency for the rock at the bottom is to fill in the excavations. This phenomenon causes frequent accidents. The cost of supporting the ground is great; indeed, it exceeds the present cost of ventilation. In the workings of the deep levels the miners have gone so far into the earth that they toil in temperatures of between 100° and 120° Fahrenheit with a relative humidity of from 90 to 100 per cent. This causes many fatal cases of heatstroke. The excessive humidity arises partly from water seepage into the mine shafts and workings. It is partly due also to the mandatory wetting down of the mine walls following every blasting or drilling operation which must be done in order to prevent silicosis, which would cause many deaths among the miners.

The Robinson Deep is now installing the greatest air-conditioning plant in the world (the Carrier system) to overcome these obstacles. The cages which carry the miners down to the workings move at a speed of two thousand feet per minute, or twice as fast as the express elevators in New York's tallest skyscraper.

That my prognostications were not entirely baseless is shown by the following appreciative article which appeared in *South Africa*, April 8, 1899:

> Turning to Mr. Hammond's experimental researches on the Witwatersrand, it may be said that his greatest and most lasting work there has been accomplished in connection with the deep levels. Mr. Hammond was one of the first to declare his unqualified belief in them as payable propositions. He urged all along that they presented no serious engineering difficulties.
>
> It was here that his American experience came to his aid. He knew that in America miners thought nothing of working at a depth of five thousand feet. Of course, everything in Cousin Jonathan's country is arranged on a scale calculated to "lick creation." Its trees, its mountains, its houses, and its stories—especially its stories— are all exceedingly tall. By analogy, then, one would expect its mines to be abnormally deep.
>
> But, although Mr. Hammond is a patriot, and therefore partial to things American, he has a frank admiration for John Bull, who in spite of his natural limitations, has managed to put in a good deal of "tall" work in the way of empire-building. Mr. Hammond has, therefore, never doubted that with British capital and British labour deep level mining would prove as successful on the Rand as it has done in America. Mr. Hammond, like Mr. Rhodes, believes in laying the foundations of empire deep as well as broad. If he makes them firm and sure at a depth of five thousand feet, that will be quite enough for the next few generations to build upon.

It is now four years ago since Mr. Hammond declared that investors and speculators had no cause to fear over-inflation in the prices of deep levels, which would ultimately reach much higher figures than those then ruling. Such an opinion, expressed by an expert who was notoriously conservative in his estimates and well-nigh insusceptible of enthusiasm, was worth a good deal, and we know now how thoroughly justified it was.

Fortunately, there were no difficult problems in the extraction and metallurgy of the ore. The gold ores of the Rand, with an average value of ten dollars per ton, are what are called free-milling; sixty per cent of the gold contents are obtained by simple amalgamation processes. The remainder contained in the pyrites associated with the gold passes into settling tanks, from which the gold contents is leached by cyanide solutions. The MacArthur-Forrest cyanide process had just been invented at the commencement of mining operations on the Rand. It was notably through the skill of Charles A. Butters, of California, and Dr. A. von Gernet, a Russian metallurgist, that this process was perfected and came into commercial use.

It was of great economic advantage to the Rand mining industry that, compared with other mining districts, but little lumber was required for timbering operations. Timber in South Africa was scarce and expensive; it had to be imported, principally from America and Australia. Almost no timber is used in the deep mines to prevent caving. Tailings, or refuse from the crushed rock, are lowered into the workings and used as filling. These may be supplemented by waste rock or reinforced by concrete pillars.

The conglomerate reefs, as they are called, flatten considerably as they approach the bottom of the syncline, or basin. These bankets are remarkably persistent, though their continuity is often interrupted. Certain sections are much richer than others. The grade of the ore has, however, been surprisingly well maintained in depth. Although the mill records at times show an apparent depreciation of the gold content of the reef, this feature is often to be ascribed to the fact that working on a large scale has made it profitable to mine and mill ores of a grade that otherwise would be left in the mine.

One of the difficult problems of the mining companies on the Rand was to secure adequate labor. Although there was always sufficient white skilled labor, there has been usually an inadequate supply of Kaffirs for both surface work and mining.

In 1898 there were employed upon the Rand 9746 whites and 88,627 Kaffirs. Today the gold mines of the Transvaal employ about 216,000 natives and 30,000 whites. The Kaffirs were largely Basuto, Zulu, Shangani, and Zambesi boys. Like house servants in China, regardless of their age these Kaffirs are called "boys." Some of these Kaffirs were recruited many hundreds of miles away. Since many came from the low "hot countries," they suffered greatly when they reached the colder altitudes of the Rand. Hundreds died on their march to Johannesburg, from pneumonia and other causes. When the boys finally arrived, always in an emaciated state, they had to be placed in the company's compound and conditioned for a month or more before they were fit to work.

Furthermore, they were of little practical use until they had learned the mechanics of mining, which required at least several months of experience. After remaining at the mines for one, two, or three years, many of them became proficient. They received an average monthly wage of about ten dollars in addition to their board and lodging. The thrifty ones soon acquired a competence. These returned to their homes with sufficient money to purchase cattle, and with these, in turn, they bought healthy wives. This enabled them to join the idle rich and to live off the labor of their help-mates, who tended the cattle and cultivated the fields.

In order to ensure a permanent supply of efficient miners, I suggested to Rhodes that we establish native villages near the mines, where boys could live with their wives and families. The mining companies were to provide them with huts and small farms on which to raise chickens, hogs, cattle, and vegetables to help support themselves.

I also thought it a good plan to attempt the civilizing of the wives so that their increasing wants would impose upon their husbands the necessity of continuous work, paralleling in that respect the duty of husbands in civilized communities. This scheme never met with the approval of the mine owners and has not been carried out.

The plan I suggested to Rhodes would have been advantageous as it would have ensured the expenditure of the wages in the country. Later when labor supply became insufficient an unsuccessful attempt was made to employ Chinese coolies.

As laborers, the Kaffirs are not only tractable, they are a fun-loving lot. They have a strong sense of justice. In our competition to secure labor we employed two brothers as compound managers. They were colonial-born, descended from a well-known English family, and spoke several of the Kaffir languages perfectly. The natives were much attached to these two, whom they called in their language The Just.

It was frequently necessary to resort to flogging to maintain order among the boys in the compounds. Afterwards the natives would come to the managers and thank them, as a dog crawls to lick the hand of its master after a deserved whipping. Because of this reputation of our compound managers for fair dealing, our companies had an advantage over others; boys coming a distance of several hundred miles would voluntarily apply for jobs with us.

Our difficulties were greatly aggravated by the incessant drunkenness of our Kaffir workmen. This was due to the right of the liquor monopoly granted by Kruger to certain of his friends. This liquor syndicate had the sole privilege to sell "Cape Smoke," a particularly pernicious form of alcohol. They could sell the liquor even within our compound. The boys often reported for work in a shockingly intoxicated condition, sometimes so helpless that they fell from the cages and were horribly mangled and killed.

We were also compelled, for the sake of filling the pockets of Kruger and his friends, to purchase our dynamite from a firm to which he had granted a monopoly. The price was excessive, but far worse than that was the fact that the quality was so poor that premature explosions were frequent and, consequently, many fatalities occurred.

Our protests to Kruger against both these outrages were consistently ignored and for this reason we held him directly responsible for the many unnecessary deaths.

Kruger realized that there would be an important mining development in Rhodesia following my favorable report. Coincidentally came my equally favorable report on the deep-level enterprise, which would largely expand the mining industry of the Rand. This he knew would result in the influx of many thousands of the British he so ardently detested, and who would inevitably constitute a menace to the Boer oligarchy. These conditions not unnaturally created on Kruger's part a genuine and, under the circumstances, a not unreasonable apprehension for the safety of his regime.

Cecil Rhodes, from the time of his first arrival in Africa, had attempted to extend the borders of British territory. He had been successful to a certain degree. Kruger's object now was to frustrate this ambition of Rhodes by enlarging the territory of the Transvaal. Through force of circumstances, these two dominant personalities were about to engage in a warfare as bitter as it was inevitable. Across the Orange and Vaal rivers Kruger's oxcarts stood square in the path of Rhodes's advance towards his "North."

CHAPTER SEVENTEEN

The Reform Movement

WHICH RIDER IN THE SADDLE?—A PICTURE OF
OOM PAUL—DR. LEYDS AS AN EVIL GENIUS—THE
UITLANDERS ARE INVITED TO THE TRANSVAAL—
THE GRIEVANCES — THE BROWN CASE — CLOSING
THE DRIFTS—WE PLAN TO REVOLT—MUSTERING
FORCES ON THE BORDER—A LETTER TO JAME-
SON—GUNRUNNING—EARTHQUAKE WEATHER

*T*he most dramatic and critical period of my life was ushered in by the autumn of 1895. Two years had passed since my arrival in South Africa. Six months of that time I had spent with Barnato, two months on the trip to Mashonaland with Rhodes. In addition, I had made a visit to London and had been to Groote Schuur for an occasional conference with Rhodes. The major part of my attention, however, had been directed towards the management of the Consolidated Gold Fields Company, and I was particularly concerned with the technical details of the new deep-level mines.

Little of my time had been devoted to politics. I had listened to the discussions going on about me and had quickly become cognizant of the Uitlander grievances—they were the inevitable topic of conversation at every dinner table. I was sympathetic, of course, but not actively interested.

On many occasions I did go so far as to say that the law-abiding miners from England were enduring ill-treatment from Kruger's government that the men I had known out West in America would never have tolerated.

Only when the Boer policy directly affected the running of the mines under my management was I forced into political opposition. It became gradually obvious to me that if the Boer policy were not radically changed a conflict was inevitable.

About this time General "Slim" (Sly) Piet Joubert, later commander of the Transvaal forces in the Boer War, put the problem to me nicely.

"There are two riders but only one horse in the Transvaal," he said. "The question is, which rider is going to sit in front—the Uitlander or the Boer?"

"General," I replied, "we Uitlanders are paying nine-tenths of the cost of the horse and nine-tenths of his upkeep as well. I think we ought to be in the saddle."

Joubert shook his head gloomily and turned away. As the leader of the liberal party among the Boers, he meant well towards the Uitlanders, but his sympathies were not strong enough to carry him to the point of acting directly against the Kruger faction. Nevertheless, he had summed up the situation concisely: two opposite ideals were confronting each other.

Before the Jameson Raid the Boers were by no means united behind Kruger. From many talks I gained the impression that the younger Boers, at least, thought reform essential. Deputations of prominent young Boers had on various occasions warned Kruger that their understanding of the justice of the Uitlander position was such that they could take no active part in any trouble that might come up in Johannesburg.

In the liberal party, led by General Joubert, were Louis Botha and many others who attained political distinction during and after the Boer War. There was little love lost between the Kruger and Joubert parties; indeed, the controversies sometimes waxed intense.

Many of the Boers themselves alleged that, at the presidential election of 1888, Joubert had lost the presidency only because of Kruger's lavish and unscrupulous use of the state's money at the polls. Moreover, Kruger's illegal ousting of Joubert supporters from the Volksraad was common knowledge.

The Joubert faction did not agree with Kruger's conviction that the Uitlander was fit only for plundering. Chief Justice Kotzé, himself a nonpartisan, told the burghers in October, 1894, that "No one . . . will deny that the country is at present in a very critical position. . . . It depends entirely upon the people whether the impending change is to take place peaceably or to be accompanied by violence."

The Boer liberals (as well as the Uitlanders) had definite grievances. They vigorously objected to the swarms of Hollanders and Germans who were pouring into the country and filling the lucrative offices. Governmental expenditures had been augmented from about $750,000 in 1886 to upwards of $18,500,000 in 1896. The salaries paid in 1896 amounted to about $150 per head per annum for the total male Boer population. In defense of their position, the Kruger followers ascribed the protests of their political opponents to the younger and more liberal Boers' exclusion from these perquisites of office.

Additional bitterness among the anti-Kruger Boers was engendered by the granting of monopolies to Hollanders and Germans. Most influential of these foreign spoilsmen was the Java-born Dutchman, Dr. W. J. Leyds (Leijds), who ultimately became state secretary and was known as Oom Paul's evil genius.

Leyds is accused of having once prevented Kruger from redressing some of the Uitlander grievances at a time when the president was influenced momentarily by the reform element among the Boers. He accomplished his purpose by threatening to expose Kruger's past financial indiscretions unless the spoils system was continued for the benefit of Leyds and his associates in the Netherlands Railway.

Another spoilsman was Eduard Lippert from Hamburg, who, for his questionable services to Kruger, had been rewarded with the dynamite monopoly. Ostensibly this had been done to foster a local industry; actually, the dynamite was imported from abroad and sold at a price sometimes as high as twice its former cost.

The government of the Transvaal was in the hands of Stephanus Johannes Paulus Kruger, known to his own people and to the world as Oom, or Uncle, Paul.

He had been president of the South African Republic, commonly known as the Transvaal, since 1883 and there was every probability that he would remain in office indefinitely. Nothing short of an internal revolution or the impairment of his faculties seemed likely to shake off his control over what was a mere simulacrum of a republic, inasmuch as it did not derive its just powers from the consent of the governed.

From Kruger's birth in Cape Colony in 1825 to his death in exile in 1904 his life was full of adventure. He had shared the hardships and dangers of his parents in the Great Trek. His education had been derived not from books, but from trekking, fighting, and hunting on the frontier. One could readily believe the many tales of his courage. The story of how, his thumb having been badly wounded, he himself cut it off with his knife had become a household legend.

I met Kruger first in 1893 in connection with the revision of the mining laws of the Transvaal. He was then sixty-eight years old. His massive frame still showed evidences of that brute physical strength which had become proverbial. A huge nose, a large firm mouth, keen eyes partially obscured by swollen lids, were set in a heavy, rugged face surrounded by a ragged fringe of beard. His forehead sloped back to where the long grizzled hair swept up in a defiant mane. In spite of his dignity of bearing, the impression I received was one of cunning rather than of intelligence.

He lived in an unpretentious one-story wooden building where he was frequently seen on the small front piazza, puffing at his pipe of strong Boer tobacco. He received me in the parlor which was fitted out in typical mid-Victorian style with horsehair furniture, and artificial flowers under glass globes. A marble-topped center table held bulky volumes among which was prominently displayed a Bible bound in pressed leather and titled in large gilt letters.

Oom Paul's religion had a decided touch of the fanatical. He belonged to the narrow and uncompromising Dopper sect of the Dutch Reformed Church. His speeches were peppered with Biblical quotations. He was a fundamentalist in every sense of the word. To him the first book of the Bible was literally true.

He even firmly believed that the world was flat. The stubbornness of this belief is illustrated by an anecdote told me by Captain Joshua Slocum, an American who visited Kruger while circumnavigating the globe in a thirty-foot sailing boat.

At the end of a short but pleasant interview in Pretoria, Oom Paul asked him, "In what direction, Captain, do you intend to continue your voyage?"

"I'm going right around the world, Mr. President," replied the captain.

"Don't lie," warned Kruger in all seriousness. "You mean across the world."

Kruger was born out of his time. He might have been a great leader, given a patriarchal society; there was no niche in the Twentieth Century Hall of Fame for a shepherd peasant leader. His very greed for land, and more land, for his burghers was against him. He wanted a succession of Dutch farms, each to include thousands of acres: he wanted Zululand, Bechuanaland, Matabeleland, Mashonaland, Swaziland, Stellaland, and a road to the sea. By devious methods he played one faction against another in his endeavor to attain these ends.

On the one hand was a simple, patriarchal, pastoral society; on the other, an urban industrial civilization. The reason for this schism between the Uitlander and the Boer of the Kruger type was not hard, therefore, to comprehend. The Boer burgher was in no way interested in mining; he was a peasant with the conservative, reactionary, and suspicious nature of that class. But he was more than this: he was cunning, brave, and stubbornly intent on keeping what he regarded as his birthright.

Those who possess a country invariably hate the invader. The question is often asked, "Why did the Uitlanders go to the Transvaal, if they were not wanted?" The answer is, they were wanted. With this in mind Kruger, in 1884, asked foreign capital, by a formal invitation in the London press, to come in and develop the mineral resources of his country. In return, he promised investors protection for their interests and a fair share of influence in the government. English investors, particularly, were attracted in answer to his invitation. The resulting activity of the Uitlander led within two years to the discovery of the famous gold deposits of the Witwatersrand near Johannesburg.

This gold strike produced a further great influx of foreigners. In 1895, out of the 150,000 whites in the Transvaal 85,000 were Uitlanders; of the 65,000 Boers only 25,000 were males over sixteen. There were almost two adult Uitlanders to every adult Boer.

Nearly all of the 750,000 native blacks were opposed to the government, because of the harsh treatment they had always received at the hands of the Boer. They were of no importance politically.

The Uitlanders held first place in the country not only numerically, but also industrially and financially. They had purchased from the Boers more than half the land in the Transvaal, and owned more than nine-tenths of the assessable property.

The Transvaal was on the verge of bankruptcy. Furthermore, its inhabitants were constantly jeopardized by native wars. With the anticipated increase of man power through an influx of Uitlanders and with the wealth they could produce, Kruger knew he could cope successfully with these two emergencies provided he remained in supreme political control.

Having regained confidence after the recession of the economic crisis and the native menace, Kruger reverted to his old policy of "the Transvaal for the Boers." This attitude has been duplicated in Latin America, China, and many other parts of the world. Foreign capital has exploited the natural resources of these countries and the native standard of living has been definitely raised by the wealth produced. Although the natives themselves had never done anything to realize on this wealth, they as well as their governments have always resented bitterly that it should leave their country in the form of profits to those who had taken the risk and performed the labor. But in all his schemes for territorial acquisition Kruger was blocked by one man—Cecil John Rhodes.

Rhodes had become to Oom Paul the epitome of all things he hated and distrusted. Again and again Rhodes tried to deal with Kruger. Even on the return from our Matabeleland trip in 1894, he stopped at Pretoria in a final effort to come to some sort of understanding as to the future of South Africa. Both men wanted a united country, but each for his own purposes and for his own people. The interview resulted in an impasse. This obstinate and obdurate Boer was virtually the only man Rhodes was never able to win over.

Kruger's personal detestation of Rhodes was extended to include almost all Uitlanders. His suspicion of us and of our motives was proof against all our attempts to attain what we considered our rights. He listened to the respectful petitions of the Uitlanders with grunted "Ja's," pulled at his pipe, and spat. Our spokesmen went away with the feeling that they had been talking to a stone wall—so impassive, so unimpressed, so adamant was he to all appeal of reason.

The effect of this uncompromising attitude was to unite the Uitlanders against a foe which threatened us all. In reality, we Uitlanders had little in common; not only were we of different races and languages, but so long as we were allowed social, political, and economic justice, it seemed of slight importance to us at that time whether the Vierkleur or the Union Jack waved over Johannesburg.

Prior to 1895 there had been several occasions on which friction between Uitlander and Boer had reached the breaking point. Kruger went to Johannesburg in 1890, on one of his annual visits to the towns of the Transvaal. The Rand was in the midst of a mining depression of great intensity. The president was cold and far from tactful and his speech to the populace did not tend to calm the undercurrent of rancor caused by his cavalier dismissal of the petition which the Uitlanders had seized this opportunity to present. That same evening the crowd became unruly, a riot ensued, and the angry mob trampled the Boer flag underfoot. Kruger was so incensed that he did not return to Johannesburg for five years.

Kruger said to Sir Henry, later Lord, Loch, the high commissioner of Cape Colony: "The Uitlanders remind me of a baboon I once had, which was so fond of me that he would not let anyone touch me. But one day we were sitting round the fire, and unfortunately the beast's tail got into it. He flew at me furiously, thinking that I was the cause of his accident. The Johannesburghers are just like that. They have burnt their fingers in speculations and now they want to revenge themselves on Paul Kruger."

During the early days of the Boer Republic, years before any Uitlander problem, there had been a great deal of political unrest. Kruger, as a member of the party then out of power, not only drew up lists of grievances but committed acts which smacked far more of revolution than anything ever done later by the Uitlanders in Johannesburg.

I had the satisfaction afterwards—when satisfaction was difficult to find—of reminding Kruger that he himself had once been a rebel and that he should now have some sympathy with such fellow rebels as myself and my Johannesburg accomplices.

Since the Uitlanders had come primarily for business and not political reasons, it was many years before they began to combine against the Boer government. Such a revolt would never have been brought about by injustices like the administration of the liquor and dynamite monopolies in themselves. Nor would the sickness and the high death rate resulting from lack of a clean water supply and adequate sewerage system have been sufficient incentives for action.

It was the sum total of various irritations that fired the mounting hostilities. Some individuals were activated by one set of grievances, some by another. For example, there was the question of education. Out of $310,000 allotted to Johannesburg for this purpose, less than $4000 was used for the Uitlander children, although they greatly outnumbered the Boer children and the Uitlander parents supplied the money to build and support the schools. Moreover, English was not taught in the schools. The Uitlander children had to learn Taal, the debased form of Dutch used by the Boers.

One of the most outrageous grievances was the Boer assertion of their right to draft Uitlanders for service in the native wars. More than a hundred English subjects were commandeered by the Boers for their expedition against the native chieftain Malaboch, and compelled to provide their own horses and arms. The five men who refused to obey the summons were imprisoned.

In June, 1894, plans were laid by the Uitlanders for their forcible rescue. The British high commissioner visited Pretoria to discuss the matter, and privately reported that the Uitlanders were so aroused that, if he had not managed them tactfully, they would have flared into revolution. Loch declined to mediate with the Boers. But later he wrote Kruger that, unless the Uitlander grievances were redressed, revolution was inevitable, and he concentrated an armed British police force on the Bechuanaland border ready to protect the Uitlander if it came to bloodshed.

Loch at the same time informed the Colonial Office that in case of an uprising, the Uitlanders were bound to win if they had rifles; obviously they could not fight Boer marksmen with their fists.

OOM PAUL (1825-1904)

PRETORIA, THE CAPITAL OF THE TRANSVAAL

In conversation with Lionel Phillips at this time, Loch would seem to have hinted at the desirability of obtaining arms to defend Johannesburg pending British intervention. He subsequently denied this interpretation of his remarks. He claimed he had simply meant that without enough rifles to defend Johannesburg no revolution was possible. However that may have been, Phillips bought himself a rifle, and it was jocosely said that the policy of secretly arming the Uitlanders really began with him.

Loch was far more vehement against the Boers than were the Johannesburg mine owners. This is shown by the fact that after the 1894 demonstration the Chamber of Mines disclaimed all violent measures, and assured Kruger of its support.

The unequal administration of justice touched the community even more closely than the commandeering of Uitlanders. No Uitlander was assured of a fair trial in the courts. Kruger and his Executive Council could bring such pressure to bear upon the Transvaal Supreme Court that it bowed to his dictates. In 1897 the condition became so scandalous that the Boer judges themselves closed the court, declaring it was impossible to administer justice under the coercion to which they were subjected by the executive branch of the government.

This is illustrated by the case of an American named Brown. Brown had staked out mining claims in a district thrown open by the government for pegging. Unfortunately, some of Kruger's official family had been anxious to secure the same claims; hence, they induced Kruger to declare Brown's locations illegal. Brown, of course, appealed to the Supreme Court for validation of his title. When the verdict was handed down in Brown's favor, Kruger dismissed the judges. He then had the Volksraad pass a law that court decisions were subject to revision by the Executive Council of the Transvaal.

Although certain members of the court resigned in protest, it was, nevertheless, a heavy blow to the Uitlanders to find that this last method of securing justice was closed to them because of the influence of Kruger and his entourage.

Among the abuses greatest public prominence was given to the non-possession of the franchise by the Uitlanders. Although we had founded and built Johannesburg, we had no voice in its civic affairs. The town was created as a mining camp under a mining commissioner. Furthermore, the civil government denied to the Uitlander a free press and right of public meetings. A Boer policeman could at his own discretion disperse any crowd of more than seven.

Prior to 1882, only one year's residence or the possession of land had been required of the immigrant or Uitlander for burgher privileges. At that time the law was amended and five years' residence was requisite, but the entries in the registration books were deliberately falsified by the Boer officials so that few were admitted to the franchise. Then, in 1890, the requirement was increased to fourteen years' residence; furthermore, the Uitlander must be thirty years old, have property, and belong to a Protestant church in order to vote. Every demand made on Kruger to grant the franchise was steadfastly refused.

Pointing to the Vierkleur, he would say, "You see that flag? If I grant the franchise, I may as well pull it down."

The Boers were by no means of one mind as to the justice or the expediency of Kruger's policy regarding the franchise of the Uitlanders. In 1895, thirty-five thousand Uitlanders signed a petition asking for political representation. A prominent member of the Volksraad named Jeppe addressed that body in a speech worthy of Patrick Henry:

"This petition has been signed by practically the entire population of the Rand. It contains the name of the millionaire capitalist on the same page as that of the miner; that of the owner of half a district next to that of a clerk. It embraces also all nationalities. And it bears, too, the signatures of some who have been born in this country, who know no other fatherland than this republic, but whom the law regards as strangers. Then, too, there are the newcomers. They have settled for good. They have built Johannesburg, one of the wonders of the age. They own half the soil; they pay at least three-quarters of the taxes. Nor are they persons who belong to a subservient race. They come from countries where they freely exercise political rights, which can never be long denied to free-born men. Dare we refer them to the present law, which first expects them to wait for fourteen years, and even then pledges itself to nothing? It is a law which denies all rights even to their children born in this country. What will become of us or our children on the day when we shall find ourselves in a minority or perhaps one in twenty, without a single friend among the other nineteen, among those who will then tell us they wished to be brothers, but we by our own act made them strangers in the republic? Old as the world is, has any attempt like ours ever succeeded for long?"

Kruger always pretended to believe that the political grievances were trumped up. He felt, and perhaps justly, that, if the Uitlanders were given the franchise, they would vote for an Uitlander president, or at least a progressive Boer of the anti-Kruger faction.

Many of us were on the Rand only temporarily. We were increasingly busy with our own affairs. Consequently, any demands for political rights on our part would have been unlikely had conditions been tolerable. I believe Kruger was aware of this. But he had established his way of doing things and he never believed sufficient pressure could be brought to bear on him to compel a change.

Terrifically heavy taxation without representation was another major grievance, illustrated by the case of the Netherlands Railway Company. A monopoly was granted by Kruger for a line through Portuguese territory to Delagoa Bay to connect the Transvaal with the coast. His idea was to divert traffic from the British-controlled roads approaching from the Cape and Natal. He hated railroads, but, since they appeared to be inevitable, he intended that at least the Delagoa Bay line should not be British-owned. Hence, the Dutch were given the majority of votes in a corporation shared among Dutch, Germans, and Boers.

Not only was the cost of construction to be paid for by taxing Uitlanders, but Kruger intended by coercive methods to compel all freight entering the Transvaal to come in over the Netherlands Railway; he wanted to cut our throats financially. He arranged that mining shipments consigned to the Rand via the Cape and Natal lines should be held back for months after arriving at the Transvaal border. And he set up a tariff schedule so prohibitive as to make it necessary for us to unload machinery and supplies at the railhead of the Cape line, reload into oxcarts, and cross the Vaal River by fords, or drifts, in Johannesburg. The Boers were enraged at our simple expedient and threatened to close these drifts across the Vaal to all freight of foreign origin.

When this situation developed and I informed Rhodes of the state of affairs, he wired me to come to Cape Town for a conference. On my arrival a private meeting of the leading political authorities of the Cape government was held at Groote Schuur. I explained the point of view of the Johannesburg mine operators. I showed how handicapped we were in our operations, and how the success of the whole mining industry was jeopardized by the actions of the Transvaal government.

Only a few days later Kruger proclaimed the drifts closed as from October, 1895.

Had not some action been taken, this would have been a heavy blow to the mining industry because its aim was to force the mining companies to submit to the extortionate freight tariff of the Netherlands Railway Company. But Kruger had overreached himself.

Since the Pretoria Convention of 1881 the Transvaal Republic and the Orange Free State had led a practically independent existence except for somewhat tenuous obligations to Great Britain included under the term "suzerainty." In closing the drifts Kruger had placed himself in an untenable position in respect to his treaty provisions. Cape Colony—the inhabitants of which, both Cape Dutch and English, were as one on this issue—decided to appeal to the home government for assistance, and pledged its support with men and money if England would enforce her treaty rights.

After careful consideration, the British government informed Kruger that the drifts must be reopened and allowed to remain open.

Kruger had some of the attributes of a clever diplomat. Once fairly caught, no false pride prevented him from yielding. He was like a poker player who, when he has a weak hand, bluffs, but is

careful not to carry his bluff too far lest it prove costly. Kruger re-
scinded his order.

The Reform Movement, as I have explained, had been tardy in
inception and was slow to gather momentum. It had begun with
conversation, was continued in press discussion, and was protracted
by fruitless deputations to Pretoria.

Protests were being made through two bodies. The first was the
Transvaal National Union, of which Charles Leonard was chairman. Although more vocal than influential, it had long been
carrying on agitation for constitutional rights and had issued much
literature in behalf of the unenfranchised.

The second body of protest was the Chamber of Mines, composed
of influential businessmen. Although Kruger never granted a
charter of incorporation, it met frequently for business reasons and
often presented statements of abuses and grievances to the Volksraad.

The Reform Movement as a whole was Fascist rather than Bolshevik in its nature. Direct action was finally undertaken by a group
of hard-headed, successful, conservative men of affairs, not by hot-
headed, irresponsible radicals. It was the moneyed element in the
revolt that finally assumed the leadership. But it was not until the
late summer of 1895 that we of the mining interests actively associated ourselves with the movement. Only as a last resort will
men representing vested interests risk property and life by entering
into a revolution in behalf of good government.

Enemies of the Reform Movement tried to create the impression
abroad that the revolt was fostered with the idea of securing control
of the mining interests of the Transvaal for Rhodes's Chartered Company. This preposterous conception was not effectually combated
until it was seen that the ownership of the mines was in no wise
affected by the outcome of the Boer War four years later.

Nevertheless, the drifts episode had showed conclusively that
there was no more to be gained by simple protestations. Moreover, the support of the British government had heartened us tre-
mendously. The indignant conversations began to concern themselves more and more with possible action.

There was no definite plan at first, but certain of us gradually
assumed leadership: Charles Leonard, the head of the National

Union; Lionel Phillips, a partner in Wernher, Beit and Company; Colonel Francis W. ("Frank") Rhodes, an officer with distinguished military record, and brother of Cecil Rhodes; George Farrar, an important mine owner; and myself.

My entry into the movement was due to the long-continued and exasperating series of government regulations which jeopardized the successful operation of the mines. I could not carry on my work efficiently, and I felt a heavy responsibility towards the people who had invested large sums on my professional recommendation.

Through this informal group, all arrangements were made. We selected men in whom we had complete confidence, were willing to assume risks, and whose co-operation we regarded as essential. Because of its failure our project may seem foolhardy now, but we who were in charge of the enterprise were not of a type likely to commit ourselves to forlorn hopes.

The skeleton of a plan began to develop as follows: First, money would have to be obtained with which to finance the movement; second, the support of Rhodes would be necessary, because he, as head of the Cape government, would have it in his power to make it succeed or fail; third, British recognition would have to be obtained should the necessity arise; fourth, an armed force would have to come to the aid of the Johannesburghers when and if the revolt started. The smuggling in of guns, the choosing of trustworthy adherents, and the formulating of a code of communications were included within the activity of those who later became the recognized leaders of the Reform Movement.

Historians have frequently asked to what extent Rhodes participated in this affair. He has been charged with inspiring the movement in the interest of Great Britain. I can categorically deny this accusation, which was largely the result of Boer propaganda, paid for by Uitlander taxes. The part he played in the revolt was chiefly financial, though he was unquestionably an important factor in our plans.

An account was opened in the books of the Chartered Company, headed *New Concessions,* on which Colonel Frank Rhodes was entitled to draw. Of the $300,000 used before the account was finally closed, almost $100,000 was handed over to Dr. H. A. Wolff for stores and supplies. The major part of the balance was put in an account in the Standard Bank of South Africa, at Johannesburg, under the head of *Development Syndicate*. This stood in the names of Colonel Frank Rhodes, Lionel Phillips, J. Percy Fitzpatrick, and myself. There was also an account at the Standard Bank at Mafeking, and, finally, the *Pitsani Camp Account* on the books of the Chartered Company out of which the immediate expenses of the armed force on the border were to be paid.

In addition to this financial assistance, the Chartered Company furnished personal aid through its agents and employees.

Everyone will admit that Rhodes was in a difficult position. As premier of the Cape Colony, he was forced to rely on the support of the Cape Dutch who would have been instantly alienated by anything that bore the earmarks of a British attack on Boer independence. He was endangering his position as the most enterprising and constructive force in the development of South Africa.

Rhodes had, of course, a large vested interest in the Rand mines. The minor persecutions to which we were subject naturally reacted on him, but he was also aiming at a political goal. Although he saw no practicable way to paint the map of the Transvaal British red, he did see hope for a customs union, a railroad convention, and an ultimate confederation of autonomous states. This would have been part and parcel of his Cape-to-Cairo dream in which he saw Boer and Briton working together toward the same end. The suspicious stubbornness of Kruger had hitherto effectually blocked any inclusion of the Boer republics in the Rhodes march north.

Another impelling reason for Rhodes's co-operation was the fact, now universally conceded, that Kruger, through his Machiavellian state secretary, Dr. Leyds, was intriguing actively with Germany and Holland to make their influence dominant in the Transvaal. In spite of Boer hostility to the British, I doubt whether the Boers would long have endured other foreign dominance. They were not psychologically inclined for the role of a subject people. The very essence of the Boer was his individuality; he was not the type to submit to the goose-step tyranny of Germany.

Rhodes's financial and political support alone was not sufficient for the success of our plan. It was recognized that Great Britain's attitude would be decisive. If the revolt should be proved to be spontaneously generated from within, we believed Great Britain would be bound to intervene and support our just complaints.

In the summer of 1895 came the retirement of Loch, whose relations with Rhodes had become extremely tense. Rhodes asked for the reappointment of Sir Hercules Robinson, whose experience with South African affairs had been long and intimate, but this did not prove a happy choice. In the past Robinson and Rhodes had worked together to conciliate the Cape Dutch. He was now not likely to do anything to weaken his position with them. Moreover, as he was a man of seventy and set in his ways, he found it difficult to follow Rhodes's sudden shifts in political strategy.

The question of whether Joseph Chamberlain, British colonial secretary, knew of the Uitlander plans at the time is largely academic. But we believed that once the lives and possessions of British citizens were in jeopardy, we could force the home government to support us.

Through Rhodes we made contact with Dr. Leander Starr Jameson at Bulawayo for military assistance. The name of Jameson was then one to conjure with. The Boers themselves had a high opinion of the administrator of Rhodesia's military powers, due to his able handling of the Matabele War. His inclusion in the scheme would not injure our case with Great Britain, because he would come as a last resort to prevent bloodshed, and not to lead a revolt.

Jameson's role was to be secondary. He was to take a position on the Transvaal border at Pitsani in the English protectorate of Bechuanaland, a hundred and eighty miles west from Johannesburg. He was to concentrate there a force of fifteen hundred men, all mounted, fully trained, and equipped with field pieces and machine guns. Each man was to bring a spare rifle to arm us in Johannesburg. The reason to be given out for his presence was the necessity for a show of force to overawe the restive natives.

It was distinctly understood that Jameson was not to move from Pitsani until he had received word, not only from other leaders of the movement, but from me personally. In the presence of Rhodes, Jameson and I shook hands as a solemn pledge that he would not cross the border until I gave him the signal. Rhodes had told him to remain at Pitsani for six months if the Reformers should need that amount of time for preparations. As Rhodes tersely remarked, "The only justification for revolution is success."

Jameson came twice to Johannesburg to make personal arrangements. His first visit was in September, 1895. We thought then that we could muster nine thousand capable men in Johannesburg when the time for revolt should come.

His second visit was in November. At that time he was given a letter drafted and signed by Leonard, Colonel Rhodes, Phillips, Farrar, and myself. It was to be for his own protection, and was to justify his incursion in the eyes of the world. It read as follows:

Johannesburg

Dear Sir,

The position of matters in this State has become so critical that we are assured that at no distant period there will be a conflict between the Government and the Uitlander population. It is scarcely necessary for us to recapitulate what is now matter of history; suffice it to say that the position of thousands of Englishmen and others is rapidly becoming intolerable. Not satisfied with making the Uitlander population pay virtually the whole of the revenue of the country while denying them representation, the policy of the Government has been steadily to encroach upon the liberty of the subject, and to undermine the security for property to such an extent as to cause a very deep-seated sense of discontent and danger. A foreign corporation of Hollanders is to a considerable extent controlling our destinies, and in conjunction with the Boer leaders endeavouring to cast them in a mould which is wholly foreign to the genius of the people. Every public act betrays the most positive hostility, not only to everything English, but to the neighbouring States.

Well in short the internal policy of the Government is such as to have roused into antagonism to it, not only practically the whole body of Uitlanders but a large number of the Boers; while its external policy has exasperated the neighbouring States, causing the possibility of great danger to the peace and independence of this Republic. Public feeling is in a condition of smouldering discontent. All the petitions of the people have been refused with a greater or less degree of contempt; and in the debate on the Franchise petition, signed by nearly 40,000 people, one member challenged the Uitlanders to fight for the rights they asked for, and not a single member spoke against him. Not to go into details, we may say that the Government has called into existence all the elements necessary for armed conflict. The one desire of the people here is for fair play, the maintenance of their independence, and the preservation of those public liberties without which life is not worth living. The Government denies these things, and violates the national sense of Englishmen at every turn.

What we have to consider is, What will be the condition of things here in the event of a conflict? Thousands of unarmed men, women, and children of our race will be at the mercy of well-armed Boers, while property of enormous value will be in the greatest peril. We cannot contemplate the future without the gravest apprehensions. All feel that we are justified in taking any steps to prevent the shedding of blood, and to insure the protection of our rights.

It is under these circumstances that we feel constrained to call upon you to come to our aid, should a disturbance arise here. The circumstances are so extreme that we cannot but believe that you and the men under you will not fail to come to the rescue of people who will be so situated. We guarantee any expense that may reasonably be incurred by you in helping us, and ask you to believe that nothing but the sternest necessity has prompted this appeal.

CHARLES LEONARD
LIONEL PHILLIPS
FRANCIS RHODES
JOHN HAYS HAMMOND
GEORGE FARRAR

The date was purposely omitted on the understanding that it should be filled in only if and when the Reform leaders should call on Jameson to come to their rescue.

Meanwhile, hope for a peaceful solution had not been abandoned. Kruger continued to look with suspicion on every overture, however friendly. When he was finally persuaded to visit Johannesburg again to open the first agricultural show, five years after the episode of 1890, he regarded our demonstrations of welcome as absolutely insincere and again maintained his distant attitude.

Deputation after deputation from Johannesburg put its case strenuously, and at length he brought the interview to a close by saying, "If you want your rights, why don't you fight for them?"

When Kruger's challenge reached my ears, I said, "That's a fine idea."

As one of the German Reformers put it, "This is the last straw that broke the camel's back that killed the goose that laid the golden egg."

Many doubters were now convinced that we must arm. This did not necessarily mean revolution. Conceivably, if we had gone back to Kruger, after securing the guns, and then demanded reforms, declaring our intention to fight unless they were effected, reforms would have been conceded. This may have been Loch's idea in 1894.

We had no legal right to possess arms without a Boer permit but a burgher could possess an arsenal if he so desired. Much apprehension had been aroused among us because a fort was being built on the hill commanding Johannesburg. The Boers might even bombard the town, as they had frequently threatened to do. Moreover, there were rumors that German military instructors and German arms were coming to their help.

We wanted to take action before the Boers had time to add to their present armament. We dared not wait until they were fully equipped to put down an uprising.

We had no difficulty in importing guns and ammunition from England and transporting them as far as Kimberley. There they were received by Gardner Williams, the American mining engineer in charge of the De Beers diamond properties. To get them from Kimberley to Johannesburg was a far more difficult matter to arrange.

It not only involved the great risk of seven years' imprisonment for smuggling guns, but must inevitably take considerable time.

We finally devised a system which worked successfully but slowly. Williams, assisted by men he could trust, loaded the guns and ammunition into empty Standard Oil drums. Each of these was provided with a false bottom and contained enough oil so that, if the spigot should be turned by the customs inspectors, a convincing trickle would follow. They were consigned to me at Johannesburg.

There were some exciting moments in connection with this gunrunning. I was accustomed to ride with Colonel Rhodes every day before breakfast. One morning I heard the fast gallop of his horse. He threw the reins to the Kaffir boy who was holding my horse ready saddled, hurried into the house and thrust into my hands a copy of the *Standard and Digger News*.

"Look at this, Jack!"

He had it open at the story which described a collision between two trains at De Aar. One of these trains carried a shipment of guns from Kimberley. We realized that some of the drums might have been torn open in the collision and their true contents revealed.

"Jack," said Frank Rhodes, "you and I have the fastest horses in this part of the country. If necessary we can make a bolt for Natal where we'll be out of danger of extradition. We could even go on to Rhodesia, where we'd be absolutely safe."

We rode directly to town and left our horses discreetly around the corner from my office. We were greatly relieved to find a telegram from Captain Harry Holden, whose duty it was to keep me informed of the progress of the oil drums in transit.

THERE HAS BEEN A COLLISION ON THE ROAD BETWEEN TWO TRAINS ON ONE OF WHICH ARE SOME OF OUR FRIENDS BUT THEY ARE ENTIRELY UNINJURED AND WILL ARRIVE AT JOHANNESBURG TOMORROW BE SURE TO SECURE PROPER HOTEL ACCOMMODATIONS FOR THEM.

All our messages were transmitted in such improvised codes. The usual notification of the despatch of a consignment of guns was

AM SENDING YOU A DIAMOND FULL OF FIRE.

Dr. Harris was known as Cactus; Colonel Rhodes, Toad; Jameson, Zahlbar; Rhodes, Umbegangen; Leonard, Zampilio; and Johannesburg, Giovano.

Without any attempt at secrecy, I had the Standard Oil drums containing the guns stored at the different mining properties. In spite of all we could do, however, the rifles came in all too slowly—much more slowly than we had expected. If there was to be a revolt, we had to obtain rifles in far greater quantities.

It had occurred to us that the Boer arsenal at Pretoria, only a little over thirty miles away and the key to any Boer defense, could be taken by a sudden surprise attack. About 15,000 Martini rifles, ammunition for them, and three or four Maxims were stored there. These arms were kept in several galvanized iron buildings surrounded by a weak brick wall, one side of which was then being rebuilt. Although during the day there were about a hundred artillerymen on guard, after ten o'clock at night all but a few were sure to be sound asleep. By timing our attack properly, we would capture as many guns as we could carry away on wagons. The rest we would put out of commission.

I had obtained a lease of property just outside Pretoria, ostensibly for prospecting purposes. There I assembled fifty hard-boiled Americans of an adventurous spirit who were supposedly prospecting for gold.

They knew, as well as I did, that there was no gold in the vicinity, but were quite content to humor my whim so long as they were paid for it. Most of them had been discharged from companies under my control for good and sufficient reasons, including drunk and disorderly conduct. The mine managers, totally unaware that anything out of the ordinary was intended, remonstrated against my giving employment to men they had dismissed. They said this was subversive of discipline. I told them not to worry; experience had taught me how to handle such men, and, indeed, I found them tractable and not altogether uncongenial.

Towards the end of the year when the situation had become genuinely serious, I tried by subterfuge to induce my wife to take the family to Cape Town. She suspected there was some reason back of my insistence and refused to go. Finally, I took her into my confidence and told her what we were intending, and what dangers she would run, not only from the revolt, but also from a resultant uprising of the native population. Even after this disclosure, she resolutely refused to leave Johannesburg, and there she stayed throughout all the trouble.

There was no danger of our running short of food. We had stored enough supplies to last two and a half months; there were enough further stocks in the town to ensure its holding out for three months against a siege. Our volunteers had little experience in drilling together, but most of them had been in Africa for some time and were not only good horsemen but excellent shots as well. The South African Light Horse, which rendered splendid service in the Boer War, was largely recruited from these men.

In the early part of December, James Bryce, authority on government and politics, stopped off at Johannesburg on his way back from a trip to Rhodesia. He could not actually prove that anything out of the ordinary was going on, but no person of sensibility could fail to suspect that something was toward. I would find him at my office when I came in in the morning; I would find him at my home when I arrived there at night. Nothing I could do or say would shake him off. He had a charming personality, and I enjoyed his company except when he asked too-pertinent or embarrassing questions. I finally told him that he possessed all the necessary attributes of a first-class American newspaper reporter.

I did have in mind one further idea about which I kept very quiet. It seemed to me that once the arsenal at Pretoria was captured it would be a relatively simple sequel to take Oom Paul himself back to Johannesburg with us. I felt confident that, when subjected to this other environment, he would prove more receptive to our ideas.

With all these various activities going on in Johannesburg, the atmosphere reminded me of what we Californians used to call earthquake weather.

CHAPTER EIGHTEEN

The Revolt of the Uitlanders

ARRANGING THE DETAILS OF "FLOTATION"—I
LAY OUT JAMESON'S ROUTE — THE DOCTOR BE-
COMES RESTIVE—THE TRANSVAAL GROWS SLIGHTLY
AWARE — SETTING THE DATE — THE FLAG INCI-
DENT — PUBLICATION OF THE LEONARD MANI-
FESTO—AN AFTERNOON CALLER—JAMESON STARTS
TOO SOON—FORMATION OF THE REFORM COM-
MITTEE—AN UNUSUAL NEW YEAR'S EVE PARTY—
KRUGER EXTENDS AN OLIVE BRANCH—WILLOUGH-
BY'S FATAL BLUNDER—JAMESON SURRENDERS AT
DOORNKOP—WE LAY DOWN OUR ARMS—UNDER ARREST

*M*ark Twain once remarked that people were always talking about the weather, but no one ever did anything about it. So all of our discussions must have seemed to Jameson who, throughout December of 1895, was chafing for action just across the border at Pitsani in Bechuanaland, thirty-seven miles from Mafeking on the border of the Transvaal. We, too, felt impatient, engrossed with our own plans and preparations at Johannesburg.

Jameson's troops began to assemble early in the month. They were in two divisions. The Bechuanaland police force of one hundred and twenty, under command of Major Raleigh Gray, was at Mafeking. The main body of Chartered police, under Jameson himself, was at Pitsani. Lieutenant Colonel Sir John Willoughby was to have the active military command of the combined forces, amounting to four hundred and seventy men.

It was the middle of the South African hot season. The oppression weighed heavily upon our spirits. Action was an effort, although we realized that we must act as swiftly as possible.

Jameson, equipped for action, restlessly impatient, accused us of apathy. He was wrong. His chief problem was to hold his forces, many of whom were volunteers owing him only nominal obedience. He overlooked our difficulties. He ignored the fact that we had multitudinous and vexatious details to handle, the omission of any single one of which might ruin our plans. With the psychology of the military man, he discounted the importance of our problems and the necessity of our aid. Unfortunately, we did not realize that this was Jameson's attitude although we were in constant communication with him by messengers; meanwhile, we proceeded as rapidly as we were able.

Back in November my wife and I had gone by train to Kimberley where I had an appointment to meet Rhodes for a discussion of various phases of our preparations. From there we proceeded to Mafeking, and then, in order to study the topography of the country, returned to Johannesburg by Cape cart and laid out the best route for Jameson to follow.

Sir John Willoughby did not approve altogether of the route I recommended; he had a vague idea of besieging Boer settlements on his way to Johannesburg. But Dr. Jameson took my view that the chief consideration was expedition in getting to Johannesburg to secure relief for the city.

When my wife and I arrived at the Transvaal border, we were stopped by a military doctor who informed us that there was an epidemic of smallpox just over the line, and we should have to produce satisfactory vaccination scars before we would be allowed to pass. Since mine was on my arm, I was speedily approved. My wife, contrary to the Victorian custom, had been vaccinated on the leg. She was much embarrassed, but made the best of the situation; she quickly lifted her dress to the necessary height and as quickly dropped it. In equal embarrassment, the young doctor signed her quarantine record.

After we had gone a short distance beyond the border, my wife suddenly turned to me and said, "My goodness, Jack, I showed him the wrong leg."

This experience was the only touch of humor in what was a very serious undertaking.

Along the road from Pitsani to Johannesburg, Dr. Henry Wolff, an intimate friend of Jameson, under our direction established stage stations ostensibly in connection with mining developments in that section. These stations were stocked with food to supplement Jameson's commissariat.

It has been alleged that we failed to carry out our agreement to provide changes of cavalry mounts for the Jameson troopers. As a matter of fact, Jameson had not suggested any such arrangement as obviously it would have been impossible to send several hundred cavalry mounts without at once arousing the suspicion of the Boers. In fact, there were few horses of this kind aside from those owned by the Boers, from whom we would have had to purchase them.

Meanwhile, in the early days of December, Jameson's restlessness increased. He did not understand the newer political complications of our situation and his uncertainty accentuated his impatience.

Jameson usually showed good judgment in selecting men who could serve in a confidential capacity but he made a mistake in his choice of a well-known young Englishman to convey a message to me. On his arrival in Johannesburg this young fellow happened to meet two old Eton schoolmates. They celebrated the reunion by imbibing too freely. Jameson's messenger became very confiding and told them the plans of the Reform Committee.

The next morning his two friends came to see me, expressed great regret at what they had to tell me of the night before, but assured me that I need feel no concern: they would give up their proposed big game shooting trip to the North and would remain in Johannesburg and give what assistance they could to the Reform Movement. They thought Jameson's messenger should not be entrusted with other important communications, however.

I called the messenger to my office and he finally confessed his breach of confidence. I reprimanded him severely and then told him to return in an hour as I had a most important message to send by him to Dr. Jameson, and said that he must guard the letter at all costs, and to deliver it personally into the doctor's hands. This was the letter:

> My dear Jameson:
>
> For God's sake don't send any more damn fools like the bearer of this letter to me. He has divulged the entire plans to two Englishmen who are here with us. It will not make any difference as they are loyal and will help us all they can; *send the bearer* to the interior of Africa where he will be lost for months.

Jameson read my letter immediately to the young man and sent him on a mission some hundreds of miles away.

Two years afterwards at a dinner in London I escorted a young lady to the table. I noticed that she was unusually disagreeable. None of my efforts at conversation were successful; she remained frigid and answered only in monosyllables. I tried to break through the barrier by asking if she had ever been in Africa, America, and other countries. The reply was "No." I was at a loss to account for her attitude.

After dinner was over, I asked my hostess about the young lady I had had the pleasure of taking in to dinner, as I had not caught her name when introduced. Her answer solved the puzzle. She was the sister of Jameson's messenger.

On December 12th, Jameson wired me frantically, to "inform weak partners more delay more danger. . . . Do all you can to hasten the completion of works." We had been making every effort to bring these weak partners into line and consolidate our tactical position. We knew Rhodes's co-operation was assured, but we felt it equally necessary to obtain the personal support of Alfred Beit, whose interests on the Rand were as great as those of Rhodes himself. Furthermore, I relied on Beit's sagacity and foresight and wanted the advantage of his personal influence. His partners, Lionel Phillips and Percy Fitzpatrick, had given invaluable service to the cause, but a number of men in Beit's employ at Johannesburg had not been particularly zealous in the movement. Rhodes was as desirous as we that Beit should come in person to enlist the active co-operation of his lukewarm employees so that the Consolidated Gold Fields would not be left holding the bag and that we would present a united front to the Boers.

Volunteers from Cape Town were now joining Jameson's camp and some even came to Johannesburg. We had so little use for them that finally Colonel Rhodes had to wire Major Robert White, Willoughby's chief of staff, to send no more heroes until January, as we had neither room nor equipment for them. We had but a fraction of the rifles required for arming our own volunteers.

With the approval of the other leaders, I wired Rhodes on December 18th, and said the "flotation" would have to be postponed until Beit could come to Johannesburg. A few days later Beit wired back from Cape Town that he could not come at the moment because of illness, and inquired as to the reason for the hitch in our plans. He said he did not want his illness to interfere with the date of the "flotation"; he could not understand why the revolt should not take place immediately.

On receiving assurance that he was heartily in sympathy with our plans, we set midnight of December 28th as the provisional time for the beginning of the revolt, but we soon found that the date would have to be changed and the "flotation" would have to be postponed. Therefore, we immediately sent Jameson a wire in code, saying that the rising would not take place as planned on the 28th, and that he must not move until he received further instructions. Jameson's only reply was to wire Colonel Rhodes that he did not see how he could delay beyond December. The reason for our change of plans was that, in the first place, in our haste we had neglected to take into consideration that the Christmas season was an important religious festival for the Boers, and that Pretoria would be thronged with burghers. This would prevent, or at least make very difficult, our proposed attempt on the arsenal.

In the second place, even then not enough arms had arrived. We had as yet only a thousand rifles, which was but a small fraction of those actually needed.

Most disturbing of all, certain of the Reformers had brought from Cape Town inflammable news that Jameson intended to insinuate the British flag into the proceedings and carry it into Johannesburg, and that Rhodes had agreed to the plan.

This caused great consternation in our ranks. Many of us, particularly the large American contingent, were not British subjects, and many of the British themselves were averse to changing the flag.

To settle this point, we sent a committee to Cape Town to tell Rhodes that we would take no action if Jameson insisted on hoisting the British flag, and also to inform Rhodes of our state of unpreparedness. Assurance was at once sent back that the apprehension over a possible change of flag was groundless. Nevertheless, it was apparent to me by Christmas Day that many in our ranks had a profound distrust of Jameson's attitude which was only equaled by Jameson's lack of confidence in our zeal.

Jameson naturally feared the possibility that the Boers might discover our real plans. Moreover, his forces were being constantly depleted; his men, who were not yet acquainted with the purpose of their assembling, had begun to quit him. He became more and more worried. He notified us that he might be obliged to act prematurely. The telegraph wires were vibrating with activity.

Dr. Rutherfoord Harris, secretary of the Chartered Company, who was working jointly for Rhodes and the Reform Committee at Cape Town, did not help to allay Jameson's fears when he wired him, December 23rd, "We suspect Transvaal is getting aware slightly."

It was obvious from the messages we were receiving from Jameson that he was attempting to hurry us. We realized that he might even be trying to force our hand and to make the "flotation" independently of us. We were confident, however, that we had convinced Jameson of the need of postponement.

One week seemed sufficient time to clear up the flag incident, so we set January 4th as the second provisional date on which the rising at Johannesburg and our attack on the Pretoria arsenal should take place. In order to blind the Boers to the imminence of this event, an open forum for the discussion of Uitlander grievances was scheduled and announced to take place January 6th—two days after the uprising. The agenda was taken from a manifesto drawn up by Charles Leonard, after a consultation with Rhodes at Cape Town in October, and later with Phillips, Colonel Rhodes, and me. The carefully annotated heads of topics were as follows:

(1) Full representation in the Councils of the State in proportion to our numbers and vested interests; being the majority of the people we claim the right to be included in a true government of the people by the people for the people; (2) Proper control of public moneys and true responsibility to the people; (3) Absolute independence of the courts and the raising of the status of the judges; (4) The possession and control of our railways and public works; (5) The abolition of monopolies; (6) Free trade with the neighbouring States of South Africa in all products thereof; (7) A settled policy which, while guarding the legitimate interests of the South African Republic zealously, shall foster the goodwill of the other South African States and strengthen the bonds of commerce and good feeling between us and them; (8) Pure administration; (9) Equal rights for the English and Dutch languages.

This "sweetly reasonable" document, as the *Standard and Digger News* called it, was signed by Leonard as chairman of the Transvaal National Union and published December 26th.

Kruger's only comment when he read it was: "Their rights. Yes, they'll get them—over my dead body."

Nevertheless, the proposed mass meeting accomplished its purpose: it deceived the Boers as to our actual plans. Apparently it never occurred to them that we would move before that date.

On December 26th, 27th, and 28th, urgent telegrams were sent by Dr. Harris to Jameson that he must not move.

Basil Williams says in his book, *Cecil Rhodes:*

Throughout the 26th, 27th, and 28th telegrams of increasing urgency were being sent to Jameson from the Chartered Company's office, bidding him stand fast. Dr. Harris was evidently moved almost to tears by the hesitation of Johannesburg, and concludes one of his telegrams "Ichabod"; but he makes it quite plain to Jameson that he must not move: "ALL OUR FOREIGN FRIENDS ARE DEAD AGAINST FLOTATION AND SAY PUBLIC WILL NOT SUBSCRIBE ONE PENNY TOWARDS IT EVEN WITH YOU AS DIRECTOR. . . . WE CANNOT HAVE FIASCO."

In fact, message after message went to Jameson urging him to be patient. "It's all right if you'll only wait," reiterated Harris, while at the same time adjuring Sam Jameson, in Johannesburg, to "Keep the market firm."

Jameson either could not, or did not care to, understand the urgency of our need for delay. As I have just said, he was afraid the Boers were beginning to wonder why he was training soldiers so near Johannesburg. But Dr. Harris notified him not to worry about any suspicion his armed force might create. He told him it did not matter if people thought he was threatening the Transvaal; he was within his rights in keeping the force there. On December 27th, Jameson wired his brother Sam:

LET J. H. HAMMOND TELEGRAPH INSTANTLY ALL RIGHT.

I replied:

WIRE RECEIVED. EXPERTS' REPORT DECIDEDLY ADVERSE. I AB-
SOLUTELY CONDEMN FURTHER DEVELOPMENTS AT PRESENT.

This statement seemed definite enough to me and to the Reform Committee. Sam Jameson also telegraphed to the doctor on December 28th:

IT IS ABSOLUTELY NECESSARY TO POSTPONE FLOTATION
THROUGH UNFORESEEN CIRCUMSTANCES UNTIL WE HAVE C. J.
RHODES'S ABSOLUTE PLEDGE THAT AUTHORITY OF IMPERIAL
GOVERNMENT WILL NOT BE INSISTED ON.

After my telegram had gone, I began to wonder more and more what Jameson intended to do. His past actions had certainly not been of a kind to instill faith in his patience and self-control. He was obviously fretting, and no one knew better than I how fatal any impetuous action on his part might prove. However incredible it might seem that Jameson should actually plan to start without receiving word from the Reform Committee and from me personally, even that remote possibility had to be guarded against.

We decided to take such steps as would make premature action on his part impossible. Captain Holden was sent on horseback across country to Pitsani. Major Heaney, a West Point graduate for many years associated with Jameson in Rhodesia, went by special train to Mafeking. Both these Jameson adherents bore the same message, and we were certain that one or the other would be delivered by Sunday, December 29th. They were to inform the doctor that the guns were arriving so slowly that we had as yet only a few more than a thousand rifles all told and hardly enough ammunition to last through an hour's steady firing.

Consequently, if Jameson moved, he would, to use his own favorite expression, "ball everything up."

The sending of these messages relieved our minds. It did not occur to us that the doctor would make any decisive move after he had heard the facts at first hand.

Rhodes himself made one final effort, December 29th, to stop Jameson. "On no account whatever must you move. I most strongly object to such a course."

Unfortunately it was Sunday and the telegraph office could not get through to Mafeking. Even if the wire had been delivered, it is doubtful whether Jameson would have heeded the command.

Saturday, December 28th, Kruger returned to Pretoria from a tour of the principal Transvaal towns. When he was informed of a rumored uprising, he said he did not believe it. Even so, he remarked, his burghers should remember that if they wanted to kill a tortoise they must wait until he sticks his head out of the shell.

Kruger had barely reached his home when he was approached by a deputation of Americans who had gone to Pretoria independently, without the sanction of the men in control of the Reform Movement. The group included those very men for whose disciplining we had desired Beit's presence. They were received civilly enough. Like Napoleon, Kruger was accustomed to losing his temper principally for effect. After he had heard the Committee's proposals for a peaceful solution, he asked, "If a crisis should occur, on which side shall I find the Americans?"

The deputation answered, "On the side of liberty and good government."

To this the president replied, "You are all alike, tarred with the same brush; you are British in your hearts."

He became really irritated, however, when the Americans asked, "If we take the oath of allegiance, will you then not trust us?"

He replied, "This is no time to talk about these things—I can promise you nothing."

We did not expect that anything would happen in the next few days. But at noon on Sunday, December 29th, came a telegram which threw us into a fresh state of alarm. It was addressed to Dr. Wolff and read:

> MEET ME AS ARRANGED BEFORE YOU LEFT ON TUESDAY NIGHT, WHICH WILL ENABLE US TO DECIDE WHICH IS BEST DESTINATION; MAKE ADV[OCATE] J. W. LEONARD SPEAK, MAKE CUTTING TONIGHT WITHOUT FAIL, HAVE GREAT FAITH IN J. H. HAMMOND, A. L. LAWLEY AND MINERS WITH LEE METFORD RIFLES.

We concluded that Jameson was making a final bluff in an effort to force action. We were still perfectly sure that the arrival of our personal messengers would have effectively leashed Jameson.

Unperturbed, I went about my regular business in connection with plans for the revolt. Early Monday afternoon I attended a meeting to hear the results of the Saturday interview between the American delegation and Kruger. We appointed a committee of three to go to Pretoria on Tuesday and once more lay our demands before the president.

I returned to my office a little before four o'clock. Shortly afterwards, I was waited upon by Sammy Marks, one of Kruger's intimate business associates. I knew the man well as I had been the consulting engineer of mining companies in which he had large interests. I was well aware of the fact that he had not called merely to pass the time of day. Marks, evidently nervous and excited, began immediately to discuss current rumors. I was sparring for time until I could ascertain his true object, when the door opened and a clerk handed me a slip of paper. On it was written:

"Jameson has crossed the Border."

I was thunderstruck!

In a voice as steady and unconcerned as I could manage, I asked, "What's that you were saying, Sammy? You think it looks as though there might be bloodshed?"

"Well, they're saying around town that you've run in thirty thousand rifles. That looks like fighting to me."

"So that's it," I thought to myself. "Kruger knows Jameson's started and he's trying to find out what we're up to."

A little American bluff seemed indicated. I said nonchalantly: "Oh, I wouldn't want to say exactly how many guns there are, Sammy. But I hardly think it's quite as many as that."

I was twisting the slip of paper in my hand while watching the effect of my words. They seemed to be going down well, but I knew how important it was to make Marks believe that we were better prepared than was actually the case. I felt certain that, if Kruger should suspect our woeful state of unpreparedness, Johannesburg would be attacked before Jameson could get within a hundred miles of us. That would be the end of the Reform Movement.

"And how about the artillery, Mr. Hammond? Is it true you've got thirty cannons?" queried Sammy, unable to conceal his eagerness. I remembered with amusement the mining pumps covered with tarpaulins that we had hauled through the streets to give the impression of cannons. The sight of these had succeeded in giving rise to the rumor.

Nevertheless, I kept up the game. "If they're saying that, they're probably exaggerating. You know how people talk, Sammy."

I could see that Marks had swallowed the bait. He lost no time in saying farewell. The door had barely closed behind him when I dashed to my secretary's room. "Marks has gone! Tell Fred to follow him and not let him out of his sight."

Fred soon reported that Marks had left by special train for Pretoria.

Some months after my release from jail in Pretoria, when good feeling had been re-established between the individuals of the Reform Committee and their Boer friends, Marks told me, as a good joke on himself, what he had reported to Kruger after his interview with me.

"Mr. President, I fear there is going to be bloodshed in Johannesburg. I saw hundreds of men marching and drilling, several cannons being hauled through the streets, all the Uitlanders are armed. I know this for a fact. I got an admission from my friend, Hays Hammond. He's had charge of my mines and I have absolute confidence in him. Hammond practically admitted to me that there were at least thirty thousand rifles and thirty cannons."

My next move was to get in touch with the other leaders. They had already received the news from Lawley, who had rushed into headquarters waving a telegram and shouting, "It's all up, boys. Listen to this! 'THE CONTRACTOR HAS STARTED ON THE EARTHWORKS WITH SEVEN HUNDRED BOYS; HOPES TO REACH TERMINUS ON WEDNESDAY.'"

And so vanished our carefully laid designs for taking the Pretoria arsenal. All we could do now was to revamp the plan to fit the altered circumstances.

Within fifteen minutes messengers were on their way to call together those Reform leaders who had not yet heard the news. We still believed that, whatever the reason for his action, Jameson must be supported.

Before eight o'clock that evening we had organized an emergency Reform Committee. We sent telegrams to Rhodes and to Sir Hercules Robinson at Cape Town, urging that the latter should come at once to avert civil war.

Ever since word had first come that Jameson was on the way, women and children had begun to leave the city in large numbers. We heard that the Natal train had been wrecked with many casualties. This cast an added gloom over everybody. The refugee women and children who remained were given bunks at the clubs. As matter of precaution, all canteens had been closed so that no Kaffirs could obtain liquor.

By midnight the alarm caused by Jameson's premature start had subsided; the streets were quiet. After working nearly all night, at four o'clock I reached Heath's Hotel, to which I had brought my family, and was just on the point of going to bed when I was called back to the Reform Committee, which had decided to meet in perpetual session.

We had appointed subcommittees for replacing the Boer police in the town, for mounting Maxims on the surrounding hills, for securing provisions, for distributing such guns as we had, and for providing for the relief of the women and children who had been called in from the mines. The Johannesburg *Star* of Tuesday, December 31st, carried our proclamation asking the inhabitants to commit no overt act against the Boer government. Our telegraphic communications with the outside world were that day cut off by the Boers.

No shops opened on Monday; all were tightly shuttered with wood or corrugated iron. The Boer police vanished from the streets and our own emergency force took control.

Before nightfall we had distributed the rifles from the courthouse; squads began drilling in the streets. Some twenty thousand men must have volunteered, but there were arms available only for a few hundred, and no way of securing a further supply. Including the fifteen hundred rifles rushed in after Jameson had started, which were concealed in freight cars under a thin layer of coke, there were no more than twenty-seven hundred altogether.

The extremely sultry day turned into a calm moonlit night. The excitement on the streets gradually died down.

Although Johannesburg was pre-eminently a British community, there were many Americans there. Prior to the last few months of the conspiracy, we had taken no aggressive political position, and even then we were not actively interested except when the Boers planned to commandeer Americans as well as British for service in their native wars. At that time I called a secret meeting of several of my mine managers and invited T. B. Brown (known as Barbarian Brown) to be present. I had first encountered Brown when he was editor of a newspaper in Idaho. He was an American and we knew him to be a paid spy of Kruger, although Brown did not suspect that we were aware of this.

The meeting was held in Victor Clement's home at the Simmer and Jack mine, of which he was manager. After swearing all to secrecy, we took an oath that if any of us were commandeered the first shot fired would be aimed at the Boer commander. This secret resolution was quickly reported to Kruger, with the result that there was no commandeering of Americans.

A meeting was called New Year's Eve to hear the report of the American deputation who had just returned from Pretoria. Over five hundred Americans, including mine managers, mechanics, foremen, and carpenters, attended. Captain Thomas Mein, manager of the Robinson mine, was in the chair. Brown reported for the deputation. Although he was pro-Kruger in his sordid sympathy, he was forced to admit that Kruger had given them no satisfaction and it was his own opinion that nothing further could be done.

Mein announced from the platform that the meeting had been called to decide whether the Americans would give their support to the revolution then brewing against the Boer oligarchy. This was as far as he got.

Brown and his fellows had decided to break up the meeting by making it impossible for anyone to speak. So loud was the uproar that, just as I made my somewhat belated entrance into the hall, Captain Mein was about to adjourn the meeting in despair.

Perceiving that the situation was practically out of hand, I walked rapidly down the aisle, mounted the platform, and raised my hand for a hearing.

"What's going on?" I demanded. "Sit down, everybody. . . . Brown, I consider that the report you've brought back from Kruger is an insult. We don't want any Kruger men in this hall. Whatever talking is going to be done in this room is going to come from the platform."

The hubbub gradually subsided, particularly as threatening gestures from the American miners under my management lent authority to my words.

When the room was quiet enough, I said, "I respectfully request that everyone who is not an American leave the room."

The few English who had dropped in slipped peaceably away.

I then explained in simple terms the situation confronting us. "You all know exactly what we're here for. I don't need to tell you the difficulties under which we've been working, or how unjustly we've been treated by the Pretoria crowd. All I'm going to ask you is one single question. Don't you agree with me that we've now reached the same point as the signers of the Declaration of Independence when they announced that 'it was their right and their duty to throw off a despotic government, and to provide new guards for their future security'?

"That's all there is to it," I explained. "You won't find anything in the Declaration of Independence that limits this principle to latitude or longitude. It's a clean-cut issue to be faced by us Americans here and now.

"You know as well as I do that we won't stand for having a British flag hoisted over Johannesburg. All we want is justice from Kruger and his grafters. You can rely on me that I'll shoot any man who hoists any flag but the Boer flag."

The assemblage applauded vigorously. The vote was immediately taken and, out of the more than five hundred present, all but five voted to take up arms against Kruger. The George Washington Corps of one hundred and fifty members was at once organized for active service, and pledged its support to the revolutionary cause.

As soon as this meeting was over, I rushed back to the Gold Fields offices where the Reform Committee was discussing proposals brought by Kruger emissaries known for their progressive sentiments. We called them the Olive Branch delegation. Among them were Eugene Marais, editor of the leading Boer newspaper, and Malan, Joubert's son-in-law. The delegation were favorable to our cause, and some of them were personal friends of members of the Reform Committee. They had brought from the Boer government letters of introduction to Lionel Phillips and myself. We refused to receive them in the capacity of a deputation from Kruger unless they came accredited to the Reform Committee of Johannesburg. This stipulation was immediately accepted.

That Kruger was willing to negotiate with the Reform Committee as the representative body of the people of Johannesburg, and not as outlaws, is a fact that was subsequently ignored at our trial.

The meeting lasted until midnight. The gist of the Boer proposals was contained in the famous statement: "We come in fact to offer you the olive branch; it is for you to say if you will take it; if you are sincere in your professions, you will."

We discussed the question of grievances; and came to an agreement on most of the important issues except the granting of the franchise to Catholics and Jews, to which Kruger had always been unalterably opposed. As we had many Catholics and Jews on our Reform Committee, we could not yield on this point.

The delegation told us that Sir Hercules Robinson had sent a letter to Jameson commanding him to turn back; they expected him to obey. They further asked us to send a deputation to Pretoria to meet a Boer commission there. Many of our committee felt that this was merely a ruse on the part of the Boers to gain time, but we accepted the invitation and sent the deputation.

On the following day, at a meeting of the Reform Committee at its headquarters in my office, in the building of the Consolidated Gold Fields Company, every man raised his hand and swore allegiance to the Boer flag which I had procured and had raised over our headquarters, where it remained throughout the crisis.

C. D. Rudd, Rhodes's partner, then at Cape Town, sent a message of protest against this usurpation, saying that we would thereby embarrass the Gold Fields Company. I sent back a prompt reply that I considered the Company was already up to its neck in the revolt and I could not see how it could be further embarrassed. I suggested that he come up personally and discuss the matter with the Reform leaders, knowing that this invitation would not be accepted.

The sixth edition of the *Star,* Tuesday, December 31st, carried the headlines that Jameson was only a few miles away. Unofficial messengers scurried back and forth between his camp and the town. Rumors of all kinds were rife. The populace was raised to a pitch of high excitement by Jameson's proximity. He had become a hero, and there was much pressure to have the citizens go out to meet him and conduct him in triumph into the city. There was a total misconception among the people as to the seriousness of the situation.

Up to this time, with the exception of the Reform leaders, the people of Johannesburg had been kept in ignorance of the number of guns in the possession of the Reform Committee. They were under the impression that there were many times the number we actually had. Obviously it would have been fatal to the cause if the truth had been made public.

On Wednesday, Sir Jacobus de Wet, the agent of the Cape government at Pretoria, was sent for by Kruger, who told him to announce to the Reform Committee in Johannesburg that they should follow a constitutional course. This same day we learned that the letter of invitation, which we had given to Jameson undated, had been made public. Percy Fitzpatrick, one of the leading members of the Reform Committee, says in his book *Transvaal from Within:*

> The public by this time knew of the letter of invitation; it had been taken on the battlefield and news of it was telegraphed in, and apart from this the writers had made no secret of it. But what the public did not know was the efforts made to stop Jameson and the practical withdrawal of the letter before we had started.

We could no longer ignore the fact that he had started in clear violation of our intent; he had tried to "make his own flotation."

The leaders of the Reform Committee and other members who had inside information were deeply incensed against Jameson for what we justly regarded as his betrayal of us.

I asked Jameson when I saw him after his release from Holloway Prison in London why he left Pitsani against our protest. He said that his men were deserting him and the Boers were getting very suspicious and if he had not started then, he never could have come in. I told him that it would have been much better if he had never started.

Lionel Phillips went to Pretoria where he met the government commission on Wednesday noon and detailed our position at Johannesburg. He said he did not know why Jameson had started, which was true, but he aroused the suspicions of the Boers, who already knew him as one of the signers of the Jameson letter of invitation. They gave him the impression, however, that our grievances would be redressed. He informed them that we leaders would be personally responsible for Jameson's leaving peaceably as soon as he arrived.

After Phillips returned to Johannesburg, at eleven the same night, he addressed a great crowd waiting for news in front of the Consolidated Gold Fields Building. Speaking from the balcony, he said the Boer commission had assured us of earnest consideration of our grievances. He declared again to them that Jameson must have made a mistake, but that he and the other leaders had offered their own persons as guarantors of Jameson's safety. This proposal had been rejected by Kruger, who, nevertheless, had asked for and received a full list of the Reform Committee members. Phillips stated further that Sir Hercules Robinson was going to Pretoria as mediator, and that there was to be an armistice pending his arrival and negotiations.

The crowd kept interrupting Phillips with cries of "How about Jameson? . . . What are you going to do about Jameson?"

Phillips knew how to handle the mob. He shouted: "We intend to stand by Jameson. Let's have three cheers for Dr. Jim." The response was hearty, and the crowd slowly dispersed.

Thursday morning came, and still no word from Jameson as to why he had started. There were rumors that he was fighting near by; the *Star* published an edition every hour recounting Jameson's supposed progress; doctors, ambulances, and volunteer nurses went out to get the wounded.

J. J. Lace, one of our committee who had accompanied the messenger sent by the high commissioner to intercept Jameson, returned with the news that the doctor had actually received Robinson's proclamation, to wit:

> Whereas it has come to my knowledge that certain British subjects, said to be under the leadership of Dr. Jameson, have violated the territory of the South African Republic, and have cut telegraph wires, and done various other illegal acts; and whereas the South African Republic is a friendly state, in amity with Her Majesty's Government; and whereas it is my desire to respect the independence of the said State;

Now, therefore, I hereby command the said Dr. Jameson and all persons accompanying him to immediately retire from the territory of the South African Republic, on pain of the penalties attached to their illegal proceedings; and I do further hereby call upon all British subjects in the South African Republic to abstain from giving the said Dr. Jameson any countenance or assistance in his armed violation of the territory of a friendly State.

Lace told Jameson that the Uitlanders were powerless to help him; that they had warned him to that effect, and Jameson admitted having received our messengers before he started from Pitsani. Indeed, the messengers had accompanied Jameson on the Raid. Lace also told Jameson that we could not understand why he had started. He received a feeble answer which was not a satisfactory explanation.

When Lace left he knew that Jameson realized fully that we were powerless to help him. Jameson feigned that we had allowed him to come in and then deserted him.

About daybreak on Thursday, January 2nd, Colonel Rhodes and I, who had been sleeping on the floor in my office, were awakened by the arrival of bugler Valle of Dr. Jameson's force. He told us that he had left Jameson but a few hours before; that Jameson was progressing surely but slowly on his way to Johannesburg. We carefully catechized him as to Jameson's condition, and he assured us that Jameson did not expect armed support from Johannesburg. Valle was of the opinion that Jameson would reach Johannesburg within a few hours.

Even if Jameson had needed any support, it would have been impossible to give it to him as we had but few mounted men and a small amount of ammunition. Furthermore, Johannesburg would have been left entirely at the mercy of the Boers who were massing on the outskirts of the town, and once the Boers got into Johannesburg and found that we did not have any armed men, there would have been much bloodshed.

The Reform Committee decided this (Thursday) was the time to seize the fort at Johannesburg, which by now had been well provided with guns sent from Pretoria by the Boers. I felt that this should be delayed no longer: if Jameson was such a short distance away, his arrival might be the signal for a Boer bombardment. To help me out, I had secured the assistance of a well-known American saloon owner, and a small group of us were at his place discussing the ways and means of carrying out our plan to take the fort. One of our fellow conspirators, who previously had been an ardent advocate of the scheme, now began to suggest difficulties. Since this did not correspond with his earlier enthusiasm, I said: "There isn't going to be any monkey business about this. You're going into the fort first, and I'll be right behind you. If I see the slightest sign of anything wrong, I'll shoot you."

At this crisis there came a tap on the door. The American opened it and received a note. It was written in Dutch, so he handed it to the hesitating conspirator, who, with barely concealed satisfaction, announced:

"Jameson has surrendered at Doornkop."

Assuming this an excuse for further postponement of our attempt to capture the fort, I said firmly, "That's a lie! Jameson hasn't been captured."

All too soon, however, the truth of his statement was verified. Willoughby had left the prescribed trail to go off cross country to Doornkop, where a battle had resulted in the defeat and capture of Jameson and his officers. They were already on their way to Pretoria as prisoners.

I returned to the Reform Committee headquarters. We learned immediately that a considerable Boer force had gone to the fort after Jameson's capture. This, of course, compelled us to abandon our plans for seizing the fort.

Another crowd of Johannesburghers had gathered in front of the headquarters building. Ugly as had been the mood of the mob of the previous night, this one was in noticeably worse temper. There were threats to blow up the building with us in it. Reiterated cries were uttered: "What about Jameson now?"

Several of the members tried to speak from the balcony, but were howled down. Finally Sam Jameson appealed for quiet and was recognized.

"I beg you, for my brother's sake," he said, "to maintain a spirit of calm restraint. We have done everything in our power for him, and used our very best judgment. In face of the complicated circumstances, no other course could have been taken."

Had any other member of the Committee made this statement, his words would have carried no farther than the balcony rail, but since this was the great Dr. Jim's own brother, the people listened to him. The tension was relieved, and the crowd melted away.

I was dead tired. When I reached the hotel at midnight, I took off my clothes for the first time in three days and nights and got a much-needed rest. The worst had happened, and for the moment there was nothing more to do.

On Friday it was difficult to untangle truth from fiction in the maze of rumors afloat in the town as to the terms on which Jameson had given up his arms. We understood that before he surrendered it had been stipulated that he and his men were to be spared, but Boer reports gave out that the surrender was unconditional. Further stories said definitely that his own life was to be forfeited.

The Committee issued a proclamation that, during the armistice pending Sir Hercules Robinson's arrival, no hostile move should be made. The entire town was in the depths of depression. Armed Boer troops began to appear on the outskirts. A few of our recruits continued to drill in a half-hearted manner in Government Square; otherwise everything was quiet, and remained so over the week-end.

The plight of the Reformers was pitiable. The revolutionary atmosphere was a combination of Armageddon and a psychopathic ward. Our aspiration for reform had not abated, but untoward facts confronted us. The proclamation of the high commissioner; the appeal to save the lives of Jameson and his men; the promises of the Boer government that our grievances would be redressed, made confusion worse confounded as to our course of action. The leaders were, indeed, in a quandary.

We could not imagine why Sir Hercules Robinson was so slow in arriving at Pretoria. Later we learned that he had quickly found out that the news of Jameson's invasion was true. He already had in his possession a cablegram from Chamberlain—who had seen the Leonard Manifesto—stating that Great Britain would support the high commissioner in keeping the peace. After he had issued a proclamation, and had seen to it that Jameson had received it, there followed the arrangement with Kruger by which Sir Hercules was to go to Pretoria to effect a peaceful settlement.

He had been summoned from his country villa early on Monday morning, December 30th. He finally left Cape Town at nine P.M., Thursday, January 2nd, accompanied by a trained nurse. He arrived at Pretoria just on the eve of the Boer sabbath and Kruger, in accordance with the strict Dopper views, postponed discussions until Monday, January 6th. Although Robinson arrived at Pretoria on Saturday evening, it was not until the next day that he cabled Chamberlain that the state of affairs was critical. The Boers, he said, were getting out of hand, and demanding the execution of Jameson. He was certain the Transvaal would insist upon the disarming of Johannesburg before negotiating, although he admitted the Johannesburg people wanted the safety of Jameson and his men guaranteed first; otherwise, they would fight.

Between Saturday and Monday the high commissioner made no effort to inform himself fully of the conditions, though he could and should have learned these, if necessary from Jameson himself. As stated, his first official interview with Kruger was on Monday, January 6th. After this meeting he despatched another message to Chamberlain.

Robinson had expressed to Kruger his regret for the Raid, and thanked the Boers for their moderation. Kruger had definitely stated that Johannesburg must disarm unconditionally and would say nothing about the prisoners. Furthermore, he would allow only twenty-four hours for his ultimatum to be accepted. Without further investigation, Robinson accepted Kruger's dictate and advised Johannesburg to disarm.

Chamberlain wired back his approval of Robinson's procedure up to this point.

Many of the Reform Committee suspected that there might be a trap concealed under the Boer offers; at the same time, we had come to realize that a struggle would be hopeless. When Sir Hercules sent us a further telegram stating that we would forfeit all "claim to sympathy from Her Majesty's government . . . as the lives of Jameson and the prisoners are now practically in their hands," we felt there was no alternative to submission. As we trusted entirely the assurances of the high commissioner that we should be fairly dealt with, we did not insist upon any written guarantee of safety. At that time we did not know the terms of Jameson's surrender.

January 7th, Robinson wired Chamberlain:

> I HAVE JUST RECEIVED A MESSAGE FROM THE REFORM
> COMMITTEE RESOLVING TO COMPLY WITH THE DEMAND OF
> THE SOUTH AFRICAN REPUBLIC TO LAY DOWN THEIR ARMS,
> THE PEOPLE PLACING THEMSELVES UNRESERVEDLY IN MY
> HANDS IN FULLEST CONFIDENCE THAT I WILL SEE JUSTICE
> DONE THEM.

The next day he put himself even more definitely on record: "I will confer with Kruger as to redressing the grievances of the residents of Johannesburg."

In a further cable of the same day he explained his position more fully: "I intend to insist on the fulfillment of terms as regards prisoners and consideration of grievances."

After he had been informed that the Boer government believed the Uitlanders had not given up all their guns and ammunition, he told the Executive Council that the onus rested on the Transvaal government to prove guns and ammunition were still being concealed, and that, if any hostile step were taken before this had been clearly demonstrated, "I should consider it a violation of the undertaking for which I had made myself personally responsible to the people of Johannesburg, and I should leave the issue in the hands of Her Majesty's government."

No words could have more plainly stated Robinson's intention at that time to stand by his agreement with us.

On January 6th an ultimatum was delivered to us from Sir Hercules by Sir Jacobus de Wet, the British agent, and Sir Sidney Shippard, administrator of Bechuanaland. It amounted to a demand that we surrender our arms: otherwise, we could not claim any sympathy either from the British government or from the rest of the world; the lives of Jameson and his men would be forfeited.

Bitter as was the decision, we determined to surrender. De Wet assured us over and over that this was the advice of the high commissioner and also of the Queen and that if we complied with their demand, "not a hair of our heads would be touched."

Later de Wet stated this was merely his private opinion, but at the time he used every argument to induce us to give up our arms.

January 7th, de Wet and Shippard addressed the crowd from the balcony of the Rand Club, asking them to accept the ultimatum. Shippard made a particularly good speech, again promising that, if the arms were given up, Jameson and the Reform leaders would be saved.

Wednesday, January 8th, eighteen hundred guns were handed in. The Boers angrily charged us with bad faith and said there were many more. We told them they were entirely mistaken; that at the most we never had possessed more than twenty-seven hundred and their assumption that we had thirty thousand was erroneous. Furthermore, we had no artillery to amount to anything. They were still suspicious, going so far as to search the lowest levels of the mines.

This was the case of "the engineer hoist with his own petard" since the Boers' estimate of the number of guns in the possession of the Reform Committee was based upon the intimation Sammy Marks had been given by me.

Johannesburg was rapidly returning to normal. The wives of the mine workers went back to the mines, the Transvaal police once more took over the town, the military companies were disbanded, the Committee began to catch up on sleep.

The Boer officials had let drop meaningful remarks about arresting the ringleaders of the conspiracy. I assured my wife, however, that Great Britain could not allow this after having made promises of protection. We refused the offer of Simpson, the surveyor for the Consolidated Gold Fields Company, to supply the four leaders with horses to take us to Natal should the threat of arrest become imminent.

Up to the last moment I believed we were in no danger, but on

Thursday evening, January 9th, after the Boers were finally convinced they had secured all the guns, they began to round us up. Kruger issued a proclamation of amnesty for all but the "chief offenders, ringleaders, leaders, instigators, and those who have caused the rebellion at Johannesburg and suburbs." We were to be arrested immediately. They had no difficulty in picking out their victims since we had obligingly handed over our membership list.

I was at Heath's Hotel when, at quarter to nine in the evening, Lieutenant Pietersen sent up his card. I knew what this meant. I scribbled on the back of the card: "If you promise that I will not be handcuffed or submitted to any indignity, I'll come down. I'll blow out the brains of the first man who lays hands on me."

He sent back word that, on his honor as a gentleman, he would observe these conditions.

With my gun in my pocket, I descended to the lobby. Tossing it on the bar, I said, as debonairly as I could under the circumstances: "Let's have a drink together, Lieutenant. It may be the last one I'll get for a long time."

CHAPTER NINETEEN

The Trial

CHARGED WITH HIGH TREASON—TAKEN TO JAIL—
NO FIT PLACE FOR "GENTLEMEN"—THE WHIMS
OF JAILERS — GEORGE FARRAR MAKES A GOOD
HOUSEMAID — MEASURES FOR RELEASE — MY WIFE
PAYS A VISIT TO OOM PAUL — THE TRUTH ABOUT
THE RAID — PRELIMINARY HEARING — OUT ON
BAIL—THE GUARDED HOUSE—A CASE AGAINST SIR
HERCULES—INDUSTRY PARALYZED ON THE RAND—
A GRIM JUDICIAL FARCE—CONDEMNED TO DEATH

I had the distinction—if it could be so considered—of being among the first arrested.

"What's the exact charge, Lieutenant?" I asked Pietersen.

"Inciting to rebellion and high treason," he gravely replied.

"That has a serious sound. Well, there's nothing to do about it. Let's go," I said resignedly.

A closed carriage waited in front of the hotel, and we climbed into it. The driver touched his horse and at once we rattled away over the red dirt streets to the Johannesburg jail. For several hours thereafter carriages straggled up to deposit hapless committee members who greeted each other with mock gaiety. The last victim of the night's roundup was Colonel Frank Rhodes, who appeared at two-thirty in the morning.

About an hour later a file of mounted police wheeled into position in front of the jail. By the flickering light of candles, lanterns, and lamps, we re-entered the carriages. The police deployed around us as we moved off through sleeping Johannesburg to the Park Station, where a special train was waiting to take us to Pretoria.

Many of the prisoners were burdened with huge bags and rugs —as much luggage as they would have taken on a holiday trip. Unfortunately, it had never entered their heads that they would have to be their own porters. Since I had only one small bag and a pocketful of chocolate, with which my wife had thoughtfully provided me, I could not refrain from joking them about their elaborate preparations for a week-end visit to Pretoria.

I have heard that there were about two thousand Boers laagered along the route, and felt some apprehension should they learn the identity of the passengers in the train. Their only acknowledgment of our presence, however, was to hail us derisively as the "New Transvaal Volksraad."

We were more fortunate than we realized at the time. Those of the Committee who were not taken into custody until the following morning endured real abuse. A crowd of vindictive Boers met them at the Pretoria station, and a shower of stones and brickbats forced them to make the last few hundred yards to the jail on the double-quick. Old Captain Mein, who could not keep up with the others, suffered the most in running this gauntlet.

Pretoria was in no way prepared to receive political prisoners. There had never been any; consequently, the officials had to put us in the jail for ordinary criminals, mostly negro.

Just as day was drearily breaking, we were ushered into the brick enclosed courtyard. On one side of the gate was the guard room; on the other, the jailer's house. Lining the inside of the walls were the narrow cells. On eagerly asking where Jameson and his staff were quartered, we were shown a small building to the right of the entrance some distance from our cells. Having come first, the Raiders were best served, since theirs was the only building with windows. We were told that we could have no communication with them; neither Raiders nor Reformers were permitted to cross the chalk lines around what was already known as the Jameson cottage.

After having been assigned to our separate cells, we were lined up in the yard and conscientiously searched. Phillips, Farrar, Rhodes, and I were then placed in a small cell twelve feet square, which reeked indescribably of the Kaffir prisoners who had previously occupied it. The only ventilation was through a narrow grille over the door. The earthen floor was vermin-infested; almost covering it were four filthy canvas cots, two of them bloodstained. I shuddered at the sight and smell, but managed to pull myself together sufficiently to despatch a cheery telegram to my wife.

The corrugated iron sheathing caught the heat from the semi-tropical sun and retained it throughout the night. The humid and fetid air made rest impossible. To make conditions worse, I had been ill for some time with Zambesi dysentery. The first three nights we were locked in from six to six. Then the prison doctor insisted that the door of our cell, which led into a small inner court, should be left open at night. This afforded us some slight relief.

The influx of sixty-four prisoners at one time crowded the jail to capacity. Among these sixty-four there were seven Americans, twenty-three English, sixteen South Africans, nine Scotchmen, one Welshman, one Turk, seven from other countries. In one cell, twenty-two by fourteen feet, were herded thirty-five of the Reformers. When the outer door was shut at night, they had no air except what passed through a narrow opening into the inner Kaffir quarters. Save for a narrow gangway down the middle, the floor was covered with small mattresses.

Sanitary arrangements were entirely lacking inside the cells; outside, they were little better. There was a tap in the yard, and an open furrow through which ran a noisome trickle of town water. This had to serve as the common washroom for the two hundred and fifty inhabitants of the jail, one hundred and fifty of them black. It was a miracle that we did not all succumb to typhoid.

My wife's thoughtfulness stood the four of us in good stead. We munched chocolate as we tried to accustom ourselves to our new surroundings. No food was served us until noon. For the first few days our sole diet was the same as that provided for the Kaffirs. At six in the morning when the cell was unlocked, tin pannikins of mealie meal, as they called corn meal, were set in rows in the yard.

Near by was a bucket of coarse salt which we had to crush with stones on the cement steps before it could be used. Dinner at twelve was coarse, tasteless, boiled meat, and half a pound of bread. Supper at five was again nothing but mealie meal. What little appetite we could muster for this disgusting pap was not sharpened by encountering Kaffir hairs in the food.

Several of us were soon in such bad physical condition that arrangements had to be made for better food. Our lawyer, J. W. Sauer, eventually succeeded in securing permission to have our meals sent in from the Pretoria Club at irregular intervals. We had to pay for this luxury, of course.

Du Plessis, the head jailer, a cousin of Kruger, himself admitted that the prison was no fit place for "gentlemen." Nevertheless, he was stern and strict, even going so far as to have us searched whenever he thought it expedient. Prison regulations varied from day to day. Our jailers were subject to whims, but bribery of one kind or another usually produced amelioration of some particularly abhorrent regulation. Sometimes the prisoners were confined to their cells; sometimes chalk lines marked bounds beyond which they might not step; sometimes no visitors would be admitted.

During the first week of our imprisonment my sister Betty secured a visiting permit from the landrost and came bearing several green-lined umbrellas. These were a special boon because the temperature often rose to 105° in the shade. Moreover, the fact that Pretoria lies in a basin makes its climate more enervating than that of Johannesburg, which is on the high veldt.

The days passed with wearisome slowness. We were too restless to spend much time reading or writing letters. Marbles became a favorite pastime. There was little opportunity for exercise, although the pedestrian English—when allowed—walked indefatigably round and round the compound. Captain Mein increased his reputation as a raconteur, and was usually surrounded by groups listening to his illimitable store of western mining anecdotes.

During the daytime most of us were to be found attired in pajamas and dozing torpidly in the few feet of shade available. Lace was the only one to keep up appearances; each morning he sedulously clad himself in his brown suit, pink shirt, and straw hat. For a time it was rumored that the prison authorities intended to humiliate us by putting us in prison garb. This alarmed some of my fellow prisoners more than it did me. I told them that the worse treatment we received in that respect, the more flagrant the violation of the conventional treatment of political prisoners, the greater would be the sympathy aroused for us throughout the world. The Boer government evidently reconsidered their intention and prison garb was not inflicted upon us.

The receipt of small comforts from home aroused disproportionate pleasure. My own misery was alleviated somewhat when my wife sent me a trunk containing linen, flea powder, ginger snaps, Shakespeare, beef essence, and soap.

As time went on, the prison regime became less severe. Ordinarily we were allowed to receive visitors daily between two and four except on Saturday, which was supposedly cleaning day, and on Sunday, which was holy. These guests brought us news from the outside world.

Business was said to be practically suspended on the Rand, most of Johannesburg's leading men being in jail. Our property had been put under interdict. The Johannesburghers had sullenly watched Commander Piet Cronje's shaggy-faced Boers parade through their town. These were the same men who later proved themselves such valiant soldiers in the Boer War.

The report came to us that the Hollanders were more rabid than the Boers against us. Kruger had proclaimed an amnesty to all but the "principal criminals," and asked the inhabitants of Johannesburg to let him go before the Volksraad with the motto: "Forgotten and Forgiven."

Kruger had finally agreed with the high commissioner that Jameson and his officers should be sent to England for trial instead of being summarily shot as at first had been threatened. On January 19th they left for Natal, and we heard later that they were cheered along the way. Sir Hercules, his task only partially accomplished, had returned to Cape Town five days earlier without deigning to take cognizance of our plight.

Kruger was reported to have said, "I would pay more heed to a petition from fifty of my burghers than to one from the whole of Johannesburg!"

The high commissioner had practically ceased negotiations after securing Jameson's release. On January 14th he notified Chamberlain that he was leaving Pretoria. Chamberlain cabled back that he was perplexed because nothing had been done about the reforms or the Reformers. He said it was Robinson's duty to use "firm language": "Send me a full report of the steps that you have already taken with regard to this matter, and of the further action that you propose."

Robinson replied that nearly all the leading Johannesburg men were in jail charged with treason, the cases would be tried, and he would regard it as ineffectual and impolitic to urge any reforms at the moment.

Chamberlain's reply was another order for Robinson to resume negotiations at once. Robinson excused himself on the ground that we were being treated well, and were represented by able counsel. "The [Transvaal] Government seem acting within their legal rights, and I do not see how I can interfere." The next day he stated definitely, "No promise was made to Johannesburg by me as an inducement to disarm," and that between himself and Kruger, "the question of concessions to Uitlanders has never been discussed."

Robinson had been in Pretoria for ten days. He had not gone near Jameson. The only information he had requested was statistics as to the number of prisoners, of killed, and of wounded. He had made no effort whatever to get in touch with the Reformers, either personally or through his staff. Moreover, it had been his representations to Chamberlain as to Jameson's extreme danger that had induced us to disarm, and we had received by messenger his assurance of protection for ourselves. We realized fully that the mental vigor of the high commissioner was on the wane and that he was ill; nevertheless, in my opinion there has never been a worse betrayal of trust by a high official of the British government than was shown by him at the time of the Raid.

It has always seemed to me ironical in high degree that, for his eminent services, Sir Hercules should shortly after have become Lord Rosmead.

As soon as Jameson left for England to be tried, we four leaders were moved into his cottage. In one of its two rooms we slept; the other we used as a sitting room. Farrar, driven by a desire for cleanliness, kept house for us, and was so efficient in his domestic role that Colonel Rhodes offered to hire him as a housemaid if they ever got out of jail. It seemed to be a pleasant diversion for Farrar to tidy up our quarters, so I humored him. No valet has ever proved as efficient as my multimillionaire valet, George Farrar. Whenever my wife visited me, he found a sympathetic listener; she told him she had had to cope with the same problem. She also told us more of conditions outside and laughingly commented on the Boers' careful scrutiny of her handbags for possibly concealed cannon when she arrived at Pretoria. Her husband had acquired a reputation as an adept in gun smuggling.

From the time we first went to jail, pressure and influence were brought to bear on Kruger from all sides to effect our release. With the exception of the four leaders and Fitzpatrick, secretary of the Reform Committee, who had been added in place of the absent Leonard, the rest of the Reformers, after nearly three weeks' incarceration, had been let out on bail of $10,000. Naturally they were not allowed to leave Pretoria before the trial.

As soon as Secretary of State Richard Olney heard of my arrest he cabled Manion, American consul at Johannesburg, to take instant measures to see that I received fair play. Since my wife felt that he had not accomplished anything towards that end, she decided to take a hand herself. Accordingly, she composed a cablegram which she despatched under my name, January 30th, to Senator John P. Jones, of Nevada, asking him to submit copies to Generals Miles and Schofield. All three men were influential family friends.

She knew that any concern I had for my personal safety had not allowed me to forget the question of Uitlander grievances. The cable began with the statement, "The Transvaal is a small unenlightened retrogressive community, under the government of a narrow oligarchy, giving a bad, inefficient administration; monstrous monopolies; corruption rampant." It continued with a more detailed description of the condition of the Uitlanders, and pleaded that our government urge the granting of our demands and the fair treatment of the prisoners, particularly the American ones. "First urge the reasonableness of our claim; then warn the Transvaal. . . . Urge our government to act immediately. . . . Enlist sympathy in our favor."

This cablegram was given wide publicity in America through the Hearst and other newspapers. There were many meetings of mining engineers throughout the United States, urged by my old friend Dr. R. W. Raymond, secretary of the American Institute of Mining Engineers, and the result of the activity of these friends was a deluge of demands on Secretary Olney to take action in my case. The State Department finally issued a notice through the press to the effect that the files were being swamped by petitions, and said that everything possible would be done by the government without any further petitions, to which Olney added that he would not feel "justified in making any personal appeal to the President of the South African Republic on behalf of Mr. Hammond." The Senate and the House of Representatives, however, felt less diffident. Almost the entire body united, May 1st, in a petition to Kruger to pardon me, saying they would esteem such action an especial compliment to Congress as well as to the people of the United States.

One amusing, and to me most heartening, aspect of this sympathy at home was occasioned by the offer of Texas miners to rescue me by force if the government would be so kind as to provide a transport for them.

Sir Julian Pauncefote, British ambassador at Washington, had already suggested to Olney that it might be a good idea to put my case unofficially before Lord Salisbury, the British prime minister, who would then undoubtedly do what he could for me. Olney afterwards told me that he had believed this indirect method of proceeding in my case might help to ease the strained situation arising out of the Venezuela crisis.

I received tangible evidence of British sympathy when Sir Jacobus de Wet brought to the prison a cablegram from Salisbury, offering British protection to me and other American prisoners. I told de Wet to express my appreciation and thanks, and then added: "British subjects don't seem to be receiving any great amount of support at home. Since I recognize that my own government is equally powerless, I prefer to go it alone."

Towards the end of January my wife, who was seriously ill, decided to beard Oom Paul himself. It was common knowledge that, despite his gruff manner, he had a kind heart. She had the idea that they would find some ground for mutual understanding. My old friend Sammy Marks, who had tried to pump me so unsuccessfully a few weeks before at Johannesburg, accompanied her. They found the President sitting in his parlor with other Boers who regarded her with a scowl.

Kruger was filling his pipe from a moleskin pouch, and, on Mr. Marks's introduction, shook hands with my wife. He then lit his pipe and puffed at it as he solemnly regarded her.

She tells the story in her own diary:

> Mr. Grobler, the pleasant faced young man, grandson and secretary to the President, observing that I was trembling with fatigue and suppressed excitement, offered me a chair. We sat opposite each other, the President in the middle. I spoke slowly, Mr. Grobler interpreting. This was hardly necessary, President Kruger answering much that I said before it was interpreted. I could understand him perfectly from my familiarity with German and especially Platt-Deutsch.
>
> I explained that I had not come to talk politics. "No, no politics," interrupted the President in a thick loud voice. Nor had I come to ask favour for my husband, as I felt assured that the honesty of his motives would speak for themselves at the day of his trial; but I had come as a woman and daughter of a Republic to ask him to continue the clemency which he had thus far shown, and to thank Mrs. Kruger for the tears which she had shed when Johannesburg was in peril.
>
> President Kruger relaxed a little. "That is true she did weep." He fixed me with his shrewd glance. "Where were you?" he asked abruptly.
>
> "I was in Johannesburg with my husband."
>
> "Were you not afraid? What did you think I was going to do?"

THE OFFICES OF THE CONSOLIDATED GOLD FIELDS COMPANY
OF SOUTH AFRICA

UNDER GUARD AT JOHANNESBURG

"I hoped that you would come to an understanding with the Reformers."

His face darkened.

"I was disappointed that the Americans went against me," he said.

Sammy Marks rose and left the room. I was seized with one of those sudden and unaccountable panics and, from sheer embarrassment—my mood was far too tragic to admit of flippancy—blurted out, "You must come to America, Mr. President, as soon as all this trouble is settled, and see how *we* manage matters."

Kruger's face lighted up with interest.

"I am too old to go so far."

"No man is older than his brain, Mr. President," and Kruger, who knew that in all the trouble he had shown the mental vigour of a man in his prime, accepted my praise with a hearty laugh. This was joined in by the Boers from the other end of the room.

Mrs. Kruger refused to see me, and I liked her none the less for her honest prejudice. I stood to go. President Kruger rose, removed the pipe from between his teeth, and, coughing violently, gave me his hand.

Mr. Grobler escorted me to the gate. "Mrs. Hammond, I shall be very glad to serve you in any way possible to me!" he said with courtesy.

"Then will you say to Mrs. Kruger that I am praying to the same God that peace may come?"

Mrs. Kruger—Tante Sanne, as the Boers called her—relented enough later to see the wives of several of the Johannesburg Reformers. When they asked her to use her influence in behalf of the prisoners, she replied: "Yes, I will do all I can. I am very sorry for you all, although I knew that none of you thought of me that night when we heard that Jameson had crossed the border, and we were afraid the President would have to go out and fight, and when they went and caught his old white horse that he had not ridden for eight years. But all the same I am sorry for you all."

Bits of information about the Jameson Raid had trickled into prison through visitors and occasional newspapers. From these I was able for the first time to piece together in detail what had happened outside Johannesburg during those eventful days of late December and early January. Subsequently I became acquainted with the full case for and against Jameson.

General Gordon once said, "England was never made by her statesmen; England was made by her adventurers." Jameson knew only too well the exploits of Lord Clive and other famous adventurers of British history. Recalling the astounding results of his own audacity in the First Matabele War, he now decided to allow his personal motives to dominate his course of action; he impetuously subordinated the welfare of the people of Johannesburg to his overweening ambition.

Despite our explicit instructions to Jameson, which he had received from both Heaney and Holden, at three o'clock in the afternoon of Sunday, December 29th, he paraded the troops at Pitsani, and read to them our letter of invitation. Then he explained that he did not intend any hostilities; he meant only to help the inhabitants of Johannesburg in their extremity and to ensure the granting of their just demands.

Such was Dr. Jim's magnetic personality that he had no difficulty in securing the adherence of his five hundred troops to his mad enterprise of rushing to the rescue of the women and children of Johannesburg, or, as Alfred Austin, poet laureate, designated them— "the girls of the gold reef city." Even Holden and Heaney threw in their lot with their hero, Jameson, and accompanied the column. Colvin, Jameson's biographer, says that after Heaney had delivered his message, Jameson paced back and forth and then said, "I'm going."

"Thought you would," said Heaney.

"And what are you going to do?" said Jameson.

"Going with you," said Heaney.

"Thought you would," said Jameson.

The enthusiasm among the Raiders outran their caution. The Johannesburg Committee had given careful instructions to Jameson to cut the wires to Pretoria before he started. The soldiers assigned to this task were so exhilarated from the effects of the canteen's having been thrown open to celebrate the departure that they found themselves unable to distinguish between certain wire fences and the telegraph lines; by this most deplorable error the line to Pretoria was left intact, while that to Johannesburg was cut. The Boers were thus informed of Jameson's departure for Johannesburg only a few hours after he had left Pitsani; it was eighteen hours before any information reached us.

At six-thirty on this Sunday evening the Pitsani column started with five hundred troopers (not the fifteen hundred he had promised, nor the fifteen hundred rifles he was to bring to the Reform Committee), and at five the next morning were joined by the column from Mafeking at Malmani, thirty-nine miles from Pitsani. In addition there were about seventy Kaffirs to act as carriers, and to drive the eleven carts with provisions and ammunition for the eight Maxims, the two seven-pounders and the one twelve-and-a-half-pounder.

The column followed the road or rather cart track, which led from Malmani to Krugersdorp. On Tuesday morning it reached the first stage station and after a short rest the march was resumed.

Wednesday at noon the column reached the outskirts of Krugersdorp, the western terminus of the railway line running along the Rand through Johannesburg, only twenty-one miles away. Scouts reported that Boer troops were holding a strong position in front of the ridges which were honeycombed with mine pits and dotted with tailing dumps.

Jameson was now forced to abandon his cherished but inevitably futile hope of reaching Johannesburg without bloodshed. When Willoughby reached Krugersdorp a few shots were exchanged with the Boer forces. Except for occasional sniping, which caused a few casualties among the Raiders, the Boers made no attack.

When Jameson ascertained that the Boers were defending the road we had laid out for him, he consulted with Willoughby as to what should be done. While this discussion was going on, they observed two youths, apparently from a neighboring farm, who had been viewing the progress of the battle with interested eyes. Thinking that a native could logically supply the most accurate topographical information, Willoughby asked, "What's the best road from here to Johannesburg?"

One of the young men, a loyal Boer, replied in perfect English, "If you follow this road to the right about ten miles you'll come to Doornkop, and from there you can't miss the way." Under ordinary conditions ten miles would have been nothing for the column, but after three days of marching and the recent fighting, men and horses were hungry and exhausted. The troopers dropped in their tracks to snatch what rest they could. Early the next morning the bugler sounded boots and saddles. Willoughby took the road to the right—straight into the Boer trap.

The circle of rocky hills surrounding Doornkop was already occupied by Cronje's troops. As Jameson's column defiled into the swampy vlei, the Boers fired down upon them. After an hour's fight, eighteen of the Raiders had been killed and forty wounded. Jameson, realizing that he was hopelessly outnumbered and out-maneuvered, ordered the white flag hoisted. He then had Willoughby send Cronje, commandant of the Transvaal forces, the following:

> We surrender, provided that you guarantee us safe-conduct out of the country for every member of the force.

The commandant answered literally as follows:

> Officer—Please take note that I shall immediately assemble our officers to decide upon your communication.

About thirty minutes later Willoughby received the following:

> I acknowledge your letter. The answer is that, if you will undertake to pay the expense which you have caused the South African Republic, and if you will surrender with your arms, then I shall spare the lives of you and yours. Please send me a reply to this within thirty minutes.
>
> P. A. CRONJE,
> Commandant, Potchefstroom

Willoughby immediately replied, accepting the following conditions:

> I accept the terms on the guarantee that the lives of all
> will be spared. I now await your instructions as to how
> and where we are to lay down our arms. At the same
> time I would ask you to remember that my men have
> been without food for the last twenty-four hours.

Thereupon the guns were surrendered to the Boers. Later Commandant Malan, though well aware of the conditions upon which they had surrendered, told Jameson that he would not guarantee his life nor the lives of the other leaders, but would hand them over to General Joubert for judgment.

It was then, of course, too late to offer resistance, and Jameson and his officers were escorted to Pretoria as prisoners of war.

From a study of the evidence available, I am convinced that the Boer intent at the time was to secure Jameson's surrender as simply as possible, and that the later deliberate suppression of the terms was Kruger's idea of diplomacy in dealing with us in Johannesburg.

After the Raid, Willoughby and some of his officers lost their army commissions. Willoughby tried to defend himself by suggesting that Chamberlain, as colonial secretary, knew in advance of the proposed invasion and approved it. The story was based on certain telegrams exchanged between Dr. Rutherfoord Harris and Chamberlain relative to the transfer of Bechuanaland to the Cape government.

A whispering campaign was carried on by Chamberlain's enemies in an endeavor to implicate him. Rhodes definitely acquitted Chamberlain at the Parliamentary Inquiry; furthermore, in the many talks I had with Rhodes afterwards, he never even hinted that Chamberlain had had anything to do with the Raid. It is preposterous to assert that a statesman of Chamberlain's acumen could have been party to the Raid. He would have realized how greatly that would embarrass Great Britain in her foreign relations. But undeniably both Chamberlain and the high commissioner did know that Jameson had troops at Pitsani. I feel satisfied that Chamberlain has been completely exonerated from complicity in the Raid.

After Doornkop, Jameson was exceedingly bitter against the Reform Committee. He alleged that we had failed to send troops to his assistance, and that the Raid would not, as Rhodes put it, have "gone off like a damp squib" had we fulfilled our part of the bargain.

To the impartial reader the role played by Jameson in what might be described as a Comedy of Errors, had it not had such tragic consequences, fixes upon him the responsibility of the "damp squib."

According to our understanding with Jameson, he was to come to us. It was never for a minute contemplated that we should go to his assistance. Furthermore, there was never at any time any indication from Jameson that he required support from Johannesburg. His own telegram of December 27th to his brother—"Let J. H. Hammond telegraph instantly all right"—proves that he understood he was not to start until I had given the word.

In the preceding chapter I have carefully shown what steps were taken by us in Johannesburg to prevent his starting, how he utterly disregarded both the commands of Rhodes and the proclamation of Sir Hercules Robinson, and lastly how, through the inexplicable stupidity of his chief military officer, Willoughby, he was captured.

The case of the Reform Committee against Jameson's accusation was summed up in the February 17, 1896, issue of the Johannesburg *Times,* while we were still imprisoned. It read in part:

> We would again . . . direct the attention of the [Transvaal] Government to the conduct of the Reformers when Dr. Jameson crossed the border. They kept the people from assisting the filibuster, at the danger of being lynched by their own supporters, sacrificed their reputation, their popularity, their power, and the cause so dear to their hearts. They swore allegiance to the Transvaal flag, they put down disorder with a strong hand, they prevented a shot being fired, although the Boer patrols fired in defiance of the armistice. When they could have easily escaped during the two days of confusion following the Jameson invasion, they waited quietly, and when called to lend their powerful assist-

ance, in persuading the armed Uitlanders to lay down their weapons, they did so faithfully and effectively. . . . Not one of the men now in gaol had to be chased, or made the slightest attempt to escape. And no one supposes that with their wealth they could not all have devised some means of getting away if they had wanted to. They stood like men, and deserve some consideration from the Government, from Johannesburg, and from the world.

In time Jameson came to admit that he might not have been entirely free of blame for what had happened, though he failed to make a public statement to that effect.

Sir Robert Williams, one of his intimate friends, met Jameson at the Burlington Hotel in London after his release from Holloway Prison and asked him, "Well, Doctor, whose fault was it that the thing failed?"

"Everybody's fault," Jameson answered, "mine included."

If I may have seemed too hard on Jameson in the criticisms I have just made on his conduct in the Raid, I should like to temper this by saying that, for the man himself, I always had the greatest admiration and affection.

Dr. Jim was equally ready to take up the scalpel or the sword. During the Boer War, he heard that one of the bravest of his old Rhodesians had been badly wounded and could not survive without a surgical operation. Although himself in ill health and worn out by fatigue, the doctor jolted all night over the veldt in a Cape cart drawn by two scrawny mules. He arrived at dawn and performed a long, difficult operation that saved his former comrade's life. This action was done in the same quiet manner with which he used to take from his belt the last piece of biltong and give it to a hungry sentry in the days when he was pushing the frontier north of the Zambesi. Instances of this kind endeared Jameson to the people of Rhodesia.

During those prison days the whole Jameson affair was a subject for speculation rather than certain knowledge. My wife graphically describes the preliminary trial in her book, *A Woman's Part in a Revolution,* from which I quote:

> Monday, February 3rd. The preliminary trial of the Reform Committee prisoners was called this morning. The hearing was in the second Raadzaal. Although the accommodation for the public was limited there was a large crowd of Johannesburghers present.
>
> Shortly before ten o'clock an armed escort marched up to the jail for Messrs. Hammond, Phillips, Farrar, Fitzpatrick, and Colonel Rhodes. The other Reformers stood in a bunch at the entrance of the hall. All the principal government officials were present. Sir Jacobus de Wet appeared, accompanied by Honorable J. Rose-Innes, Q. C., one of the leaders of the Cape Colony bar, who had come from the Cape to watch the case on behalf of the Imperial Government.
>
> Punctually at ten the State Attorney, Dr. H. J. Coster, took his seat, and, beginning with my husband's name, called the accused into court.
>
> The sixty-four prisoners were assigned to rows of cane-bottomed chairs in the northwest corner of the building. The proceedings were in Dutch, and continued throughout the day. With the exception of a few, none of the Reformers understood Dutch. The hall was without ventilation, and overcrowded, and sixty-four more bored and disconsolate-looking men, I believe, were never brought together. Some of them fanned vigorously with their hats, others gave themselves up to circumstances and sank into apathy. On the second day, profiting by experience, fans and paperbacked novels were brought into the court room by the arraigned.

There were also present many prominent officials of the Transvaal Republic.

Since the proceedings were in Dutch, we had little idea of what was going on. The testimony of each witness was read back to him in a free translation by the interpreter. Thereupon he was asked to sign the notes of his evidence, the accuracy of which he had to take on faith.

The second day of the hearing, I was too ill to attend. My wife, who immediately noticed my absence, came at once to the prison.

After one look at me, she said, "I'm going to get you out of here, Jack."

Feeling too miserable to be moved, and in dread lest hospital conditions be even worse than those to which I had become more or less accustomed, I replied, "I'd rather stay here than go to the prison hospital."

"I've a better plan than that," she answered reassuringly, and hurried off. So successful was her intervention with the Transvaal officials that, before the end of the day, I had been moved into a small cottage in Pretoria. My wife, her maid, and my sister Betty were permitted to be with me. Captain de Korte, a Dutch officer serving with the Boers, lived with us in the house. Thirteen men formed the exterior guard.

Although living conditions were vastly improved by this transfer, prison regulations remained in effect; surveillance was close. All letters and telegrams were censored by Captain de Korte, and all visitors had to have permits. The ladies were allowed to leave the house only twice a week. De Korte, although strict, was most considerate, even to the point of wearing civilian clothes instead of his uniform in the house. The guards were careful to see that we did not escape. One soldier remained always at the bedroom door while we slept, and two others were posted just outside the window on the veranda. My wife and I could never exchange a private word. Sometimes we wrote a message which would be burnt at the bedroom candle as soon as read.

The illness which I had contracted on my trip to Rhodesia had been aggravated by my distressing experiences in the jail, and I was exceedingly weak. A few steps were sufficient to exhaust my strength; I appeared to be growing steadily worse. In great anxiety of mind, my wife summoned Dr. Murray, our family physician, from Johannesburg. His representations of my state of health induced the Boer officials to give permission for me to drive out daily, but I was too ill to avail myself often of the privilege.

Since I did not improve, my wife decided I ought to be taken to Johannesburg where the higher altitude produced a more bracing climate. To everybody's surprise she secured consent to remove me to my own home. At the same time Phillips, Farrar, and Frank Rhodes, who also had suffered in health, were transferred from the Jameson cottage, with its mildewed walls and damp floor, to new quarters just outside Pretoria.

Each of us was to pay the entire cost of his detention and to deposit $50,000 in sovereigns as bail. Since it would have taken me too long to raise the money elsewhere, I accepted Barnato's kind offer to supply the necessary currency.

With his usual impetuosity, Barney was causing a great furore at the time by being one of the first to threaten to close down or sell his mining properties. His explanation was that it was no use trying to operate them with all his associates in prison.

The prospect of getting out of Pretoria gave me strength enough to survive the train journey. De Korte and nine soldiers accompanied us and at the Johannesburg station turned us over to a new guard. These local Vrywilligers hurried us off before I could even exchange a word with the members of my engineering staff who were there to meet me.

I was kept in even closer custody at my own home in Johannesburg than had been the case at Pretoria. At night there were two guards instead of one outside the bedroom door; one was posted at each of the windows, and more were scattered outside. These extraordinary precautions seemed somewhat fantastic in view of the fact that I could not have tottered around the block. When Captain de Korte came to see me without securing a permit, the commander of my guard was so angered that he lodged a complaint.

The same afternoon on which we returned home, February 18th, there was an appalling explosion at Fordsburg, one of the suburbs. Our son, Jacky, then seven years old, had been digging with a miner's polepick in the garden. When extracted from his refuge under the bed, his comment was, "When I was digging in the garden and that terrible noise came, I thought I had dug up hell."

Our superstitious Kaffirs were under the impression that the sun had burst.

Actually fifty-five tons of nitroglycerine had exploded, wounding seven hundred persons, killing eighty, and rendering fifteen hundred homeless. This shocking catastrophe was entirely attributable to the negligence of the Netherlands Railway. Since Fordsburg was the section of town occupied by the poorer Boer inhabitants, there were virtually no Uitlander casualties. Nevertheless, the Uitlanders at once turned over the Wanderers' Club to the homeless and opened subscription lists for relief of the sufferers. In a few hours they had raised $325,000, the railway supplied $50,000, while the Boer government contributed $125,000.

Kruger himself hurried from Pretoria and thanked Johannesburg for coming so nobly to the rescue of the afflicted. Speaking, as he always did, in the manner of a predikant, he chose as the text of his speech, "Blessed are the merciful, for they shall obtain mercy."

In spite of the improved climate and better care, my health failed to improve at Johannesburg. It was finally arranged, on doubling my bail to $100,000—which my friend Barney again supplied—that I might go to Cape Town for a few weeks pending our trial, with the hope that the sea air would prove beneficial. By this time the members of my guard and I were on such friendly terms that, before we parted, they asked to be photographed with me. I willingly agreed to this request. While we were wishing each other good luck over a bottle of champagne in the garden, the carriages were waiting in front. My wife sent Jacky to hunt me up. He returned with the report, "Papa is playing with his guard outside."

By way of diversion Jacky accompanied me on my trip to Muizenburg, the sea resort near Cape Town. My wife was to follow us next day. On arrival at Muizenburg I joined Joseph Story Curtis, another of the Reform Committee. He had been partially paralyzed as a result of his prison hardships and never recovered sufficiently to stand trial.

Through the kindness of Miss Louise Rhodes, sister of Cecil, I was given the cottage in which Rhodes subsequently passed away.

Fortunately for Jacky, my wife arrived as per schedule. The boy had complained several times a day that his clothes were too small and uncomfortable. I appeased him temporarily by telling him that he was growing very rapidly and would soon be a man. As soon as his mother came, however, the cause of his discomfort was perceived. It seems I had been putting his trousers on hind part before.

As soon as I arrived I was besieged by queries, "What do you think Rhodes is going to do?" I found that the political enemies of Rhodes were assiduously spreading the report that he had deserted Jameson and the Reformers. This I most emphatically denied, expressing the opinion of the Reform Committee that we were convinced Rhodes had made every possible effort to prevent Jameson's departure from Pitsani.

That Rhodes had resigned as premier of Cape Colony, on January 5th, and had gone to London before our trial, did not in the least indicate desertion of us. We realized that even if he remained in Africa he could be of no help to us, and any attempt by him to influence Kruger would only result in incensing the Boer president. The Committee believed there was some possibility of Rhodes being of service to us in London. This belief was justified by what I learned from Rhodes when I saw him in London for the first time after my release from prison.

Rhodes's reason for leaving South Africa so soon after Jameson's surrender was to attend a meeting of the Chartered Company. He was attempting to re-establish confidence and, in behalf of the investing public, steady the South African securities market, which had precipitously tumbled to practically nothing. I was convinced that Rhodes would return to South Africa as soon as possible and go to Rhodesia to take measures against the Matabele, who had revolted on March 24th because of Jameson's absence in England awaiting trial. This was exactly what Rhodes did. He reached Bulawayo at the end of March, while we were still prisoners, and immediately took measures to suppress the uprising of the Matabele which I have described in a previous chapter.

While I was recuperating at Muizenburg, one of my visitors was Sir Gordon Sprigg, Rhodes's successor as premier. During the course of our conversation, Sprigg brought up the subject of the financial difficulties of the Cape Railway. There had been a great falling-off in the freight shipped over the road to Johannesburg, owing to the closing down of many of the mines and the rescinding of orders for machinery and supplies.

This gave me a logical opportunity to intercede for the Reform prisoners.

"Sir Gordon," I began, "I feel sure your personal sympathies are with the Reform Movement. I realize also that you have to conciliate Kruger, which puts you in a difficult situation politically. I'm sure, however, that some means must be devised for effecting the release of the Reformers."

Sir Gordon eyed me dubiously. "I deeply sympathize with your sufferings, Mr. Hammond, but I have no authority to act in this matter. My paramount duty is to attempt to bring business conditions in the Cape back to normal."

"That's undoubtedly true," I replied, "but the prosperity of the Cape cannot be dissociated from that of the Transvaal. You know as well as I do why business is paralyzed. I have been authorized to tell you that the Reformers—who, as you know, hold the economic interests on the Rand in their hands—intend to stop the further purchase of Boer properties, close down the mines now operating, and cancel the purchase of large orders of machinery that were to be transported over the Cape Colony Railway lines, the only way to stop this is to secure the release of the prisoners."

"Why," replied Sir Gordon, "that would tend to precipitate a business panic. Coming at the same time as the rinderpest, which has decimated the cattle, it would work untold misery to the people of the country."

"True, Sir Gordon. On the other hand, the mines could not be operated successfully under present working conditions. These conditions exist because in the past men of your political power have not made full use of their influence with the Boers in behalf of the Uitlanders. We have made an attempt toward reform and failed; now it is up to you to solve the problem."

As the time set for the trial drew near, my health had improved somewhat and I could walk about.

One day after I had returned to my hotel from a walk, a "minister" was announced and, though I doubted that any minister would care to see me, I told the clerk at the desk to send him up. My visitor's face seemed vaguely familiar; but it was not until he had divested himself of his whiskers that I recognized Richard A. Parker, one of my mining staff. Although among those ordered to be arrested, he had succeeded in escaping from the Transvaal in his clerical disguise. His mission at Cape Town was to keep me from returning to Pretoria. In spite of his reluctance to abandon his comrades and, as he expressed it, to show the white feather, I insisted on his taking the first steamer leaving the country. This was in the interest of the Reform Committee rather than out of consideration for Parker's welfare.

In addition to this personal warning, many of my friends in the Transvaal wrote me that feeling against the Reform leaders was intense and that, if I were not assassinated en route to Pretoria, I should certainly be condemned to death upon my arrival. Victor Clement, who was carrying on the operations at the Consolidated Gold Fields in my absence, also vehemently deprecated my return. He suggested that if my illness were to continue the Transvaal government could not forfeit my bail without incurring consular interference. After sentence had been passed, I could then decide whether I should return or forfeit bail. Simpson, another of my engineers, wrote me to the same effect. Even de Korte confidentially urged me by all means to remain away.

Alarm for the safety of the Reformers was increased by the rumor that certain of the more intransigent Boers intended to lynch the leaders before trial. Commandant Henning Pretorius, a prominent Boer official, had visited Cape Colony shortly after the Raid. There he found that the original beam used to hang the five Boers condemned by the British after "Slagter's Nek" had been built into a Boer farmhouse at Cookhouse Drift. He had purchased the beam and brought it back to Pretoria. With sinister intent, the local newspaper, *Volksstem,* then published a description of the 1816 executions, and called on the people to avenge themselves on the Reformers. Chamberlain was informed of this threat; he cabled Kruger that the president would be held personally responsible for the safety of the Reform leaders. Pretorius thereupon made the excuse that he had brought back the beam to be placed in the National Museum; Kruger increased the guard around the prison.

Without my knowledge my friends had used every argument to induce my wife to prevent my returning to Johannesburg. She says in her account:

Mr. Manion, the Consular Agent, and Mr. R. E. Brown, an American just arrived in Cape Town from the Rand, took me aside and laid the case in all its bare brutality before me. *To allow my husband to return to Pretoria was for him to meet certain death.* If he were not lynched by the excited Boers, he was sure to get a death sentence. Mr. Brown showed feeling as he plead with me to use a wife's influence to save her husband's life. My head was swimming. I could only repeat in a dull, dogged way: "He says his honour takes him back. He is the father of my sons, and I'd rather see him dead than dishonoured."

Somehow I got to my room, and the page-boy stumbled over me at the door some time afterward, and ran for Mrs. Cavanagh. When I felt a little recovered, I put on my hat, and, not waiting for my husband's return from an appointment with Dr. Thomas, I drove to the office of Mr. Rose-Innes. He was not in, and his clerk declared he did not know when he would be in. "Very well, then; I'll wait until he does come in."

I was given a comfortable chair, and a dictionary was dusted and placed under my feet. Mr. Rose-Innes at length appeared. He was greatly astonished to find me waiting for him. I began abruptly: "Dear Mr. Rose-Innes, I am in need of a friend; my distress is so great that I can no longer distinguish right from wrong." I told him everything; showed him the letters which I had received, and, facing him, asked, "What is my duty? I can appeal to my husband for my sake, to save

378 The Autobiography of John Hays Hammond

the life of our child [she was an expectant mother]—
and perhaps dissuade him! *My God, it is a temptation!*"

Mr. Rose-Innes sat deep in thought.

"If you think his going back is a needless throwing
away of a valuable life," I began, with a timid hope beginning to grow in my heart—"I will chloroform him
and have him taken to sea!"

Mr. Rose-Innes leaned forward, and took my hand
gently between his own: "Mrs. Hammond, your husband is doing the right thing in going back; don't try to
dissuade him. If he were my own brother I would say
the same"—and I accepted his decision.

We returned to Pretoria.

Just before my scheduled departure, however, I became so ill that
my friends petitioned the Boer government for a stay. The only
reply was an abrupt notification from State Attorney Coster to
American Consul Chapin that I must be on hand for the convening
of the High Court in Pretoria at ten o'clock, Friday, April 24th.

On the eve of the trial Coster agreed with our chief advocate,
Wessels, that, if the leaders would consent to plead guilty to the
charge of high treason, he would permit the rest of the Reform Committee to plead guilty to a merely nominal offense. Wessels assured
us that if we should plead not guilty, there would certainly be a trial
of long duration with an inevitable verdict against us. We had also
the alternative of claiming there had been an arrangement with the
Boer government which had been broken by our arrest. The final
choice was to accept Coster's proposal and plead guilty, realizing that
conviction in any case was a foregone conclusion.

Many of the Committee objected to admitting guilt, but Coster
insisted that, if this bargain was to be made, the pleas would have
to be uniform.

So far as the leaders were concerned, we were of one mind in agreeing to accept whatever punishment might be decreed for us in order
to exculpate so far as possible the other Reformers, many of whom
had been induced to enter the revolution by our example. Coster's
strategy in persuading us to plead guilty would be of definite advan-

tage to the Boer government; they would avoid having their dirty political linen washed before an eagerly awaiting world.

Once the arrangement had been reached, Coster and Wessels discussed the form of law under which the case would be tried. The Transvaal courts operated under the Roman Dutch law, save where special statutes had been passed. Coster said the statute law, mild in term, applied to our case, although he qualified this by admitting that the trial judge had the power to rule otherwise. This, our attorney informed us, was extremely unlikely.

Considerable difficulty arose over the choice of a judge to preside at the trial. Three out of the five Supreme Court justices were disqualified because they had acted as emissaries in the preliminary dealings at the time of the Olive Branch negotiations between the Reform Committee and the Boer government. A fourth was admittedly too much of a Boer partisan; the fifth was a liberal and, although it was his turn to preside, he was passed over by Coster— he could not be relied upon to render a sufficiently severe sentence. Consequently the government decided on Gregorowski to conduct the trial. This judge had recently come from the Orange Free State and had been appointed Chief Justice of the Transvaal in place of Kotzé. Gregorowski was so noted for his severe sentences upon all offenders save Boers that he had been given the sobriquet of "the hanging judge."

All these points had been decided upon before I started on my journey from Cape Town to Pretoria with Dr. Scholtz in attendance. Since my name had been telegraphed on ahead, at each station beyond the border many Boer farmers came into the car to satisfy their curiosity about the criminal. By the time we had reached Johannesburg, Dr. Scholtz decided it would be impossible for me to continue the journey. We wired that I would arrive at Pretoria on the following day by the noon train. This accounts for my absence the first day of the trial.

Wessels explained to the court that my illness would prevent my attendance before Monday, and applied for postponement. When this was refused, he pleaded guilty to high treason for the three leaders present, and a copy of this plea was signed by the accused. On my arrival at Pretoria the document was brought to me, and I affixed my name as evidence of my concurrence in all that had been done.

Monday morning the trial was resumed in the great Market Hall, quickly converted from the dispensing of food to the dispensing of justice. An hour before the trial began a great crowd had assembled at the main entrance, although it was known that admission was by special ticket only. The guards at the gate were so conscientious on the first day that some of the accused themselves would have been turned away had they not been identified.

With the other leaders I made my entrance into a room already packed with jurymen, witnesses, press representatives, and favored visitors, both men and women. On the floor, covered with coconut matting, had been placed long plain forms for the accused, the witnesses, and the officials. Facing the main entrance was a large carpeted dais, raised about a foot from the floor. Green baize curtains had been hastily arranged to produce the proper judicial dignity, while piles of documents and books provided the legal atmosphere. Many women were already on the platform, and it was difficult to find room for late arrivals. Fifty or more local police were scattered throughout the hall to quell any possible disorder.

At the rear of the hall the judge occupied a temporary bench raised a foot and a half above the dais, before which were tables and chairs for the bar. On the left was the witness stand; on the right, accommodations for a supernumerary jury. The press was represented by a large group from the leading European papers.

The prisoners were conducted to seats between the dais and the barricade on the right, and facing the witness box. The acoustics were naturally poor so that, with the exception of the judges and advocates, few of those present could hear what was going forward.

Coster presented the case for the state in a restrained and quiet manner. We were startled, however, when he read into the record the evidence captured from Major White at Doornkop. This was the first inkling we had that the state was in possession of such proof.

At the time of Jameson's surrender at Doornkop the Boers captured Major Robert White's despatch box, containing diaries, notebooks, codes, cipher keys, and worst of all, the letter of invitation which we had given to Jameson undated on condition that he use it only when so ordered by us. Now, to our astonishment and consternation, we learned that the date of the letter had been filled in as of December 20th, and that Major White, as magistrate in Bechuanaland Protectorate, had certified it as a true copy. Furthermore, while in the jail in Pretoria, he had confirmed his own affidavit. Later he said he did not remember anything about this, but the charge was made that he had made the confirmation in exchange for the return of some of his private papers. We subsequently learned that, without authority and unknown to us, Dr. Wolff had actually filled in the date at Jameson's request.

When Coster finished, Wessels first entered a written statement setting forth the motives which had activated us and explaining why our so-called rebellion had been no more than constitutional agitation. He ended his defense with an eloquent plea for clemency.

To the amazement of all, Coster then jumped to his feet and, in contrast with his previous quiet manner, burst into a violent diatribe against the Reformers. Wessels objected, but was overruled. Coster acted like one possessed. He ran up and down the platform, waving his hands in the air. His voice rose excitedly until the words "Hangen bij den nek!" repeated over and over, warned us that our agreement was to be abrogated. Even with only a rudimentary knowledge of Dutch, we could make out only too well that he was urging sentence under the Roman Dutch law instead of the Transvaal statutes.

At the termination of his harangue, court was adjourned until the following day. It was apparent now that the rumors of a severe sentence were to be uncomfortably confirmed.

The next morning, Tuesday, the town swarmed with burghers. The state artillery was omnipresent and troops were massed in Market Square to prevent any demonstration. The audience was packed tightly into the extemporaneous courtroom. A feeling of ominous suspense pervaded the hall; the atmosphere of agitation was conveyed by a perpetual shuffle of feet, a flutter of fans, subdued whispers, an occasional clank of arms, the constant sound of footsteps passing to and fro in the rear.

Judge Gregorowski took his seat. He smiled slightly as he made an apparently jocular remark to an attendant. Then, recovering his solemnity, he made the unexpected and significant request that the court be cleared of women.

When the last of them had vanished through the great doors, the judge began to pass in review the evidence before him, making no reference to the statement on our behalf that had been submitted the day before. He reviewed the statute law and gave his reasons for setting it aside in favor of the Roman Dutch law. His voice droned on interminably.

He brought to an end his summing up of the legal aspects of the case about an hour after court had convened. Just as he finished, a small wooden dock, large enough for only four men, was carried in over the heads of the assemblage, and set down before him.

He then stated that the signatories of the Jameson letter were directly responsible for shedding burghers' blood at Doornkop. He was prepared, he said, to pass upon them the only sentence possible under the Roman Dutch law. Whatever hope there might be for mercy must lie in the hearts of the Executive Council and in the magnanimity of the president. Certainly, in no other quarter could there be the slightest grounds for hope.

"Lionel Phillips, George Farrar, Francis Rhodes, John Hays Hammond!" called the registrar.

We were led into the dock. The sheriff called for silence; there was a pause until a complete hush had fallen.

"Lionel Phillips, have you any legal reason to urge why sentence of death should not be passed upon you?"

The firm response was "No." After a pause, Gregorowski carefully adjusted the black cap on his head, and pronounced sentence.

The same words were intoned to Colonel Rhodes and George Farrar, the interpreter repeating them in English until he broke down under the strain. Half-suppressed exclamations of protest and horror began to break forth, in spite of the threatening attitude of the soldiers and attendants.

In no way perturbed, Gregorowski now turned to me. Angered by the Boer treachery to a point where fear could play no part, I looked steadily at the judge and repeated the same bleak monosyllable.

The room had become so still that I could clearly distinguish his solemn words. "The sentence of the court is that you be taken from this place where you are now, and be conveyed to the jail at Pretoria, or any such other jail in this Republic as may be appointed by law, that you be kept there till a time and place of execution shall be appointed by lawful authority, and that you be taken to the place of execution to be there hanged by the neck till you are dead.

"May Almighty God have mercy on your soul."

TAFT AND MYSELF

THE AUTOBIOGRAPHY OF

JOHN HAYS HAMMOND

Illustrated with Photographs

VOLUME

2

FARRAR & RINEHART · INCORPORATED

On Murray Hill, New York

Contents Volume Two

List of Illustrations

CHAPTER TWENTY

In Pretoria Gaol

THE DEATH CELL—SENTENCE COMMUTED —FRIENDS
IN NEED—SMUGGLED SAUSAGES—SUICIDE OF A
FELLOW PRISONER—TWO HUNDRED MILLION BIG
BUGS —THE MISPLACED HUMOR OF MARK TWAIN—
"MAGNANIMITY BY INCHES"—THE BARGAINING
BEGINS—SOUTH AFRICA DEMANDS OUR RELEASE TO
RESTORE PROSPERITY—PRICED AT $125,000—
WELCOMED BY JOHANNESBURG—THE SELECT
COMMITTEE OF THE CAPE OF GOOD HOPE—A NOVICE IN
INTERNATIONAL LAW—"REVOLUTIONS ARE EXPENSIVE"

*A*s I stepped from the dock, the spectators were so emotionally stirred that an old man collapsed directly in front of me. I stooped to lift him and was reminded of my status by a swift blow from the rifle butt of a guard.

Du Plessis, the head jailer, seated himself beside me in a closed carriage, and we started off at a quick pace for the jail. As we neared the gates, a delivery wagon carrying a coffin passed and entered the prison gate just ahead of us. My nervous tension was so great that the most macabre circumstance would have seemed funny. I pointed out the coffin and asked Du Plessis, "Is that for Phillips or for me? It looks as though it would fit either of us."

Du Plessis made no comment. The English claimed he was gross and brutal, and were resentful of his methods. I, on the contrary, considered that only the characteristics of a jailer should be looked for in a jailer. We were in prison and not at a party. Du Plessis and I respected each other's position and got along without friction.

News of our sentence had preceded us. Even the guards were visibly moved. The other prisoners, who had been given a sentence of two years and a fine of $10,000 each, were marched through the streets. As they filed within the prison gates, Dr. Leyds stood smiling at them, unable to suppress his evident satisfaction. The sinister character of Kruger's chief counselor was at this moment truthfully revealed. Leyds hated the Uitlanders more keenly than did the bitterest Boer. It was the Uitlanders who thwarted the large-scale grafting schemes of Leyds and his associates.

Phillips, Farrar, Frank Rhodes, and I were at once placed in the death cell, and the customary formalities for those about to die were observed. The death watch was maintained for twenty hours. The silence of the night was disturbed only by the occasional subdued guttural voice of the guard and the steady hammer strokes of the carpenters erecting the gallows outside.

I was so utterly worn out with fatigue and illness that I threw myself on the nearest dirty cot and passed the night tossing restlessly from side to side.

When daylight finally came I sat up and all four of us looked disconsolately at one another.

"What sort of night did you pass, Jack?" asked Frank Rhodes.

"I'm afraid I didn't sleep much," I replied. "How about you, Frank?"

"The same," Colonel Rhodes sighed.

At this moment the door was thrown open to admit a messenger. He announced that he had been sent by Dr. Leyds who had interceded with Kruger in our behalf.

"Gentlemen, I have the honor to inform you that the death sentence has been commuted."

I had risen to my feet at his entrance. As soon as he finished speaking, I asked quickly, "To what?"

"Life imprisonment."

"Oh, hell!" I exclaimed disgustedly and turned on my heel.

Leyds's emissary seemed taken aback by our reception of his news.

He had evidently been told to bring back an accurate report of our joyous excitement and expressions of gratitude. But Leyds was not a good psychologist. He had underestimated the moral stamina of the leaders and had felt sure that they would be deeply grateful for his intervention, so that he might appear before the world in the role of one who is generous to a defeated enemy.

The messenger asked rather stiffly, "Is there any message you would like me to convey to Dr. Leyds?"

"Not so far as I am concerned," I said shortly, and asked the others, "How do you feel about it?"

They agreed that thanks were uncalled for.

It had suited the Boer purposes to keep us on the rack as long as possible and then, by proclaiming an act of clemency, to impress the world with Boer magnanimity. After several days in the death cell, we were moved back to the Jameson cottage, and then informed for the first time that on the very afternoon of the trial our sentence had been commuted to fifteen years' imprisonment. So even the message Leyds sent us under the guise of mercy was a cruel lie.

The decision as to the commutation of our sentences had not been arrived at without extended argument. The Executive Council had taken several votes. At each ballot two recalcitrant Boers had insisted they would be satisfied with nothing less than having us hang as high as Haman.

Krüger himself favored milder punishment—he hated the idea of blood guilt. He was astute enough to realize the effect on the world at large if so drastic a revenge were taken. He was fully aware that there were definite bounds beyond which he could not pass without precipitating intervention by the British government.

Finally, he won over his opponents by telling them the leaders would become martyrs if they were hanged, but that as hostages they might prove of considerable commercial value to the Boers. The virtual certainty of ultimately being able to extort large fines was so enticing that the Council voted unanimously not to hang us.

Many of my friends in the United States and Europe assured me later that they had had no fears for my life, but the Uitlanders had been far from convinced that the matter would end happily. There was no telling what might happen. Because of their limited knowledge of circumstances, it was natural for outsiders to be confident of our safety, but we were living in the midst of a Boer populace inflamed by race hatred to a point where the possibility of foreign complications was stubbornly ignored.

The news of our conviction, cabled all over the world, brought an immediate reaction. Messages were received from all quarters urging the exercise of the presidential pardoning power.

One of the most generous responses to my need did not come to my attention until I returned to America some years later. Harry Davis, a mining promoter, asked me, "Have you been to see John W. Mackay yet?"

"Why, no, why should I? I hardly know him."

"Hasn't anyone told you of his efforts on your behalf when you were in Pretoria Gaol?"

"What did he do?"

"He offered me $100,000 to use in any way I saw fit that might help you and said he'd add another $100,000 when that was gone."

This generous gesture certainly merited acknowledgment. The next morning I called on Mackay, who was then head of the Mackay cable system. When I tried to thank him for his kindness, Mackay interrupted, "Let's not talk about it."

"But," I protested, "I have to talk about it. I'd have done it long ago if I had known anything about it before yesterday."

"Look here, Hammond. I'm an older man than you, but I bet I can lick you and I'll do it right here if you mention the matter again."

Mackay was truly beloved by miners of the West. After his death I met many of his old friends and from them learned of his innumerable kindnesses and his great generosity. When his estate was settled it developed that Mackay had given hundreds of thousands of dollars to old chums of his, and had always done it so quietly that no one but the recipient knew it.

The report of my plight brought Robert W. Chapin and his wife from Cape Town to Pretoria. Chapin was acting American consul in the absence of Consul Manion, and Mr. and Mrs. Chapin were old-time friends of my wife and myself; indeed, "Bob," as well as three of Mrs. Chapin's brothers, and I had been intimate friends during our Yale schooldays. Mr. and Mrs. Chapin went to see Paul Kruger

the morning after the trial. They found him in one of his prophetic
moods, awaiting divine inspiration. To their appeals for mercy he
said, "I tell my generals to show mercy on the battlefield; but the
penalty of murder is bloodshed."

Barney Barnato, whose reactions were always immediate and unrestrained, called at once upon my wife and told her not to worry:
he would stay in Pretoria just as long as the prisoners were in jail.
When I repeated this remark, the almost universal response was that
Barney was bluffing as usual. I maintained that he would keep his
word, and he did. He became active on our behalf immediately.

With his innate love of theatricality he put a mourning band
around his hat and crape on his sleeve and went to the Pretoria Club.
There he happened on Gregorowski. Barney planted himself in
front of the judge and began to denounce him roundly for his conduct of the trial.

Gregorowski responded in Dutch: "Mr. Barnato, you are not a
gentleman. I was appointed to put down rebellion, and I have done
so to the best of my ability."

Barney could not understand him, and countered with, "Maybe
you're right, but still you're a damn rotten judge!"

For a time Gregorowski was exceedingly unpopular; when he returned to Bloemfontein there was a demonstration against him.

My last news of him came just after the Boer War. James Barnes,
war correspondent, writer, and big game hunter, brought me a message from Gregorowski to the effect that, if the judge had known
about Paul Kruger at the time of the Reform Committee's trial what
he found out later, he would have condemned Kruger to death instead of the four leaders.

Some of the more cool-headed residents of the Rand were made uneasy by anti-Boer demonstrations, which tended to perpetuate the
race antagonism it was to our interest to subdue. They rightly believed that our cause would be injured by too violent condemnation
of the Boers. George Farrar's brother, Percy, had notices posted
throughout South Africa urging the Uitlanders to be moderate in
their expressions of opinion while negotiations on our behalf were
going forward.

Barnato, whose threat to close his mines had caused widespread concern, was persuaded to confine himself to more temperate efforts. Nevertheless, he worked night and day for our release. He gave $25,000 to the Boer government to alleviate the distress caused by the Raid, and told Kruger this donation ought to warrant the release of his nephew, Solly Joel.

When Kruger refused even to discuss the subject of prisoners, Barney adopted a new mode of procedure. He ordered two great marble lions as a gift for the president, to be presented on his birthday in October. Oom Paul pretended not to know what lay hidden under the tarpaulins on his front porch, and the pleasure evinced by these two grown-up children over the secret helped to bring a spirit of amity into the dealings between Boer and Uitlander. On Kruger's birthday, a religious service was held in the parlor, and then the two lions were unveiled in all their gleaming majesty. In a halo of whiskers, these three monarchs of the veldt confronted the camera.

Immediately after adjournment of the court that convicted us, a petition for commutation of sentence had been drawn up and circulated among the Boers themselves. We knew nothing of this. Botha was one of the signers. Even the chairman of the First Raad, Schalk Burger, expressed keen sympathy for many of the convicted men, and said they would be well advised to leave the decision to the government.

The opinion of the liberal Boers as to "this grim judicial farce" was well summarized in a letter to the Johannesburg *Star*:

> . . . the resolute and fearless demeanour under the trying ordeals through which they [the Reform Committee] have passed has gained for them increased respect and honour from the many thousands here and elsewhere in South Africa, who make common cause with them in striving for those just and righteous reforms which are the inalienable heritage of every free-born citizen—a cause which must eventually succeed, however mighty the opposition may be . . . Johannesburg has been asked to suppress all demonstrative excitement lest the interest and safety of its leaders be prejudiced,

and it has loyally responded to the request, although the feelings of its citizens have been strained to break- ing point . . . I am a son of the soil, with not a strain of English descent, and by choice a Republican, but I have the Englishmen's love for fair play; and admire their sense of honour and love of liberty; hence it is a keen humiliation to feel that an indelible blot has been cast upon the escutcheon of this Republic by the events of this week.

Immediately upon our arrival at the jail, the prisoners were searched and all our money, jewelry, tobacco, matches, and pipes were taken away. Tobacco was always contraband and had to be smuggled in.

Jail regulations were ultimately relaxed in respect to visitors, books, and papers. Except for spasmodic censorship, we could write and receive letters freely. The most unpleasant aspect of our treatment was that we were once more put on Kaffir rations, but soon most of the Reformers' wives arrived in Pretoria and were moving heaven and earth to better conditions for their husbands.

Mrs. Solly Joel used to come into the prison with the crown of her hat filled with cigars, a bottle of cream under her skirt, and a brace of ducks (too well broiled to quack) concealed in her bustle. Mrs. Clement wore a huge sausage around her waist. In the big sleeves of the period the ladies were able to conceal tins of sardines, beef essence, condensed milk, and other delicacies. After a short while, however, the rules were again modified so that food could be sent in from the Pretoria Club, as had been done during our first imprisonment.

I used to obtain an additional tidbit from Sullivan, a trusty em- ployed in the prison hospital kitchen. One evening he brought me a chop; while I was devouring it, he asked, "Want to know how I got in here, Mr. Hammond?"

"Why, yes, Sullivan; as a matter of fact I've been wondering, but I didn't like to seem curious."

"Could you stand a hard-luck story?"

After receiving a sentence of fifteen years' imprisonment, I felt sure a regulation hard-luck story would cheer me up.

Sullivan needed no encouragement. "I was working for a Boer who had a store near Pretoria. He went out one night, and forgot to lock the safe—the damn careless cuss. I could see all the coin just begging to be used, and I'd had a hot tip on the market that very day. I thought I could make a quick cleanup and put the money back before the stingy old Boer found out I'd borrowed it. Just as I'd taken it from the safe, damned if the old fellow didn't come back. He thought I was stealing, when I was only borrowing.

"The judge asked me whether I'd taken the money and I said I had, but I told him the Boer had no right to leave his money around like that. He wouldn't listen to me. He said five years was the penalty for my kind of borrowing. So I said to him, 'I'll make you a sporting proposition, Judge, I'll toss you double or quits.'

"He didn't see the joke. He gave me a nasty look and said, 'Five years more for contempt of court.'

"I had a chance at him later. I was working on the road gang when he went by one day. I dodged the guard, made a quick dive, and would have finished him proper if I hadn't been dragged off. They gave me some more time for that, but it was worth it."

I agreed with Sullivan that the punishment does not always fit the crime.

I should like to tell another story about Sullivan, which I am sure will amuse the younger generation, who blush very little at such things—the older generation may skip if they find it indelicate. One of the cockney English prisoners was talking with Sullivan one day, and protesting against the treatment he was receiving. "Sullivan, these Boers can't put an Englishman in stocks like this and get away with it, can they?"

Sullivan said: "The hell they can't. They are doing it, aren't they, and they are getting away with it. Just look around you and see all the Englishmen and how they are being treated.

"Let me tell you something," continued Sullivan, "these Boers can do anything they want to with you, except one thing."

Sullivan's friend was all ears by now and he asked eagerly what that one thing was.

"They can't put you in the family way," said Sullivan.

Several years later, on one of those dreary days that characterize the London winter, my secretary said there was a man waiting to see me.

"What sort of fellow is he?"

"Well, he doesn't look much like a gentleman, sir."

"That's fine, show him right in. I'm sick of Bond Street haberdashery and Oxford accents."

My visitor was Sullivan, and I was doubly pleased.

"Well, if it isn't Sullivan!" I greeted him. "How did you get here? The last time I saw you, you had several years ahead of you yet. How'd you manage it? Over the wall?"

"No, sir. Right through the gate like the rest of you gentlemen. I bought my way out with the money you and the other Reformers gave me when you left. I'm trying now to get back to my family in Ireland, but I hate to go looking like this!"

I could understand that, for he was a bedraggled-looking object.

"Surely it didn't take all your money to get this far! Why don't you buy yourself a decent suit of clothes?"

"Would you believe it, Mr. Hammond," he replied ingenuously, "I was robbed last night on the dock at Southampton."

"No, Sullivan, to be quite frank with you, I wouldn't believe it."

I started to reach in my pocket but thought better of it. "I'll go with you right now and get you a suit and buy you a ticket. That is the only way you'll ever get to Ireland."

I fed and clothed him and saw him safely on the train. At the last moment, I relented and provided him with cash for tips, though I suspect it was promptly diverted into the till of some tempting pub.

I did not begrudge him this; in the jail at Pretoria I had luckily found a substitute for a pub myself. Among the prisoners were two I remember with special gratitude: A. L. Lawley, an Englishman who had helped build South African railways, and F. R. Lingham, an American who had spent many years on the western cattle ranches of the United States. They had no social graces, but no fault could be found with the quality of their friendship.

All prisoners were, of course, deprived of liquor in any form. Occasionally, at what seemed to us exceedingly long intervals, Lawley and Lingham would manage to have a bottle of whisky smuggled into their cells. I had a standing invitation to attend on these gala occasions.

They would bribe a friendly guard to unlock the door of my cell. I would follow him stealthily, keeping to the shadows, until we reached the haven of the Lingham and Lawley quarters. There I would remain until anxiety for the safety of my guard would drive me back to my cell.

After their release, these men did not forget the friendship formed in prison. They returned as visitors with much the same ideas for my escape as had been presented on two previous occasions.

"Look here, Hammond," Lingham burst forth eagerly as soon as we were alone. "We've got everything fixed up. All you have to do is to get over the wall; we'll throw a rope over for you and will have horses hidden near by. In two days we'll be over the Natal border. Before any extradition papers can be served, we'll be safe in Rhodesia. What about it?"

Their offer warmed my heart. But they admitted the impossibility of taking Phillips, Frank Rhodes, and Farrar along with us. One prisoner might escape unnoticed, but it would hardly be possible for the inmates to walk out in any numbers without the Boer guards becoming "slightly aware." Since I still hoped for release and exoneration, I told them I was grateful but could not accept their friendly offer.

My cell mates had one favorite diversion. All three were accomplished whist players. For some inscrutable reason they considered a fourth indispensable to their game. They would carefully pin blankets around the cell so that no ray of light would betray them. Then they would crouch like gnomes over a small candle end stuck on an old wooden box.

Since I was neither an enthusiast nor a good player, they would draw lots to see who would be the unfortunate one to get me for a partner. The "Oh, hell, I drew Jack" was distinctly uncomplimentary to me. Not only was I pressed into service, but the stakes were higher than I could afford. I was always relieved when the bit of candle guttered to a smelly death in a pool of grease. The

IOUs often had to be gathered up in the dark, but none of them went into my pocket.

The local papers reported monotonously from day to day that sanitary arrangements at the jail were to be completed almost immediately. Meanwhile, we suffered from the overpowering fumes of carbolic acid powder which was liberally strewn from one end of the compound to the other. This did little to alleviate our discomfort; it simply substituted one insupportable odor for another.

As if I had reached the nadir of human misery, my health began to mend almost from the moment I received the death sentence. Prison conditions had a contrary effect upon my fellows. One by one they succumbed to illness of one sort or another.

The district government surgeon, Messum, did what he could towards improving sanitation. He informed the inspector of jails that the sheds were too small and unhealthy for the number of occupants, that vermin had rapidly spread from the native quarters to those of the political prisoners, and that the lives of the older Reformers, as well as those who were ill, were endangered.

Dr. Messum made particular mention of Fred Gray, who was showing signs of acute melancholia and threatening to commit suicide. Poor Gray had been especially upset by the fact that the Boer government had just confirmed the sentence of banishment against the Reformers. In his Wednesday report, Messum recommended Gray's immediate release; Thursday was Ascension Day, a public holiday; on Friday the landrost was so busy signing visitors' permits that the doctor's letter received no attention until noon. Meanwhile, to use the words of the Johannesburg *Times,* "The enforced idleness, the terrible ennui, the heart-sinking, brain-snapping suspense in which they have to drag through the weary hours—all these form a punishment which the most remorseless arbiters of fate could not render more horror-inspiring."

Early Saturday morning, May 16th, Gray borrowed a razor and cut his throat. The universal horror aroused by this act was heightened by the fact that he left a widow and six children. The tragedy formed the only topic of conversation, even in Johannesburg, and the expression of grief there was almost as profound as within the prison itself.

When the time came for the removal of Gray's body, we formed a solemn procession and reverently carried his coffin as far as the gates. Ten thousand people attended his public funeral in Johannesburg. Several hundred conveyances followed the hearse to the grave in a spontaneous tribute to one who was regarded as a martyr. Conspicuously placed among the floral offerings was a wreath bearing a card, "In memoriam, F. Gray; from his friends in prison." Despite the fact that he was a suicide, he was given Christian burial. The clergyman who pronounced the final words at his grave said his epitaph should read, "Tortured to a cruel death by murderous suspense."

To offset the feeling of depression, we were cheered a few days later by an afternoon of humor and hopeful good omen. "The Star of the Stars and Stripes," as the Johannesburg *Times* called Mark Twain, was on a round-the-world lecture tour, and took advantage of an engagement in near-by Johannesburg to pay a social call on the American prisoners. I had great hopes for the effects of this afternoon on our spirits as I was familiar with Mark Twain's genial personality and witty conversation. While I was a student at Yale, I met him a number of times at Hartford, Connecticut, where I often went to spend week-ends with General Franklin, president of the Colt Arms Company.

In the glare of the South African sun which beat into the courtyard, Samuel Clemens, with his white hair and spotless linen suit, was a refreshing sight. I grasped his hand warmly in both of mine. "Mr. Clemens, I'm certainly glad to see you again. How did you ever find your way into this God-forsaken hole?"

"Getting into jail is easy," replied the humorist. "I thought the difficulties arose when it came to getting out."

I smiled appreciatively and introduced him to the rest of our company. He was particularly struck with the martial demeanor of Colonel Bettington, who had been one of the Committee's military commanders.

"This is a pretty dull sort of place, Colonel. Killing time, eh?"

"I suppose so," replied Bettington. "I'm a soldier and must kill something."

"You've got all the big bugs here, haven't you?"

"Yes, two hundred million were in my cell last night." The colonel rubbed his shoulders.

"What! Two hundred million big bugs?"

"Good Lord, no! Two hundred million pounds in good hard English money."

"Where do you keep it?"

The colonel pointed to Solly Joel, leaning against the wall. "There's some of it standing over there. Barnato Brothers, you know."

"And what's he doing in here? Hasn't he enough money to buy himself out?"

"So far he hasn't had any success, but we still have hopes."

After an hour or so of amusing conversation, Mr. Clemens prepared to depart, refusing our invitation to wait until we were ready to leave.

As he left the prison yard, a cub reporter accosted him. "Mr. Clemens, how did you find living conditions in the prison?"

"Why do you ask?"

"Some of the prisoners have complained to Kruger that the jail was no fit place for gentlemen. Although the president replied he was not aware that jails were intended for gentlemen, just the same we'd like to have your impressions."

"Has Mr. Hammond, or any of the other Americans, made any complaint?"

"No," admitted the youth; "the grievances were urged by their friends."

"Well," said Mark Twain, "I am not surprised that Mr. Hammond has made no complaint. I knew him as a young engineer out in Nevada where he used to spend a good deal of his time in mining camp hotels, and compared with those accommodations Hammond is now living in luxury."

The reporter carefully noted this down on his pad and Mark Twain went on to say that he was really greatly pleased with the jail; he had found some very charming gentlemen there, and he thought it was an ideal rest cure for these tired businessmen. He only regretted his stay was so short that he could not take advantage of the peaceful conditions in the jail to rest his own tired nerves. He said he could not imagine a place where one would be less troubled by the importunities of his creditors and the only feature he did not like about the jail was that there were too many lawyers among the prisoners, and somehow or other he never could hit it off with lawyers.

Next morning a very sharp criticism of the jail authorities appeared in this Boer paper, which was one of the Joubert papers hostile to Kruger. The article declared the jail was supposed to be a place for punishment and *not* a pleasant rest cure, and the paper called upon the government to take drastic measures of a punitive nature. The prison authorities responded by diminishing our rations, which had been none too liberal before.

None of the prisoners had seen this news item, and we could not account for the increased severity of our jailers' treatment of us; conditions had seemed intolerable before. Some friends on the outside, however, learned the reason and at once sent a deputation to Bloemfontein, several hundred miles south, to intercept Mark Twain, who was on his way to Cape Town to sail for England. As soon as he saw the paper containing his interview, and realized its unfortunate consequences, he hastened back to Pretoria to make clear to President Kruger that he had merely been trying to be humorous. In truth, he considered our quarters disgraceful and quite unfit for political prisoners. His explanation was apparently satisfactory; the severity of the discipline was once more relaxed.

Several years later I met Mark Twain in New York and was invited to a delightful luncheon. He told this story as a joke on himself and promised redress by giving me a banquet whenever I cared to name the day.

In the latter part of May, my wife was taken seriously ill, and the Boer government allowed me to go to her at Johannesburg. Du Plessis came with me as guard but after twenty-four hours of home life he became bored and returned to Pretoria, leaving me to my own devices.

As soon as my wife was out of danger I returned voluntarily to prison. It amused me to find a heavy guard lined up at the station and to be marched solemnly into the jail. One of my jailers considerately offered to relieve me of my small hand bag, but I determinedly maintained my grip on what was a precious load of contraband tobacco.

By this time the prison authorities knew that none of us would take advantage of Boer trustfulness, and other Reformers were also granted week-end privileges.

During one of our numerous conversations, Du Plessis told me Kruger was curious to know why the Reformers had pleaded guilty. I asked Du Plessis to tell the following story to the president with my compliments.

"A Texas horse thief had stolen an animal from the very judge before whom he was later brought for trial. The judge, as an interested party, wished to prevent any criticism of partiality, and turned over the case to a subordinate court officer, saying, 'Proceed with the case while I go for a rope.'

"Tell His Honor, the president," I said, "that the Reformers were just as likely as the horse thief to get a fair trial."

Du Plessis told me afterwards that Oom Paul shook with laughter at the joke. It was too apt to seem funny to us.

Negotiations for our release had begun almost immediately after our imprisonment. So long drawn-out and involved was Kruger's policy towards the Reformers that it became known as "magnanimity by inches." For some time the leaders were definitely excluded from any arrangement that might be made. The other prisoners were asked to send in individual petitions in which they admitted the justice of the sentences imposed upon them, expressed regret for what they had done, and promised to behave in the future. Almost to a man they refused.

The result was a compromise. On the one hand, the authors of the petitions had to take into consideration the extremist Boer opinion that penitence was a condition precedent to release; on the other, many prisoners were reluctant to admit any guilt.

A way out was found in a formal application to the Executive Council to have the sentences reviewed. Each application had to contain an explanation of the circumstances under which the prisoner had joined the Reform Movement, and set forth any extenuating factors he could urge in his own behalf.

The suicide of Gray probably hastened a decision. On May 20th, ten of the prisoners were released, twenty-four had their sentences commuted to three months, eighteen to five months, and four to one year. A. Wools-Sampson and W. D. Karri-Davies refused to submit any petitions; consequently, their cases were not considered.

By this time there had been a strong revulsion of feeling in South Africa in favor of the prisoners. Part of the solicitude on our behalf was undoubtedly due to the Boers' belated realization of the economic benefits the Uitlanders had bestowed upon them. The country was facing financial ruin. Railroads were going bankrupt, options on Boer properties were not being taken up, the rinderpest was now within their borders, a plague of locusts had destroyed crops, and many of the mine owners had threatened to close down.

The little seed I had planted in Sir Gordon Sprigg's mind now began to bear fruit. In every single one of the South African towns, in some of which only Dutch was spoken, and including such a stronghold of conservatism as the Orange Free State, a concerted movement got under way to effect our release. J. Bryant Lindley, an American who had lived in Cape Town for many years, directed this movement. It was generally felt that there had been gross discrimination towards prisoners who had pleaded guilty to the same offense, and that some were being held by the Boer government as political pawns.

The gathering pressure of public opinion eventually had its effect. On May 30th, with the exception of the leaders and the two impenitents I have just named, all the prisoners were released on the payment of $10,000 and, in lieu of banishment, a promise to keep out of Transvaal politics for three years.

So far as the four leaders were concerned, the government would make no public statement except that it was busy. But privately it was intimated that, if we were prepared to pay for our liberty, the matter could probably be arranged. Our attorneys sent a letter to the Executive Council suggesting some monetary arrangement, and offering $40,000 as ransom for each of us.

At once there arose loud Boer professions of reluctance to accept what they termed blood money. But they were a thoroughly practical people not unacquainted with high finance and assessed a value of $250,000 on each of the leaders. I protested that this asking price was too high for me, although my fellow prisoners could have paid the sum without feeling its loss.

Meanwhile, some of the Reform Committee, now once more free, had swallowed their pride and gone to Kruger to petition for our pardon. This was the famous "dog interview." Kruger maundered on about dogs, and how the little dogs had been punished but the big dog (Rhodes) had escaped, and how dogs crawled to lick their masters' boots after being punished.

He would make no definite promises.

There was one thing far more effective than this attitude of humility, and that was the rising tide of sentiment throughout South Africa: from the Cape Parliament, from the inhabitants of Natal, from the Orange Free State, and even from the Afrikander Bond, which Kruger could not afford to antagonize.

Overwhelmed by the unanimity of protest, Kruger hastened his policy of "magnanimity by inches," and little by little his price came down to $125,000. This payment was to be accompanied by an expression of appreciation of his generosity. We replied that we would rot in prison before we would both pay him and thank him for accepting our money. We would either pay or thank; we refused to do both. This created a temporary impasse which lengthened our period of detention by several days.

At this point, a delegation of one hundred and fifty mayors of South African towns arrived at Pretoria to petition in person for our release. Kruger could delay no longer. On June 11th—five months after our arrest—we leaders were set free without having to express our gratitude. My fine of $125,000 was paid by Cecil Rhodes as an advance on the profits due me according to the understanding arrived at in my first interview with him at Groote Schuur.

We had to choose between banishment and nonparticipation in Transvaal politics for three years. Colonel Frank Rhodes chose the banishment and was escorted over the Natal frontier, whereupon he promptly joined his brother Cecil who was engaged in fighting the Matabele. Phillips, Farrar, and I, together with a handful of Reformers still remaining in Pretoria, boarded a special train, provided not by the Boer government but by the citizens of Johannesburg.

Johannesburg, which had offered to pay the ransom, celebrated our release wholeheartedly. Several thousand people met the train as it pulled into the station. The crowd lifted the Reform leaders to their shoulders and carried them to a victoria, which was then drawn triumphantly through the town. The next evening we were guests of honor at a banquet presided over by Barney Barnato.

Karri-Davies and Wools-Sampson remained in jail. When I returned to South Africa in 1897, I went to see them. I told them they were giving great concern to those who had formerly been in prison with them, and that many of their friends thought they should accept Kruger's offer of release. Particularly if Boer and Briton should come to blows, their presence as hostages in Pretoria Gaol might prove an embarrassment to their own government.

They were already an embarrassment to Kruger, who was becoming increasingly anxious to be rid of them. After having served thirteen months, the Boer government expelled them as a compliment to Queen Victoria on her Diamond Jubilee.

Before the Raid had taken place, I had already decided to move my headquarters to London, where I could continue to act as consulting engineer for Rhodes's mining interests. The important technical problems had been solved; I had the utmost confidence in the ability of my staff to carry out all operating details. Had it not been for the Raid, I should have gone sooner. I now wound up my affairs in Johannesburg as quickly as possible.

While still in prison I had reserved passage for myself and my family on the *Drummond Castle* from Cape Town but the delay in coming to terms caused us to miss the sailing. Kruger's dilatoriness in opening the jail doors had undoubtedly saved our lives. The *Drummond Castle* went down off Ushant, only two of her passengers and crew being rescued.

By a curious coincident there were Hammonds on board. My son Harris, then at school in England, saw this name on the list of those missing. But the same day he received word from his guardian in London that we were not on the boat.

Many times in my life I have been touched by the attitude of the men working under me. Certainly elaborate and formal expressions of esteem cannot always be taken at face value; but with so many years intervening, and with the loyalty of my associates still warm in my memory, I should like for various sentimental reasons to quote a letter which meant much to me.

THE CONSOLIDATED GOLD FIELDS OF SOUTH AFRICA, LIMITED.

Johannesburg, June 20, 1896
South African Republic.

John Hays Hammond, Esq.
Johannesburg.
Dear Sir:

It is with feelings of great sorrow, that we, the members of your staff are about to part from you.

Our respect for you as a man, our admiration for you as an Engineer, and our affection for you as a friend, is most strong.

An ambitious man is inclined to allow nothing to stand in his way in the attainment of his ends. You, on the contrary, have always been anxious to further the interests of those who have been associated with you, and have guarded their interests more zealously than your own. You have never allowed an opportunity to pass, where there was a chance to advance some one whom you felt deserved it. The kindness and consideration you have shewn, has endeared you to us in the strongest degree. You have drawn us to you, not by your great success, but by a genuine and lasting feeling of affection.

It is scarcely necessary for us to speak of the great work you have done on these Fields, or of what the Rand owes to you. That is too well known. We simply speak to you personally, that you may understand our feelings for you, and our sorrow that you are to leave Johannesburg.

That health and happiness may attend you and yours is our most earnest wish.

V. C. CLEMENT

S. B. CONNOR

EDWARD MELVILLE

POPE YEATMAN

W. LEONALD HOLMS

H. C. SIMPSON

F. M. WATSON

E. H. GARTHWAITE

W. WYHERGH

E. H. BOOTH

S. J. TRUSCOTT

E. KEMPER-VOSE

R. M. CATLIN

A dozen or more Reformers traveled to Cape Town on a special train as guests of the Cape Colony government. We were cheered as we pulled out of Johannesburg, and cheered again at Bloemfontein, in the heart of the Boer country.

From the newspapers I had learned that a Select Committee of the Cape of Good Hope House of Assembly proposed to determine, if possible, the exact connection between Rhodes and the Raid. When I reached the Cape Colony border I was not surprised, therefore, to receive a summons to appear before this committee on June 23rd.

It was well known that the Select Committee was being run by an anti-Rhodes faction, actuated by political animus. The chairman was W. P. Schreiner, a brother of Olive Schreiner and formerly a member of Rhodes's cabinet.

I made up my mind in no way to add to Rhodes's difficulties by incriminating him or exposing him to further criticism. Furthermore, Rhodes had his hands full with the uprising of the Matabele in Rhodesia and was unable to defend himself in person.

On the other hand, a refusal to testify might involve me in considerable red tape and compel me to remain in Cape Town for some weeks. The situation was particularly embarrassing to me since my wife was shortly to be confined, and I was anxious to have her in England. But after we had discussed the subpoena she told me she would rather have her baby in Cape Town than have me go against the dictates of my conscience.

I arrived just in time to present myself at the place and hour specified. Following a preliminary verbal skirmish, Mr. Schreiner asked me certain questions which tended to incriminate Rhodes.

I declined to discuss Rhodes's connection with the Reform Movement. The committee reiterated its questions, but I still would not reply. Helpless in the face of my refusal, they asked me to withdraw for a few moments while they discussed the policy they should adopt. They intimated that they could hold me as a material witness if I continued recalcitrant.

In about half an hour I was again summoned before the committee, and was asked on what grounds I refused to give this testimony. I replied out of the depths of my ignorance of international law: "I'm not a British subject. I've already paid the Boer government for my share in the rebellion. As an American citizen traveling from one friendly republic to another, I'm not obliged to give evidence against my will, and any attempt on your part to extort it is entirely *ultra vires*."

I was pleased to note the perturbation of the committee and realized that I was actually within my rights in taking this stand.

I was asked once more to retire. When I reappeared, they said they would have to take legal advice and would notify me whether or not I should be detained in Cape Town. Thereafter, they confined their questions to other matters.

This gave me an opportunity to place on record the Reform Committee's relations with Dr. Jameson and to demonstrate that his precipitate action had been largely responsible for the failure of the Reform Movement.

Somewhat to my surprise, Mr. Schreiner and other members of the committee invited me to lunch with them next day. They complimented me on the loyalty I had shown to a friend, and particularly on the legal correctness of the stand I had taken. I admitted to them then that, even as I was laying down the precepts of international law, I had been uneasily wondering whether Grotius and

Puffendorff would have approved my incursion into their special field.

That very afternoon, two weeks after my release from Pretoria Gaol, my family and I set sail from Cape Town.

My wife was as much pleased as I to get away from South Africa. "Revolutions are expensive games to play," she said.

We landed at Plymouth, July 11, 1896, and immediately took a house at Bickley, near London. In August my third son, Richard, was born. For the next four years London was my business headquarters and my home.

CHAPTER TWENTY-ONE

The Aftermath of Revolt

*F*ollowing the months of African sturm und drang, life in London was calm and peaceful. My headquarters during the first year were the Consolidated Gold Fields offices, at 8 Old Jewry; later I established myself in Threadneedle Street. My time was divided between work for the Rhodes interests; trips once or twice a year back to South Africa to inspect the mines of the Consolidated Gold Fields and other companies which I represented as consulting engineer; and in building up a new clientele in London. At Rhodes's special request I had renewed my engagement with the Consolidated Gold Fields.

Almost as soon as I returned to London in July, 1896, I realized a feeling on the part of the British public that the Reformers had been responsible for the failure of the Raid. We had been selected as scapegoats and were being ridiculed in journalistic lampoons and music hall skits. The opprobrium was undeserved and I could not understand why Jameson had so long kept silent. We Reformers had not been able to speak in our own defense while we were still in South Africa, for fear we would do Jameson an injury pending the preliminary hearings of the High Court of England against him and his principal officers. These hearings had dragged on for months, during which time the Reformers suffered in silence. We felt aggrieved at Jameson for allowing charges of cowardice to be alleged against us. Of course, we did not expect Jameson to incriminate himself, but he must have known that the sole responsibility for the failure was his own.

The first charge brought against Jameson and fifteen of his officers was in the Bow Street Police Court:

> That they with certain other persons in the month of December, 1895, in South Africa, within Her Majesty's Dominions and without license of Her Majesty, did unlawfully prepare and fit out a military expedition to proceed against the dominions of a certain friendly state—to wit, the South African Republic, contrary to the provisions of the Foreign Enlistment Act, 1870.

On June 15th, after three and a half months of preliminary proceedings, Jameson and five of the fifteen officers were picked out for trial. The indictment contained twelve separate counts.

The trial began July 20, 1896.

Ian Colvin in *The Life of Jameson,* says:

> The jury were asked to find upon a series of questions—as to whether or not the defendants were engaged in a military expedition from Mafeking and Pitsani Potlugo against the South African Republic, and whether Pitsani Potlugo was under the dominion and sovereignty of the Queen.
>
> The motive for asking the jury for this sort of verdict is suggested by the illustration used by the Chief Justice:
>
> 'Of course you remember the shipwrecked crew who, finding themselves on the ocean without

any means of obtaining food, sacrificed the life of one of the persons of the boat.'

Clearly, the Bench feared that the sympathies of an English jury would go against State policy.

The jury retired at 4:20 in the afternoon, and debated their verdict for an hour and five minutes.

When they returned it was with an answer in the affirmative to all the questions on the paper.

'That amounts, gentlemen,' said the Chief Justice, 'to a verdict of guilty. Do you now find against all the defendants a verdict of guilty?'

'My Lord,' the foreman replied, 'the jury have thought fit in answering these questions to append a rider: "The jury consider that the state of affairs in Johannesburg presented great provocation." My Lord, we have answered your questions categorically.'

'Then I direct you that, in accordance with those answers, you ought to find a verdict of guilty against the defendants.'

Here Sir Edward Clarke rose to his feet, 'My Lord,' he said, 'I wish . . .'

'I cannot allow any intervention,' said the Chief Justice.

'My Lord, I am calling attention . . .'

But the Chief Justice was determined to have his way: 'I cannot allow it, Sir Edward Clarke,' he said. 'At this moment I cannot allow it.' And then to the jury: 'Gentlemen, I direct you that in point of law that amounts to a verdict of guilty, and it is your duty to see if you cannot come to an agreement.'

'My Lord,' said the foreman, 'there is one objection to that. We answered your questions categorically. We cannot agree upon a verdict.'

'That,' said the Lord Chief Justice, 'is a most unhappy state of things. If there is one juryman objecting to a verdict he ought to reconsider the matter. These questions, answered as they are, amount to a verdict of guilty and to nothing else. They are capable of no other construction, and therefore I direct you—and I direct my observations particularly to the gentlemen to whom you refer as disagreeing with the rest on the verdict—that you ought all to find, in accordance with these findings, a verdict of guilty.'

The jury hesitated for a time and consulted among themselves, and at last the foreman yielded the point:

'My Lord,' he said, 'we are unanimous in returning a verdict of guilty.'

Against this skilful and masterful piece of shepherding Sir Edward Clarke proposed to appeal: he wanted to ask for a new trial, but Jameson and his officers refused to allow him: they preferred to take judgment.

Jameson and Sir John Willoughby were sentenced to imprisonment for fifteen months at hard labor. Major Robert White was given a sentence of seven months, and Colonel Grey, Colonel Henry White, and Major Coventry, each five months at hard labor.

Jameson was taken first to Wormwood Scrubs, dressed in prison garb and treated like a common criminal, but shortly afterwards was moved to Holloway Prison and became a "first-class misdemeanant." Jameson was in bad health, suffering from gallstones. In November, 1896, he was operated on and shortly afterwards released from further punishment. He moved to his chambers in Down Street.

On the very day of Jameson's sentence, July 27th, Richard Harding Davis, whose influence on the press at that time was great and whose attitude was therefore important, remarked to my Yale classmate, Colonel George Creighton Webb, that he "would rather be in Jameson's shoes than in those of John Hays Hammond." He went on to express his contempt for me and the other leaders of the Reform Movement, and called us cowards because we failed to keep our promise to go to Jameson's aid.

Webb spoke up in my defense. "That shows you don't know the inside facts about the Raid. If you're interested in getting both sides of the story, I'll arrange to bring you and Hammond together, and then I'm sure you'll change your views."

Webb arranged a dinner at the Savoy. Without informing me of Davis's preconceived ideas, he induced me to recount my adventures. I related the more familiar details and in addition I described the many attempts on the part of Boer Secret Service agents to extort confessions from us in order to involve Rhodes and in that way escape punishment ourselves. But I asserted with pride that not one had turned state's evidence and betrayed a fellow prisoner or implicated any other person.

Early in the conversation Davis's incredulity showed that he was in the other camp. By the end of dinner he was half convinced that his first impression of the Reformers had been wrong. But I wanted him to verify my statements and offered to put him in touch with Captain Harry Holden, Jameson's intimate and trusted friend. From him he could get many particulars confirming my version. Davis interviewed Holden and was fully convinced. Since he was first and foremost a newspaperman, he composed a feature story and cabled it to the American newspapers. He did the Reformers a great service. Davis and I struck up a personal friendship which remained unbroken throughout his life.

After Jameson's release from Holloway Prison, and while he was convalescing at Down Street, Rhodes returned to London. At the urgent request of Rhodes, Maurice Gifford, and other friends of Jameson, I reluctantly accepted his invitation to come to see him. Gifford brought the message and said that Jameson wanted to talk over old times with me and had promised not to mention the Raid.

I had always been fond of Jameson and was really sorry that he was so ill, but I still resented his implication that the Reformers were cowards. Gifford tried to reassure me, saying that Jameson had never included me in his contempt. I insisted that we had all worked together and should be judged together.

"You mustn't be too hard on poor old Jameson. He's been through a lot and he's ill."

"I guess you're right, Maurice, we'll let bygones be bygones."

In spite of our determination, the Raid inevitably came up in our conversation. Apropos of Jameson's coming to our assistance I resorted to an allegory to avoid unpleasantness.

"Once there were two neighbors. One had built himself a house of which he was inordinately fond. In this house he had a laboratory in which he carried on chemical experiments. The other had made a fire engine of his own invention.

"The chemist one day hailed his neighbor, saying, 'My good friend, tonight I shall try a delicate experiment, which, if it fails, will burn up my house and family. Will you stand by with your crew in my back yard, and come to the rescue if you are needed?'

"The neighbor was pleased at the prospect of trying out his fire engine and gladly agreed. The chemist returned to his test tubes. Presently there was a commotion outside; he threw open the window and called out, 'See here, you fellows, don't turn on the hose until I call.'

"But the firemen were carried away by the idea of an actual test of the engine. The water suddenly burst forth, the excited neighbor directed the stream on the chemist's windows, and it crashed through the glass. This so startled the chemist that he upset the lamp, and the whole elaborate structure went up in flames."

Jameson smiled grimly and the subject was dropped.

Jameson's health improved, and during the next few months we resumed our old friendly relations, but I did not see him again in London after he gave his testimony before the Select Committee appointed by Parliament to inquire into the circumstances of the Raid, the incursion by armed force into the South African Republic. His testimony was given in the summer, and then Jameson returned to Rhodesia to resume his position as administrator. On my last trip to Rhodesia shortly before the outbreak of the Boer War, I spent a night with Jameson at his camp on the veldt, where there were a group at dinner including Lady Sarah Wilson. We did not meet again until the coronation of King George V in 1911.

Jameson served in the Boer War, and was present at the siege of Ladysmith. After the war he took an active part in the political life of Cape Colony and was prime minister of that colony from 1904 to 1907. He received a baronetcy in 1911—Sir Starr Jameson. He became president of the British South Africa Company (Chartered) and held this position until his death, November 26, 1917.

In February, 1897, while I was on one of my business trips to South Africa, my wife's diary, *A Woman's Part in a Revolution,* was published in London. This small volume was described by James Bryce as "one of the brightest, freshest, and most graphically vivid and direct of all the accounts that have appeared of one of the most curious and interesting episodes in modern history." Her account of the Raid did much to allay prejudice against the Reformers.

While the Second Matabele War was still in progress, Rhodes had received a summons to appear before a Select Committee of Parliament. The committee was appointed "To inquire into the origin and circumstances of the incursion into the South African Republic by an armed force and into the administration by the British South Africa Company, and to report thereon, and further to report what alterations are desirable in the Government of the territories under the control of the Company."

When Rhodes received the summons he answered: "The investigation can wait. I am busy fighting the Matabele."

After the Matabele were suppressed, Rhodes started for London—to face the "unctuous rectitude" of his countrymen, as he expressed it—via Durban and Cape Town. In both places he was given great ovations. In January, 1897, he arrived in London where he was welcomed with a demonstration also, from all except some of the stockholders of the Chartered Company who considered he had jeopardized their interests to carry out what they pleased to call his own selfish political policy.

On the day of his arrival I went to see him at Burlington House, his headquarters whenever he was in London. His sitting room was already filled with friends. When I appeared in the doorway, Rhodes rushed to greet me, and grasped me by the hand. It was our first meeting since the Raid.

"Hammond, my dear fellow, you don't know how glad I am to see you."

He then drew me aside into the bedroom where we could talk privately. He seemed eager to explain his apparent indifference to the fate of the Reformers. This had been one of the focal points of criticism of him.

I replied to his first words: "You don't need to explain. I fully understand your position. You had your hands full with the Matabele. The Reformers never doubted your sympathy for them."

Kruger's animosity to Rhodes had prohibited him from intervening for the Reformers.

Later I was told by those who had been with Rhodes in Rhodesia that, when the news of our death sentence reached him, he exclaimed, "Good God! Surely Kruger wouldn't dare to do a thing like that." For the rest of the night he paced up and down his tent, chafing at his utter powerlessness to help us out of our dilemma.

The anguish of mind which had afflicted him since the Raid was shown by his remarks to my wife when he saw her for the first time since they had parted in South Africa. The Baroness Burdett-Coutts, one of the dominant figures in the later Victorian era, gave a dinner and reception in honor of Rhodes. From his position beside the baroness in the receiving line, he caught sight of my wife and left his place to welcome her.

"I am so glad to see you again, Mrs. Hammond. Many things have happened since you and I last met. I remember that you asked me then whether I had ever spent a sleepless night, and I said, 'No!' But since then I have spent many sleepless nights. Often in my adversity I have recalled the pleasant visits we had at Groote Schuur. I suspect that you then looked upon me as being afflicted with the 'big head.' I must have seemed to you so cocksure and self-satisfied. Is that not true?"

My wife's reply was tactful, but did not confute his conjecture.

He answered her unspoken criticism. "Mrs. Hammond, I have had a serious setback; but I trust that eventually I shall profit by this. My perceptions are now awakened to many things which formerly I did not recognize or realize."

The proceedings were impressive enough to have frightened any ordinary man. A committee of the House of Commons were just "plain folks" to Rhodes. At the trial he, the accused, dominated the scene. While the examination was in progress he called for beer and a sandwich and between mouthfuls answered the questions put to him.

The morning of the second day of the Select Committee's investigation I was to have breakfast with Rhodes at Burlington House.

I caught an early train from Chislehurst, where we had moved. Two gentlemen in the compartment with me were discussing the testimony Rhodes had given the previous day. They were obviously friendly to him, although they regarded many of his answers as evasive and feared an unfavorable impression had been created by his attitude.

I repeated the gist of the conversation to Rhodes over the breakfast table. After a moment's reflection, he replied:

"Perhaps that is true. So much has happened since that many of the details have slipped my mind."

"Don't you think it would be a good idea to tell that to the committee?" I asked. "The public is evidently getting the impression that you're trying to conceal something."

He immediately summoned his attorney, Hawksley, and got in touch with Alfred Beit and George Wyndham, asking them to come to the hotel. After discussing the matter, we agreed that every effort must be made to counteract that impression.

When the hearings were resumed later that morning, Rhodes frankly stated that he did not remember the dates or wording of certain messages, but he said he was willing to assume full responsibility for all telegrams and letters sent in his name by myself, Jameson, or any of the others who had figured prominently in the Raid. He added, he would go even further and would take upon his shoulders full responsibility for all that happened. This courageous attitude brought forth praise from all England, even from his political enemies.

Punch, which had not always been favorably inclined towards Rhodes, printed a cartoon representing the "great man" as a giant tied to the ground by his Lilliputian investigators. One of these was Labouchère, the editor of *Truth,* who had charged Rhodes with profiting on the stock market through the Jameson Raid. This made Rhodes so furious that "Labby" was forced to withdraw the accusation, admitting it had been based upon vague and totally unfounded rumor.

Although Rhodes was acquitted of having ordered Jameson to invade the Transvaal, the conclusion of the committee was that the Raid should be condemned without qualification, because by it "public confidence was shaken, race feeling embittered, and serious difficulties were created with neighboring states."

When the hearing was over, Rhodes still had to deal with his stockholders. Their resentment was not lessened by the bill which Kruger had rendered: £677,938 for material damages; and a cool million for intellectual and moral injuries.

Unless the Raid had left the Republic morally bankrupt, the latter item would seem rather steep.

Both claims were promptly rejected by the Chartered Company. Perhaps the shareholders considered that Kruger had already profited enough from the Reform Movement; the Reform prisoners had, after all, paid him almost a million dollars in ransom money.

Ultimately many of these stockholders revised their unfavorable opinion of their leader. In 1899, I went with Rhodes to the last meeting of the Chartered Company in London at which he was destined to preside. The hall of the Cannon Street Hotel was filled to capacity and the crowd overflowed into the corridors. In front of the building a throng had gathered to catch a glimpse of the man who was the first since Wellington so completely to capture the imagination of the British world. The uproar became deafening and the calls for Rhodes insistent. He put his arm around my shoulders and drew me to the balcony overlooking the vociferous assemblage. This ovation marked the final stage of Rhodes's return to the Olympian heights.

During the year following the collapse of the Reform Movement, the progressive Boer element had forced the appointment of a government commission to investigate the Uitlander grievances. A thorough and impartial examination was made and a report of seven hundred pages drawn up. The whole constitutes a damning indictment of the government, as the following extracts from the report of the commission testify:

> Your Commission are pleased to state that at present there exist all the indications of an honest administration, and the State, as well as the Mining Industry, must be congratulated upon the fact that most of the mines are controlled and directed by financial and practical men who devote their time, energy, and knowledge to

the mining industry, and who have not only introduced the most up-to-date machinery and mining appliances, but also the greatest perfection of method and process known to science. But for these a good many of the mines now producing gold would not have reached that stage. . . . When the fact is taken into consideration that up till now the mining industry must be held as the financial basis, support and mainstay of the State . . .

Your Commission entirely disapprove of concessions, through which the industrial prosperity of the country is hampered. Such might have been expedient in the past, but the country has now arrived at a state of development that will only admit of free competition according to republican principles. This applies more especially to the gold industry, which has to face its own economical problems without being further burdened with concessions that are irksome and injurious to the industry and will always remain a source of irritation and dissatisfaction.

As to the sale of liquor:

It has been proved to your Commission that the Liquor Law is not carried out properly, and that the mining industry has real grievances in connection therewith, owing to the illicit sale of strong drink to the natives at the mines, and they wish especially and strongly to insist that the stipulations of Article 16 of the law shall be strictly enforced. The evidence given on this point proves that a miserable state of affairs exists, and a much stronger application of the law is required.

Regarding explosives:

Before entering on this subject, we wish to put on record our disappointment with the evidence tendered on behalf of the South African Explosives Company, Ltd. We expected, and we think not unreasonably, that they would be able to give reliable information for our guidance respecting the cost of importation, as well as of local manufacture, of the principal explosives used for mining purposes; but, though persistently questioned on these points, a few facts were elicited and we regret to say that they entirely failed to satisfy us in this important respect. . . .

The Mining Industry has thus to bear a burden which does not enrich the State or bring any benefit in return, and this fact must always prove a source of irritation and annoyance to those who, while willing to contribute to just taxation for the general good, cannot acquiesce in an impost of the nature complained of.

The nature of this report was a surprise to President Kruger and his entourage, who denounced Mr. Schalk Burger and others who had signed the report as being traitors to their country, i.e., the Transvaal.

In spite of my connection with the Reform Movement, I retained the friendship of many of the Boers, particularly among the younger men, and when I was in the Transvaal in 1899 they asked me again to take up the cudgels in defense of Johannesburg community and the Uitlanders generally.

I did not care to undertake such a mission to Kruger, but there seemed no way out of the difficulty. I did stipulate that I be furnished with an interpreter who could be depended upon to render my conversation verbatim. Because of Oom Paul's well-known tendency to sudden wrath, I feared that his sycophants might be led to temper my remarks in translation.

There never was any trace of personal animus in my dealings with Kruger, although I naturally deplored his intolerance, fanaticism, and obstinacy. In fact, he seemed to have some regard for me, which I suspected was mainly due to his admiration for my wife. On many occasions he referred to her as a "grand woman" whom he held in the highest esteem because she had remained to face danger and to help her husband.

When I arrived at Kruger's home in Pretoria, the president greeted me with the question, "How is my sister?" I must have shown my bewilderment, because he continued, "I mean Mrs. Hays Hammond; she is my sister because we both believe in God." I thanked him and assured him that she was in good health.

I then said that I had just come from London and had called specially to tell him about the feeling of the people of England regarding his treatment of the Uitlanders. I said I was convinced that there would be serious trouble unless he adopted a conciliatory attitude at the meeting he was to have within a few days with Sir Alfred Milner, the high commissioner. Kruger replied that so long as Queen Victoria lived there could be no war. I insisted he was wrong; although Queen Victoria was opposed to war, and wanted to end her days in peace, eventually the pressure of sentiment throughout her dominions would force her to protect the rights of British subjects in South Africa.

Kruger remained undisturbed. "That's all right, I'll come to an agreement with Milner."

A few days after the meeting of Kruger and Milner at Bloemfontein, I spent an evening with the high commissioner at Cape Town. In the course of our political discussion, he told me what had occurred at the interview.

Because of Kruger's reputation for craftiness, Sir Alfred Milner had been uncertain of his ability to cope with him. Kruger first made offers which Milner promptly turned down; they were not adequate to secure redress of the grievances of the Uitlanders. Kruger repeatedly said that, if he made further concessions, he would not dare face the Volksraad. He employed his histrionic talent so effectively as to bring tears to his own eyes; the only reaction in the mind of the Englishman was disgust.

Despairing of reaching any satisfactory compromise, Milner told Kruger it was futile to prolong the discussion and rose to go. Kruger now perceived that his disingenuous tactics had failed; he drew from his pocket a proposal of terms from the Boer government which were far more liberal than any previously discussed. Milner was incensed by this duplicity, stated that even these additional concessions were unsatisfactory, and abruptly terminated the conference.

After the Bloemfontein meeting there was unmistakable evidence that the Transvaal and the Orange Free State were preparing for war.

On October 9, 1899, these two republics sent their ultimatum to England and two days later the Boer War began. The Boers fired the first shot and Kruger directed war operations until the British came within striking distance of Pretoria. He then departed unobtrusively to seek aid in Europe. He never returned. Tante Sanne, too old and ill to face the uncertain future, was left to the kindly understanding of the British. She died a few months later. For the few remaining years of his life, Oom Paul lived in comfort on the large fortune he had amassed during his years of power. In 1904 he died in exile, near Vevey on the shores of Lake Geneva.

I have always believed that the "little Englander" attitude of the Liberal party towards the Boers, largely inspired by political considerations at home, was responsible for Kruger's obstinacy in refusing to settle the Uitlander grievances. There is no doubt that Kruger was tenaciously holding to a policy of noncompromise in the expectation that the Liberal party would eventually return to power.

General Smuts, while attorney general of the Transvaal, in February, 1899, told Fitzpatrick that the Boers would stick it out until there was a change of government in England. "The Liberals will come into power, and this time we shall get all we want."

The diplomatic entente between Kruger and Germany naturally grew more intimate after the Raid, though it had already begun in the early nineties with the inauguration of Germany's policy of colonial expansion. It had been rendered more secure by the Kaiser's bestowal of the Order of the Red Eagle upon the president of the Transvaal Republic.

Kruger, in his fear of Rhodes's imperial schemes, had turned to Germany, whose rapidly growing influence had not yet become a serious menace. By playing one power against the other, he hoped to maintain Boer autonomy. He and his people were imbued with a sense of numerical inferiority which made them bluff. In the end, this proved their undoing.

Some months before the Jameson Raid, Kruger had spoken at a banquet given by the Pretoria Germans in honor of the Kaiser's birthday. In the homely figures of speech which he habitually used, he compared the Transvaal to a little child who had to wear small clothing. "When a child's clothes are made, they must not be made to fit a man; but as the child grows up, it requires bigger clothes— the old ones will burst. . . . We are growing up, and although we are young, we feel that if one nation tries to kick us, the other will try to stop it. . . . I feel certain when the time comes for the Republic to wear still larger clothes you will have done much to bring it about. . . . I wish also to give Germany all the support a little child can give to a grown-up man. The time is coming for our friendship to be more firmly established then ever."

Kruger had previously allowed Dr. Leyds to go to Germany to secure the promise of the Kaiser's aid in the event of an Uitlander uprising at Johannesburg. When the Raid took place Kruger's expectation of support from the Kaiser was more than justified by the famous Kaiser-to-Kruger telegram:

> I HEARTILY CONGRATULATE YOU ON THE FACT THAT YOU AND YOUR PEOPLE WITHOUT APPEALING TO THE AID OF FRIENDLY POWERS HAVE SUCCEEDED BY YOUR UNAIDED EF- FORTS IN RESTORING PEACE AND PRESERVING THE INDE- PENDENCE OF YOUR REPUBLIC AGAINST THE ARMED BANDS WHICH BROKE INTO YOUR COUNTRY.

Queen Victoria's indignation at the Kaiser's action was so out- spoken as to amount to a reprimand. The Kaiser's own advisers pointed out how near his telegram had brought Germany to the brink of war; he thereupon tried to explain away his hasty and ill- advised act.

Kruger, whose bravery has never been questioned, is reputed on good authority to have said: "I have no more use for the Kaiser. I have a contempt for any man who is afraid of his grandmother."

In March, 1899, Rhodes visited Berlin and there had an interest- ing interview with the Kaiser. The conversation touched upon the Kruger telegram.

"What's your feeling about it?" asked the Kaiser.

"So far as your interests are concerned, I think it was a great mis- take, Your Majesty. But you unwittingly did me a service."

Rhodes went on to say that at the time of the Raid he was looked upon as a bad boy who needed punishment. His own people were quite ready to perform this task, but their wrath was diverted towards Germany by the prospect of the latter's interference and he had got off.

Arthur Balfour said to Fitzpatrick: "The Kaiser is an extraordinary fellow—one does not know if he is mad, has some deep-laid plan, or is just puffed up with vanity. You will hardly credit it, but only a few days ago he wrote privately to his grandmother, the Queen, enclosing a complete plan of campaign which he had ordered his general staff to prepare for the use of the British army against the Boers."

This was practically the plan adopted independently by Lord Roberts in the Boer War.

On my last trip from South Africa to London I took passage on the *Dunvegan*. I was on deck talking with Sir James Sivewright when I saw Dr. Leyds come aboard. I still had a vivid recollection of how he had blocked all our attempts to bring about a rapprochement between Boer and Uitlander. Moreover, there was no doubt that the major part of the blame for our prison treatment rested on his shoulders.

Sir James accosted him with the remark, "Here, Dr. Leyds, I fancy you and Mr. Hammond have met before."

"I think," I replied, "that I had the honor on a previous occasion."

"Yes," responded the doctor with a cool smile, "I recall we have met before."

Thereafter, Dr. Leyds and I saw nothing of each other until the steamer stopped at Madeira to take on coal. Our staterooms were on the same side of the ship and directly exposed to the dirt and noise of coaling operations.

The captain said to me: "I was afraid you'd be kept awake in your stateroom. Since I have to be on the bridge all night, I've made arrangements to shift you to my cabin. Would you object very much to sharing it with Dr. Leyds?"

"Certainly not," I said.

When I entered the room Dr. Leyds was already there. We bowed

A CONTEMPORARY CARTOON

RUDYARD KIPLING

coldly. We undressed in silence. I was preparing to take the cot and leave the bed to him when the steward entered.

"The bed has been prepared for you, Mr. Hammond," he announced.

His tone was decisive. Realizing that on a British ship feeling against the Boer secretary of state was intense, even among the stewards, and that the question of which should have the bed might involve national prestige, it seemed advisable not to protest.

I pulled the covers up to my chin and, just before snapping out the light, I wished Leyds a formal "Good night."

The response was even more frigid. The darkness concealed my involuntary smile at the irony of having my implacable enemy for a roommate. I still marvel at my moderation in not throwing him overboard, for my contempt and hatred for Dr. Leyds had not in the least diminished since Pretoria days.

During the Boer war, I made many addresses in America on behalf of Great Britain to enlighten the American people as to the circumstances that had led to hostilities. The consensus of opinion in the United States was undoubtedly anti-British. Boer propaganda had been extraordinarily effective. Acting on the maxim, "One tale is good before the other is told," the Boers had been shrewd enough to get in the first word.

In 1902 while in London I was asked to make an address at a banquet given me by Lord Albert Grey. I knew that among the guests would be many of the leading colonial statesmen then in London attending a conference on imperial relations and that I should be expected to express an opinion on South African affairs.

A few days before this occasion I had dinner with Joseph H. Choate, Hay's successor at the Court of St. James's.

"I have to make a speech two nights from now and I dread it," I remarked. "If only I had your gift of expression, I'd know what to say and how to say it."

Choate replied: "Why, you're the very man for the job. You have all the background. I've often heard you say how much you admired the Boers who did the fighting. In your opinion, it was

men like Kruger and Leyds who caused all the mischief, wasn't it?"
I agreed.

"Well, then, it seems to me there's a logical analogy between the end of our Civil War and present conditions in South Africa. Why wouldn't it be a wise move to point this out to the peacemaking diplomats? Tell them how magnanimously Grant treated Lee at Appomattox, but how everything was ruined by the harsh treatment meted out to the South by our reconstruction politicians. These men gathered here in London are responsible for the future of Great Britain in South Africa. Much will depend upon the spirit in which they approach the negotiations."

I used Choate's suggestion as the keynote of my address. I began by deploring the fact that American sympathy lay with the Boers; that this seemed particularly unjust, since we now had the opportunity to reciprocate the sympathetic attitude of Great Britain during our war with Spain. I told them not to take too seriously the professions of friendship made by the Newport element; this was no real index of American thought.

As I was testing out the temper of my audience, I was encouraged by the "Hear, hear," uttered by Lord Beresford, which evoked further approval from other distinguished guests.

In conclusion, I pointed out that Boer and Englishman together had to work out the political and economic destiny of South Africa. I urged a peace settlement that would grant to the Boers at once what they would ultimately and inevitably attain by their superior political strength. *Bis dat qui cito dat.* My sentiments were vigorously applauded. Mr. Choate later added his congratulations, and said that my speech had contributed in some measure towards the granting of generous terms to the conquered.

It has always been a source of satisfaction to me that the Peace of Vereeniging proved my contention that, in the end, magnanimity is the wiser and more statesmanlike policy.

If the Reform Movement had been successful, I believe a *modus vivendi* between Boer and Uitlander would have been established. If, through diplomatic intervention, the full rights of the Uitlander could have been secured, enlightened self-interest would thereafter have made it to the advantage of all South African states to compose their differences for the common welfare and the Boer War would have been postponed, if not averted.

Of course, there are no ifs in history, but it is interesting to speculate on what might have happened if the Boer War had not broken out in 1899. In the intervening years Germany had built strategic roads in German Southwest Africa as a military threat to the whole British position from Cape Town to the headwaters of the Nile.

Germany's African ambitions were undoubtedly grandiose. She planned to build up an enormous legion of black soldiers as an inexhaustible reserve of cannon fodder. With her roads, with her disciplined host of native levies, with the aid of the well-armed, skillful, and courageous Boer Army, in 1914 Germany would have struck a blow in South Africa which might well have overwhelmed all possible opposition on the part of the British South Africans and the pro-British Dutch, and would have helped to give her that world-victory she so nearly secured by the suddenness of her attack upon Belgium and France. Her treasury would have been replenished with the gold of South Africa; naval bases at Durban and Cape Town would have placed her submarines within easy striking distance of every sea route south of the equator; the resources of the South American continent would no longer have been at the disposal of the Allies; the participation of India and Australia in the war would have been seriously hampered.

Immediately following the outbreak of the World War, certain irreconcilable Boers made a compact with the governor of German Southwest Africa to announce the independence of South Africa and to declare war against England. Germany promised to send help from Southwest Africa, and, in the event of a German victory in Europe, to recognize the South African claim to full independence. Furthermore, Germany was to have Walfish Bay, and the new South African Republic was to be allowed to compensate itself with Portuguese-owned Delagoa Bay.

Botha obtained possession of this treaty and tried to dissuade the rebels from joining forces with the Germans in 1914. Failing in this, he headed a volunteer commando of Boers in what is regarded as a remarkable campaign, captured the rebel leaders, and put an end to the movement for revolt in the Transvaal.

Even before the Raid, Botha and I had been good friends. At the Imperial Conference in England in 1907, Botha and Jameson struck up a friendship. Many of the British extremists never forgave the doctor for dealing with Botha.

"Are you aware," argued one of them, "that Botha˘ was one of those men who wanted to shoot you at Pretoria after the Raid?"

Jameson smiled. "Ah," he said, "Botha was always right."

It was largely owing to the co-operation of Jameson and Botha that the Union of South Africa was formed in 1910, with Botha as its first prime minister. Moreover, many of the Reform Committee prisoners became identified with South African politics after the Boer War, and held office under the Union government. Prominent among these was Sir Percy Fitzpatrick, who defeated Botha himself in a friendly but strenuous contest for a seat in Parliament.

In 1911, General Botha was in London as the special ambassador from South Africa to the coronation of King George V; I was special ambassador from the United States.

Botha greeted me with, "It's been some years since we met, Your Excellency."

"The last time we were together, General," I replied, "I didn't meet you; I saw you in the courtroom when I was sentenced to death. I'd like to thank you now for being one of the first to start the petition for commutation."

"Isn't it extraordinary," he exclaimed, "that you and I should meet again under the present circumstances!"

"Not any more so than that you and Dr. Jim should have held high office under the same government. By the way, are you and the doctor still friends?"

"Indeed, yes," he answered, "I had the pleasure of recommending him, as well as several other old friends of yours on the Reform Committee, for the Honors List. I think he is the salt of the earth and as soon as this affair is over, I'm going with the doctor on a fishing trip to Scotland."

The following day I had luncheon with Jameson, and asked him his opinion of Botha. Jameson, at that time leader of the political opposition to Botha's government, answered, "He's as good a friend as I have."

That evening I dined with King George and was able to furnish him with some sidelights on South Africa, that seemed to interest him. I repeated my conversations with Botha and Jameson, and expressed the belief that, so long as men of their quality held the political control of South Africa, Great Britain might be confident of a loyal colony.

CHAPTER TWENTY-TWO

London Days

*T*he years during which I made London my business headquarters were among the most enjoyable of my life and gave my wife and me an opportunity to know something of the color and the grace of English life at a fascinating period in its history. It was just before the machine age, and the twentieth century irrevocably changed its social aspects and made anachronisms of traditions that in their time were both sound and delightful. After the informal, relatively isolated, and occasionally rough life in Africa these few years came as a very acceptable contrast.

The family was united again for the first time in some years. Immediately upon our arrival, we took a house at Bickley in Kent, where Dick was born. Harris had been at school in Malvern for several years and we resumed our role as his parents, a responsibility which Lady Elizabeth Cust had kindly undertaken in our absence. Now Jack was also put in school, at Eastbourne.

I had settled down in my office in Threadneedle Street, with Kelsey, who had been with me in South Africa, as my secretary. Even now I was never in England for a very extended period, still having to do the traveling which an engineer's career exacts. My first commitments were, of course, to Rhodes and his concerns. Nevertheless, I found time to investigate and consult for other persons and companies. I traveled widely, sometimes on business, sometimes for pleasure. I made occasional short trips to Italy, France, and Germany, and to Switzerland where I was interested in building a tramway system. I made several trips to Africa and an extended journey through Russia, at the invitation of Count Witte, to study its natural resources. In 1899 I made my last voyage to South Africa. This chapter, therefore, is titled with a latitude to say nothing of longitude.

Many mornings, when I was in England, I would go up from Bickley, or from Chislehurst where we later lived, to my office in the City. I soon discovered that I must either change my American habits of business hours or find a great deal of unoccupied time on my hands, after arriving in London for the day's work. The English indubitably get their work done, but to the American, accustomed to arriving early at his office, it is a mystery how they do it. They come to work, not so long before lunch, spend a generous hour at lunch, and just as they are getting into the stream of the afternoon's business, they stop for tea.

Although I may have found this disconcerting, it afforded me time to pursue one of my favorite pastimes, that of indulging myself as an amateur antiquarian and also to reflect that Americans have much to learn from this method of organization, for many of these seeming gentlemen of leisure are among the most efficient businessmen in the world.

I have seen many different countries during my life and have always been interested in things of historical significance and particularly those bearing on the artistic and material development of civilization. In old London now called "The City," the remnants of the old Roman walls, some of them running to lengths of a hundred feet or more, first absorbed me. I would often go to the British Museum and search into books for information on various engrossing ruins I had seen and at one point my mental picture of the early Roman city was so vivid that I felt competent to undertake its reconstruction.

I followed the fortunes of both Ben Jonson and Dr. Samuel Johnson through alleys, bystreets, and taverns; in fact, it was at the "Old Cock" tavern in the Strand, the "Mitre" in Chancery Lane which Dr. Johnson entered by way of the "Cat and Fiddle" alley, that the doctor often held forth with Boswell. But it was at the "Turk's Head Inn" in Gerrard Street, Soho, that members of the Literary Club founded by Johnson—Goldsmith, Boswell, Burke, Sir Joshua Reynolds, and Garrick—more often met. These coffeehouses were most attractive landmarks on one's ramblings.

Visiting places described by the inimitable diarist, Samuel Pepys, was an unfailing delight. Pepys, who lived in what is now the City, describes the Great Plague of 1665 and the fire which came the following year, lasted three days, and swept away almost the whole of old-time London. But the fire was a blessing in disguise as it effectually destroyed the germs of the plague and led to the building of better streets and better houses. It is an injustice to regard Pepys as a philanderer and a socialite—to use the objectionable modern term—for he was an energetic man of affairs and rendered conspicuous service in the upbuilding of the British Navy when he occupied the responsible position in the Admiralty.

In what is now the crowded section of London, around the Hotel Cecil, there were many secluded spots, "Where one would live in the world but not of it, or, of the world but not in it." I have found recreation in those spots.

I have enjoyed an occasional visit to the country churchyard at Stoke Poges, where Gray's *Elegy* was written and where he is buried. This is one of my favorite poems, and it gave me infinite delight to have my children voluntarily memorize it at an early age.

As a lover of Chaucer, at times I would trace the course of his travels as far as possible along the old Canterbury Road. I could well appreciate the charm of the Canterbury Road in lovely spring days and understand what charm meant when he said, "Than longen folk to goon on pilgrimages." Perhaps the fact that

A Coke [cook] they hadde with hem for the nones,
To boille the chiknes with the mary-bones

may have added to the zest with which the old pilgrims undertook their journey.

In its historical interest ancient London appealed to me more strongly than did any other European city with the possible exception of ancient Rome.

My curiosity and interest in these literary traditions were insatiable; if mines had no longer offered a livelihood, I believe I could have done rather well for my family and myself as a tourist guide.

In the evenings and over week-ends my wife and I entertained many friends we had known in both America and South Africa and people we now met in London. Richard Harding Davis was with us frequently, and a charming companion we found him. In the evenings at Bickley we would sit and talk for hours. It was here that he not only developed the idea for his novel *Soldiers of Fortune,* but wrote part of it. My literary friends tell me that it is difficult for the subject to recognize himself in fiction. This may be true, but I doubt if any of my friends would have seen in the six-foot, well-turned-out Clay—relatively a mirror of fashion—any resemblance to me. At any rate, I accepted the compliment and Davis and I continued our friendship until his death. Soon after my return to New York he invited me for the opening night of the play, a dramatization of this book. I enjoyed the evening very much.

It was with Davis that I first took up bicycling. In my student days at Freiberg, this sport was beginning to have a vogue, but as I gazed at the strange-looking objects with a huge front wheel and a small wheel strung ignominiously on behind, I preferred to walk. At this time in England, however, bicycles more nearly resembled those now in use.

Our garden at Bickley was a labyrinth of paths cutting in and out of many kinds of bushes and vines. To add zest to our self-instruction, we two beginners, with some misgivings, laid out a sort of bicycle steeplechase around the garden, which seemed to us as hazardous as a Mexican mountain trail. A large rosebush stood at the most difficult turn. I add, without modesty, that Davis more frequently than I found himself enmeshed in the thorny Charybdis. Poultney Bigelow, *sui generis,* was also a bicycling companion of mine in those days.

As we became more intimately a part of London life and our circle of friends widened, it became clearer to us how varied and continually fascinating was the make-up of Victorian society. It was a happy mixture of people who were active in many different capacities at the time or who had been in the past. We came to meet a number of businessmen, actors, various members of the nobility, writers, politicians, artists, and their wives. Among the friends I made in those days was T. P. ("Tay Pay") O'Connor. Tay Pay and I naturally did not hit it off on South African politics and I never succeeded in convincing him of the justice of the British cause in the South African War. I saw much of him during my last visit to London in 1929, shortly before his death, and he was "of the same opinion still." Tay Pay's bias was undoubtedly due to his Hibernian ancestry.

My friendship for W. T. Stead was founded on our mutual admiration for Cecil Rhodes who had already fortunately converted Stead to his South African policy. Stead was attached to Rhodes because of the latter's unquestioned sincerity in his efforts to promote world peace. At the time I met him Stead was editor of the *Pall Mall Gazette* and the *Review of Reviews.* He had written *If Christ Came to Chicago!* and *The Americanisation of the World.* He was a great spiritualist and his book, *Letters from Julia*—communications from the spiritual world, became famous. I never met him on any occult ground. The last time I saw him was during the coronation celebration in 1911. I was looking forward to a visit from him when he sailed from England in April, 1912, on the ill-fated *Titanic.*

Among the first of my old New York friends with whom I renewed acquaintance in London were John Singer Sargent and Edwin A. Abbey. In the artistic life of London we found some of our most stimulating friends. In fact, later when I came to know John Hay, as ambassador to England, it was with this group of intimates that we spent some of our pleasantest evenings.

My New York days had not been without such associations. When

I established my office in New York in the early eighties I met Sargent and Abbey at the old Tile Club. This club no longer exists, but it had an atmosphere so unique and charming that I should like to recall it here. In a way the Tile Club had some of the delightful features of Samuel Johnson's Literary Club, but was entirely lacking in the old-world atmosphere, obviously somewhat difficult to achieve in the basement of 48 West 10th Street, New York City, where it met monthly.

Since it was an association of artists, my calling as an engineer disqualified me. But I knew all the members intimately, among them William Merritt Chase, A. B. Frost, "Bill" Laffan, who was Charles Dana's right-hand man on the New York *Sun;* Frank Millet, F. Hopkinson Smith, Augustus Saint-Gaudens, Elihu Vedder, and Stanford White. Frederick Dielman is now the sole survivor.

The members took turns at cooking some special dish. Bill Laffan was the best cook in the crowd, but because of his laziness the members rarely enjoyed his virtuosity in this line. Frank Millet used to superintend Black Daniel, the old club steward, in the preparation of Turkish kibaab. Black Daniel was a typical servant of the old slavery days, and when he found that my great-grandmother was a Ringgold from Maryland, he, with great pride, would say, "Yassuh, I'se one ob de Maryland Ringgolds."

I was once, and only once, asked to try my hand at cooking. I had been talking of the native dishes I had learned about while in Mexico, although I failed to mention that I had never attempted to convert the recipes into actualities. I accepted the challenge, rolled up my sleeves, and from memory tried to produce tamales, chile con carne, or some other tempting Mexican dish. I'm afraid I did not stick to the recipe in the amount of condiments and highly flavored ingredients, for I was more liberal than the Mexicans themselves in the lavish use of spices and peppers. I was prepared to receive a chorus of compliments for my culinary art and it seemed incredible that the comments were, if anything, hotter than the dish I had prepared for them.

Through my Tile Club friends I came to know many others of their circle. Stanford White introduced me to Edwin Booth, who was then living at the Players' Club, in Gramercy Park. At that time

Booth was broken down in health and a recluse. Although some thought him difficult to get on with, I always found him pleasant. He asked me to come and see him often. He was interested in hearing stories about Mexico and the mining towns of our own West, in many of which he had played as a young man. He enjoyed reminiscing and was eager for news about the people he had once known and the changes that had taken place. He liked to hear about the actors I had seen as a boy when they played stock in San Francisco at the old California Theatre. We'd talk at length about such men as John T. Raymond, Lawrence Barrett, and John McCullough.

In London it was chiefly through Alfred Parsons that I kept in touch with the artistic and literary world. We had many mutual friends in the Tile Club, and he had once visited my family in San Francisco on his way home from a trip to the Orient. Parsons was a bachelor, a painter, and a most fascinating host. As an avocation to his painting, he became greatly interested in landscape gardening and laid out some of the most beautiful private gardens in England. On the walls of homes in both England and America one can still find lithographic reproductions of his *In a Copse, November.* It was a picture which caught the popular fancy, and consequently today's critics shrug and label it "Victorian."

At Alfred Parsons' "Open House" one met the wittiest and some of the most worth-while people of all sets in London, particularly the painters. It was here that most frequently I saw Abbey, Sargent, William Black, the novelist, and a host of others. In putting young and struggling artists in touch with those who had already made a name for themselves, Parsons performed a fine service.

Years later, when my wife and I went to live in Washington and found ourselves a part of the political and diplomatic life of our own country, I was immediately struck by its contrast to this same type of life in London. Not only was there in London a mingling with the world of artistic and business affairs, such as is rarely the case in America, but members of various English political parties could meet at the same table or in the same drawing room and brilliantly and without restraint or rancor discuss the most heated questions of the day. Even today this is not true in Washington. Perhaps this is due to the fact that many of our congressmen are little men, desperately worried over the outcome of the next election, harassed by lobbies and by their constituents, and more worried over their own survival than over good government, while in England statecraft is a life career and even if a man goes out with one election, he may either find an office or come back in the next. In America a man is likely to be out of office for years.

In London, Parliament is near the City, which corresponds to our Wall Street, and business and high finance are integrally connected with government. It is considered only reasonable that lawmakers should take various problems to the men who have firsthand information and the judgment derived from long experience. Indeed, many members of Parliament are actively engaged in business affairs in the City.

In Washington, politicians so far as possible avoid close contact with men of standing in business for fear of suspicion or investigation. The cry of "Wall Street" has been the death knell of many sound acts of legislation.

Another factor which added to the diplomatic or social life in London was the Englishwoman's ability to act brilliantly and intelligently as hostess at the most complex gatherings. Long before she gained the right to vote, she had an informed and accurate knowledge of "my country's politics." She is adroit at leading conversation and keenly aware of the moment when it is wise to retire from the center of the stage. Women have played an important role in the background of English politics, but they have done it with subtlety rather than publicity.

Of an evening in London one would find oneself in the midst of a thoroughly cosmopolitan assemblage. Under the same roof one might meet Viscount Grey, the statesman, Lecky, the historian, Kipling, the writer, and Lady Elizabeth Cust's son, Sir Lionel, head of the National Portrait Gallery, the Duke of Argyll, and Sir Edward Elgar, the composer and conductor. Among the charming women were Lady Vincent, called the most beautiful woman in London, and Madame Antonio de Navarro, formerly the lovely Mary Anderson of the stage. Add to these the usual sprinkling of foreign diplomats and noted explorers, the dash of leaders of great business enterprises, and the omnipresent number of beautiful and distinguished women, and the scope of interest in the inspired conversation would be unlimited. Yet one must remember that this was before the time when the business office spread into the drawing room.

I have mentioned only a few of the friends we made. My wife had a genius for bringing together our friends, and I delighted in it. Her great interest in music naturally led her to include many musicians in this circle, and one of the closest was Elgar. Years later I made a speech at a dinner given for him in New York.

Elgar was a man of the world and informed on many subjects other than music, which was lucky for me. While I might enjoy listening to the sonorous notes of his *Pomp and Circumstance,* I doubt that my appreciation would include one of his symphonies. To be perfectly honest, I have difficulty in telling one note from another, although in my boyhood days I occasionally led the band in the drum corps of my company at the school military exhibitions.

I have sat through many painful hours of opera and concert in one good cause or another, chiefly to please my wife. She was a fine musician and was studying music in Dresden when I first met her. While I was courting her, I went up from Freiberg and took her to dozens of operas and concerts. I finally developed some small appreciation of Wagnerian opera, but I must confess that this came through following the schematic structure, which appealed to me as a great feat of mechanical thinking. It has always seemed to me that Wagner would have made an excellent engineer.

Our son Dick inherited a strong musical talent, obviously from his mother. Before he was three years old he showed a decided interest in it, and would try to climb onto the piano stool to reach the keys. One of his prized toys was a little primitive phonograph. He could pick out *She Was a High-Born Lady, Follow the Man from Cook's,* or *My Lodger Is a Nice Young Man,* simply by his familiarity with the slots and dashes on the paper disks. This aptitude was developed and Dick studied music for many years in Paris. His songs and other compositions have been played or sung by Spalding, Ganz, Louis Graveure, and many others.

One of the most noted hostesses of all Victorian London was the Baroness Burdett-Coutts. She was born in 1814 and was an elderly woman when my wife and I first met her, distinguished and graceful in appearance and alert and clever in mind. The daughter of Sir Francis Burdett, she added the name of Coutts on inheriting the large fortune of her grandfather, Thomas Coutts, the banker. She was close to Queen Victoria by whom she was created a baroness in 1871.

King Edward VII spoke of her as "After my mother, the most remarkable woman in the Kingdom."

Baroness Burdett-Coutts gave much of her time to the organizing and carrying on of various charities. Her friendship with Charles Dickens came from their common interest in the poor of London. In 1881 she married William Ashmead-Bartlett, who took her name. Ashmead-Bartlett was born in America of English parents.

Her house at No. 1 Stratton Street, Piccadilly, was filled with rare paintings, porcelains, ivories, old silver, Shakespeare folios and other first editions. I frequently dropped in after business hours to have tea with the baroness. She did not interfere with politics, but she was much interested in Africa and we often discussed the problems of the blacks under the English and the Boers. At these afternoon gatherings one would invariably meet most of the nationally and internationally known people of the time.

Holly Lodge, her suburban home, was one of the most beautiful in London. On a hillside some hundred feet above London, it was surrounded by magnificent gardens, and on a clear day one could look down on the town. It was an ideal place for out-of-door entertaining. In the spring Season, she and her husband gave delightful garden parties. It was at one of these that I had one of my more serious encounters with royalty. The Duchess of Albany was being pushed around the grounds in a rolling chair. There was also present an Indian maharaja. The baroness asked me to present him to the duchess. I asked to be reminded of his name and was told that the reason the baroness wanted me to make the presentation was because she couldn't remember it. No wonder. He had about forty titles.

I started, feeling a little like Alice in Wonderland, and was making fair, if somewhat halting progress in mentioning his many titles when the young maharaja stepped forward and in the best Oxonian English said, "Kindly allow me, sir"—and finished the job himself.

Both the duchess and the baroness seemed content and I, needless to say, was relieved.

The baroness had known the Duke of Wellington in her girlhood. It is said that she refused his offer of marriage. It was her custom, each year, to observe the anniversary of the Battle of Waterloo by giving a dinner. As the years went by these dinners became nearly as important as other more official memorials.

While my wife and I were at Bad Nauheim in 1906-we received an invitation to spend this anniversary with her. We were honored but somewhat surprised to find ourselves the only guests. But she was ninety-two now and growing weaker. She felt close to us for many reasons, among them the fact that she was our daughter Natalie's godmother. Her mind was as clear and active as ever. She wore the cabochon emerald that Wellington had given her, and talked of him and his services to England and repeated stories he had told her of his campaigns and battles. It was the last time we saw her. She died a few months later.

Mr. Burdett-Coutts' brother, E. Ashmead-Bartlett, M.P., was an extreme pro-Turk. He had been an observer in the Greco-Turkish War of 1897; Richard Harding Davis had been a war correspondent with the Greeks. After the return of both these friends of mine to London, I invited them to lunch to meet each other. I thought it would prove interesting and I promised myself some light on the unofficial and inside history of the war. We were hardly seated when Ashmead-Bartlett said something about the cowardice of the Greeks. This was challenged by Davis, who flared up in defense of them and then attacked the Turks. The argument became so heated that the two almost came to blows. This would have been a serious fight as both were powerful men, and it required all my tact to quiet them. The purpose of the lunch was defeated and the subject had to be dropped. War had very nearly broken out again over the glassware and china.

Another of England's most gracious ladies is Princess Louise, the fourth daughter of Queen Victoria. The princess has always been especially kind to Americans. She understood our unfamiliarity with court life. Her receptions were simple and her warmth of personality unaffected. She was most kind to both my wife and my

JOHN HAY (1838-1905)

In Memoriam,
December 30, 1906.

ANGELA,
BARONESS BURDETT-COUTTS.

BARONESS BURDETT-COUTTS (1814-1906)

sister when they were presented at Queen Victoria's court. Her husband was the Marquis of Lorne, afterwards Duke of Argyll, whom we always enjoyed seeing. His charming simplicity is illustrated by his remark to my sister, when he heard we were looking for a house and were considering various locations: "Perhaps you'd better not think of the section around Buckingham Palace. *My wife's family* find it too relaxing." Among my literary treasures are the complete works of Walter Scott, which had been a gift to the duke from his mother, and which he gave to me shortly before his death in 1914.

I saw a great deal of Sir Edgar Vincent, later Lord D'Abernon. He was tall and handsome and wore a beard—strangely enough, becoming. Among all the English diplomats, he was one of the most versatile. He was an outstanding banker, financial adviser to the Egyptian government, and governor of the Imperial Ottoman Bank, and from 1920 to 1926 ambassador to Germany. He wrote many books, and one of the best arguments in the cause of peaceful international relations is the three-volume diary account of his activities in post-war Germany, *An Ambassador of Peace.*

The last time I saw him was when I visited England in 1929. He was just preparing to head one of those famous English goodwill tours. This one was to South America and, of course, to promote English business and commerce. He invited me to go with him to which I demurred saying that it would be impossible to get passage at such a late date. He assured me that he would arrange for the passage himself and that all diplomatic courtesies would be extended me. I hesitated again and asked him how he dared suggest that I, an American, go along, for I might be tempted to stir up some business for my own countrymen and myself.

"I'll take my chances on that," he replied. I persisted in my refusal, for I saw no reason why I should be a part of a junket to drum up trade for the British, though this was not my sole objection.

Following a good lead, however, I did make a trip to the east coast of South America a short time after.

During the winter of 1897-98 I made another trip to South Africa, and on the same boat with me were Rudyard Kipling (Rudyard was named after a place where his father and mother first met), his wife, and his father, Lockwood Kipling, the artist. They proved excellent traveling companions and we have maintained our friendly contact ever since. Rudyard manifested his " 'satiable curtiosity" by prowling endlessly from engine room to bridge getting information which, as he said, he filed away in his memory for future use.

When we arrived at Cape Town, I went, as always, to spend a few days with Rhodes at Groote Schuur and report on the mining properties in which he was still interested and of which I was still consulting engineer. Rhodes had finished with his Parliamentary Inquiry and had returned to Cape Town, once more to enter politics, and to work for his "North."

Rhodes asked me if there were any interesting passengers on the steamer and I mentioned the Kiplings. Then I asked his permission to bring them to lunch; from that meeting sprang a genuine and deep regard between these great imperialists which terminated only at Rhodes's death. Rhodes had built a guest house on his place at Groote Schuur, and Rudyard was asked to make it his winter home, which he did for several years.

My assistants, Yeatman and Webb, had met me at Cape Town to report on operations on the Rand. We made the return trip to Johannesburg together, and I invited Lockwood Kipling to accompany us.

At the Transvaal border we had to change trains and go through the customs. Precautions against smuggling had greatly increased in stringency since the old days when I had played Ali Baba with the oil drums. Yeatman and Webb seemed apprehensive. They asked me several times whether I had a pistol with me, saying that the Boers were sure to make a thorough search for arms. They believed that I, particularly, would be suspected should my identity become known. Their anxiety, though to me amusing, became tiresome.

To quiet them I bet them I would not suffer the indignity of personal search.

At the border Yeatman and Webb went ahead of me into the wire enclosure where the baggage was being examined. After they had submitted to a search of their persons for concealed weapons, the inspector turned towards me.

"Let me see your commanding officer, please!" I demanded in a firm voice.

He pointed to a man standing in the doorway. I walked over and introduced myself.

"Oh, yes, Mr. Hammond, I seem to have heard of you before. What can I do for you?"

"Do you think it necessary to search me?" I asked. "I don't deny that I have done some gunrunning over these borders in my time, but I like to do my smuggling on a large scale. I'd have no use for firearms now. I assure you my intentions at the moment are entirely peaceable."

The official smiled pleasantly, and said: "I'll see you're passed through without examination. Is there anyone else in your party?"

"Yes," I replied, "I've a friend with me." I discreetly avoided mentioning the name of Kipling as it was anathema to the Boers at that time because of the extremely imperialistic character of Rudyard's verse. Moreover, I didn't care to disturb the confidence just shown in me. The official beckoned to a porter and told him to reserve a compartment for us and to see that our luggage was put on the Transvaal train.

It was a warm day, and the official asked me whether I would join him in a glass of beer. I gladly accepted. He thereupon unlocked the door which led from the wired enclosure to the bar. While waiting for the train, we sipped our beers, smoked, and chatted.

As I leaned with my back against the bar, I could see out of the corner of my eye Yeatman and Webb staring wistfully, their anxiety this time centering on themselves rather than on me but I took no notice of them.

Finally the Boer inspector remarked: "Mr. Hammond, there are two gentlemen out there. I think they're trying to attract your attention. Do you know them?"

I glanced casually in their direction. Their gestures became more agitated. I turned back to my beer and said, "I can't place them for the moment."

But their pathetic appearance gradually worked upon my sympathies and I relented.

I turned and called, "Come on, fellows, there's just time for a quick one before the train leaves."

When I was back in England in 1898, I was dining one night at the Burlington Hotel in London with Rhodes and two or three other friends. Rhodes received a cablegram from Kitchener, saying, "We have whipped the Mahdi. Your brother Frank well. I will win my bet." I asked Rhodes what the bet was and he said that he had made a bet with Kitchener that he would extend the railroad from Cape Town farther north than Kitchener would extend it south from Cairo, within the next five years.

The Cape-to-Cairo railroad was most dear to Rhodes and was an old point of contention between Rhodes and me. I pointed out to him again that the cost of maintaining the Cape-to-Cairo road would be greater than the economic returns would ever warrant, and that he ought to take into consideration the fact that all freight for western Europe and England would have to be transferred from railroad to ships at considerable expense and there would be no saving of time. Also, very little time would be saved by passengers who chose the land route. Rhodes, however, was so committed to the completion of this project that after a few arguments which became somewhat heated the subject was dropped.

Later, in lunching with Baron Reuter, of the Reuter News Agency, I remarked that at last the English had another great general. He said, "Of course you refer to Kitchener."

"Yes," I replied; whereupon he said, "You are entirely mistaken in your estimate of Kitchener."

Reuter then went on to say that the Battle of Omdurman was not one that would reflect great credit on Kitchener's generalship, since as a matter of fact he narrowly escaped defeat owing to lack of precaution in his advance. The Mahdists, it seems, had led him into an ambuscade and if it had not been for the remarkable bravery of a force of a few hundred soldiers under General Kelly, one of Kitchener's officers, in relaying, charging, and dispersing the enemy, thus affording Kitchener time to reorganize his column, the British would have suffered a serious defeat.

Neither did Kitchener's career in the Boer War, a few years later, add luster to his laurels as a military commander. It was fortunate for the British cause that Lord Roberts was in command early in the war; he superseded General Buller, who had got the British Army involved in many difficult situations. Kitchener was, however, a great executive, and I think he must have had many of the qualities of General McClellan in our Civil War; a great organizer but not a great fighter. We all recall Lincoln's impatience at the inaction of General McClellan; the President good-humoredly sent word to McClellan that if he did not have any use for his army he wished the general would lend it to him.

In the great World War, Kitchener failed to rise to his opportunities, not realizing the supreme need of sufficient munitions to carry on a war of that character. Only the perception and energy of Lloyd George retrieved that blunder.

All over the world, when I set up an office, people came to me with mining propositions. Sometimes they were sound, sometimes worth investigating, at other times tragic or comic. The most tragic, I think, was the case of Whittaker Wright who came to me after I had established headquarters in London.

"Mr. Hammond," he said, "I have some gold properties in Australia. I'd like you to look them over and come in with us as consulting engineer. We've a fine board of directors as you'll see by this list."

I took the paper and noted suspiciously the inclusion of many titled directors. Since I was familiar with Wright's questionable mining reputation, I suspected that these noble lords were being prepared for fleecing.

Wright held out the inducement of a yacht for my accommodation if I would go in with him; even so, I refused.

Only a few months later Wright's financial structure toppled. He had tried to freeze out his partners by bearing the market and buying in at the bottom, but he overstepped the bounds of legality.

At his trial, he might have embarrassed those well-known gentlemen who, in return for substantial directors' fees and through misplaced confidence in Wright, had lent their respectable names to his enterprise.

There was consternation in London. But Wright refused to give any evidence involving others. He had even destroyed all records which might have inculpated some of them. Perhaps fearing his own high resolve might weaken, he took some cyanide of potassium from his pocket as he left the dock and, before the guards could prevent, he had swallowed a fatal dose.

Since it was during these years in London that I first met John Hay, whom I consider one of the finest Americans I have ever known, I should like to digress long enough to tell something of our relationship.

Trifles often help to turn acquaintance into friendship. Soon after I met him I heard one day that he was ill. Stopping at a florist shop, I selected some flowers, and wrote a card, "From John Hay's Hammond." This pleased the fancy of the genial diplomat, and after that we saw a good deal of each other.

Although I had not known Hay before, I had, of course, heard about him from boyhood. I was ten years old when Lincoln was shot; John Hay had been his most confidential secretary. The imagination developed in his early career as writer and journalist, tempered by his legal training and matured by intimate association with Lincoln, together with the terrific events at the Capital during the war and the President's assassination, gave his mind a balance and a varied brilliance that cannot be forgotten by anyone who heard him talk or has read his letters. Hay was the ideal diplomat. As ambassador to England and later as secretary of state in this crucial time of financial crisis and our war with Spain, he more than any other American cemented our bonds with England. The English admired and liked him no less than did his fellow countrymen.

It was just at this time, during the Spanish-American War, that he and I became so intimate. Through the co-operation of Rhodes, I acted in sort of liaison capacity between Hay and certain important personages in the British government. Hay was very anxious to meet Rhodes in an informal way, so when Rhodes next came to London, I arranged a luncheon for Ambassador and Mrs. Hay, Mr. and Mrs. Rudyard Kipling, Rhodes, James M. Barrie, my wife, and myself. We had a delightful time and enjoyed a spirited talk for two or three hours. Rhodes then told Hay the whole story of South Africa as only he could tell it, and Hay was won over to Rhodes and his aspirations. When Hay returned to the United States in 1898 and became secretary of state under McKinley, he was able to impress upon the President the true situation in South Africa.

When the Spanish-American War first broke out, I was in London and was greatly pleased to see how English public sentiment in general favored us. All the other nations of Europe sympathized with Spain. As evidence of the British sympathy to the American cause, they often referred to it as the Yanko-Spanko War.

During this time, I happened to sit next to General Lord Wolseley at a dinner and I asked him how he thought the conflict would end. Wolseley said: "You know I am in sympathy with the United States, as I served in your Civil War as a British observer, and I have a very high regard for the American soldier, but I am much afraid that your country will be rushed into the war by politicians, and your country is not prepared. It takes a lot of preparation to transport troops, even for a short distance. England with her great navy and merchant marine would find it difficult to move troops to any part of the world in a short time, and I am afraid that the United States might be set back, but, of course, ultimately you will win, and I hope you do." Subsequent events proved the justness of this criticism.

After enjoying Hay's companionship while he was in England, I did not see him again until we met at Bad Nauheim in 1906. I had had pneumonia in America, after visiting the Utah Copper Company. The weather was very cold and I had to walk through the snow for two or three miles down to a canyon to the railroad. It was bitterly cold; there wasn't a drop of liquor at the Utah copper mine, as the superintendent would not allow it about the place. I've always believed that if I had had some whisky I might have escaped pneumonia, but then I might not have seen John Hay again.

My wife really inveigled me into going to Bad Nauheim. While I was recuperating, she tried to get me to make the trip there, but I refused. Then she pretended that she had heart trouble; she thought she ought to go to Bad Nauheim and take treatments. I was naturally greatly concerned, so we went. The result was that I got the treatments, and her heart trouble quickly disappeared.

John Hay was completing his treatments at Bad Nauheim under

Dr. Groedel. During this time the American ambassador to Germany was Charlemagne Tower, who later became a good friend of mine. He came to Bad Nauheim with an invitation from Kaiser Wilhelm for John Hay and myself to visit him in Berlin. We would have enjoyed such a visit exceedingly and were disappointed that we could not accept the invitation, but our physicians strongly urged us not to leave until after the completion of the cure. We asked the ambassador to express our regrets to the Kaiser, with the hope that we might be able to visit him at another time. Unfortunately this occasion never presented itself, as the "reisender" Kaiser was away on one of his frequent trips by the time we were ready to leave the baths.

Mrs. Hay went to Paris for a few days and left her husband under the care of my wife and me. We used to meet with other friends daily at five o'clock to listen to the band and drink tea, chocolate, or beer. Hay called our meeting the "Catch Your Eye Club"; whenever we saw an American any of us knew, we would catch his eye and invite him to come over to our table. For obvious reasons it occurred to me that it was more fitting to call ourselves the "klätscherei" or gossiping club.

Hay was a delightful companion during those days at Bad Nauheim. We talked naturally of many of the presidents including Lincoln. Hay told me: "I sat up with Lincoln the night the election returns for his second term were coming in. He was far from confident; in fact, he was exceedingly nervous. I have been with several presidents on similar occasions and not one of them showed any confidence in being re-elected."

During one of our conversations he told me that King Leopold of Belgium was importunate in seeking a meeting with him. Hay said: "I know what the old codger has in mind; he wants to explain away the atrocities in the Congo, and I am not going to see him." The king arrived the next day, so Hay left word at the desk of the hotel that his doctors had ordered him to see no one and he was not to be disturbed. Then he and I went off for a long walk. About five o'clock, he said: "Let's go back now. I guess the old rascal has come and gone by this time." When we reached the hotel there was King Leopold in an armchair in front of the elevator, waiting for Hay.

There was nothing left for Hay to do but make an apology and talk with the king.

That evening Hay told me that the king had not wanted to talk about the Congo at all; instead, he talked about the Manchurian Railway. Hay added, "He is really a very likable fellow."

Royalty does not move without being noticed. Robert Williams told me long afterwards that he feared King Leopold's visit while I was there meant that I would secure from him the Katanga concessions, and this fear impelled Williams to hasten to a conclusion his own negotiations for that property.

There was a curious thing about Hay. With all his intellectual power and the fair degree of his earlier success as poet, biographer, and essayist, it is said that after he went to England he was always sorry he had published any books in lighter vein. Perhaps he feared the accusation of being literary would interfere with his importance as a statesman.

Hay's greatest obsession was his contempt for the United States Senate, which had turned down the Hay-Pauncefote Treaty, though it was finally signed in November, 1901.

Hay was a man of quick wit, as is illustrated by the following anecdote. He, William M. Evarts, at that time secretary of state and likewise famous for his wit, and the British lord chancellor, who was paying a visit to America, went sightseeing to Mount Vernon. The British chancellor turned to Secretary Evarts and said: "That is a pretty tall story about Washington throwing a dollar across the Potomac. It is a very wide river."

"Oh," replied Evarts, "a dollar went farther in those days."

Then Hay capped the climax by quickly saying, "George Washington did something better than that; he hurled a sovereign across the Atlantic."

Our visit together at Bad Nauheim was destined to be our last. John Hay was anxious to return home, but Dr. Groedel advised him not to go back to America and start any business until he had finished his nach kur. Unfortunately Hay disregarded this advice and returned home. He spent a few weeks in Washington in the heat of the summer and then went to his home in New Hampshire. He died there, the day I arrived in the United States.

In London, in 1898, I had received a new business proposition. My arrangement with Rhodes allowed me to accept other work in South Africa, of course, provided it involved no injury to his interests. Therefore, no professional ethics were concerned when Leopold Hirsch, head of the great stock brokerage house of L. Hirsch and Company of London, informed me that his client J. B. Robinson, later Sir Joseph, wished me to take charge of his gold-mining properties, the Randfontein Estates.

I had heard a great deal about Robinson's unpopularity among the ,mining operators of the Rand; he was especially jealous of Rhodes, his avowed enemy. His astuteness in negotiating land purchases from the reluctant Boers are still far-famed in the Transvaal.

In 1886 he was almost penniless. Hearing of the discovery of gold on the Rand, he had persuaded Alfred Beit to back him to the extent of one hundred thousand dollars in the purchase of farms in the Witwatersrand district. Since the partnership did not thrive, it was decided to divide the property. Robinson's share, the Langlaagte, produced nearly five million dollars in five years but he was disgruntled because that of Beit proved much richer.

Robinson carried on a long private feud with Rhodes, paying extravagant prices for diamond fields wherever and whenever he thought it possible to injure the De Beers Company. He boasted that, since he was now worth sixty million dollars, he could afford it. Because Rhodes and Kruger were inimical, he affected to be an adherent of the latter. Afterwards he broke with Oom Paul because, as he said: "Kruger is so corrupt he can be bribed by anyone. I've done it myself."

Because of his eccentricities, Robinson had few friends on the Rand, and was likened to a "rogue elephant." For that reason I told Hirsch quite frankly that I would not consider seriously any offer made by Robinson, since I believed I could not get along with a man of such arbitrary disposition.

When Hirsch reported this to Robinson, his only reply was, "Well, at least bring Mr. Hammond to have tea with me some day at Dudley House."

Some weeks later I accepted this invitation.

It was interesting to observe a man who utterly lacked aesthetic appreciation living in one of London's most famous and beautiful houses. He was proud of it because it was expensive. He was incapable of realizing that the value of such an architectural treasure could not be estimated in pounds, shillings, and pence.

He asked me bluntly why I objected to becoming associated with him. With equal candor, I answered that, according to report, no self-respecting man could remain long in his employ.

"Can you be more explicit?" he asked.

"For one thing," I replied, "I've been told by your engineers that you interfered constantly with their work."

"True, Mr. Hammond, I've employed many men in whom I have afterwards lost confidence. But if I paid you as much as I expect you to ask, I wouldn't dream of trying to run things myself. Furthermore, I'd agree to give you absolute control of all mining matters."

"I'll have to think this over for a few days, Mr. Robinson," I answered as I took my leave.

I sent a cable at once to Harry H. Webb in Johannesburg in whose estimates of ore values I had great confidence. I asked him to let me know whether it would be possible to make the Randfontein Estates property a financial success if there were sufficient working capital and if it were under my absolute control.

On the strength of Webb's favorable assurances I accepted the position with Robinson, and selected Pope Yeatman to become general manager.

A few months later I went to South Africa and made a personal examination of the properties. Without any hesitation our recommendations were accepted, and we had the satisfaction of seeing our policy carried out.

When Rhodes and other friends heard that I had become consultant for Robinson, they told me I could not get along with him for three months. Actually, I remained his consulting engineer for two years—that is, until my return to America. Other mining men who knew Robinson were amazed when I told them I had found him one of the most liberal men with whom I had ever done business. He gave me his unqualified support and, after I had resigned, did the same for Yeatman, whom he retained as general manager.

Towards the end of 1899 I came to the conclusion that it would be desirable to transfer my headquarters to New York. My reasons were due partly to business conditions and partly to sentiment.

I sought out Rhodes at Burlington House to tell him of my decision. Rhodes expressed regret, and asked whether I could not be persuaded to reconsider and instead go back to South Africa as general manager of all his interests there.

I hesitated for a moment, and then shook my head. "I'm sorry but I can't do it. I appreciate your offer, and I know how important the position is, but it's not in my line. It's a job for an administrator. Right now all that mining on the Rand amounts to is cutting salaries and reducing operating costs. You know the kind of work I like—solving new technical problems or pioneering in new districts. There's plenty of territory in the United States and Mexico still left to explore."

Rhodes nodded in agreement. "But wouldn't you be interested in politics? I feel confident I'm going to have a new lease of political life, and I'd hoped to have you work with me."

"I'm certain your career has hardly begun yet," I answered him, "and I should regard it as a high honor to be associated with you, but South African politics don't seem to be in my line. I confess I've had enough politics."

I then gave my final reason. I told him that, in spite of my fondness for England, I did not wish my children to become expatriates. Harris was almost ready for college. If I were to remain longer in England, the natural thing would be for him to continue with his friends to Oxford. I recalled my own happy years at Yale, and liked to picture my sons receiving their education in a similar environment. It seemed to me that I could recapture some of my early enthusiasms through their experiences. I looked forward to seeing them take their places in the small college world.

Rhodes understood and sympathized with my feeling, and so we parted. This was my last talk with him; in a few months he was besieged by the Boers in Kimberley.

While dining with me in New York on March 26, 1902, Lord

Albert Grey received a cablegram from Dr. Jameson saying that Rhodes would not survive the night. This came as a great shock to us, though we had known that his days were numbered.

Not merely did I wish my children to be educated in the United States, but I desired to renew my business connections here. At the beginning of the Spanish-American War the price of American securities had dropped considerably, though I had not the slightest doubt that with the ultimate victory of America they would rise again.

Because I had been out of touch with American investments for so long a time I asked the advice of Otto Kahn, who was then in London. Accepting his suggestions, I sold out a large part of my South African mining securities, and invested the proceeds in American enterprises. Once again, I threw in my fortunes with those of my own country.

CHAPTER TWENTY-THREE

Russia

AN OFFICIAL INVITATION TO RUSSIA—WITTE THE
STATESMAN—DODGING THE NIHILISTS—EXAMINING
THE URAL MOUNTAINS—OUT FOR THE WORLD'S
PLATINUM SUPPLY—AN OASIS IN SIBERIA—THE
INDUSTRIAL DEVELOPMENT OF RUSSIA—WITTE
NEGOTIATES PEACE WITH JAPAN—A SECOND
JOURNEY TO RUSSIA—I GIVE THE CZAR GOOD
ADVICE—BARON ROTHSCHILD AND THE JEWISH
PROBLEM—THE UNITED STATES ABROGATES HER
COMMERCIAL TREATY WITH RUSSIA—THE U.S.S.R.

While I was in London, a fresh opportunity presented itself to enlarge my mining experience. In the winter of 1897-98 the financial firm of L. Hirsch and Company was working with Serge Julievitch Witte, the Russian minister of finance, to stimulate the investment of English capital in Russia. Leopold Hirsch had several interviews with Gregory Wilenkin, the Russian government's financial agent in London, and with Dr. Rafalovitch, who acted in a similar capacity in Paris.

As a result of these conversations, Witte invited me to come to St. Petersburg with Hirsch and make a survey of Russia's industrial potentialities, particularly the mining resources.

Our party consisted of Hirsch, his friend, Captain Money, a retired English army officer who managed the details of the trip, and myself. Almost immediately upon our arrival at the Hotel Europa, a droshky was ready to take us to the Ministry of Finance.

I looked forward to meeting Witte, the man who almost single-handed was attempting to change the course of his country's history. At once he reminded me of Cecil Rhodes. Both were over six feet tall and proportionately broad, and would dominate any assemblage by size as well as personality.

Witte had fine clear eyes, set far apart. His face, though intellectually distinguished, bore an expression of sadness. No other Russian I have ever met had his drive, his energy, his ability to cut through red tape. Yet, blended with this practical activity was a certain Oriental imperturbability which contrasted sharply with Rhodes's nervous energy and responsiveness. It is not likely that the possibility of failure had ever occurred to Rhodes before the Jameson Raid; from Witte one gathered that he was prone to envisage the eventuality of disaster.

At that time Witte was regarded as the magician who was about to metamorphose the somnolent Muscovite with his cannikin of vodka into the busy happy workman with a full dinner pail—a plan that had the merit of never having been tried in Russia. In the eyes of the world, Russia was a land of vast and incalculable natural resources awaiting only the fructifying touch of foreign capital.

Witte was one of the most highly qualified of the great statesmen of his day as an empire builder, although perhaps in the economic rather than the political sense. Rhodes was interested in the industrial development of a country chiefly as a means of expanding the British Empire territorially; that is, his aspirations were pre-eminently political, while Witte's paramount interest was for the economic expansion of his country. In his ambition to bring Russia to a high state of industrial development, Witte was willing to sacrifice such frontier territory as was not essential to the country's political integrity. He fully comprehended the political weakness of an overextended empire.

Like Rhodes, the Russian statesman was deeply sensible of having a mission to perform. Either would have been a great factor in the history of any nation and would have exerted commanding influence. Both were exceptionally self-reliant and resourceful; both were dictatorial. Rhodes was the more willing to compromise, but even Witte was at times compelled to make concessions in order to maintain position and influence.

Witte had a far more difficult problem. At court he had to face a camarilla opposed to any economic or political change that would militate against its control of Russian affairs. Also, he had to compel a hidebound bureaucracy and an ignorant populace to subscribe to his plan. On the contrary, Rhodes could appeal with confidence to the enlightened self-interest of the Englishman.

Witte was the ablest and most farseeing man who has guided Russia. He was born in the Caucasus in 1849. His father was a minor state official of Dutch descent; his mother belonged to the Russian nobility. He attended school at Tiflis and then went to Odessa for further education.

In the ordinary course of events he would have become a member of the local bureaucracy. Instead, he went into the employ of the Odessa Railway Company. In a few years he had become general manager of the Southwestern Railway Company, and there he won his technical reputation handling troops and supplies during the Russo-Turkish War.

Business opportunities in Russia at that time were decidedly limited. Advancement through merit was possible up to a certain point; thereafter favoritism played a dominant role. Witte's opportunity came when he was commanded to run the imperial train over his road on a schedule he considered too fast for the Little Father's safety. He absolutely refused to obey orders, and this obstinacy brought him to the Czar's attention.

The Czar recognized that, although honesty and ability are essential for business success, the real test of a man's value to his employer is the manner in which he conducts himself in an emergency; there are times when judgment must override rules, regulations, even the orders of a superior.

There were in the ranks of the Russian nobility few men capable of handling efficiently the portfolio of national finance. Witte was offered this position, but declined. After much persuasion, he agreed to accept the specially created post of director of railways, and in 1892 became minister of ways and communications. Finally, when

Vishnegradsky fell ill, Witte took over the duties of minister of finance, and in 1893, in his forty-fourth year, received the formal appointment.

I was familiar with Witte's aims and generally in sympathy with them. He was convinced that Russia must be tributary to industrial countries so long as it remained exclusively agricultural, and there could be no extensive development of Russian resources without capital. This must be sought abroad. He had to persuade foreign money that Russia was a safe place for investment. In spite of every type of opposition and intrigue, he succeeded in initiating his program.

One of his major victories was to put Russia on the gold standard. First he stopped the speculation in Russian rubles on the Berlin Bourse, and then contracted the paper currency. This financial achievement had been carried through the year before my visit.

The foundation of Witte's economic theory was "educational protection," which resembled the ancient and honorable plank in our Republican party's platform. Witte put high duties on raw materials and manufactured products which could be produced in Russia, although he knew that this policy would result in higher prices to the Russian consumer and that any measure touching the consumer's pocketbook would be unpopular. He deliberately accepted this unpopularity.

The tariff provoked German hostility. Witte welcomed these reprisals because they gave him an excuse to throw off German industrial domination. At our first interview he frankly stated that this was his object in seeking the aid of English capital.

"Isn't the real reason, M. Witte," I asked, "that you have sucked the Gallic orange dry?" France had supplied Russia with large funds.

Witte's face remained impassive. I continued, "Have you also considered seeking American capital?"

He looked at me for a moment, and then said: "Mr. Hammond, the United States is not an international money power. You are occupied with building up your own country. You have not yet reached the stage where you can afford to export capital."

There was enough truth in the statement so that I could not counter his observation with any conviction.

From Witte's office we went to his home for luncheon. With great show of politeness, Hirsch and Money insisted that I be the one to accompany the minister in his small droshky. I climbed in and seated myself beside the great man. My involuntary smile and glance of understanding betrayed my thoughts to my English companions, who showed signs of embarrassment. Witte did not trouble to hide his own amusement at their discomfiture. They had apparently taken to heart the recent publicity given by the European press to nihilistic attempts on the lives of Russian officials. Their droshky remained discreetly distant from ours.

Mme. Witte presided over the luncheon table. She was a charming and highly intelligent woman who, I felt, understood Witte's plans and was a constructive influence in their accomplishment. The conversation ran chiefly in political channels, and both M. and Mme. Witte expressed opinions which, in certain diplomatic circles, might have been regarded as unnecessarily frank.

Witte showed particular interest in Rhodes and what he had been trying to do in Africa. The conversation turned naturally to the English attitude towards Russia. Since I lived in England, but was not English, I felt free to express my opinions.

"M. Witte, you have asked me several questions about Rhodes, and I have tried to tell you my estimate of him. It seems to me that if Rhodes were autocrat of England and another like him held the same position in Russia, these two would be able to settle the differences between their respective countries. The English autocrat would concede Russia's necessity for a Window on the Mediterranean, provided Russia would cease agitation on England's Indian frontier. Both men would recognize that, for the peace and welfare of the world, the two countries should harmonize their foreign policies."

"Of course you know, Mr. Hammond, that I, as minister of finance, have little influence on the foreign policy of my country, but you may rest assured that I know how essential it is for Russia to be friendly with England."

When we were ready to start back to the office, Hirsch—his fears calmed by the fact that we had arrived for luncheon intact—expressed a desire to ride with Witte.

"No," demurred Witte. "You'll pardon me if I seem to consider my own safety. Mr. Hammond will prove a more efficacious bodyguard, because he is an American. I am sure the Nihilists would show him more consideration than they would an Englishman, in spite of the fact that England is well known to be the asylum of 'persecuted Nihilists.' "

Any apprehension I may have had was now allayed, and I relaxed sufficiently to take an interest in the strange city life through which I was passing. Each time I attempted to look about me, I found my view obstructed by the corporeal majesty of the driver. Witte explained to me that the private coachmen were selected from the fattest of their class. The importance and standing of the master was gauged by the weight of his coachman.

This was an interesting sociological sidelight, but I was more comforted by the thought that our driver might serve as a shield from an assassin's bullet. And it occurred to me that armor plate would be an acceptable means of enlarging a coachman and protecting his master.

In order that I might have an accurate picture of the occurrence of minerals in Russia, I had sent ahead several engineers under S. J. Truscott, one of my most competent assistants in South Africa and author of the recognized standard work on Rand mining. He is at present professor of mining at the Imperial College of Science and Technology in London. A preliminary report was awaiting me at St. Petersburg. On the basis of this report I laid out my route to include the most likely prospects. We had permission to examine the Crown properties and authority to open them up if they proved worth while.

Witte had warned me to be on guard against German interference. He had also advised me under no circumstances to attempt to bribe a Russian official. Although the graft scandal was greatly magnified, it seems that little of the money paid to the middlemen for their influence in high places ever accomplished its object.

My party of inspection included Hirsch, Money, and a German interpreter. Everything was done to facilitate our preparations. The minister of transportation, Prince Khilkov, who had learned practical railroading as a locomotive engineer on one of our western lines, placed his private car at our disposal. One room was given up to an enormous map over which we all pored endlessly. The five-foot gauge used on all Russian railroads produced a smoothness of motion that was very agreeable. The tedium of the long trip was relieved by frequent stops at stations where all the passengers were served glasses of hot tea. I have never been able to accustom myself to the English preference for their bitter boiled beverage, but I succumbed without a struggle to the attraction of this liquid as served from the Russian samovar. We lived well: smoked salmon, caviar, bortsch, veal, and cheese appeared often on the menu.

Our first detailed examination was to be made in the Ural Mountains at Ekaterinburg, where shallow prospecting shafts had been sunk on the gold veins in anticipation of my arrival. None of these properties was worth exploitation, however, and the prospects so far developed were not available for purchase. It was near these shafts that the Russian royal family was murdered; their bodies were cremated and the ashes of the bones, with buttons and other indestructible objects from the wearing apparel, were thrown into the shafts, where they were later found.

The platinum deposits were more tempting as a business proposition. Ninety per cent of the world's supply at that time came from the Urals. Since it had to be sent abroad for refining, English firms had secured the monopoly of the manufactured product and could establish its market price. Platinum was then selling at about $5.00 per troy ounce, and Russia was producing about two hundred thousand ounces a year. In 1912 the price in New York had risen to $45.00 per ounce, and at the depth of the depression, in 1932, was still $36.45. Colombia and Canada are now important producers, and in 1932 California produced two thousand ounces as a by-product from working the auriferous gravels.

Hirsch was planning to secure a monopoly of the platinum deposits, and to make an agreement with the Russian government whereby the ore might be reduced and refined in Russia. As a preliminary step we secured options on all the important properties except that of Count Schouvalov, of the Russian diplomatic family. On our return to St. Petersburg, we approached Count Schouvalov on the subject. He expressed willingness to join in the proposed amalgamation, and invited us to luncheon for the purpose, we assumed, of discussing details. After luncheon the count explained that he did not handle his financial affairs himself, but would turn us over to his business agent.

Our plans eventually came to nothing because we put too much dependence upon the honesty of the Schouvalov representatives. While Hirsch and I were absent in England awaiting final decision on this property, Belgian financiers secured it. Our ambitious scheme for cornering the world's platinum market had to be abandoned.

After a few days spent in investigating the mineral potentialities of the Urals, we resumed our trip by way of the Trans-Siberian Railroad. From its terminus at Marinsk, in South Central Siberia, we started south with native guides and two troikas on a trip of several hundred miles to the headwaters of the Yenesei River in the Altai Mountains. Sometimes by muddy roads, sometimes by rocky trails, we made our way through the rolling, sparsely wooded hills of this rarely visited portion of Russia.

While we were still in St. Petersburg, Witte had secured for us a government order enabling us to commandeer conveyances and horses wherever and whenever we should need them. This document proved particularly efficacious when we arrived one night, long after dark, at a small village. Everybody was drunk, including the mayor. We needed a change of horses immediately as we were in haste to catch the weekly train from Marinsk. We seized the mayor, stuck his head under a pump, righted him again, and shoved the order under his nose. Sobered by the sight of the imperial seal, he promptly produced fresh horses.

Traveling in a troika over the almost impassable Siberian roads is comparable in discomfort only to a journey in a dead-ox wagon over the rough trails of western America. Hirsch moaned disconsolately at each jolt. Hitherto his greatest physical exertion had consisted of cantering along the bridle paths of Hyde Park or reeling in salmon or stalking deer on his estate in Scotland.

On the northern slope of the Altai Mountains we found a hospitable host and comfortable quarters at the Ivanisky estate, the only one of any importance within a wide radius. In fact, it was two hundred and fifty miles from the nearest railway and a thousand from any important town.

Ivanisky was over eighty. Forty-odd years before he had been sent as a political exile to Siberia. There he was joined by his wife. Under the laws regulating exiles, those who agreed to discontinue political activities were allowed considerable latitude after a time and could take up their residence in Siberian localities remote from police supervision. Ivanisky was now at liberty to return to Russia, but he told me he preferred to spend his remaining years in Siberia. His relatives and nearly all his friends were dead, and he had succeeded in creating a civilized form of living in the wilderness.

In his youth Ivanisky had acquired some knowledge of mining, and had found employment in a small gold mine owned by a fellow exile. At the latter's death he had inherited several hundred acres of gold-bearing gravels, or placers. The working methods were crude, but produced from fifty to a hundred thousand dollars a year, depending upon the amount of work done upon the mine, which in turn varied with the income he required. I examined the property and made him an offer. Without hesitation he turned it down. He admitted the sum was fair but he considered it far safer to keep his gold in a bank of gravel than to deposit it in any bank of Siberia.

Ivanisky found diversion in his lonely life in raising trotting horses. The Altai country was not at all adapted to this purpose, there not being a level acre within many miles of his stables. Nevertheless, he had laid out a half-mile undulating track and had even sent his head trainer to California to study scientific breeding methods.

This genial old gentleman delighted in dispensing hospitality, and provided pleasant entertainment. The sole amusement for him and his wife during the long winter nights was to listen to the raucous music ground out by a primitive phonograph. Its repertory was almost entirely made up of negro minstrel songs and the so-called humorous dialogues of the day. The old couple did not understand a word of English.

Since they were eager to know exactly why they were amused, I translated the jokes and songs into Russian through our German interpreter. Whatever faint elements of humor might once have existed must somehow have evaporated in my rendition, and I fear that unwittingly I did these simple old people a disservice. They never laughed so heartily after that.

Using Ivanisky's estate as a base of supplies, we outfitted for a trip into the mountains. Our route lay through a country devoid even of trails and, though it was May, great patches of last winter's snow still lay on the northern slopes. Fortunately, our sure-footed Cossack ponies were able to avoid the treacherous places encrusted with thin ice. Before advancing over questionable ground, they would snuff off the covering of soft snow and delicately paw at the suspected spot. Thanks to their amazing sagacity, we met with no mishap except an occasional tumble into a snowbank.

One night a mounted messenger from Marinsk arrived at our camp with a telegram. When we had left St. Petersburg, the Spanish-American War was in progress and the American ambassador, Ethan Allen Hitchcock, had promised to keep me informed as to the result of the naval engagement which then seemed imminent.

The whole evening was devoted to deciphering this message. It had been written in French, the language of diplomacy, and so transmitted to Moscow, translated into Russian there, and then forwarded to Marinsk. When it finally reached us, our interpreter translated it from Russian into German, and I made an English version for Hirsch and Money.

The text had been so mutilated in transmission that all we could make out was that there had been a battle between Cervera's fleet and our own. It was impossible to be sure which side had won, although the Americans seemed to have been victorious. Naturally, I preferred this interpretation. In spite of many telegrams of inquiry, we never did know exactly what had happened at Santiago until we reached Moscow.

We were almost as much out of touch with the world as were some Americans I once heard about who raised foxes on an island off the coast of Alaska. Trips were made from the island twice a year to deliver the skins and to get provisions for the colony. At these times they would pick up a file of papers dating back to their previous trip, and would conscientiously read them in the proper order from the earliest issue to the latest. During the Spanish War, they were so interested in events that they reversed the process and read from last to first.

On our way back to Marinsk, we broke our journey for a day at Ivanisky's home. The entertainment began early and was continuous. We were not accustomed to champagne toasts and "no heeltaps" in the morning. Bumper followed bumper all afternoon and evening, alternating with caviar and hors d'oeuvres. At midnight we sought our beds, tired but happy.

To our consternation, breakfast consisted chiefly of champagne. But we managed to present a steady front and converse fluently until it was time to start.

As we stepped into our troika, Ivanisky bade us farewell: "God speed you, but pardon the lack of true Russian hospitality of which I am guilty. You are the first guests who have ever left my house sober."

With pardonable pride, we thanked him and settled down for a few moments' quiet before we reached the river which cut across the road. There on the brink of the river stood young Ivanisky to bid us farewell. He had taken a short cut and driven furiously to arrive ahead of us. He proudly pointed to his own troika where we saw a case of champagne.

At this point we broke down and abjectly pleaded incapacity. Pointing to the rain-swollen torrent, we explained that, even perfectly sober, we would find it difficult to keep the dugout from capsizing. As we climbed into the troika on the farther side, we caught a glimpse of Ivanisky junior. In each hand he held an upturned bottle from which the precious contents were flowing to the ground. Then, according to Russian custom, he dashed the empty bottles on the rocks.

On our return to St. Petersburg, we saw Witte again. I told him that the natural resources of Russia offered most attractive opportunities for the investment of British capital. The physical geography of many parts of Russia and Siberia strikingly resembled our own West, and for that reason I was inclined to be especially enthusiastic over the prospects. It was apparent that the problems in Russia were similar to those encountered in the United States.

The construction of railroads was going steadily forward under Witte's constant pressure. But many other problems had not yet been seriously considered. Improved methods of agriculture were vitally needed, and with them the erection of grain elevators at strategic points. Furthermore, refrigerator cars were required to move perishable products over the vast distances.

I told Witte that I was greatly impressed with his plans for an intensive industrial development of Russia and Siberia. I then pointed out certain factors which would prevent foreign capital from seeking Russian outlets. In the first place, the laws of Russia were not favorable to such investment. Certain legal clauses made confiscation possible without what citizens of other countries would term "due process of law." Witte acknowledged this objection and expressed his willingness to modify the legislation regarding tenure of property by aliens.

The second obstacle was the control exercised by the Russian bureaucracy over all phases of Russian economic life. Its blighting hand reached to every smallest detail of administration. If English capital were to be interested, much red tape would have to be eliminated.

Most important of all to capital was the alarming state of the political situation. Sir Nicholas O'Connor, the British ambassador, Mr. Ethan Allen Hitchcock, the American ambassador, and I had a joint interview with Witte. The seizure of Kiaochow by the Germans had been followed by the Russian appropriation of Port Arthur and Dalny in Manchuria. Furthermore, in 1896 Russia had secured permission from China to construct the Chinese Eastern Railroad. While I was in Russia, the Trans-Siberian was extending a spur to Port Arthur.

These preparations for the economic and political exploitation of China were being viewed with the profoundest suspicion by England. She could not help believing that the Bear was on one of his ever-recurrent prowls and would be unlikely to content himself with such honeypots as had already fallen to him.

Witte admitted that little could be done about English capital until the political horizon cleared.

My first Russian trip brought no concrete results, but it did bring me in touch with the Russian Empire.

I next saw Witte at Portsmouth in the summer of 1905. My observations in Russia in 1898 had convinced me that American commercial interests in the Orient would be best served by a Russian victory in the Russo-Japanese War.

I made an address before the American Academy of Political and Social Science at Philadelphia in which I firmly stated my views. This came to Witte's attention, and he was prepared to regard me as a genuine friend to Russia at a time when Russian friends in the United States were few: from Roosevelt down, the American populace was inclined to sympathize with the Japanese. Witte seemed honestly pleased to find one American who was prepared to give him sympathetic hearing.

He talked with me frankly about the problems he had to face. He had come to the United States as peacemaker against his will. The war had not been of his making. He regarded it as the work of a court cabal. As an economist he recognized only too well the disaster war would inevitably bring to Russia. It represented the downfall of his hopes for a regenerated nation. The Russian treasury had been depleted, foreign loans could be obtained only on ruinous terms, and the army and navy had been decisively defeated.

In confirmation I recalled that in 1898 Witte had expressed opposition to the Russification of the Far Eastern territory. He had been unquestionably an advocate of world peace: he realized that the enormous cost of their national defense put the European nations under a severe handicap in trade competition with America.

Witte conducted himself with remarkable sagacity although he was no diplomat by training. He recognized American hostility and set out to counteract it. A hater of publicity, he allowed himself to be photographed as much as the American press desired and in this way did much to overcome the prevailing pro-Japanese sentiment. His old friend, Dr. E. J. Dillon, long a British newspaper correspondent in Russia, gave him valuable assistance in winning over the American press. When the Japanese insisted on secrecy at the peace sessions, he declared for the admission of newspaper correspondents. The representative of autocracy, he conducted himself with democratic simplicity. Although fully cognizant of Jewish antagonism, he paid a visit to the ghetto in New York City. At no period of his life did he show himself more favorably than during the negotiations.

He had come to the peace conference shackled by the instruction that he was to surrender not one inch of Russian soil or pay one kopeck of indemnity. Many people regarded his attitude as one of sheer bluff. But he really believed Russia "had only just begun to exert her full strength and to attain co-ordinated effort in her military plans." He pointed out that Japanese credit was practically exhausted, and that she could not extend her military operations much farther westward because of the increasing distance from her base of supplies. Furthermore, Russia was at the moment negotiating with French bankers for a loan with which to prolong the war.

Although Russia did cede half of the Island of Saghalien, this was due entirely to the Czar's personal intervention. Witte was generally regarded as having scored a great diplomatic victory at Portsmouth because Russia was not burdened by the imposition of a war indemnity. His reputation as a statesman was greatly enhanced by this victory, although the tardy expression of appreciation of his imperial master caused him deep chagrin; he was not even given his title of Count Witte until some time later.

During the years since I had seen Witte, we had fought and won our war with Spain. The United States had projected itself on the European vision, not only as an economic but as a political world power. I jestingly reminded Witte of the statement he had made to me in 1898 about our financial provincialism.

"You are right," he replied, "in asserting that the United States is now a star of the first magnitude in the financial heavens, but it will be long before she becomes an international banker."

He could not foresee that a decade after this discussion America would have lent almost as much money to the countries of Europe as the total sum of England's foreign investments.

In 1910, Gregory Wilenkin, the same financial agent of the Russian government with whom I had previously dealt in London, came to the United States. He tendered me an invitation on behalf of M. Kokovtzov, successor to Witte as minister of finance, to visit Russia again. The object this time was the development of Russian industries by the use of American and English capital expended under American auspices.

Remembering that the outcome of my former trip had been abortive, I wanted assurance of Russian sincerity. Wilenkin told me I had been chosen because of my previous survey, and also because the government believed that my recommendation would convince hesitant investors of the soundness and profitability of Russian opportunities.

Taking my wife and Jack with me, I started for Russia late in November. The news of my departure had been cabled ahead to Berlin where I planned to stop a few days. When I arrived I found reporters from German newspapers prepared to interview me. I did not wish news of my true object to get about, and supplied no more information than was necessary to allay suspicion. My few days in Berlin were mainly occupied in securing political and economic information from Ambassador David Jayne Hill as to the relations between Germany and Russia.

Heretofore, about two-thirds of the trade of Russia had been in the hands of the Germans, who were making every effort to keep it there by preventing the extension of commerce between Russia and other nations. I learned that a large part of United States exports to Russia were going through German channels and were being credited to that country. Germany, of course, enjoyed the advantage of proximity to Russia and most favored nation clauses under the Treaty of Bjorke, made by Witte in 1905. Through political pressure applied by Germany on Russia, at that time in the throes of the Russo-Japanese War, the treaty was tantamount to establishing a German economic protectorate over a large section of Russia, and had become a heavy burden on her industry.

I felt that, since Russia had within her boundaries most of the raw materials required for her basic industries, her natural policy should be to establish a protective tariff adequate to build up her home manufactures. The greater earning capacity thus created would result in higher standards of living, and with her immense population she would provide a great home market for her own industrial products.

It is my confident opinion that under the right kind of government and increased industrial development Russia would have been able to create in the not remote future a national wealth greater than that of any other nation in Europe with the single exception of Great Britain.

While we were in Berlin, Herr Emil Rathenau, head of the Allgemeine Elektricitäts Gesellschaft, an immense corporation comparable to the General Electric Company, and father of Walther Rathenau, called at our hotel and asked for John Hays Hammond. When he was shown into our suite, I found that he did not wish to see me. He wanted to consult my son Jack, whose developments in radio had already gained him a position of repute in the scientific world.

Later we dined at the Rathenau home and found the whole family deeply interested in current world problems. Herr Rathenau in particular had a great admiration for the Kaiser, to whom he gave much credit for the industrial expansion of Germany because of the close contact he maintained with the leading industrialists.

M. Wilenkin, who had accompanied us from London, arranged that we should be shown every courtesy at the Russian frontier. Our baggage was passed without examination and a private car was attached to the St. Petersburg train. I was cordially received in the capital by the various ministers of the Czar, including not only Kokovtzov, but Prime Minister Stolypin, his minister of foreign affairs Sazonov, as well as the ministers of commerce and agriculture, Timaschev and Krivoschein.

W. W. Rockhill was then American ambassador to Russia, but owing to strained relations over Manchurian railways he had not yet been able to present his credentials to the Czar. I was careful not to involve him in any way in my affairs. Because of my known personal relations with Taft at that time it would have been unfortunate had my visit borne any official tinge.

To get the imperial imprimatur on my agreement with the government officials, an audience was arranged for me with the Czar at his palace of Tsarskoe Tselo, some fifteen miles from St. Petersburg. Although the audience was scheduled for four in the afternoon, the Foreign Office sent me careful instructions to present myself in evening dress. Nothing was said as to the type of waistcoat prescribed. In order to be on the safe side, I wore a white one and carried the ordinary black evening model in my pocket, prepared to make a lightning change if necessary.

Somewhat amused at my own trepidation over meeting the Autocrat of all the Russias alone, I took the train and was set down at the station. It was already dark but I managed to make out a gorgeously arrayed Cossack standing at the door of a royal equipage. It was the only vehicle at the station. I peered in all directions, but could see no other passenger for whom it might be intended.

Since I was unable to speak Russian, I could make no inquiry. Without further formality, I stepped into the carriage, the Cossack shut the door, and off we drove. After a short ride we stopped at a small building which I was certain could not be the palace. Nevertheless, the Cossack opened the door of the carriage. It was apparent that I was expected to alight. I was taken to a small reception room where it was so warm that I removed my overcoat and sat down.

After a few minutes, I was summarily hurried back into the same carriage and driven furiously down the same hill I had just ascended. I lowered the window and poked my head out. In spite of vigorous protests delivered in English, German, and French, that I did not want to go back to the railroad station, the driver remained impassive. I had given up trying to make him understand when the carriage turned suddenly into a side road, and delivered me at the imperial palace.

This time I had to wait but a few moments before the Czar, attired in Cossack uniform, appeared. He advanced quickly, shook hands cordially, and offered me a chair. Then pleasantly, in perfect English, he expressed the hope that I was enjoying my stay in Russia.

I knew that imperial audiences were customarily short, and thought I could not afford to take up half this valuable time in verbal exchange of courtesies. Therefore, I disregarded the diplomatic usage which prescribed that the Czar should lead the conversation.

"Your Majesty," I began, "I feel honored by your confidence in me, and I assume you wish me to speak frankly, and not take up your time with pleasantries."

"Yes, Mr. Hammond," he replied, "I want you to be perfectly frank."

"I can reassure Your Majesty that, were I so indiscreet as to betray any confidence you might place in me, you could remedy this by nominating me for the Ananias Club, formed a few years ago by President Theodore Roosevelt."

"I've heard about that club," the Czar admitted with a smile.

"Well," I went on, "if Russia is to go on a constitutional basis, Your Majesty will find an Ananias Club an exceedingly useful institution."

The Czar then expressed curiosity as to why the United States had been so sympathetic with Japan during the Russo-Japanese War. I told him a certain degree of American sympathy inevitably had gone to Japan as the smaller nation. Also, there had been an impression that the war had been fomented by concession seekers belonging to the court camarilla. Mustering all my courage, I suggested that the Russian government might have forfeited some American sympathy because of the frequent Jewish pogroms.

The Czar did not seem angered: "I can understand the American point of view in the latter case. But there are six million Jews in Russia—more than half the number in the entire world."

"Couldn't the administrative regulations which restrict Jews to certain congested localities be modified?" I asked. "Wouldn't a policy of dispersion eliminate the sore spots?"

His Majesty told me with a smile that the idea had already occurred to him.

I then introduced the subject of the advantages Russia could obtain by the use of American capital for its industrial development. "We are best fitted," I urged him, "to understand your problems because they are so nearly identical with those of our own West."

This was the same argument I had used years before with Witte.

"Also," I continued, "you will find it profitable to employ Anglo-American rather than German capital. The Germans aim to stifle the growth of a Russian bourgeoisie and, if they succeed, it will retard Russia's financial and commercial independence."

Emboldened by the Czar's acquiescence in my views, and absorbed in my mission, I continued to give him good fatherly advice as to how the interests of Russia, politically and economically, could best be served.

At the conclusion of our conference, the Czar assured me of his approval of the plans I had outlined and, wishing me succēss, bade me a cordial au revoir.

Immediately following my audience, Sazonov called to see the Czar, who told him that he had just had an interesting and informative interview with a man who spoke to him as "man to man and not as subject to sovereign."

The following day Baron Rosen, for many years the popular Russian ambassador in Washington, called at my hotel and left the following note:

> Hotel de l'Europe
> St. Petersburg
>
> January 15, 1911
>
> I have just seen M. Sazonov who told me that you had had a prolonged audience with the Emperor and that His Majesty was very greatly pleased with you.
>
> ROSEN

Ambassador Rockhill was also gratified with what I had accomplished and predicted that my visit would prove a great advantage to America's commercial relations with Russia, adding that I had also done much to promote the entente cordiale of the two nations.

An interesting dinner was given for us by M. Kokovtzov, at which M. and Mme. Stolypin, M. and Mme. Sazonov, and other prominent members of the Russian government were present.

Stolypin was always regarded as a leader of Russian reactionary officialdom. Several attempts had already been made on his life. In fact, he had a badly mutilated hand as the result of a bomb thrown a few years before.

Stolypin expressed a great desire to see America, but when my wife asked him to give us the pleasure of reciprocating his hospitality, he shook his head and said, "You little realize the danger my presence would bring to your peaceful household."

A few months later he fell a victim to the bullet of an assassin at the Royal Opera.

The result of my visit was most promising. I had the assurance of the highest Russian officials that, so far as consistent with Russia's treaty obligations with other nations, preference would be given to American and English capital in the various enterprises we were to undertake.

Entirely at my own expense I sent two American experts, A. P. Davis, chief of the United States Reclamation Service, and W. W. Mackie, who had worked for me in mapping out the reclamation of the Yaqui Valley, to make an investigation of the agricultural recources of the southeastern part of the Russian Empire and particularly to report on the feasibility of irrigating the Hungry Desert of Turkestan.

The reports of Davis and Mackie were presented by me to the Russian government and formed the basis of developments recently undertaken by the Soviet government, employing Davis as advisory engineer.

The investigation of the Stewart brothers who had erected the grain elevators along the Great Lakes confirmed the opinion I had formed in 1898, that Russia would benefit by having a similar system. At that time I had ridden through field after field of crops unharvested because of lack of storage and transportation facilities. There was still a crying need for refrigerator cars, and this was provided in the concession from the government.

In a tentative way, better equipment for loading and unloading cargoes in Russian ports was also discussed with the departmental heads.

It was my ambition to achieve in Russia the crowning work of my career as one of those "unprincipled American exploiters" who are arraigned so often at the bar of public opinion for their ruthless exploitations of the defenseless foreigner.

When I left Russia I was convinced I had with me the most important packet of commercial opportunities ever to be of such prospective benefit to two nations. I had succeeded not only in opening up a great field for the profitable investment of American capital and the expansion of her commerce, but also in breaking the economic shackles which held agricultural Russia subject to industrial Europe.

In Berlin, where I remained a few days to look into the much-vaunted efficiency of German industries, the object of my visit to Russia was freely discussed by the press and considerable apprehension, I learned, was created in German official circles.

From Berlin I went to London, where I found a keen desire among financiers to participate in the Russian enterprises.

Lord Rothschild was particularly interested to know not merely what I had accomplished, but whether my plans would have any effect upon the unhappy status of the Jew in Russia.

"I know from your pleasant business and social relations with Barnato, Hirsch, and the Guggenheims that you must sympathize with our efforts to alleviate the misery of our persecuted brethren."

"The Jewish question in Russia, as the Czar himself admitted, is undoubtedly 'difficult'," I replied. "The Jews have been subjected to every conceivable form of ignominy and, as all humanitarians will agree, have been cruelly maltreated. The issue has developed into a vicious circle of crimination and recrimination between the government and the Jewish population. The authorities justify themselves by claiming that, if Jews would abstain from participation in revolutionary politics, they would be treated more liberally; the Jews retort that, if they were treated more liberally, there would be no occasion for them to seek redress through political activities."

Rothschild pondered over my comments and then said: "Suppose for a moment that the Jewish bankers in London should participate in financing these projects of yours. Would Russian anti-Semitism extend to Jewish bankers in London?"

"Yes," I replied honestly, "there is universal resentment against the Jewish bankers of Europe, and also of America, because they lent money to Japan during the Russo-Japanese War. This has been used as a rallying cry by the liberal party of the Kadets."

A few days later I sailed for America. When I reached New York I was greatly surprised to learn that the government was seriously considering the abrogation of our commercial treaty with

Russia, in retaliation for the refusal of that government to grant America's request for passports into Russia for American Jews.

I studiously avoided any action that might be represented by President Taft's political enemies as an endeavor to influence legislation on this subject. As a matter of fact, the passport question was never at any time discussed between the President and myself. Moreover, I fully realized that any attempt to frustrate the movement would be futile. But I did warn my Jewish friends that the desired passports never could be secured by threats of hostile legislation against Russia.

The United States did abrogate the commercial treaty. The resultant ill feeling utterly destroyed any hope of carrying out my plan of obtaining American capital for Russia.

Although my mission failed, the theory on which I was proceeding was correct. There are in Russia extensive deposits of iron, coal, lead, copper, gold, platinum, and other valuable minerals, and petroleum in addition to its vast agricultural and timber potentialities.

Under the right kind of government Russia would be found an attractive field for foreign investors. As I told Witte in 1898, the vast opportunities grip the imagination of Americans, because the problems presented in the industrial development of Russia would not be new to the American captain of industry.

Furthermore, in the new era Americans would enjoy a significant advantage over the peoples of other countries, because there can never be political jealousy between Russia and the United States. Russia has always held America in high esteem and admiration, and the Russian people feel a sincere friendship for Americans.

Russian labor may be lacking in technical skill, but it is the opinion of Americans who have conducted mining and other industrial operations in that country that a most efficient class of artisans could be developed from the great Russian proletariat.

While it is true that the Russian peasant is illiterate and densely ignorant, he possesses exceptional resourcefulness. Contrary to the popular impression, he has a peaceful and kindly disposition, but his limited knowledge of the world makes him an easy prey to any political and economic doctrines foisted on him by unprincipled agitators.

In 1898 the fundamental laws of Russia described the power of the Emperor as "autocratic and unlimited," but after the opening of the first Duma, following the revolution of 1905-06, the word "unlimited" disappeared, although the name and principle of "autocracy" was jealously preserved. The *Almanach de Gotha* described Russia as "a constitutional monarchy under an autocratic Czar." It was still a question whether the emphasis should be placed on "constitutional" or on "autocratic." The definition itself connoted the transition period through which the empire was passing.

But in 1910, so far as was observable on the political face of Russia, the revolutionary spirit had become modified, and the nation seemed destined to attain a more liberal form of government through political evolution rather than bloody revolution. Russia seemed on the eve of great industrial expansion and prosperity.

Yet within the brief period of seven years a world cataclsm brought forth a Bolshevik Samson who pulled down the temple of the mighty Russian Empire, a temple that was erected on the quicksands of political oppression instead of upon the solid foundation of the "consent of the governed."

To judge the potentiality of Russia as an important industrial nation by the progress she has made since the establishment of the Soviet government would be a mistake. Russia has not as yet had a fair opportunity to demonstrate her capacity in industry. In spite of the efforts of the Soviet government to develop industrial classes, progress has been disappointing even to the rulers themselves. Internal political conditions have made it impossible to attain the industrial development that would have been achieved under such a government as our own, free from political oppression and dictation in matters of industry.

The political theory of government at present obtaining in Soviet Russia is absolutely opposed to the fundamental economic principles of national development adopted by other nations.

Collectivism removes the stimulus and incentive for individual effort, without which achievement is doomed to failure.

The war against the Russian bourgeoisie is a mistaken policy inasmuch as that class has proved to be the backbone of industry and commerce throughout the world.

The political situation in Russia is well known. The will of an insignificant minority is imposed by force of arms upon a helpless majority of Russians. Our government has recently recognized the Union of Soviet Socialist Republics. Protagonists for recognition hold that every nation has a right to determine its form of government, and for this reason Russia was entitled to recognition. This, of course, is true so far as the activities of that form of government do not seriously affect other governments. However, the avowed Communist program of Russia is

> The dictatorship of the proletariat is nothing else than power based upon force and limited by nothing— by no kind of law and by absolutely no rule.

> LENIN, *Complete Works,* Vol. xviii, Page 361.

> "The American Communist Party must be improved and Bolshevized. For that end we must work in order to forge real revolutionary cadres and a real revolutionary leadership of the proletariat, capable of leading the many millions of the American working class toward the revolutionary class struggles."

> STALIN, in address, May 6, 1929.

> "The conquest of power by the proletariat is the violent abolition of the power of the bourgeoisie, the destruction of the machinery of the capitalist state.
> "We proclaim openly that our design can only be realized by the violent overthrow of the entire traditional social order."

> (The above policies were formally adopted and promulgated as the Communist program by the Sixth Congress of the Kommintern of the Communists' Internationale, which was held in 1925 in Moscow.)

This program is obviously a challenge to other nations to defend their peculiar forms of government. It is for this reason that I have consistently been opposed to the recognition of Soviet Russia. That Russia has not repaid the United States for loans made to the Kerensky government does not seem to me an insuperable objection to recognition. Other nations are in default in respect of loans we have made to them. The confiscation of American property in Russia comes under a different category and we should insist that our citizens be compensated.

I do not believe that there is danger of the overthrow of our government by the Communists. America is not fertile soil for revolutionary activities, but there can be little doubt that their insidious attempts to accomplish this are a serious menace to industrial peace. It would seem that Russia herself is pursuing a fatuous policy in antagonizing the rest of the world in her attempt to overthrow the government of other nations with whom her policy should rather be a spirit of co-operation.

We have incontrovertible evidence of further activity in many of our universities, and worst of all is the plan to Sovietize the youth of the country through the Young Communists League which is financed by older Communists.

Had there been unanimity among the foreign governments in refusing diplomatic recognition, I believe the Soviet regime would have long since ceased to function. Lack of uniform purpose has been due to the subordination of a great moral issue to the desire of developing commerce with Russia, and even this desire has failed of realization.

CHAPTER TWENTY-FOUR

The Turn of the Century

I BRING MY FAMILY BACK TO AMERICA—
HORSECARS TO TRAMWAYS—THE PURCHASE OF THE
CAMP BIRD MINE—EDISON TAKES JACK THROUGH
HIS LABORATORY—AUTOMOBILING IN THE 1900'S—
WASHINGTON SOCIAL TRADITION—THE STRIKE AT
TONOPAH—HOW STRATTON SOLD HIS MINE—THE I. W. W. IN
CRIPPLE CREEK — GOLD DREDGING ON THE YUBA RIVER

*I*n December, 1899, after an absence of seven years, my family and I returned to New York. For the second time my name appeared on an office door in the Mills Building.

The business of a consulting engineer is made up of constantly shifting activities which call him without warning from one end of the earth to the other. My first summons was to Mexico to examine the El Oro and Esperanza gold mines. This experience will be described in the next chapter.

I had also secured a concession to install the first hydroelectric plant in Mexico to furnish power for irrigation. D. O. Mills, Charles A. Coffin, and others furnished capital and we built what is now known as the Guanajuato Power and Development Company, supplying current to the mines and irrigating systems in that district.

The extension of transmission lines over the mountainous country was an expensive undertaking. As might have been expected, there was a good deal of pilfering by the Indians, particularly of the large insulators on which the high tension lines were strung on the poles. Finally, the foreman offered twenty-five cents reward for each insulator returned. When I first went to Mexico in the early eighties I had bought my own chickens over and over again from my servants; and once more I had to spend hundreds of dollars for the company buying back insulators from the Indians. This trade was not always an advantage to them, however. After the line was put in operation, we occasionally found a dead Indian at the foot of a pole—in trying to make a little extra money on insulators he had been electrocuted.

With the backing of Wernher, Beit and Company, Henry A. Butters and I were now planning to electrify and extend the Mexico City horsecar system which we had lately purchased. I had already had some experience with tramways, for in 1895 Butters and I together had laid out the Cape Town tramway system. After the completion of this system, he and I started a similar type of project in Geneva, Switzerland. There we encountered the same obstructionist tactics from the politicians that we met later in Mexico. We were constantly threatened with a rival franchise until, in exasperation, we said, "When you clean out your bad politicians, we'll build you a tramline." But the interference continued and, after laying out the road and solving the engineering problems, we left the matter to a group of French investors who seemed better fitted to deal with petty officialdom.

Although my family could not accompany me on my professional trips, it was sometimes possible to have them near me. This was the case at Glenwood Springs in the Rocky Mountains, where I went for my health in the summer of 1900.

My wife and I were much interested in what we heard of the archaeological discoveries of the Mesa Verde region south of us. We outfitted at the Wetherill ranch in southern Colorado and set off exploring, taking Jacky with us. The country we had to traverse was almost without trails, and water was scarce. But despite its discomforts, the outdoor life proved of great benefit to me. Our enjoyment was enhanced by poking about among the cliff dwellings which had been preserved intact by the dry air of the desert. We found them practically as they were when abandoned by the Indians several hundred years ago.

COUNT WITTE (1849-1915)

TRAVELING IN A DROSHKY

The winters of 1900 and 1901 were spent at Del Monte, California. One of our chief pleasures was to get up at five in the morning and ride with the cowboys in the roundups.

Del Monte brought to my mind many interesting and pleasant associations. In 1879, I accompanied my father and Governor Leland Stanford, president of the Southern Pacific Railway, Mr. Charles Crocker, vice-president, on a trip to Monterey just after the completion of the railroad to that terminus. They were looking for a site for the proposed new hotel and station. On the train going back to San Francisco, Governor Stanford asked my father to suggest a name for the hotel. Father said he thought Del Monte an appropriate name, but Governor Stanford seemed to think it inappropriate as there were no mountains in the neighborhood. Then my father explained that there was a fine grove of oak and other trees and that in Spanish "Del Monte" also means "of the grove." This name was finally adopted.

My brother Dick was employed to survey the grounds and construct roads through the property, which involved many thousands of acres. It was he who built the famous Seventeen Mile Drive on the Monterey peninsula.

Dick had a very constructive mind and together with Page Brown, San Francisco architect, laid out the beautiful section now known as Burlingame, not far from that city.

While we were at Del Monte, President McKinley and John Hay dined with us. My wife, full of enthusiasm over the archaeological interests of the Mesa Verde, concerning which she had delivered a lecture before the American Association for the Advancement of Science in Denver, persuaded the President that the region should be made into a national park.

During these early years of the twentieth century we took a house at Lakewood, New Jersey. We were so well pleased with it in itself and with its accessibility from New York that we made it our winter home for several years. There our daughter Natalie was born.

Thomas A. Edison, who lived at East Orange, was then working on a new process to extract gold from South African ore. He had encountered difficulties and asked me to come to see him in the hope that I could shed light on his problems. I was soon able to demonstrate that the obstacles were insuperable in the economic use of his process.

Jack—who was about twelve at that time—was with me, and we eagerly accepted Edison's invitation to go through his laboratories. He showed us the models of his first phonograph and complained that well-known musicians scorned to sing for his machine; with a quiet smile he added that he did not blame them. That was in 1901. He prophesied, however, that we should all live to see the time when the best of them would be glad to do so.

He gave Jack some original sketches of the first phonograph model, and it may have been the contact with Edison that stimulated my son's interest in the study of electricity.

Ten years later Edison wrote me: "I see that your son has adopted inventing as a trade. If he has a commercial instinct, he will succeed; if not, the poorhouse will be his ultimate destination."

On several occasions Edison said to me: "Every time I see you, you are wasting your time in civic matters, politics, or public affairs. Why don't you stay with your profession and be at the head of it?" He did not entirely follow his own counsel, for later he adventured into discussions of educational and social problems.

One of my first engagements in the United States was the examination of the Camp Bird mine, owned by Thomas F. Walsh, and located in Ouray County, Colorado. This examination was made jointly with Hennen Jennings, who was for many years with Wernher, Beit and Company on the Rand and rendered distinguished service in the development of the mining industry. In his South African work he was associated with Henry C. Perkins, another American mining engineer. At this time Jennings was living in London.

A favorable report had already been made on the Camp Bird property by T. A. Rickard and F. W. Bradley, who, in spite of experience and reputation, seem to have lacked the proper qualifications for evaluating mines. Rickard was at the time consulting engineer of the Venture Corporation of London. This organization had been formed to promote mines, particularly on the western hemisphere. Frederick W. Baker was the chairman and moving spirit.

On Rickard and Bradley's recommendation a short-time option on the property had been secured by our clients, the Venture Corporation of London and their associates. The estimate of net ore in sight made by Rickard and Bradley was about six million dollars. Our clients had deposited this amount, the purchase price, in a New York bank to be paid if Jennings and I approved.

Although we found some rich ore bodies, we estimated the net value to be less than three million dollars; there was nothing to warrant the investment of six millions. Our London clients accepted our recommendation to turn down the proposition.

The next year a recurrent attack of malaria necessitated another summer at Glenwood Springs. Walsh came to see me there and again brought up the question of the sale of the Camp Bird.

"I heard you recommended your clients not to buy my mine, Mr. Hammond."

"Yes, I did. I thought your figure was much too high."

"I'd like to talk with you about it again. You see, it isn't entirely a question of money with me. I've already made several millions out of the mine, but I don't want to be tied up any longer. I've been in these mountains for many years. My children are growing up. I want them to have an education and some social life, and I'd like to play around in politics myself. There's nobody I can trust to manage the mine properly. My manager, John Benson, can't stand the high altitude any longer, and I don't want to train a new man."

"Well, Mr. Walsh," I replied, "I'll arrange for another examination and make you a new offer based on what I find."

On this understanding I sent for A. Chester Beatty. On my first examination I had noticed the skill and efficiency with which this young graduate from the Columbia School of Mines was doing his work. He was then employed by his brother-in-law, T. A. Rickard.

"How much are you making, Beatty?" I had asked.

"Twelve hundred a year."

"That's not much, is it?"

"It does for me. I still have beer tastes though I hope to get to champagne some day."

"How'd you like to come to me for twice that amount?"

"I'd come for nothing," he caught me up eagerly.

"Well, I haven't any place for you now, but you're on my payroll from this minute, and when I find something for you, I'll let you know."

One of the first tasks I assigned him was that of sampling the Camp Bird after my conversation with Walsh.

When Beatty had finished his work, I joined him and checked up on the results. Our report was most thorough in details and positive in conclusions. This second examination confirmed the values previously found by Jennings and myself.

I then discussed the purchase price with Walsh on the basis of two and a half million dollars' worth of net ore in sight. "You've already had a valuation from Rickard and Bradley which is much higher than mine. You and Benson are practical miners with a lot of experience. Why don't you employ other engineers to ascertain the correctness of my report?"

"I'm perfectly satisfied to accept your estimate of the value of the ore reserves."

Three million dollars cash was agreed upon. I advised Walsh to take part of this in stock, and offered a certain additional payment if and when ore should be extracted beyond the purchase price of the mine.

I then cabled to the Venture Corporation that I was on my way to London to make a personal report. The time of the option being short, I had to leave the necessary legal work to be done in this country. Samuel Untermyer represented the Venture Corporation; Charles S. Thomas, formerly governor of Colorado and subsequently United States senator, represented Walsh.

The cash payment was made to Walsh according to agreement. But when the contract drawn up by Untermyer and Thomas reached London, there was some ambiguity as to the additional percentage payment due on future ore developed. The London attorney of the underwriting syndicate was greatly disturbed; he pointed out that, according to the phraseology of the contract, we were at the mercy of Walsh. He could legally have claimed a large sum of money. I told them that the lawyers were wrong in certain important mining technicalities and that I was sure Walsh would not take advantage of the lawyers' ignorance, but would accept the verbal understanding he and I had made.

I hurried back to Colorado and met Walsh and Governor Thomas, to whom I explained the anxiety of my London clients.

Walsh said: "I haven't read the contract. I left it entirely to Governor Thomas."

"Well, Walsh," I replied, "you and I are both mining men and you know very well I'd never have agreed to a contract like this."

I pointed out the error. His immediate response was, "You're quite right, Hammond; that wasn't our agreement at all."

He turned to Governor Thomas. "Charlie, change that to Hammond's understanding. He is right as to our agreement."

Walsh had the right to send expert accountants to check up mine output and engineers to report on underground developments. When he was asked by the Camp Bird Company why he did not avail himself of the privilege, he replied that so long as I was their consulting engineer he needed no one to protect his interests.

Walsh, honest himself, gave others credit for possession of the same quality.

The Camp Bird turned out to be profitable for all concerned, but the rich ore that added so much profit to the company was later developed under my personal direction in a section of the property not opened up at the time Hennen Jennings and I made our examination.

Walsh aspired to social position and attained it. He made friends in high places, among them Albert, King of the Belgians. He died a wealthy man.

When the Walshes became my neighbors on the North Shore of Massachusetts, which had become our summer home, our children saw much of each other. My son Jack and Vinson Walsh acquired automobiles of the same make, in which they used to race each other. In order to keep them within bounds, their parents formed an automobile club, and invited them to join. They felt highly honored at this attention from their elders and accepted with alacrity. As soon as the fathers had paid the boys' dues, these same fathers hastily passed a by-law imposing fines and removal of license on any member who was reported for speeding.

There was one occasion on which I myself fell a victim to the same speed mania. Jack and I were coming home one night from dinner with the Walshes when a car tried to pass us. Jack imperceptibly opened the throttle. I sympathized mildly when he shouted above the noise, "It's Vinson!"

As the other car slipped past, we heard a defiant challenge.

Jack's feeling of outrage was transmitted to me. I said nothing as the speedometer needle began to creep up. We skidded around corners, madly raced on the straightaway, and my elation equaled his as we triumphantly passed the other car. Jack honked derisively.

That night there was no reprimand of Jack, and no one reported to the Automobile Club that one of the committee members had been speeding.

The last time I saw Vinson was at Newport an hour or so before he drove his car off a bridge, killing himself and seriously injuring his sister.

Jack was not the only one to give me a wild ride. Henry Clay Frick taught me that automobiling could hold new terrors. His home was at Pride's Crossing, about nine miles from Gloucester. One day Frick telephoned me that E. H. Harriman was visiting him, and asked whether I would like to take a spin with them around Cape Ann.

"I'd like to show you my new French car."

"I'll be delighted," I replied.

"All right, we'll be there in fifteen minutes."

"Better make it twenty," I replied as I hung up the receiver.

He was at the door in fifteen minutes. We started on the twenty miles of narrow, winding, unpaved Cape Ann roads. The chauffeur took the curves on two wheels and whenever we came to a village seemed to prefer the sidewalks to the streets. Hens squawked, horses reared, New England ladies scuttled into doorways. So loud was the rattle and bang of our vehicle that we were spared most of the vituperation which followed in our wake. Once we slowed down long enough to catch some salty comments which for a moment made me think I was in Billingsgate rather than in the main street of Gloucester.

We slithered to a stop at my front door.

Harriman and I had no breath left with which to swear, but Frick was not at all discomposed. He said, "Harriman, how do you like the wonderful scenery of Cape Ann?"

Harriman's trains never could travel fast enough to suit him, but now he gasped: "To tell the truth, Frick, your French chauffeur went so fast I didn't see much of it. Another time I think I'd better ask Hammond to take me in his car. I'd really like to see the scenery!"

"Sorry I won't be able to go with you," responded Frick who, even on the golf course, had a mania for speed. "When I go riding, I have to go fast enough to dodge bullets." This remark referred to his experience at the time of the Homestake strike, when he was shot by Alexander Berkman.

Shortly after our return from South Africa my wife and I were invited to be the guests of honor at a dinner given by Mrs. John R. McLean, whom I had known as a young girl. She was Emily, the daughter of General and Mrs. Edward F. Beale. Her parents and my parents had been intimate friends in our early California days. Mrs. McLean was known as one of the leading hostesses of Washington. Upon starting for the dining room, we were somewhat surprised to have our hostess express the hope that we would not be offended at not being given the seats of honor—she had to follow the established rule of precedence. We were not offended, of course, but I was interested in this phase of Washington etiquette, which was then new to me.

It was on this occasion that I met Admiral Dewey, recently returned from his victory at Manila Bay. He told me how humiliated he felt at the criticism leveled at him by the American public for having given to his new wife (the sister-in-law of Mrs. McLean) the house which had been presented to him by the people of the country in recognition of his exploit. He said that it was the only gift he could have made to his wife. At this time Dewey was being groomed as a Democratic candidate for the presidency. He told me that the "boss" Democratic politician said to him, "Keep quiet and don't say nothing."

In 1903 I resumed my position as consulting engineer of the Union Pacific and Southern Pacific railroads, united under Harriman's control. My chief function was to examine mining districts and to determine whether it would be profitable to connect them by spurs to the main line. If it seemed to me that the ore bodies were sufficiently extensive I advised favorably.

I fell into the habit of lunching frequently with Harriman at his office. I considered him the greatest of our railroad builders, greater than Jim Hill or Paul Morton, or Ripley of the Santa Fe, all of whom I knew intimately. His great fault was his impatience at what seemed to him the slowness of others in grasping his ideas. His pronounced unwillingness to delegate responsibility was brought home vividly by an experience I had with him.

At that time I owned the Mount Whitney Power Company, which was supplying power for irrigating the newly developed citrus fruit belt near Visalia, California. I pointed out the profits Harriman could make by running an electrified branch line into the San Joaquin Valley for which we would furnish the power. Harriman told me to go ahead and secure land for the right of way without letting it be known that the Southern Pacific was the purchaser. Meanwhile he went abroad for his health.

I secured the necessary options and then went to Judge Lovett, president of the road. Julius Kruttschnitt, vice-president and general manager, was also present.

I said, "I need twenty-five thousand dollars to exercise the options."

Lovett replied, "I'm sorry, Mr. Hammond, but I can't give it to you."

"But both you and Kruttschnitt were present when Harriman told me to go ahead. Don't you remember?"

"That's true," Lovett agreed, "but neither Kruttschnitt nor I has authority to make the payment."

"Well, then," I suggested, "why don't you cable Harriman and get it?"

"Harriman doesn't want to be bothered with business, and we'd rather not."

This struck me as a childish and inefficient way of doing business. I knew that the Santa Fe would jump at the chance to get into the citrus belt, and I couldn't let Harriman down. I left the Southern Pacific office determined to advance the money out of my own pocket.

HYDRAULIC MINING

THE BUNKER HILL AND SULLIVAN MINE

A present-day view showing concentrators, powerhouse, shops, change house and electric power lines at the mouth of Kellogg Tunnel

THE BUNKER HILL AND SULLIVAN MINE

*A print from an old picture taken at the time of its development,
showing the original concentrator and circuit work*

When Harriman returned from Europe, I told him of the difficulty I had encountered, and how I had had to use my own money to pay for his right of way.

"Here's Kruttschnitt," I said. "There isn't a better railroad man in the country, and yet you won't give him the power to handle a small matter like this. Why, I've seen you send for him to come all the way from Chicago to New York for a fifteen-minute interview. On top of that you sometimes keep him waiting for days. And he's your highest salaried man! But you'll let me come in and take up an hour over some trivial detail. It would save you time, money, and worry if you'd delegate a little more authority."

Harriman merely smiled. The next time he went to Europe, however, his subordinates were granted more leeway, and on his return he admitted that the wheels of the locomotives had gone around just as well during his absence.

One of the projects I suggested to Harriman was a sixty-five-mile spur track from Sodaville to Tonopah, Nevada. Up to this time the ore had been hauled over the desert by mule team.

My first connection with Tonopah had come from W. C. Whitney, with whom I became well acquainted after my return from London. He asked me to become consulting engineer for the Tonopah mine in which he had a large interest. I accepted this position.

Tonopah was one of the richest strikes made in Nevada in recent years. In twenty years $125,000,000 was taken out—nearly half of which came from the original mine—with a profit in dividends of $32,000,000. In the year of grace 1902, this camp was almost as "bad" as Bodie or Tombstone had been twenty-five years before. It was the last wild town of the West, though Goldfield, discovered a few years later, is entitled to honorable mention in this respect.

The discovery of the Tonopah district was the result of pure chance. As in the case of every famous strike, there were innumerable tales as to who was the discoverer and how the find had taken place. Prospectors necessarily lead lonely lives and must entertain themselves. They take to yarning much as sailors do, and eventually convince themselves of the truth of their own stories.

One day as I emerged from the shaft of the Tonopah, I found James L. Butler discoursing learnedly to a party of enthralled eastern tourists on the geological phenomenon which had led him to the discovery of the mine. When he caught sight of me he stopped abruptly. While he was still Lazy Jim Butler, rancher and prospector, he had told me quite a different tale.

I went on my way smiling. Butler had gone back on his burros in a most unsportsmanlike manner. The burro certainly has "a nose for a mine" even though he may not have horse sense; he is a worthy precursor of the modern geophysicist, as in the case of Kellogg's burro of Coeur d'Alene fame.

According to Butler's early version, in the spring of 1900 he and his wife set out from Belmont, Nevada, for a near-by district called the Southern Klondike. They camped one evening in a desolate spot at the foot of a hill. The next morning, finding that the pack burros had strayed, Butler set out uphill to find them. In order to speed them on their way back, he picked up a rock and was about to hurl it in their direction when he noticed it was mineralized quartz.

Mrs. Butler also claimed to be the finder. She said that while she was sitting on a rock pile waiting for her husband to find the burros, she saw a piece of loose rock that glinted with yellow specks. Gallantry impels me to accept her version.

Like the good prospectors they were, the Butlers gathered up some specimens and carried them the remaining ten miles to Southern Klondike. There Butler submitted them to the camp assayer, who refused to test them without the customary fee. This the Butlers could not produce, but they were undiscouraged by the rebuff. They picked up more fragments on their way back to Belmont, and took them to the young district attorney, Tasker L. Oddie. Butler offered Oddie a quarter interest in the mine if he could get an assay made.

Oddie took the samples to Walter C. Gayheart, an assayer, and in lieu of the usual fee of ten dollars, offered him half of his own share for making the assay. Gayheart agreed to this proposal and made a test in his spare time. The ore was found to run several hundred dollars per ton in gold and silver.

Every foot of ground anywhere near the richest outcrop of Mizpah Hill was immediately staked and restaked. Not having enough money to develop the claims, the original locators leased them on a percentage basis. Four million dollars were taken from surface digging the first year. Butler then sold his holdings to Philadelphia capital represented by O. A. Turner, C. R. Miller, and other eastern investors.

In 1901 the Tonopah-Belmont Company was formed with John W. Brock, president; Tasker Oddie, general manager; Key Pittman, attorney. As I have said, I was employed by this company as consulting engineer and spent considerable time in developing the property and erecting a mill for treatment of the ores.

It is interesting to note that fortunes made out of this mine enabled three men to devote their energies to politics. Pittman became leader of the silver faction in the Senate, Oddie was a senator and also governor of Nevada, and Miller was elected governor of Delaware.

While I was consulting engineer for Tonopah, I was asked to make an examination of a mine at Cripple Creek, Colorado, known as Stratton's Independence. This was at the time the greatest gold producer in that famous district.

Its original owner, William S. Stratton, had started out as a carpenter, but he was ambitious and in his spare time took lessons in assaying. Then he attempted prospecting on his own, and discovered the Independence mine.

The Venture Corporation had been trying to find outlets for its surplus money, and Stratton was now approached and asked how much he would take for his mine. It had not previously occurred to him to sell but he realized from the eagerness of their representatives that the highly favorable report submitted by T. A. Rickard had made the Venture Corporation exceedingly anxious to buy.

Stratton was invited to come to London at the company's expense to meet the board of directors. He proved no more tractable in England than in the States. As a last resort, it was decided to give him a banquet. At the appearance of the first course, they offered him five million dollars for his mine. He promptly turned it down.

As the dinner proceeded, the price rose to five and a half millions. Stratton showed some sign of interest, but was still unwilling. When the figure reached six millions, his eyes opened wider and he began to pinch himself. But his head had started wagging in the negative and he could not seem to stop it.

Except for the price, the contract was ready for his signature. At six and a half millions the pen was placed in his hand. But he said he liked his mine; he couldn't bear to part with it.

In desperation seven and a half million was written in and his fingers were firmly closed around the pen. Still unable to believe his eyes or his ears, he affixed his signature.

When I met him some time afterwards, I asked, "What would you have done if I'd offered you a check for five million dollars for the property before you had been approached by the Venture Corporation?"

"I'd have jumped at it!"

The Venture Corporation offered a large block of stock to some of my clients in London. I was at Glenwood Springs at the time. They cabled me to examine the property and advise them as to the purchase of the stock on the basis of ten million dollars for the property.

The manager of the Independence was ill when I arrived at the mine, and the foreman accompanied me on my tour. Although the foreman had known me by reputation and realized I was not easily to be deceived, he suggested that we begin our examination on the upper levels from which the pay ore was being taken. I suspect that he hoped I would devote most of my time to examining that part of the mine. I simply remarked that as the future of the property depended upon the value of the ore found in the deepest workings, I had better start my inspection at the bottom of the shaft.

When we reached the lower levels the character of the development work showed me at once that the grade and amount of ore had fallen off. The foreman admitted that the recent developments in depth had not been encouraging. In order to confirm my conclusion, I sent engineers to sample the mine. Their report convinced me that the estimates made by Rickard and his associate engineers had been altogether too favorable.

When my cabled report was made public in London, there was a crash in the market quotation of the stock. In spite of my unpopularity among those who were gambling in the shares of the company, the Venture Corporation employed me to replace Rickard as consulting engineer for the Stratton Independence mine. Under my management the shaft was sunk deeper by several hundred feet, but crosscuts and other exploratory work proved conclusively that the rich ore bodies had petered out.

While I was still engaged in this work there was a labor strike in the Cripple Creek region. Our employees admitted they were not dissatisfied with the conditions of their own employment, but claimed they had been compelled to join the strike under the over-whelming pressure of the I. W. W. organization, which had already closed the neighboring mines. The district was under martial law, so we supposed we would be safe in operating the mine with those men who had defied the strike order.

We took all possible precautions to protect our miners. One night after an inspection of the underground operations I ascended the shaft and returned to the manager's house where I was staying at the time. I had just gone to bed when word came of a bad accident at the mine.

Dressing as we ran, the manager and I hurried back to the shaft house I had just left. It was a shambles. Dismembered bodies were tangled with wrecked machinery. In an attempt at sabotage, some I. W. W. member had greased the brakes of the hoisting engine. As the cage, filled with men, rose to the surface, the brakes refused to grip and the cage shot up into the gallows frame. The engineer, helpless in the face of this horror, ran screaming from the spot.

I was overcome by this brutal deed.

When I heard a few days later that the I. W. W. were sending a delegation to the Camp Bird mine, I saw to it that I got there first.

Immediately I called a meeting of miners, mill hands, foremen, and clerks. "Have you any complaints against the company?"

"No!"

"Do you like your manager?"

They said he was all right. He had risen from the ranks, worked with them, and shared their risks. In fact, they thought him the best manager they had ever worked under.

"Do you get along with your cook?"

There was nothing to complain of about the food.

Having run through the list of possible grievances, I pointed out that I had always dealt frankly and fairly with them. I told them

I was gratified with the work and that, though I had great confidence in the manager, I was always ready to discuss any important questions with the men. I reminded them that we had tried to make their winter hours in that isolated spot as pleasant as possible. There was a comfortable clubroom equipped with gramophone, magazines, and other means of recreation.

My words were received with approbation. Then I came to the point. "Tomorrow there is a gang of I. W. W. coming up here from Cripple Creek to get you to strike. Do you want to meet them here and let me be present while the matter of grievances is discussed?"

One man shouted, "We haven't any kick coming!"

Another rose and said, "Just leave it to us, Mr. Hammond; we'll take care of 'em!"

Instead of allowing the I. W. W. deputation to reach the mine, the miners sent a committee of their own down the narrow mountain road to a strategic point about a mile and a half from the mill. There they met the invaders.

With menacing gestures, the leader of the Camp Bird contingent shouted: "You damn butchers, what are you doing here? Go on back where you came from. You're going over the cliff quick if you don't get the hell out of here!"

Miners of the old type were honest, courageous, and took great pride in their work. I could invariably rely upon their loyalty in an emergency. I never had a walkout in any mine under my management.

One reason for the popularity of my mines, I realized, was the fact that I paid top wages. I did not do this in order to draw men away from the other mines, but because they deserved it. Furthermore, at a time when mining was much more hazardous than it is now, and when mine owners did not always employ doctors, I saw to it that medical attention was available at each of the mines in my charge. I also worked to secure the compulsory adoption of safety devices.

Soon after my return from London, I had become interested in dredging alluvial gravels at Oroville, California. Because of my extensive examinations of the section around the Yuba River at the time I was employed as expert on the United States Geological Survey, and subsequently as consulting engineer of the Mining Bureau of California, I believed that the Yuba and its tributaries presented an exceptionally attractive field for similar operations.

I suggested the idea to Jeff Doolittle, whom I had known some years before when he was in charge of hydraulic operations in Placer County. In spite of the fact that he was an expert on auriferous gravels, he inclined to the opinion that the difficulties were too great. The river bed was covered with many feet of debris, swept down from hydraulic operations in tributary streams. "I myself have washed down millions of yards," he remarked.

Prior to this time, forty feet was the greatest dredging depth attained. If we wanted to operate successfully, we had to build a dredge of much greater depth capacity.

Finally, I persuaded Doolittle that the project was feasible and agreed to secure the necessary capital. Because of my enforced absence in London, I had E. A. Wiltsee obtain an option on a thousand acres in the heart of what subsequently developed into the most profitable dredging area in the world.

Also, I made an arrangement with Fred W. Bradley for drilling tests. In addition to depositing funds for that purpose, I left him my power of attorney to handle the option—an act I was later to regret. Bradley's first report to me was favorable.

I had known Bradley for a long time and had considered him thoroughly honest. In 1890 I had been looking for someone to assist Clement, and Bradley had been recommended to me. During a blizzard I had traveled on snowshoes to a mine in the Sierra Nevadas which Bradley was then operating. I remained with him two days. I was impressed with his ability as a manager and engaged him as assistant for the Bunker Hill and Sullivan.

When Clement went to South Africa with me, Bradley was made manager of the property and proved himself a good executive. In recognition of his services I had given him an option for a year at a very low price on a large block of the B. H. & S. stock. Clement also gave him an option for a block of the same stock.

About three years later Bradley came to London to see me on other mining matters and told me he would like to exercise his option on the B. H. & S. stock. I told him that his option had long since expired; nevertheless, I would let him have the stock at the same price, though Clement refused to let Bradley have any stock.

Some months after securing the Yuba option, I was much surprised when R. D. Evans, a Massachusetts investor interested in mining ventures, called at my New York office to ask whether I would be interested in a gold-dredging proposition.

"That depends," I answered. "Where is it?"

"California."

"What part?"

"Yuba River."

I smiled. "Old man, you're a little late. I already have an option which controls dredging on the best part of that river."

He smiled in turn. "You mean you had an option until last week. Now I have it. I bought your option from Bradley, who wasn't going to renew it."

It was through W. P. Hammon, who was engaged in dredging operations not far from the Yuba, and Colonel Forbes that Evans had secured the property.

I was astonished. "I can't understand why Bradley should have changed his views as the last reports from him were favorable. I'd advise you to go slowly. Maybe he's found poor values, or too much clay. You'd better see him again and make sure the property is worth developing."

I suggested to Evans that he have further tests made by Charles Hoffman, a specialist in auriferous gravels who had been in Siberia with the Lena Company. These confirmed Bradley's first estimates of rich possibilities. Evans then formed a syndicate in which he offered me a fifteen per cent interest, which I purchased.

When I later examined the titles to the claims Evans had secured on taking up our original options, I found that Bradley himself had taken up options on some adjoining claims and had sold these to Evans at a profit. While I still had the property under option I had told my friend Cyrus H. McCormick that if the tests being made by Bradley came up to my expectations I would give him and other of my Bunker Hill and Sullivan associates the opportunity to invest in the enterprise. I had sent him Bradley's preliminary reports indicating that his first tests were exceedingly favorable. Later, Mc-

Cormick wrote to Bradley asking how it was that I had confidence in the property in spite of his adverse report. Bradley replied that Evans and I had nothing to lose by our investment: if it proved worthless, we could dispose of our interest to my English clients. As a loyal friend, McCormick showed me this correspondence and I immediately wrote Bradley expressing my utter contempt for him, and warned him to keep at a safe distance from me. This he carefully did.

Then I started suit against him for restitution of the money he had received for his options. The San Francisco fire destroyed the essential records just before the case was to be called. Also Doolittle, one of my most important witnesses, died suddenly about this time. I was compelled to drop the suit.

There was more than one reason for my indignation against Bradley. He had been basely ungrateful for professional favors I had done him. More than that, in order to cover his own unethical transactions, he attributed dishonorable motives not only to me, but to R. D. Evans, a high-principled man who had acted solely on Bradley's recommendation in the purchase of the property. Bradley persisted in expressing to my friends his belief that the property was of no value, even after dredging operations had shown a large profit and the phenomenal value of the property was proved.

The success of the Yuba operations has many times over justified the confidence I had in the soundness of the idea, and all credit is due W. P. Hammon for his skillful handling of the technical and business problems.

Much of my enthusiasm for the career of a mining engineer has been caused by the evidence of what technical knowledge and skill have accomplished. An old-time miner, with a five-dollar outfit of pick, shovel, and sluice box, could not have visualized the development of great dredges for use on alluvial gravels. Had he been asked whether it was worth while to wash twenty-five hundred pounds of gravel to recover thirteen cents, his comments would have been unprintable.

The first two dredges on the Yuba, costing $190,000 each, started operating in August, 1904. Eighteen dredges have since been constructed on the property at a cost of $4,723,000, paid out of earnings. These dredges have extracted 481,000,000 cubic yards, or more than was taken from the Panama Canal. Each dredge can operate profitably on gravel which returns no more than seven cents a cubic yard, although the average yield is over twelve cents. The Yuba Company's latest electrically operated dredge, with bucket capacity of seventeen cubic feet, costing nearly a million dollars, will dredge to a depth of 140 feet instead of the 65 feet reached by our earlier dredges. From 1904 to 1933, with a capital of $750,000, the company took out $37,500,000 in net profits.

All this statistical information is not a prospectus for the company; its shares have never been placed on the market and are still largely held by the original investors.

Subsidiary companies of the Yuba are operating in a smaller way in other parts of California and Montana, as well as carrying on dredging operations for tin in Portugal.

I have also been interested in the extension of dredging operations in Colombia, South America, on properties for which I obtained and transferred the option to the Oroville Dredging Company.

Recently the Oroville company secured from my old firm, the Consolidated Gold Fields of South Africa, an interest in gold gravels in New Guinea. The property is about a hundred miles from the coast and exceeding difficult of access, owing to dense jungles and high mountains. The estimated cost of a road, built through the lowest pass in the mountain range, four thousand feet above sea level, was in excess of $1,000,000. This road would have had to be cut through trackless, fever-ridden jungles peopled by head-hunters and cannibals. Moreover, because of torrential tropical rains and subsequent washouts, the upkeep of the road would have been prohibitive.

The only hope of success in the enterprise lay in the possibility of having the proposed dredges flown in parts over the mountains and assembled at the inland base of operations. This plan was finally agreed upon and three specially designed airplanes were put into service. The twelve thousand tons of material, to construct the three dredges now in operation, were flown in without accident and in a relatively short time. These planes are capable of making three round trips a day, whereas, had a road been possible, the round trip would have taken a tractor a week. The cost of transportation is still materially less than the cost of the road originally considered. The large profits derived from the three dredges now operating have warranted the importation of a fourth, which is currently under construction.

CHAPTER TWENTY-FIVE

The Guggenheim Exploration Company

THE RISE OF THE GUGGENHEIMS—I MAKE A FIVE-
YEAR CONTRACT—ALVARADO PROVIDES FOR PAYMENT OF THE
UNITED STATES NATIONAL DEBT—MEETING WITH
DIAZ—TAKING A FLYER ON THE ESPERANZA—THE
HIGH-PRICED ENGINEER VERSUS THE "PRACTICAL
MINER"—ERROR IN THE NIPISSING—FINANCING
THE UTAH COPPER COMPANY—THROUGH THE
AIR IN AN ORE BUCKET—RIDER HAGGARD'S
HOBO—THE INTEGRITY OF THE GUGGENHEIMS

*T*he history of the rise of the house of Guggenheim to wealth and fame is comparable in many respects to that of Rothschild. Meyer Guggenheim of Switzerland had seven sons who were united by paternal guidance and fraternal loyalty. This cohesive quality which distinguished the Guggenheims would have been possibly only in a Jewish family. Even among the wives there was no friction. Each woman who married a Guggenheim became a Guggenheim herself and worked for the solidarity of the group rather than for the advancement of her particular family unit.

All were possessed of the fine old German sentimentality and kindliness. My wife and I were constantly made aware of this. For example, they would never consent to my setting out on a trip to mining property unless I was in the best of health.

So long as Meyer Guggenheim lived, he was the patriarch of the clan. Although I met him on only a few occasions, I always had a great admiration for him. After having previously made what was then regarded as a comfortable fortune in spices, he came to Philadelphia in 1848 and set himself up as an importer of embroideries.

In 1879 he put twenty-five thousand dollars into two silver mines at Leadville, Colorado. Benjamin Guggenheim was sent to Colorado to take charge of his father's mining interests. He became dissatisfied with the terms under which the custom smelter was treating his ores, which, though refractory, had a high silver content. He persuaded his father to buy fifty-one per cent interest in a near-by smelter. Meyer Guggenheim insisted that all seven sons be given equal shares in this new business he was launching for them. Out of this small beginning grew the great American Smelting and Refining Company.

Daniel, the second son, was recognized as having the greatest executive ability. For this reason his brothers acknowledged him as head of the clan and accorded him unswerving loyalty. When any decision had to be made, the others would come for judgment to "Mr. Dan," as he was called in the organization. They knew that everything he did was directed towards the advancement of the family rather than for his own aggrandizement.

Isaac, the eldest son, devoted his time to the financial aspects of the business. Simon, later senator from Colorado, was interested chiefly in the technical details of treating ores. In the early years Benjamin and William controlled the smelting operations. Murry was the salesman of the company. He would buy the unrefined ore and find markets for the refined product. Solomon was interested in all phases of administration. He was the outside man, what would now be known as the contact man.

It was natural for the brothers to extend their activities to the mining of ore so as to assure a steady supply for their smelters, which in a comparatively few years were scattered throughout the West and Mexico. The Guggenheim Exploration Company was formed expressly to locate mining properties. The Guggenheims were primarily interested in smelting and not in mining; the latter was always incidental

One of the important stockholders in the Guggenheim Exploration Company was William C. Whitney, who was not only a great power in the financial world, but had attained political eminence as secretary of the navy under Cleveland. Because of his winning personality, I had come to find his companionship most agreeable. He had often talked to me about the Guggenheims and had even suggested the possibility of my becoming connected with them. With this in mind, in 1903, he arranged a luncheon at the Midday Club for me to meet Daniel Guggenheim.

He introduced me pleasantly by saying: "This is the man I've been urging you to get for our Exploration Company. He's worth any salary he may ask."

We spent the lunch hour discussing the question of my joining the Guggenheims, and at a later meeting tentatively agreed on a salary and a five-year contract. Before signing this, I consulted Whitney and offered a substitute plan to him.

I told Whitney that personally I would rather work with him than with a company. Between us we could raise all the capital needed. I knew the western country and was sure we would be offered the cream of the new discoveries. Whitney agreed that this was worth considering.

Then I made the following proposition: Whitney was to pay all the expenses of my mining staff and back me in any venture I might recommend. At the end of two years we would figure the value of the properties I had acquired. Whitney would then agree to pay me out of future earnings what he considered the value of my contribution. I had great confidence in him and knew that any figure he mentioned would be fair.

The idea appealed to Whitney. He asked if I would be willing to take his son Harry in with me. The young man was just getting started in his business career, and this would be fine practical experience for him. Naturally, I was glad to do so.

This was as far as the scheme went, because the Guggenheims objected. They said to Whitney, "No, you have a large interest in our company and it's better to have Hammond working for the organization as a whole than for you alone."

Accordingly, I made a five-year engagement whereby I became consulting engineer and general manager for the Guggenheim Exploration Company. This contract not only covered my salary, but gave me a percentage interest in propositions taken on my recommendation. In principle it was the same as my contract with Rhodes.

My first duty was to scrutinize the company's holdings, get rid of poor properties, and install new managers wherever the present ones seemed incompetent. I was also to take charge of the various mining operations and at the same time I was to be on the lookout for new and promising ventures.

I was expected to attend daily board meetings. These were impromptu affairs which occurred almost without warning, no one could tell where. Messengers could be seen scurrying from floor to floor rounding up the executives with last-minute bulletins of where the meeting was to be held. Before long these meetings became a bone of contention between the Guggenheims and me.

The firm had invested in an unprofitable mine in Mexico, the Zaragoza. The manager kept sending monotonous and long-winded dissertations on its minor past performances and its infinitesimal future expectations. He usually guessed wrong the first half of the month, and apologized for his mistake the second half.

One day at the board meeting Murry handed me a particularly long and inept report from the Zaragoza and, as usual, asked my opinion.

I lost my patience completely. "Good Lord!" I shouted, "don't you realize that your entire investment in the Zaragoza would only pay my salary for about a month? I'd be saving money if I bought it myself and shut it down, yet you are taking up half of my working time in these endless discussions. These post-mortems are just a waste of my valuable time and yours! I can't get anything important done if you insist on talking trivialities!"

"Well!" Murry exclaimed, as I departed. "J. H. H. certainly has a temper!"

The result of my outburst was that the daily meeting was changed to a monthly one, and I attended only if I could fit it into my schedule.

But the day came when I, of my own accord, asked for a full meeting of the board of directors of the Guggenheim Exploration Company. I was ready to recommend the purchase of the Central Lead Mine of Missouri. I had learned its history from Arthur Thatcher, a well-known St. Louis mining engineer, who had been its manager before it was closed down some years previously. I secured a working option on behalf of the Guggenheims and my assistants had made drill tests to ascertain the value of the ore deposits. When these proved favorable, I made a careful inspection of the property myself.

With my head crammed with statistics and my arms laden with maps, I made a personal appearance before the directors. The maps were enthusiastically spread out on the long table and I began a lengthy, detailed, and earnest explanation. The directors wandered idly around the room evincing no interest, not even glancing at my maps.

Finally Isaac Guggenheim turned and asked, "How much money is involved in this transaction?"

I replied, "The property itself and a plant to work it will cost about a million dollars."

In a good-humored but pointed manner, Murry said: "Well, J. H. H., why are you spending so much time on such an insignificant matter. If you recommend its purchase we should buy it without further delay and not waste any precious moments of your 'valuable time'!"

My own words used against me. I laughed along with the rest and took them off to Delmonico's for lunch.

While looking over prospects in Mexico for the Guggenheims, I heard of a likely gold and silver mine at Parral, Chihuahua. The reputation of Pedro Alvarado, the owner of the Palmilla mine, had spread far beyond his own district. His peon father had been ignorant of the potentialities of his mine, but shortly after Alvarado inherited it, the Palmilla developed into a bonanza.

I have observed in the case of the nouveaux riches the desire to turn their wealth immediately into some tangible evidence of their improved economic and social status. Alvarado spent his first million in building a Mexican palace in the small village near his mine and equipping it with Parisian furnishings. One bathroom would have made his house unique in the village and certainly would have served his needs. In his desire to impress the world at large, he had twelve bathrooms installed. The possession of a piano was a sure sign of opulence, so he ordered not one but fifteen.

In the midst of his new-found riches and magnificent surroundings Alvarado retained his simplicity and kindheartedness. He established Sunday as gift day and invited the poor of the town to receive the silver pesos he himself doled out from a large basket. He was also a man of great civic pride, and made a promise to pave the streets of Parral in silver, a promise he was never able to fulfill.

Alvarado's generosity took more impressive form in a patriotic letter to President Diaz in which he offered to pay the national debt. When the affluent Don Pedro's suggestion went unnoticed by the Mexican government, he changed his allegiance and made a will providing for the payment of the national debt of the United States. After he had been swindled, as he thought, by the exorbitant charges of the American plumbers who were installing the twelve bathrooms, he cut the United States out of his will.

Within a few years he had accumulated and spent several million dollars. In his ingenuousness, he expected his wealth to last forever. He dug deeper and deeper into his mine until he struck underground springs. His pumps were inefficient and the lowest workings were soon flooded. Alvarado had never heard of King Canute's failure. He had a silver angel made and dropped this figure down the shaft of the mine in the pious belief that it would cause the waters to recede.

At that time general conditions in Mexico were unbelievably primitive with practically no hotels available. In my work I could not afford to be at the mercy of chance accommodations and found a private car indispensable. I had named it "Kya Yami," which in Zulu means One of My Homes, and it was indeed one of my homes for I spent many days and nights on the car in different parts of Mexico and in our western mining districts. The car served also as a traveling office so that members of my staff could join me on my trips and discuss business matters. Fortunately, as consulting engineer of the Harriman system I had free passes for "car and party" over the railroads of this country, Canada and Mexico, and the cost of transportation was not prohibitive as it is today.

Before I met Alvarado, he had seen the car standing on a siding and a friend of mine showed him through. He inspected it thoroughly.

As he emerged he asked, "Whose car is this?"

"It belongs to Mr. Hammond, the consulting engineer of the Guggenheim Exploration Company."

Alvarado at once replied: "I'd like to have a consulting engineer. Is Mr. Hammond a good one?"

"He's supposed to be," answered my friend. "He gets a pretty good salary."

Alvarado came to a quick decision. "I believe I will employ him."

"I don't think you can. He's already under contract to the Guggenheims."

"Well, then," countered Alvarado, "why shouldn't I buy their mines?"

"I don't think you have money enough," replied my friend.

"That doesn't worry me. I can take care of that—but if I get Mr. Hammond as my consulting engineer, I suppose the car will go with the transaction. Of course," he added astutely, "he'll have to make some allowance for its being secondhand."

But Alvarado and I never came to terms on this proposal—nor, for that matter, on the sale of the mine. Although I found him not unwilling to part with his property, his valuation was out of all proportion. Certainly Palmilla would not have been worth recommending to the Guggenheims. Eventually he sold it to an American company which has operated it intermittently, but without profit.

Today Alvarado is practically destitute, living alone in his crumbling palace and existing upon the meager sums received occasionally from those old friends who remember his former generosity.

When I went to Mexico in 1900 to examine the El Oro and Esperanza properties, John Hay, then secretary of state, gave me a letter to President Diaz, calculated to make him regard me as an important as well as trustworthy figure in the business world. Upon my arrival in Mexico City I lost no time in presenting it.

I was ushered without delay into the presence of the president, who, in spite of his seventy years, was still erect and soldierly in his bearing. Most noticeable were the white hair, white mustache, and white bushy eyebrows, the snowy lines of which contrasted with the swarthy complexion. His Mixtec Indian blood proclaimed itself in the high cheekbones and large dark eyes, half covered by drooping lids so that they gave no inkling of the purpose behind them. Like Rhodes and Witte, he had a massive frame, a fit instrument for the dominant will directing its movements.

In the memory of most people Porfirio Diaz was a cruel dictator. They have forgotten that as a young man he was in a large measure responsible for the overthrow of the French in their occupation of Mexico. Moreover, in a sense he was the first Mexican patriot in that he recognized a national individualism as opposed to the heterogeneous racial characteristics and borrowed cultures.

The idea of Mexico's coming of age became strongly fixed in Diaz's mind when he was a youth. He was a man of decided culture and learning. He went to college and later studied law at Oaxaca. Shortly afterwards—in 1847— he joined a guerilla band and fought to defend his country against the American invasion of 1848, then later to defeat Santa Anna whom he rightly considered a fool and a traitor.

From then on Diaz was definitely a military man—a rebel and a skillful revolutionary leader. In his almost fanatic belief in the destiny of the people of Mexico and his conviction that they were being grossly mismanaged by their executives, he plotted revolts against Juarez and Lerdo de Tejada.

Finally, in 1877, he entered Mexico City victorious and with the acclaim of the people he had so ably defended.

The methods Diaz used might be criticized according to the ethics of our reputedly more enlightened democracy, but his justification was that he had employed them in behalf of his country. It was Mexico's good fortune to have as her leader during these important years a man for whom the means justified the end, but for whom that end was Mexico's welfare.

Diaz understood English much better than he could speak it. With such Spanish as I had at my command we were able to understand each other perfectly. The first question the old dictator asked me was, "What can I do for you?"

"Not a thing in the world," I assured him.

He looked his surprise. "This is an unusual, if not a unique, experience for me. Should you ever change your mind, Mr. Hammond, I shall be glad to be of service."

Then he added slyly: "I hope you will not attempt any revolution here. I'm afraid you would not get off so easily as you did in South Africa."

I laughed. "No, it would never occur to me to start a revolution where none was needed. Though you yourself, Mr. President, must admit that revolutions are sometimes necessary."

Diaz made no comment, but his mustache twitched with amusement. The conversation then shifted to a discussion of the development of Mexican resources. He warned me of one obstacle I would almost certainly encounter. I would be approached by lower officials who would ask for money, saying it was necessary to square the higher politicos.

"In reality," said Diaz, "very little of the money paid in bribes goes beyond the pockets of the petty grafters. If you have trouble of this sort, come to me and I'll settle it."

Occasionally I heard from my staff in Mexico that they were having difficulties with the local authorities. I thought up a scheme. Whenever a crisis seemed imminent, I would see to it that announcements of my departure for Mexico City appeared in the local Mexican newspapers, intimating that I was going to pay a visit to Diaz. This was usually enough to bring the greedy politicos to reason before I had reached the capital.

From my first meeting with Diaz a pleasant relationship developed. Whenever I happened to be at Mexico City, Diaz sent his military aide to bring me to the palace for a little chat about my work and things in general. I was one of the earliest representatives of foreign capital in Mexico, and the president was eager to consult about many phases of industrial development in his country. He was encouraging American businessmen to invest in mining and oil concessions in order to open up the country to the industrial revolution.

His theory was that, if Mexico was to be freed from ignorance and poverty, he must make use of the enterprise and money of more progressive nations. He knew capital would not enter in sufficient amounts unless he could reduce danger and risk to a minimum by maintaining before the world a stable government. This government would have to be strong enough to protect the lives and property of the foreigners who were to be the instruments to his great purpose. Under existing conditions in Mexico, despotic rule was the only kind possible.

Diaz's attitude towards capital as the weapon he was forging to free Mexico was well illustrated by what happened one day when I called on him in company with José Casasus, Mexican ambassador to the United States.

We were kept waiting for over an hour at the National Palace while the president was conferring with his secretary of foreign affairs. Diaz seemed surprised when he saw us, and displayed irritation for not having been notified of my presence. He said that, so far as the ambassador was concerned, he was a Mexican, for whom mañana would do as well as today. As for the secretary of foreign affairs, he also could wait. But I, as one of his "collaborators in the development of Mexico," deserved instant admittance day or night, for "Mexico herself" waited on me.

Besides being a shrewd diplomat, the old dictator did not lack a sense of humor. I remember once being summoned to his summer palace at Chapultepec, one of the most beautiful places in the world. Outlined against the snowy background of the towering volcanic peaks, Popocatepetl and the White Woman, Iztaccihuatl, and located upon a conspicuous hill in a grove of ancient cypress trees, it afforded a splendid view over the Valley of Mexico.

As I looked down over the precipice I wondered how the American troops in their march on Mexico City had managed to scramble up its steep slope. I remembered that my father had been one of the leaders in the storming of Chapultepec.

Diaz and I were strolling about the grounds when a light rain, hardly more than a mist, began to fall. With a glance at my shiny top hat, Diaz remarked, "I'm afraid your hat will be ruined."

He thereupon sent an attendant to bring me more fitting headgear. I confessed that I had bought the top hat about an hour before expressly for this occasion, explaining that toppers were not de rigueur at the mines.

The attendant returned with one of Diaz's own sombreros. I made the exchange and the hat sank down over my cranium. It made an excellent umbrella, although I had to use both hands to keep it off my ears.

The thought that the skies had intervened to render futile my carefully arranged formality of appearance struck the old man as funny. He never forgot it. Whenever I appeared, arrayed in all the glory of my beaver, Diaz would glance at it gravely and utter a pious ejaculation of gratitude that he had once been able to save it from destruction. Indeed, I kept it at my hotel in Mexico City for presidential audiences. For all I know, it may still be there, or it may even have graced the head of one of the post-Diaz presidents.

During one of our conversations, Diaz asked me whether I had ever been at his birthplace in Oaxaca. I told him the story of how, in 1885, I had recaptured the baggage and ore which had been stolen from me by bandits.

He smiled knowingly. "So you were the young engineer. I heard about your exploit at the time. Mr. Hammond, you lost the opportunity of your life. If you had killed any of those bandits, I should have given you a gold medal for each one, because it would have saved me a great deal of expense. I had to send a party of rurales to clean up Oaxaca. Today you will find it as safe as New York City."

"That isn't saying much, Mr. President," I replied. "But I know what you intend to imply."

I have already mentioned that I had gone to Mexico in 1900 to look over the El Oro and Esperanza properties, located ninety miles northwest of Mexico City. J. B. Haggin, of Haggin, Tevis, and Hearst, had sold the El Oro to an English organization, which called itself the El Oro Mining Company. Before I left London I had been employed by them as consulting engineer, a position which I held for about a year.

As for the adjoining Esperanza mine, in 1899 I had secured an option on it for a group of English investors, including the Venture Corporation of London, On my suggestion, F. W. Bradley, then manager of the Bunker Hill and Sullivan, had been engaged to make an examination of the property. Bradley recommended the purchase at the agreed price of six million dollars. On the strength of his report, we organized a company in London with the necessary capital.

Before proceeding further, I pointed out to my colleagues that, since Bradley had long been one of my own assistants, it would be well to have a report from an engineer representing the prospective purchasers. Accordingly, Ross E. Browne, whom I knew to be one of the best of our American mining engineers, was sent to make another examination.

The expectation was, of course, that his report would confirm that of Bradley; we were only making assurance doubly sure. To our consternation, Browne's estimate fell far below Bradley's. His statistical analysis was so convincing that we decided not to float the company. My own examination made the following year confirmed Browne's report. The lower levels were in poor ore; the mine was en borrasco, as they called it.

I still believed that further development would open up fine mineral deposits. E. A. Wiltsee remained there to secure an option on the property. He advised Sonnenberg, the owner, to come to see me in New York. Sonnenberg accepted this advice and offered me the mine for three million dollars, exactly half Bradley's original evaluation. This was the blunder which made me first lose confidence in Bradley.

I sent Beatty and several assistants to sample and map the property thoroughly. Their favorable report, coupled with the reduced price, persuaded me to start for Mexico to conclude the purchase.

Before I could reach Mexico City, however, Sonnenberg died, and I was obliged to conduct my business with his executors. It turned out fortunately for me that this particular matter had been left solely in the hands of an honest lawyer, Luis Mendez.

There had been bad blood between the owners of the El Oro and Esperanza mines. Immediately upon the death of Sonnenberg an agent of the El Oro Company endeavored to get an option on the Esperanza property. To that end, he offered to deposit twenty-five thousand dollars for an option of thirty days, during which the company's experts could examine the mine. I reminded Mendez that Sonnenberg had promised me the option: that I had been put to considerable trouble and expense in having the property examined, and was now ready to purchase; moreover, that Sonnenberg himself had several times told me that, because of the existing feud, he would under no circumstances sell the property to the El Oro Mining Company of London. Mendez readily admitted that the estate was under moral obligation to sell me the property, and finally agreed to give me the thirty-day option without my putting up any money.

I myself felt a moral obligation to offer a fifty-one per cent interest to the Venture Corporation because they had been associated with me at the time we had formerly considered the purchase. The remaining forty-nine per cent I intended for the Guggenheim Exploration Company.

It was a Friday afternoon when I arrived at New York. The first payment on the three million dollars had to be made the following Wednesday at Mexico City. I went at once to see Daniel Guggenheim, but he displayed no interest whatever in my proposition.

I did not press the matter, but started for Whitney's cottage at Sheepshead Bay. At this critical juncture I went to him because I knew him to be a man of courage. With that ability to grasp a situation quickly which distinguished his entire career, he agreed to assist me in the undertaking. We tried to reach Guggenheim by telephone Saturday morning, but were unable to get trace of his whereabouts. Finally, it was agreed that Whitney and I should take over the property ourselves.

When I located Mr. Dan on Monday and told him what we had done, he expressed surprise. I then said: "Whitney and I are going ahead to float this company. I know that the Venture Corporation will take up fifty-one per cent. Do you want the other forty-nine? If not, we'll buy it ourselves."

He bought this section of the flotation on behalf of the Guggenheim Exploration Company, and it was not offered to the public.

The Venture's fifty-one per cent was being dealt in on the London market. When bonanza ore was discovered in a newly developed part of the property, there was a boom in Esperanza shares. I told Mr. Dan that the high price of the stock was not justified, since the bonanza ore would soon be exhausted, and the mine had no future except as a relatively slow and steady producer. Our profits were not to be derived from stock manipulation, but from the operation of the mine. As soon as earnings fell off, there would inevitably be a slump in the shares. This would reflect discredit both on the Guggenheim Exploration Company, which owned the property, and on me, who was managing it.

Guggenheim immediately agreed with me. We cabled the London brokers who were engaged in booming the Esperanza shares to the effect that, if the shares advanced higher, the Guggenheim Exploration Company would dump its holdings and break the market.

This brokerage firm, which had been a client of mine in South African days, indignantly cabled that in the future its members would not touch any flotation in which the Guggenheim Exploration Company was interested. I replied by letter that they would be given no opportunity to repeat such an unwarranted manipulation of stock, and when they realized that the conservative policy of the Guggenheim Exploration Company was for the protection of the investor and not for the profit of the speculator they would be glad to participate in that company's flotations. They came to repent of their hasty action, and many times in the future were desirous of dealing in our securities.

The mining investor is constantly obliged to take risks, even when prospects seem most favorable. In purchasing the Esperanza we were risking a half million dollars, since there was not more than two and a half million dollars' worth of net ore in sight. Moreover, most of the deeper developments seemed unfavorable.

But I knew from my previous examinations that the El Oro, on one side of the Esperanza, possessed a long shoot of pay ore; on the other extension, the recent discovery of rich ore bodies at the Dos Estrellas convinced me that the geological formation justified our risk. As consulting engineer, I ordered certain exploratory work done, and was fortunate in discovering large bodies of unusually high-grade ore in a new section of the mine. Those who had invested in the Esperanza then enjoyed a series of handsome dividends, amounting in a few years to twelve million dollars.

At a banquet, not long after opening up the new development at the Esperanza, I was seated next to my old friend, J. B. Haggin. He was evidently in an unpleasant frame of mind. In discussing mining conditions, he remarked sourly, "Well, Jack, you have a lot to answer for in mining."

"Yes, Mr. Haggin," I said, "what's your particular grievance?"

"You've ruined the mining industry with the high salaries and engineering fees you pay," he replied. "Though I'm not reproaching you for the very large salary you're now reputed to receive," he added.

"That's a matter of opinion," I said. "It's true that I've paid fairly high salaries and fees, but I get expert engineers who are really worth their salt. Mr. Haggin, when it comes to purchasing a property you still stick to the 'practical miner,' though you've made all your money through the technical knowledge and ability of trained engineers developing and operating those properties. And you haven't even paid them adequately. Your practical miner with a 'nose for a mine' is all very well, but I'm not sure that I, personally, feel complimented."

Haggin humorously mentioned having seen a cartoon from a recent issue of a London paper in which I was represented with a greatly magnified nose. According to the caption, Barney Barnato said to his brother in 1892, "They have a miner over there in America who can smell a gold mine a thousand miles away. Let's send for this man Hammond."

"I've always contended a sense of smell is not enough," I remarked. "Shall I go on?"

"Go ahead."

"Well, you brought the subject up, and I want to prove I'm right. You were the first capitalist to invest any considerable amount of money in the El Oro district. I admit you secured the El Oro mine through the recommendation of your practical men, but unfortunately, through their bad advice you afterwards sold it to some of my English clients. Following their suggestion, again, you refused to purchase the Esperanza when it was offered to you. On my recommendation the Guggenheims and the Venture Corporation bought it.

"In this very same district I secured for myself, Charles D. Lane, and Ernest A. Wiltsee an extension of the El Oro in depth. Although this ground had been condemned as valueless by the manager of the old El Oro Company, I purchased it on the recommendation of my experts and, after some development work, I sold it to the new El Oro Company at a handsome profit. Now don't you think it was good business for me to employ a more expensive but a more competent type of mining engineer?" Mr. Haggin was somewhat chagrined but had to admit the force of my argument.

I still maintain that my theory is sound and I repeat what I have said already, that I believe the specialist is worthy of his hire. Of course, even experts sometimes make mistakes. Pride goeth before a fall. Because I could not help being somewhat proud of my previous successes, it was a great shock to find that my first favorable report on the Nipissing silver mine of Canada was not justified by subsequent examinations made under my direction. This report had created a sensation on the market, because the Guggenheims had invested a large sum in the purchase of the Nipissing Company stock on the strength of my recommendation.

My optimism had been based upon estimates by engineers in whose integrity and ability I had implicit confidence. Unfortunately, they had overestimated the value of the ore; it was the first time they made an error of that kind. I accepted, and still do accept, full responsibility for my optimistic report. Shortly afterwards, as the result of a careful personal examination, I informed the Guggenheim Exploration Company that my previous estimate of values had not been justified.

I was much criticized at the time. The Guggenheims, although they admitted they had been disappointed in this particular investment, stood loyally by me. They publicly stated that their confidence in my judgment had not been shaken by this error. It was rumored that I was to resign my position with the company in consequence of the Nipissing episode. This was corrected by the following statement in various newspapers, including the New York *Herald,* December 8, 1906:

> There is no foundation for the report that John Hays Hammond, mining expert for the Guggenheims, is to resign his office as a result of the Nipissing episode. Official denial of the report to this effect was made yesterday.
>
> This statement may be taken as representing the

views of the Guggenheims in regard to the recent Nipissing developments.

There is no mining company or set of mining engineers infallible. If a mistake was made in our first views of the Nipissing property we were at liberty to rectify our attitude later. Mr. Hammond has examined the properties for the Guggenheim interests which later came under their control and have resulted in enormous profits—enough to triple the losses sustained in the Nipissing deal.

My mistake in the Nipissing had been due to placing too high a value on the stock of the company. After the Guggenheims retired, the mine still continued to produce silver and to pay dividends. Since my report, eighty-two million ounces have been mined, and $29,940,000 have been paid in dividends.

One of the outstanding acquisitions of the Guggenheim Exploration Company was the Utah Copper Company. In 1899, Victor Clement, representing Joseph R. De Lamar, purchased a one-quarter interest in Colonel Wall's Mountain of Copper, at Bingham, Utah. Up to this time there had been no development on the property.

Clement made a careful examination, running drifts and crosscuts, and engaged R. C. Gemmel, the state engineer, to do the sampling and D. C. Jackling to run the mill tests. Under a comparatively barren cap, the mountain was found to be a mass of porphyry which assayed slightly less than two per cent in copper. The ore in sight was vast in amount but of such low grade as to make unprofitable the ordinary method of mining by means of tunnels and shafts.

Clement advised the use of steam shovels to terrace down the mountain and run it through a mill. Jackling, who subsequently carried out the development independently, adopted this plan. The deterrent to this procedure was the reluctance of capital to expend an estimated three million dollars in development before one ingot of copper could be produced. The property, therefore, remained idle. Clement became involved in a dispute with De Lamar and resigned his position. In 1901 he began to devote himself to his Mexican mines.

The following year De Lamar still had his one-quarter interest in the property and Colonel Wall held a three-quarter interest. Wall was anxious to have the mine developed. He was disappointed in what he considered De Lamar's lack of co-operation, and offered a favorable option on his own interests. Clement was still convinced of the value of the deposits and had kept up his friendly relations with Wall. He now suggested that, if I could secure De Lamar's quarter holdings and interest capital in London or New York, we could take up the property ourselves. We agreed to put a hundred thousand dollars each into the venture for further prospecting work.

De Lamar was willing to part with his interest at about its cost. He told me frankly that he had no faith in the enterprise.

In January, 1903, Clement had to go to Mexico again, and we agreed that on his return we would close the negotiations. But Clement died in the hospital at Saltillo in April. I happened to be in Mexico at the same time and so was able to assist in the last sad rites for that fine engineer and my loyal friend.

When I reached New York again, I heard that Daniel C. Jackling had succeeded in closing a deal with Wall by which the MacNeill-Penrose group had acquired control of Utah Copper. The capital for extensive development was not forthcoming, however.

In 1905, John C. Montgomery, Colorado mine promoter, came to see me with the proposal that I, as the Guggenheims' consulting engineer, should interest them in financing the Utah Copper Company. I told Montgomery I was familiar with the history of the property and would recommend it. I put the proposition before Mr. Dan with a view to securing his support at our next board meeting.

There was needed, I said, someone with imagination enough to see beyond the great initial outlay and to grasp the eventual success of large-scale operation. My own faith in the enterprise was evident, since I had been willing to go into it with Clement. This demonstration of confidence, coupled with my arguments and figures, convinced Mr. Dan.

I then sent Seeley W. Mudd and Beatty to make a new examination and a thorough drill test of the property. Their report, in October, 1905, was favorable and the Guggenheim Exploration Company then underwrote a bond issue of three million dollars and bought a large block of the stock.

I became consulting engineer and later managing director of Utah Copper. Jackling was put in charge of operations. The adjacent property was acquired and consolidated for more efficient operation, and the striking success of Utah Copper under Jackling's able management is a matter of contemporary copper history.

In August, 1907, the big concentrator at Garfield went into operation. Since that time 225,000,000 cubic yards of ore and waste have been moved, or almost exactly the total yardage displaced in building the Panama Canal. At least four times this amount will have been dug before Utah Copper is exhausted as a mine.

The gross income from the sale of copper, gold, and silver has been $596,000,000. Total disbursements, including dividends, construction of plants, taxes, etc., have been $300,000,000, and the company has paid in dividends alone $185,000,000. The number of men on the Utah Copper Company payroll is about 3500, with 500 others whose livelihood comes directly from the company's operations. These men represent a high class of labor, all skilled workmen and well paid. With their families and the families of those men indirectly required for the life of a community, there is in the Bingham district a population of twenty-five thousand or more supported directly or indirectly by operations of the Utah Copper Company.

The success of working the large low-grade copper deposits by the Utah Copper Company gave rise to discoveries of deposits of this kind in other parts of the United States and in Chile, and the development of what is known as the Porphyry Copper Industry. The magnitude of operations in this industry is shown by A. B. Parsons in his book, *Porphyry Coppers.* "From 1905 (the beginning of operations of the Utah Copper Company) to 1931 inclusive, the output was $2,871,300,000 of which $50,000,000 was derived from gold and silver contents. Of this large sum $800,000,000 has been allocated to dividends and bond interest; $391,000,000 to taxes, local and federal; transportation, refining and selling copper; $840,000,-000 to supplies, fuel, equipment, machinery, and power at mines, mills, and smelters $840,000,000, for payrolls at mines, mills and smelters."

As Mr. Parsons states: "In a mining community payrolls make towns. The townspeople include a great many doctors, lawyers, school teachers, preachers, bankers, merchants, butchers, garage men, restaurant and laundry proprietors, insurance agents, hotel keepers, movie-house owners, and the employees of all these necessary members of a normal community. Even bootleggers and politicians are not unknown in some of the towns. And all these indirectly derive their livelihood from the mining or ore-treating operations. Farmers, dairymen, and poultry raisers find excellent markets for their produce in the mining town. For every man employed either directly in producing copper or in serving the man who digs or smelts, there is on the average a family of four."

In 1906, I sent my assistant, Pope Yeatman, to Alaska to examine the Kennecott Copper Corporation's property. The Guggenheims secured an interest in it on his favorable report. Later on, Yeatman and his assistants, Edward Berry and E. T. Stannard, the latter subsequently president of Kennecott, had charge of the development for the Guggenheims of the Braden Copper Company and the Chuquicamata property, both in Chile. An expenditure of many millions of dollars was necessary in the development of these properties for large-scale operation, and the attainment of the low working cost will ensure their importance as factors in the world copper production. The Incas smelted copper ores from the Chuquicamata mine in the fifteenth and sixteenth centuries.

Pope Yeatman succeeded me as managing director and consulting engineer of the Guggenheim Exploration Company. He resigned the office in 1916, after a period of nine years.

One of the properties on which I had to report for the Guggenheims was the Silver Lake mine in Colorado. I had already visited the mine in 1901 for English clients, at which time I had found that the owner was an old Freiberg classmate, Ed Stoiber, who was lacking in aggressiveness.

Stoiber's wife possessed all the traits which were missing in his kindly disposition. She was determined that Ed was not to be imposed on by anyone but herself, and relegated him to the background when there was business to be done.

On my arrival I was introduced to Mrs. Stoiber by Ed. After some preliminary conversation about Freiberg days, the talk turned to business. Mrs. Stoiber, apparently fearing that I might get the better of her husband, projected herself into the conference.

I began by saying: "Now let's see what condition the mine is in. First, how large are the profits, and what are your prospects?"

The replies were evasive and vague, and my dissatisfaction must have been obvious. Before long Mrs. Stoiber asked to speak to Ed privately, and they withdrew from the room.

In a few minutes Ed returned. "Well, Jack," he said, "I don't think this is the kind of mine your English firm would like. If I were you I wouldn't recommend it." After a moment's hesitation, he added, "I hate to advise you to do this, because I know you'll lose your fee."

"That's all right, Ed. Don't worry about that. You're an old friend—that's enough for me. I won't even bother to examine the mine."

Without further ado I returned to Glenwood Springs and dismissed the Silver Lake property from my mind.

I was much amused when, some little time after I joined the Guggenheim Exploration Company, the directors asked me to make an examination of this same mine. They had purchased it a few years before, probably led astray by the exaggerated value of the property in the opinion of Mrs. Stoiber. Having already spent a million dollars in developing it and erecting a plant, the Guggenheims thought the mine ought to begin showing some profit.

It was decided that I should make the trip with three of the brothers, Daniel, Solomon, and Simon. While plans were being made, I told the Guggenheims that I was afraid the journey would be unprofitable, and I then related the story of my first visit there.

Young Harry Payne Whitney accompanied us and did much to enliven the excursion. The train took us as far up the valley as the company's office. The mine itself lay at an elevation of thirteen thousand feet, about three miles away as the crow flies.

The ore was brought down in iron buckets traveling along aerial cable lines. Their use by employees of the company was prohibited since they were regarded as unsafe for passenger traffic. Unfortu-

THE GUGGENHEIMS

WARDNER, IDAHO

nately, the night preceding our planned inspection of the mine there was a heavy storm, and in the morning the horse trail was buried so deep in snow that it would be impassable for days to come. It was essential that I, at least, see the mine, and time pressed. I decided to go up in one of the empty ore buckets, although it was only under the strongest protest that the manager finally gave me permission to do this.

Whitney wanted very much to accompany me. He used all his persuasive wiles, first on the manager and then on me, and was greatly disappointed when I flatly refused to take him. I told him I was not going for the fun of it: it was a business necessity in which he could be of no service.

Wrapped in a heavy fur coat against the cold, I cramped myself down in a bucket. The manager telephoned that I was on my way. After swaying for a half-hour over the snow-clad rocks and gorges far below, I reached the mine and was dug out of my uncomfortable conveyance. I had barely straightened up when I saw Whitney's head poking out of another bucket approaching the landing stage.

I was angry, because I felt responsible for him, but was unable to restrain a smile at his comical appearance. I demanded, "Where did you come from, you nuisance?"

He grinned back at me, promised not to get in the way, and followed me to the office.

There we were met by a delegation of outraged miners who complained in strong language about the cook. Now, to complain of the food is the most fundamental and treasured right of a miner. I inquired whether there was any fault to be found with the supplies furnished by the company. The spokesman replied that the grub was good enough in itself, but the fault lay with the cook, who was giving them the same thing day after day. "We'll be damned if we'll stand it any longer!"

I then called the cook, and asked him whether he thought the company was furnishing suitable provisions. He admitted it was.

"Now, cook," I said, "you came here with a good recommendation, and I wonder if you're living up to it. How many ways do you know of cooking potatoes?"

"About six."

I appealed to his vanity. "And how about bread, eggs, corned beef, pudding?"

To prove his culinary art, he began to enumerate the different dishes he could make.

"All right," I said, "the men will appoint a grub committee, and each week one of them will make out a menu and submit it to you. Then you'll cook up what they want from your supplies. If you give them an occasional surprise, they'll be your friends for life."

I saw he had half a mind to leave, but I looked significantly at the snow-covered mountains. His eyes followed mine; apparently he decided he was better off where he was. I heard later from the manager that peace was reigning at the cookhouse—at least, for the time being.

Whitney watched proceedings with amusement. He followed me into the mine and all day scrambled nimbly up and down ladders and over piles of rock. His athletic prowess stood him in good stead. In the evening we went back to the mill in two buckets as we had come.

I have never seen anyone make friends more quickly with miners, prospectors, and other old-timers than Harry Whitney. He had a personal magnetism and a disarming friendliness that made him popular in the West as well as in the East. "You could beat even Teddy if you would go into politics," I used to tell him.

Harry also had his father's good judgment and generosity. In many later years of business dealings with him, there was never an enterprise in which we were associated wherein Whitney did not only urge my receiving the profits due by definite agreement, but also an additional sum to which he thought I was entitled. I, of course, declined these generous offers.

When the Guggenheims, Harry, and I arrived at Salt Lake City, my secretary told me that a man had been waiting several hours to see me. A personable-looking fellow was shown in.

He said, "Mr. Hammond, I don't suppose you recognize me."

When it was evident that I did not, he added, "I'm the 'hobo.'"

My mind flashed back to the time two years before when Rider Haggard had been a guest in my car going from California to New York. As the train wound its way over the Sierra Nevadas, I had been relating some of the famous holdups that had occurred on this same road. The scenes I had depicted were still vividly present to his mind when, late at night, he went to his compartment.

Before long James, my negro cook, came rushing into my room and in great agitation asked what was wrong with my guest. He explained that, noticing Haggard's light still burning, he had gone in to switch it off. With pistol in hand Haggard had leaped from his berth and threatened to shoot.

The next day I told Haggard that it was permissible to defend himself against bandits, but he would have to be careful with James; in addition to being the best cook I had ever had, James was also the best shot.

At breakfast Haggard regretfully remarked that he had never encountered a hobo in the flesh.

My son Harris, who usually accompanied me on these western journeys, spoke up. "There's a hobo been riding the brake beams of our car all night. I found him this morning and gave him something to eat. He's back there now."

At the next stop, Harris produced him. The hobo was grimy with dirt and cinders, ragged, and nearly frozen from the cold ride through the snowsheds and alkali desert. I introduced him to Haggard.

The hobo's face lighted up as he said, "You don't mean the famous Rider Haggard?"

"Yes," I said, "the very same man."

"Mr. Haggard," he said, "I've read all your books—some of them several times," and he rattled off their names.

I called James and told him to get our new guest washed up and give him a coat, since he was to have dinner with us.

We spent an entertaining evening listening to his tales of hobo life. Finally I asked the man whether he wasn't tired of being a tramp and whether he would take a job if I were to give him one. He accepted eagerly.

When we reached Ogden, I sent him off with a railroad ticket and a letter to the manager of a mine near Salt Lake City.

In parting, I added: "Here's a chance for you. I hope you'll stick to the job."

Now, some two years later, here was this same hobo transformed into a respectable and steady workman. He reminded me of my parting words as I had despatched him to a more profitable life, and said, "I did stay with the job, and now I have a chance to get a better position in the smelter you're building here."

I told him I would talk with the manager about him and would also write to Rider Haggard. I knew he would be pleased. The manager reported later that the man had turned out well and deserved his promotion.

On this same trip I was walking up and down the station platform with Sol Guggenheim, while waiting for a change of engines. We were discussing the notorious lawsuit then being tried at Butte, between H. H. Rogers, of Anaconda, and Heinze, the mining magnate. The bribery, corruption, and blackmail in this long and expensive litigation were causing more scandal than has been raised in any other mining case.

J. P. Morgan had said to me, "It reflects on every business in Wall Street, and it ought to be stopped."

I had been asked to serve as umpire between the parties to the suit but before I could act I joined the Guggenheims.

Sol said: "I can't understand why Rogers keeps up such a dirty mess. He may get a few million out of it, but he'll only give it right away to charity. Wouldn't you think he'd have more sense than to sacrifice his good name for that? I think it's a damn shame!"

"I agree with you, Sol," I replied, "and I'm glad to hear you've such a high ideal of business ethics. In the future I'll never have to worry about any rumors of sharp practice connected with your enterprises."

At the end of 1907, when I tendered my resignation to the Guggenheim Exploration Company on account of ill health, I was asked to renew my contract, and the Guggenheim brothers expressed regret at my leaving.

In the four years I had been with them I had formed a friendship with all the family. Although Dan and Isaac are dead, this friendship still continues with the surviving brothers.

I look back on my association with them as one of the most satisfactory periods in my mining career. This was partly due, of course, to the generous amount of my salary but chiefly to their estimable personal qualities. They backed me loyally. I found them scrupulously honest in their business methods, men of courage and broad vision, although outside of their knowledge of the smelting industry they had little personal experience in mining matters. They took an interest in their church, their charities, and social service.

I consider myself qualified to express high admiration for their business integrity, their sense of civic duty, and their solicitude for the welfare of their staff.

CHAPTER TWENTY-SIX

Prospecting in Politics

I RETIRE FROM ACTIVE BUSINESS — CLEVELAND,
MCKINLEY, ROOSEVELT — MY FRIENDSHIP WITH
TAFT — ROOSEVELT AND INDUSTRY — I FLIRT WITH
THE VICE-PRESIDENCY — TAFT'S CAMPAIGN
AND ELECTION — GOLF — MAKING A CABINET —
TAFT'S PERSONALITY — WE MOVE TO WASHINGTON

I had been in active service as a mining engineer for more than a quarter of a century. I had built up a corps of younger men on whom I could rely for efficient field work. It was not only unnecessary for me to follow activities in the field but considerations of health now made it unwise. I found I had leisure to do other things.

Up to this time I had not engaged in American politics, although in a life as active as mine one necessarily deals with statecraft and learns to know the weapons and the rules of the political game. I never cared for it. I have never fancied myself as a handshaker, a godfather to the nation's children, or a demagogue.

In America one must be "all things to all men" to run successfully for public office. Although it is the duty of honest and intelligent men to take part in the executive affairs of the nation, one reason why many industrialists and businessmen hesitate to do so is because political activity lays them open to suspicion and puts a noose around the neck of their business freedom. Also they have been accustomed to direct dealing and find themselves waterlogged by the need for compromise and the entangling routine of "parish pump politics," as Rhodes expressed it.

It is true that positions and offices were at various times offered me—some of which I would have accepted—but, unfortunately, these offers came when other conditions made acceptance impossible. As a result of combinations of circumstances, I found myself in the political arena without portfolio.

The reason—and the only reason—for my entry into politics in the early nineteen hundreds was my warm personal friendship with William Howard Taft. I liked to be with him. I admired him. His intelligence, integrity, and fine balance were qualities requisite in a leader at that particular time. He welcomed my advice and I felt that I might be of some use to him.

Out of all my family I am the only one to break away from the tradition that a Southerner must be a Democrat. My relatives thought me a misguided turncoat; I consider it independence. While still a student at Yale, I had agreed with the Republican stand on the tariff issue and my attitude had persisted and developed. But in becoming a Republican I had not renounced my allegiance to many of the time-honored principles of the Democratic party. I felt that Cleveland's election came at a time when the Republican party had been so long in power that a change was needed. Cleveland was the type of president best fitted to the occasion, and was highly esteemed by men of all parties for his level-headedness, his soundness of purpose, and his courage.

I have been personally acquainted with all the presidents from Grant on—with the exception of Chester A. Arthur—and had opportunities for close observation of their activities. Hayes, Cleveland, and some of the later presidents I knew more intimately.

The first time I saw President Cleveland was in 1886 when the appointment of my brother Richard as surveyor general of California was under discussion. Cleveland realized that Richard had strong support from California, but feared that some objection might be made to his youth: he was only twenty-seven. The position was one of great responsibility because of the predatory efforts of powerful private interests to get hold of valuable timber lands in California.

My brother's competence and record for inflexible honesty finally prevailed, and the President appointed him. After that he was locally called "general," much to the amusement of my father who really was a major.

Golden Gate Park in San Francisco owes much to my brother Dick. He was president of the Park Commissioners for several years and was especially interested in building the children's playground. In my boyhood days I used to camp and hunt among the sand dunes on which the park is built. My cousin, William Hammond Hall, a young civil engineer, imported shrubs from abroad and transformed these sand dunes into a beautiful park.

After that first meeting, I did not see Cleveland again until the summer of 1908, when I was living at Lakewood. He was desperately ill and had been moved from his home at Princeton to the Lakewood Hotel in the hope that the change would be beneficial. When they were ready to return to their home, Mrs. Cleveland was extremely anxious to get her husband away without his having to run the gauntlet of photographers who prowled around the grounds at night and lurked by day behind their black cloths on the hotel veranda.

I succeeded in throwing them off the scent by appearing with Mrs. Cleveland and the baggage in front of the hotel. She allowed herself to be photographed while the ex-President was taken out a rear door and installed in my son Jack's automobile. When we were sure Jack had a sufficient start, Mrs. Cleveland and I stepped into our waiting car and departed, leaving behind us a row of dumfounded newspapermen.

A few days later Cleveland died. I served as one of his pallbearers.

I was out of the country during most of the years of McKinley's presidency, and my occasional contacts with him were purely social. He was always kindly and good-natured, but behind this front-porch manner I divined a greater degree of stamina than many people gave him credit for. Shortly before his assassination McKinley had paid off his political debts and had begun to assert his authority.

Roosevelt, his successor in office, was a spectacular figure the world over. While I was in England, I followed with interest his vivid career in the Spanish-American War and as a forceful governor of New York State. He was a man marked by physical and moral courage, and by an inexhaustible drive. The self-made man is popular in America. Roosevelt, with a background of illustrious ancestors and ample means, substituted vigor and personal magnetism for humble origin as his method of capturing the admiration of the masses. Moreover, it was apparent that he was politically astute and would forge ahead in politics.

After my return to America I saw President Roosevelt on many occasions.. It was at the White House during his administration that my friendship for Taft, then secretary of war, was intensified and that I saw much of the famous trio, the other member of which was Elihu Root, secretary of state.

On one occasion these men, and Mrs. Roosevelt, were present at a luncheon at the White House to which I was unexpectedly summoned by wire from New York at the time of the I.W.W. trouble in Colorado.

At the table, in his impetuous manner, Roosevelt boomed jocularly, "Well, Mr. Hammond, I hear you think I'm losing my political courage!"

I was embarrassed by so blunt a statement, but understood his reference. A few days earlier I had dined with Paul Morton, secretary of the navy, and had expressed the opinion that Roosevelt should have complied with the governor of Colorado's requisition to send troops to suppress the lawless activities at Cripple Creek. I had further stated that in my opinion the refusal had been based solely on political considerations.

Morton must have repeated this conversation to the President; I was fairly caught. I frankly admitted that my sentiments had been correctly reported and that I still held them.

Roosevelt seemed amused that I should acknowledge having accused him of political cowardice. "Why," he said, "most of my friends on The Hill blame me for showing too much boldness. They say I've meddled in too many things—Panama, for example."

"Mr. President," I said, "I'd like to discuss this Colorado situation with you after lunch, explain my criticism, and hear your side of the story."

When Mrs. Roosevelt retired, the President reintroduced the subject. "You criticized me for not having sent troops to Cripple Creek at Governor Peabody's request. Peabody must have known that before federal troops could legally be sent to Colorado, the resources of the state itself had to be exhausted. He had no business asking me for help until the state militia was no longer able to handle the situation. There are plenty of people who'd like to catch me doing something for which they could impeach me. Your friend Taft will bear me out."

Turning to Taft and Root, he said, "I wish you both would send Mr. Hammond all our correspondence with the governor. He can then see for himself."

I said quickly, "There's no need of that, Mr. President. I will take your word for it."

A few days later I had to go to Colorado, and, while I was there, made a point of seeing the governor. I asked why he had issued an appeal with which he knew the President could not legally comply.

He finally agreed that Roosevelt's stand had been correct and admitted that he had hoped to avoid antagonizing either capital or labor by shifting the responsibility to the federal government.

I had been a staunch supporter of Governor Peabody, but now I freely expressed my opinion of his double-dealing and said I would make it my business to do all I could to prevent the re-election towards which he was so cautiously pussyfooting. My friends prominent in Republican politics were disgusted with Peabody's action and contributed their influence to his defeat.

During these years I was seeing Taft constantly, and our families became close friends. I often went to Washington to see him; he and Mrs. Taft came to Lakewood and New York to visit us. The renewal in 1902 of our acquaintance of Yale days, with its informal—indeed, almost accidental—quality, I count as one of the happiest events of my life. Taft later described it in an article in the *National Geographic Magazine*:

> After I returned from the Philippines temporarily in 1902, I stayed with Mr. Root in Washington while I was being subject to the grilling of a congressional committee, which cross-examined me for 30 days in the spring of that year. During that examination I ran

over to New York and went to the University Club for luncheon.

While I was there a waiter brought a card from a gentleman who was also taking luncheon, which was followed by the owner of the card, and he proved to be my old college friend, John Hays Hammond. He had been out of college 26 years, and I had been out of college 24, and we had not met since we graduated.

He had been to South Africa and helped to develop its wonderful mineral wealth, had been convicted of treason against Oom Paul and the Boer Republic, had been sentenced to death, and had only escaped by the intervention of England and the United States. He left college a mining engineer, to be engaged in peaceful occupations in the West. I had left as a lawyer, to pursue the humdrum professional life as a member of the bar in the Middle West, and had just then come back from the Orient, as the chief executive of 8,000,000 people, the oldest Christian community in the Orient.

There was a metamorphosis in the case of both of us that seemed to be striking, and when I told Mr. Root about it he said, "And they say there is no romance in this American life."

With all these comparable experiences and the opportunities for discussion which they offered, we naturally reverted to our college days. Taft had not changed greatly in character—he was the same genial Bill Taft—although his physical bulk had increased. One got the impression of a large rather than a fat man. At college he had been a powerful boy, with a decided aptitude for undergraduate politics and academic study. He was in my brother Bill's class, two years behind me. Bill was very fond of him; in fact, he broke the habits and beliefs of a lifetime to vote for Taft in 1908. Through Bill I met Taft and saw a good deal of him at New Haven, although he was two years younger. In fact, at that University Club luncheon we recalled that it was I who had initiated him into the mysteries of poker. He was not a particularly promising pupil. Some months later, however, I was badly beaten by him. When I recovered from my surprise I realized that brother Bill, a recognized authority in the game, had been coaching Taft on the quiet. I promptly went to Bill for some coaching myself. The defeat lurked in the back of my mind for years, but the opportunity to retaliate at the poker table never came.

In 1904 when Taft returned from the Philippines, where he had been governor general, to become secretary of war under Roosevelt, we first began discussing politics and the activities in which he was engaged. He was having dinner with me one day in New York. Afterwards, we strolled down Fifth Avenue; that was the quietest place in which to discuss a subject without interruption. James G. Blaine once said that a stroll on Fifth Avenue afforded him the best means of a private conversation.

Taft asked my opinion of the Panama Canal; whether the army should take over the work or whether private interests should be allowed to complete it.

I said that I believed the army engineers would probably not do as good a technical job as civilian engineers, but that there would be less opportunity for graft and less scandal if the canal were put under military supervision. Taft said that was his opinion also. Efficiency would have to give way to integrity. The remarkable ability shown by Goethals and other army officers in the digging of the canal proved my misgivings unjustified.

While Secretary and Mrs. Taft were visiting at our home in Lakewood at the time my wife and I were celebrating our silver wedding in 1906, President Roosevelt called Taft by long-distance telephone and offered him, for the second time, the post of associate justice of the United States Supreme Court. Taft was inclined to accept.

Mrs. Taft and I urged him to refuse, assuring him that many of his friends felt as we did. Had he been offered the chief justiceship, we would have raised no objection. That would, indeed, have been the achievement of his life ambition.

I based my opposition on the ground that he was the logical candidate for president in 1908. If he now accepted a life tenure on the bench, he would be shutting the door on any further political advancement. Moreover, he could be virtually certain of an appointment to the Supreme Court if a vacancy occurred during any ensuing Republican administration.

Up to this time Taft had held numerous important political offices and in every case had acquitted himself admirably: assistant district attorney and then judge in Cincinnati, solicitor general of the United States, judge of the Federal District Court, chairman of the Philippine Commission and later governor general, and at present secretary of war. Even his work in the Philippines had been thrust upon him. This proved to be practically the reorganization of a whole nation by one man. He displayed courage, diplomacy, and executive brilliance in the work, but he really did not like politics. His natural inclination was always towards the law.

Towards the end of 1907 it became apparent that Taft was to be the Republican choice for president. He was the only man above the status of a favorite son, and Roosevelt was letting out the tucks in his own mantle to make it fit Taft's shoulders.

I had recently resigned my position with the Guggenheims and now actually ventured into the field of politics in behalf of Taft. I was to spend the winter in California and my wide acquaintance there might be of value in supporting his candidacy for the presidential nomination, which was already gaining momentum in Republican circles. This proved to be true. I made many trips throughout the state and in other sections of the West and in most cases found it easy to enlist support. Oddly enough one of my most ardent lieutenants in this cause was Jack Burke, who had been my violent business enemy in the Bunker Hill litigation. Burke insisted enthusiastically that I campaign in my own behalf as running mate with Taft, a suggestion which Taft had already made to me.

On my return to New York in the spring of 1908, I called on E. H. Harriman and in the course of our conversation told him that I was now taking a hand in politics.

"Hammond," he said, displaying the American businessman's attitude, "I'm surprised at you wasting your time in politics. Your valuable abilities as an engineer shouldn't be discarded for intrigue and demagogy."

I smiled and asked him what kind of man he did want to see taking care of the affairs of the country and told him he ought to know that I wasn't likely to play cheap politics. Then I said jokingly that Wall Street didn't have enough money to "buy" me and under no consideration would I go out appealing to the mobs, and assured him seriously that I had no political ambitions for myself.

Apparently this made some impression on him. A few years later, in Washington, he asked me to come and see him and Chauncey Depew. They proposed that I run for the Senate.

I asked from what state.

"Why, New York: you live and do business there; or California, where you were born; or Idaho, where you've developed so many mines."

I thanked them both and declined, reminding Harriman that I had not changed my mind about seeking office for myself.

Harriman was definite in his approaches and opinions. He either liked a man or he didn't. For instance, there was no love lost between him and Roosevelt. When Charles D. Walcott, secretary of the Smithsonian Institution in Washington, was collecting money for Roosevelt's African expedition, he asked me to get Harriman to contribute. "Give money? No," said Harriman. "While he was president I would have gladly paid all his expenses to get rid of him, but not a cent now."

Harriman added that what particularly disgusted him was Roosevelt's posing as the discoverer of the Ten Commandments. He said, undoubtedly the big businessmen of the country at certain times in the past had been ruthless in their methods and not as scrupulous as they should have been. But at that time they had all been engaged in a free-for-all fight with devil-take-the-hindmost and did not realize how objectionable their methods were. He concluded by saying, "We will all be more conscientious in the future." If they had been, the history of 1929 to 1935 might have been a very different story.

The fact that I enjoyed a flutter in the direction of the vice-presidency should not really count against my statement that I was not seeking personal advancement. I should have liked being on the ticket with my friend Taft. My name was being mentioned in this connection in the newspapers, as were those of several others. The vice-presidency was quite open; no one seemed to have any lead.

I discussed the matter with Taft. He named two men who were seeking the nomination for vice-president, neither of whom he favored, and said he hoped I would make every effort to defeat their candidacy. He expressed the opinion that with them out of the way the situation at the convention might take such form as to allow him to give me his support, and he assured me that he would be delighted to have me as his running mate. It must be remembered that this was before the convention, when Taft's own nomination was by no means certain and it would have been sheer folly for him to commit himself. Also, I was given to understand by friends that Roosevelt had no objection to me, but Roosevelt would have all he could do in keeping the convention from a Roosevelt stampede, and in securing the succession for Taft.

I went to the Chicago convention but not as a delegate. My plan was to use my influence wherever it would be most useful to Taft.

Shortly after our arrival my friend, Arthur Sewall, brought Congressman James S. Sherman to see me. Unfortunately, I was away at the time and did not hear of Sherman's offer to be my convention manager until too late.

After many telegrams came in to party headquarters urging me to try for the vice-presidential nomination, and after John C. Montgomery, a western mining man and an old friend, had offered to be my campaign manager, I said "Barkis is willin'."

We opened an office in a hotel room and my son Harris, just out of college, came on to help. I am afraid we were just hopeful amateurs at the game. Harris tells the story of one of our negro constituents who came in one day and said to him: "Well, Mistah Hammond, yo' fathah sho' ain't takin' dis campaign ver' seriously."

"How's that?" Harris demanded.

"Well, sah, I ain't seen much of his money bein' spent aroun' heah."

Harris tells another story. One morning two negroes called to see me. They were referred to Harris, who had not forgotten the "glad hand" spirit of college days. One of the men took Harris aside and told him that the other was by far the most influential colored politician in Indiana and Illinois. Harris said he would be glad to meet him. The most influential colored politician was introduced to Harris as "my old and esteemed friend whom I have known for forty years or more. Mr. Hammond, let me introduce you to Mr. Jackson," whereupon "Mr. Jackson" indignantly drew himself up to his full height and said to his esteemed friend of forty years, "Didn't I just tell you not more than five minutes ago that my name's Johnson?"

Harris suddenly recalled that he had an engagement elsewhere.

When it was certain that Taft, the Midwesterner, was to get the nomination instead of Hughes, the Easterner, Hughes's adherents became bitter and claimed that steam-roller methods had been used in flattening out their candidate. My friends advised me that the nomination of Congressman "Sunny Jim" Sherman, the very man who had offered to be my manager, would add to the strength of the national ticket; in this way compensating the New York delegation for the rejection of Hughes. I withdrew and turned over to Sherman such potential support as I had.

Taft and Sherman were nominated. A few weeks later the Democrats at Denver once more chose William Jennings Bryan as their standard bearer, and the campaign opened.

The Republican National Committee set up headquarters at Chicago, as well as New York, in recognition of the growing importance of the West in Republican party politics. Taft resigned his Cabinet post and went to Cincinnati; he remained there until September when he took the stump for four weeks in the eastern, midwestern, and border states.

An example of Taft's fearlessness and direct honesty in meeting issues is shown by the address made in Chicago, September 23rd. The audience was composed largely of members of the organized labor groups. Taft chose to talk to them about his unpopular decisions in labor cases when he had been United States circuit judge.

"I am not here to apologize for anything which I did when I was on the bench. I am here only in view of the fact that I have been attacked on this ground, to take up those decisions, to ask your attention to them, to explain here in my humble judgment why it was necessary to reach the conclusions and take the action which I did, and then, if you gentlemen of organized labor think that this is a reason why I should *not* be selected President of the United States, you will not hear a bit of complaint from me. That is your privilege. You are electors and you have the right to judge of a man by his official action, whether it be on the bench or in any other capacity."

Taft took up several cases, analyzed them, and explained the necessity for his decisions. It was bold, franker than political speeches usually are, and met the issue squarely. It was typical of him.

Mark Sullivan says that Roosevelt advised Taft—and it must have been apropos of this speech, "Don't talk on delicate subjects—stop citing court decisions." Roosevelt was perhaps more astute, Taft was certainly more forthright.

Roosevelt's political wisdom and open support were generously given to Taft. But some of Taft's friends thought Roosevelt's public utterances were at times too patronizing. He seemed to be creating in the public mind the impression that Taft was not capable of standing on his own feet. When Governor Haskell, of Oklahoma, brought up the question of government guarantee of banks, Roosevelt took issue as though he himself were the candidate.

At the urgent request of some Taft supporters, I undertook the delicate mission of intimating to Roosevelt that in his effort to help Taft he was keeping himself too much in the limelight. I had no fear of being thrown out as I had always found him willing to listen, however violently he might disagree with me.

I told Roosevelt that I was perhaps in a better position than he to hear political gossip and that there was a lot of talk about Taft's lack of independence, and about his being forced to rely on the President for everything he did. I said that I thought it was partly because Taft had insisted on consulting him on the acceptance speech, against the advice of certain supporters who were not friendly to Roosevelt. This had made a bad impression in political circles. Taft openly declared that he felt he should confer with Roosevelt, not only out of a sense of loyalty but because he had high regard for Roosevelt's political acumen.

Roosevelt eyed me quizzically for a moment and then remarked: "I guess you're right. In the future I'll put on the soft pedal."

I tell the incident to show that Roosevelt was not always as arbitrary as represented. On other occasions I found him equally willing to discuss controversial subjects.

Shortly after Taft's nomination Roosevelt asked me to take up the reorganization of the National League of Republican Clubs. He wrote me, and also sent John A. Stewart, long identified with Republican politics, to explain how I could help the campaign by undertaking this work. The existing organization was inactive, and the clearing away of a few obstacles would rejuvenate it and I could be made president.

Frank H. Hitchcock, formerly first assistant postmaster general under Roosevelt, was at this time chairman of the Republican National Committee and Taft's campaign manager. We had to exercise considerable tact to avoid giving the impression that we were encroaching upon his province. He seemed jealous of any interference and apprehensive of not receiving due credit for success in the election.

At no time was he sincere in his support of the league; he undermined it whenever he had the opportunity. He was particularly anxious that no funds for its support should be diverted from his organization. Instead, he invited me to Republican headquarters and then was tactless enough to ask me for money. In view of the unfriendly attitude he had always betrayed, this was certainly surprising.

He complained: "When my friends induced me to accept this job, they said they'd give me ample funds. They're not doing it."

"Well," I retorted, as I turned on my heel, "I wasn't one of those friends. I wouldn't let you squander a penny of mine under any condition."

This open expression of my sentiments did not improve his feeling towards me. He had other worries, however. Whenever a difficult campaign problem presented itself at New York, he would take the Twentieth Century train for Chicago to seek advice from western headquarters. He would at once be confronted with two major problems in Chicago, and would skip back to New York on the next train. He spent most of his time railroading himself out of political realities.

The function of the Republican National Committee was to carry on party propaganda; that of the National League was to form local clubs of young and new voters in every county and city. Some thirty-eight units were organized, with a total membership of a million or more.

We could not draw on the National Committee for funds, nor did we need much money; our organizers were volunteers who gave their spare time to the work. Membership in the league involved the payment of no fees or dues, and the amounts that had to be spent for rent, literature, campaign buttons, and similar items were donated in small sums. My own party contribution was for the support of these clubs.

I appealed to the young men to interest themselves in political questions; I wanted them to be Republicans, of course, but more especially to be politically active. In my addresses I deplored the private citizen's lack of concern with local and national political questions.

It was my view then, as it is now, that good government in a democracy is possible only when responsible citizens envisage self-government as a personal and serious duty which cannot safely be delegated to professional politicians. I urged American youth to assume its civic duty and make its influence felt.

I thoroughly enjoyed the big parades of voters from our clubs which arranged for Taft's visits to the larger cities. The flickering torches, bands, excitement were an interesting and picturesque part. I liked to feel that thousands of young voters were aiding Taft's march into the White House.

After the election the Tafts went to Augusta, Georgia, to spend the winter, and invited my wife and me to accompany them. When not engaged in political discussions, the President-elect and I spent our time playing golf or attending barbecues.

We played a whole series of games which came out exactly even. On the day before Taft left for Panama, we had a final round to decide which was the better golfer. At the seventeenth hole we were still tied. On the eighteenth Taft teed off and topped his ball, which landed in a quagmire, leaving him what seemed a hopeless shot.

I turned to him and said triumphantly, "Well, old man, I guess I have you now."

With great deliberation I proceeded to drive, and made a beautiful long shot, which unfortunately hit a tree and bounced into a position fully as bad as that of Taft's ball. We both arrived on the green in the same number of shots, with my ball about six feet from the cup, and his fully thirty. There was a large gallery of fans. They seemed to inspire Taft but made me decidedly nervous. He took aim carefully and holed out by what seemed to me a miraculous putt. At this crucial moment, I flubbed and left him the victor by one stroke. He never failed to mention this victory snatched from defeat and plagued me unmercifully whenever he could contrive an opportunity.

Roosevelt often criticized Taft's enjoyment of golf. He thought it not a democratic enough game for a president, but Taft would laugh and go on playing. Just what form of exercise a man weighing over three hundred pounds should take was not suggested; possibly tennis or running, or pole vaulting.

Taft had selected golf on the recommendation of his physician. Roosevelt regarded this as a great political handicap and on several occasions warned Taft to that effect. Through Mark Sullivan, Roosevelt told him "that he should take his exercise in some form more familiar to the plebeian." "It is true," Roosevelt said, "I myself play tennis, but that game is a little more familiar. Besides, you never saw a photograph of me playing tennis. Photographs on horseback, yes, tennis, no, and golf is fatal."

For a time after his inauguration Taft took up horseback riding but he never really enjoyed it. In this connection one recalls the cablegram sent by Secretary Root when Taft was governor general of the Philippines. Taft had been seriously ill after a surgical operation and his friends in Washington were anxious about his health. When he recovered he cabled Root that he had just completed a long horseback trip into the interior of the country and felt fine. Root expressed pleasure at hearing this, but inquired as to the condition of the horse.

Taft's genial personality was as efficacious in winning him friends in the South as it had been everywhere else. On all public occasions he was greeted with sincere enthusiasm. He would rise slowly to his feet and, with his familiar chuckle, say: "I'm accepting your enthusiasm as a personal tribute and not as a sign of political approbation. Four years from now, of course, I know you'll go to the polls and vote against me."

His platform manner was peculiarly his own. He did not ingratiate an audience. He won them. To describe the "famous chuckle" to which everyone refers in remembering him, one should have the pen of a Dickens. I have never heard any other sound like it, nor expect to again. Taft's laughter was a form of physical enjoyment. It would start far ahead of the point of an anecdote, when he began to think of something that amused him and was making up his mind to tell it. It began unexpectedly and softly, grew in volume and repetition, and was used to punctuate his sentences. This chuckle started chuckles in his hearers. One of the most exciting memories of anyone who ever heard him make a speech was his ability to throw huge audiences into spasms of delighted laughter. This was neither a pose nor a trick. Taft was a great lover of laughter—and he liked to share his enjoyment.

Taft's popularity suggested to me that the Republican party in the South might be resuscitated by the formation of Taft Clubs. I hoped they could be entirely dissociated from the corrupt, carpetbagger organization which made the southern Republican politician a disgrace to his party. Hitchcock's hostility, however, quashed the idea.

If the Republican following were to be increased in the South, Taft's attitude on that ever-recurrent and troublesome problem of the negro politician had to be made clear. My southern heritage made me sympathetic with the Southerner's attitude toward the negro, politically and socially. I was afraid Taft might get into difficulties about this but was reassured when he told me that he would not think of giving a negro any important political position in the South, although if Massachusetts wanted a negro postmaster, it could have one. I said I felt sure Massachusetts would not be insistent as to that.

Taft spent much of his time in Augusta weighing carefully the make-up of his Cabinet. He talked with me freely about the various possibilities and asked whether I would accept a secretaryship. I told him I preferred to serve him in an unofficial capacity.

It has often been alleged that Taft promised Roosevelt he would retain certain members of the old Cabinet. It is quite possible that Taft in his jovial and expansive way may have remarked at one of the last meetings under Roosevelt, "I hope you fellows will come along to help in the new job the President has picked for me." But I am certain from what Taft told me that he gave no specific promise to appoint any particular individual to a certain post, and that he acted in good faith. It was in the matter of these appointments that the difficulties began which made Taft's administration so stormy a one from the personal angle. I know that when he was first considering appointments he did not intend to make George von Lengerke Meyer secretary of the navy; he had already offered me that portfolio and I had declined it, though he had Meyer in mind for a Cabinet position as a favor to Senator Lodge, to whom he felt politically indebted.

Senator Henry Cabot Lodge had a personal interest in the appointment of Meyer, to eliminate him as a possible candidate for Congress against his son-in-law, Augustus P. Gardner, who came from the same Congressional district in Massachusetts. Lodge came to Augusta to see the President-elect and asked outright, "Are you intending to put Meyer in the Cabinet?"

Taft replied: "Yes, Senator. Roosevelt has already suggested it, and I myself shall be glad to have him there." He did what he thought politically wise in the Meyer appointment, but even in this case he believed Roosevelt had made a suggestion rather than a request.

Taft certainly did not regard himself bound in the matter of James R. Garfield, secretary of the interior. In January, 1909, Taft wrote Garfield that he could not retain him.

Though he did not want Garfield in his Cabinet, he was anxious to choose a secretary of the interior who would continue the conservationist policy so dear to Roosevelt's heart. Richard A. Ballinger, as head of the General Land Office, had rendered excellent service and seemed the logical man for the job.

Taft asked me to go to New York and convey personally the offer of appointment. I invited Ballinger to breakfast and explained my mission. He said he appreciated the compliment but regretted he could not accept the post because of his limited personal means. He added that he had promised his wife to give up government work and return to his law practice in Seattle.

I reported this decision to Taft.

"Well," Taft said, "I'll get Henry to see what he can do."

Henry W. Taft, his brother, a member of the law firm of Cadwalader, Wickersham, and Taft, was apparently able to summon more cogent arguments in the line of civic duty, and Ballinger succumbed.

In place of Luke E. Wright, secretary of war, Taft appointed Jacob M. Dickinson, of Tennessee, an ex-Confederate soldier and a Democratic railroad attorney. He was a man of fine character and proved himself loyal to the President. When trouble began between Roosevelt and Taft, Dickinson told me he felt he was rendering Taft a disservice by remaining in his Cabinet, since, as a Democrat and a Southerner, he could contribute no political influence. I promised to report his attitude to Taft, although I was sure Dickinson's reasons would have little weight. Dickinson was not to be shaken from his decision, however; shortly afterwards he resigned, and was replaced by Henry L. Stimson, an intimate friend of Roosevelt.

For the appointment of Chief Justice White, of Louisiana, another southern Democrat and a Catholic, Taft was severely criticized by Republican organizations throughout the country. He had a particular interest in this office, since it was the one which, above all others, he would have chosen for himself, and regarded White as best qualified for the position. He courageously refused to consider anyone else.

The conscientious discharge of what he regarded as his duty is further evidenced by his appointment of two other Southerners as associate justices of the Supreme Court: Horace H. Lurton, of Tennessee, in 1910, and Joseph R. Lamar, of Georgia, in 1911.

Although Taft knew I wanted to remain a private citizen, two months after his inauguration he announced my appointment as minister to China. The first intimation I had of the matter was through the newspapers. Taft immediately sent for me to come to Washington.

When I arrived he greeted me enthusiastically with the words: "Well, what do you think of the idea, Jack? I knew you didn't want to be ambassador to any European country, as you saw no opportunity to render conspicuous constructive service, but you can't say that about China. We need a man there who can deal with the problem of developing her natural resources and industries. You've had that type of experience in Russia and elsewhere. In my opinion you're just the man to be minister to China."

I insisted that I couldn't do it. I told him that I appreciated the honor, that I'd rather have that post than any other in his gift, but that I'd been out of my own country many years and didn't think I should take my family away again, especially as I had children ready for college.

Reluctant to take "No" for an answer, Taft sent for Philander C. Knox, his secretary of state. Knox also urged me earnestly to accept and finally asked me whether I was declining the post because it was not an embassy: "If that's the reason, we can take care of that. We'll make it an embassy."

I explained that I felt the foreign policy was dictated by the State Department, and the envoy was merely the intermediary—a glorified messenger boy.

"Well," retorted Knox, "you've heard of such things as 'cutting the cable.'"

"Yes," I replied, "but I'm declining on personal and no other grounds."

It was embarrassing for me to have to decline after the appointment had been made public, and I also feared that it might embarrass the administration even more. Taft advised me to state my reasons frankly to the press, and to explain that the appointment had been made without my knowledge.

That same afternoon, the President, Knox, and I were playing golf at the Chevy Chase Club. In a pause in the battle I asked Knox:

"Why don't you go to China this summer after Congress adjourns and take me with you? We could study the country at first hand. You'd have the distinction of being the first secretary of state who'd ever been to the Orient."

Knox drove far down the fairway. With his eyes still following the trajectory of the ball, he remarked complacently, "Hammond, I'm just learning to play this game, and I'm not going to let anything so unimportant as China interfere."

Taft appointed Charles R. Crane of Chicago. Crane was criticized for having cast aspersions at Japan while on his way to his post. Influenced probably by Huntington Wilson, the undersecretary who at the time was doing most of the work of the department, Knox first recalled Crane and then telegraphed the news to Taft who was in San Francisco.

Taft was much concerned about this and told me that a reprimand would have been sufficient punishment, but added: "Knox is in the saddle and that's his department. If I interfere he'll say, 'If you don't let me run my department the way I want to, I'll get out.'"

In high dudgeon Crane betook himself and his wealth to the opposing political camp where, through judicious campaign expenditures, he did much damage to his former political associates. Finally, in 1920, he reached port when Woodrow Wilson appointed him again minister to China. He served there with distinction and later in other diplomatic missions.

In 1909, at Taft's solicitation, I moved my family to Washington. My wife and I had for many years entertained the hope that after I retired from business Washington might be our home.

Before, during, and after Taft's term of office, our relations were those of pure friendship. In our many hours together we talked of all manner of things, naturally of state and business matters among them. He came to ask my advice, considered it competent, and I sought advice from him on many occasions. It was give-and-take, although he sometimes thought I was too eager to be "up and doing," while I felt that his judicial mind weighed matters too long. I was always extremely careful to avoid giving the impression that I possessed inside information or that I had any special influence over the President. It is difficult to explain an association of this sort without giving rise to misunderstanding. I know that Taft appreciated my efforts not to presume on our friendship, and it is my wish to avoid the appearance of it even in these pages. Our confidences were those of friends. He was one of the best-loved friends I ever had.

My visits to the White House had their lighter moments. I was at the executive office one day when the chairman of an important New York antisaloon society was announced.

As I started to leave, Taft said, "Don't go, Jack—I may need help."

A stern-faced lady appeared in the doorway. "Mr. President," she began, "I've made this trip from New York especially to express the admiration of the members of my society for your noble action in turning down your glass when you were offered wine."

A twinkle appeared in the President's eye. "Madam, if I am to speak honestly, I must admit I'm not entitled to any credit. I'm strongly in favor of temperance, but I'm a teetotaler only because my physician advises it. I've no objection to drinking wine. As a matter of fact, many of my intimate friends drink it. For example, Mr. Hammond here."

The lady gave me a look of disapprobation, rose, swished her skirt as women did in those days—and because of the revival of fashions in dress with the years they are now doing it again, as I observe—to express disapproval, and remarked witheringly as she stalked from the room, "I'm greatly disappointed to hear this about you, Mr. President."

In the next issue of her society's paper the President was arraigned as a backslider from grace.

Taft's great bulk was made the subject of caricature and jest. It was fortunate for him that he was not oversensitive on this subject, and could joke about it himself. He once told me, with his hearty chuckle, the story of his visit, while governor general of the Philippines, to the court of Czar Nicholas. As he and Mrs. Taft alighted from their carriage at the imperial palace, there was a loud ripping sound; the seam of his trousers had burst. There was no time to return to the hotel for a change of clothes. Mrs. Taft rose to the emergency; she borrowed needle and thread from a lady-in-waiting and hurriedly sewed up the rent. Fearful that her hasty stitches might not hold during the audience, Taft moved crabwise before the Czar and on leaving backed out of the room.

In spite of his size, Taft had an unusual air of dignity. He was a jovial man—a fat man if you will—but above all a most distinguished one. His laugh, his beaming smile, his optimism, and his kindliness became famous the world over, and unlike large men generally, he was careful of his attire. Often his love of people and his delight at being with them made him seem easygoing. He was rarely on time for appointments, not because he meant to be late, but because he found himself interested in whatever he was doing at the moment and unable to break away.

Taft has been criticized for having changed his views on important matters, but in each case that came under my observation he was amply justified. I have known him to go back on a promise made to friends from whom he had every reason to expect truth, but only when he discovered they had misrepresented the facts. He disliked saying "No" because he was essentially a man of kindly impulses, desirous of doing his friends favors when these were consistent with the public interest. Politicians soon found it useless to recommend a measure because of political expediency alone or because it might be helpful to Taft's own political fortunes. The interest of the country was uppermost in all his decisions.

As I have said before, his intellectual interests were basically judicial. He admired the jurist rather than the statesman. We once passed the statue of Chief Justice Marshall on Capitol Hill together.

Noticing that Taft glanced at it, I asked curiously, "Wouldn't you rather have been John Marshall than president?"

"Of course," he replied. "I'd rather have been Marshall than any other American, except perhaps Washington—and I'm inclined to think that I'd even rather have been Marshall than Washington."

CHAPTER TWENTY-SEVEN

Debates and Battles

*T*his chapter and the following are in no way intended as an apologia for Taft's presidential career; they are merely an explanation of his attitude, expressed to me on the debated issues of those four years.

In the first place, Taft has not always received informed acknowledgment for the constructive legislation passed during his administration. He did not dramatize nor spectacularize it as many presidents would have done, but its value has been increasingly evident. Later administrations have received credit for such measures as the federal budget and a national banking system, which he had recommended long before. He did not use publicity to cut short his enemies, but quietly pursued what he believed to be the business of being president, placing accomplishment in office ahead of ambition for re-election, and paying little attention to the fact that his deeds were being currently obscured by the sound and fury of his political opponents.

It is undoubtedly true that politicians of long experience were able to upset legislation and commit sabotage because of the unorthodox and unselfish way in which Taft conducted himself, but I believe this to be a devastating commentary on the fundamental condition of American government and not on the character of President Taft.

Many people considered that Taft would have become a second John Marshall had he given up his whole career to the bench. Some of his friends, partly misled by his own preference for the law, thought his going into politics was a mistake. In fact, the popular estimate of Taft as president is more or less confused with a conviction that he would have accomplished greater things as a jurist.

In 1908 the country did not need a fighting leader such as Roosevelt; it needed a president who would carry out the general program laid down by Roosevelt and promised in the party platform.

Unlike some presidents, Taft took the party platform promises seriously and used them as a legislative program. Among other things, he strengthened the Interstate Commerce law so that appeals could be taken from the commission to the Court of Commerce. He instituted the parcel post and postal savings bank systems, secured the passage of the income tax amendment, encouraged many bureaus for government scientific research and supervision, and urged a bill providing that campaign funds and their uses be made public.

Had there been any issue requiring direct action, I am sure Taft would have risen to meet it. Obviously, he did not carry a chip on his shoulder nor did he welcome controversy.

Naturally the first question confronting any president is the vexing problem of official appointments. Taft was, with his usual balanced timing, slow to make up his mind. With four or five names under consideration for a particular job, he would spend many days and still have come to no decision as to which candidate to appoint. He was as precise and as thorough in weighing a man's qualifications for office as he would have been in the courtroom in deciding on a question of life and death. While this was admirable, it was often irritating.

I used to tell him that he was wasting too much time in dealing with patronage. I asked him why he did not select one of these men, and, if he seemed all right, appoint him. What difference did it make if his recommendations were based on the selfish motives of the man's backers?—he might be good in spite of them. I added: "You can find out as much as you need to know about him in twenty-four hours. If you make casual appointments fast enough, the press will be kept busy reporting them instead of filling the pages with criticism of your selections. While this is going on, you can be making up your mind about the really important appointments. That's the way Roosevelt did."

On one occasion only did I interfere in Taft's political family. Charles D. Norton, who was then secretary to the President, had been assuming unusual authority and pretending to have a greater degree of influence over the administration than he actually possessed. In the presence of newspaper correspondents, at his summer White House at Beverly, Massachusetts, Taft had several times jocosely referred to Norton as "underpresident" and his "alter ego."

Norton was a Chicago businessman, whose fine appearance and ingratiating manners invariably created a favorable first impression. In time, however, everybody except the President began to see that Norton's practice of setting one person against another was seriously damaging Taft's prestige.

Various people, both representatives of the press and members of the Cabinet, asked me whether I would not protest against Taft's being misrepresented by Norton.

"You are closer to Taft than we are," some of the Cabinet urged, "and your position is a disinterested one. The President won't let us say a word against Norton."

I replied that I was sorry but didn't see how this concerned me at all, that I couldn't understand how they had allowed themselves to get into such a humiliating position. I asked them why they didn't write individually to the President and tell him that they would be forced to resign if he insisted on keeping Norton.

On thinking this matter over, I decided that anything which concerned Taft so intimately was my problem also. For Taft's own sake, such a situation must not be allowed to continue.

Accordingly, I went to the White House and found the President in the executive office. "Mr. President," I began, "I'm sure you'll recall that on the way to your office in the State, War and Navy

Building one day shortly before your nomination I pointed to the White House and asked, 'Bill, do you see that building? You'll soon be living there.' You replied that I was pretty optimistic. I asked you then to make me a promise. With all our admiration for President Roosevelt, we agreed that he often acted impulsively without seeking advice from his friends or without making sure information was not being kept from him. I asked you to promise me that, when you were in the White House, I should always have the privilege of telling you anything that concerned your welfare, however disagreeable it might be. You shook hands on that, didn't you? Now I've come to tell you about Norton."

Taft listened to me attentively. Then he said, "Thank you, Jack."

We shook hands and I left. Within a few days Norton handed in his resignation. Charles D. Hilles succeeded him.

Hilles never was afraid to tell the President what he thought about anything. He said to Taft once, "I'm going to resign unless you get rid of Postmaster General Hitchcock or get him under control."

Fortunately there was no need for Hilles to resign as he and others of us finally did succeed in curbing Hitchcock's pernicious political activity.

Almost at the beginning of his administration Taft had to make a choice as to which of the two elements in the Republican party could be persuaded to join him in helping to carry out Roosevelt's policies. On the one hand were the old standpat Republicans, to whom party allegiance was paramount. They were regimented under such leaders as Senator Nelson W. Aldrich, chairman of the Finance Committee, and "Joe" Cannon, speaker of the House. These men knew exactly how to go about securing the results they wanted, although their methods might not have been approved by reform elements.

Taft has often been accused of not knowing how to handle politicians and of not having political flexibility. His plans were thoroughly thought out before he launched them and he was not inclined hurriedly to readjust a program because of changing circumstances. His critics point to his association with Cannon and Aldrich, who during the last two years of Roosevelt's administration had bitterly opposed him. They claim that these "unscrupulous politicians" led Taft around by the nose. This is emphatically not true.

Actually he used them instead of being used by them, although the public was not generally aware of this. When Roosevelt's insurgent partisans later attacked Taft on these grounds, his defense was that an antagonized Cannon or Aldrich would have wrecked the legislative record of his administration.

Taft had come into office personally endorsed by Roosevelt and his political household. He believed he had a right to call upon them for aid, but they promptly deserted him.

He turned then to the leaders of the Old Guard. As he explained to me, "They were my enemies when they were Roosevelt's, but since his friends have deserted me, I've had to accept the help they brought me." He had no great personal friendship for either of them nor did he always approve of their methods. But his aim was progressive legislation, and he realized that they were the only instruments to serve his ends.

Aldrich was an artist in steering legislation. He knew exactly how many Senate votes he could count upon. If an additional one was needed, he would hold out bait to Congressional ambitions. The promise of a desirable committee position or even such a trivial thing as the bestowal of a larger office in a better wing of a government building often proved irresistible.

Aldrich never spoke much in the Senate. It never disturbed him when Robert M. La Follette, of Wisconsin, the archrebel of the party, thundered for hours against the System (referring to Wall Street affiliation), the tariff, or predatory wealth. Aldrich, Brandegee, and their followers, confident of results, would meanwhile be pleasantly lunching in another room. When the time was ripe, Aldrich was certain that his cohorts would go into action and deliver the votes. This method of procedure gained him his reputation for political cynicism.

Far less in numbers but headed by the redoubtable La Follette, and including Dolliver, the veteran, experienced Cummins, and the oratorical Beveridge, the radical Republican movement was monthly gaining strength.

I used to divide these insurgents into four classes. First came the Simon-pure socialistic element, masquerading as Republicans. To these the Democrats were welcome.

THE TAFT FAMILY AND MYSELF

PORFIRIO DIAZ (1830-1915)

Second were the unintelligent intellectuals, the theorists without any practical knowledge of governmental affairs.

Third came the unctuous rectitudists, the reformers, and the fanatics concerning whom I thought no statement could be more apt than that often quoted by Arthur T. Hadley from one of the old philosophers, "Virtue is more dangerous than vice because the excesses of virtue are not subject to the restraints of conscience." In this latter class belonged what Roosevelt himself termed the "lunatic fringe." Its members had the same high ideals and the same Jesuitical belief that the end justified any means which had inspired the extreme abolitionists of the 1850s and 1860s and the prohibitionists of the 1920s.

The fourth insurgent class was the same Progressive element. Many of these Progressives remained my friends, although I have always regarded their desertion of Taft as a betrayal of the party and responsible for Taft's failure to secure a second term.

In 1910 the Progressives still stood for control of the Republican party from within by public-spirited and patriotic members. This meant the reduction of power of the old-line machine politicians. It was increasingly apparent that there was danger of a split in the Republican ranks as the Progressives as well as the Democrats gained ground in 1910, although the insurgent Republicans at that time were not advocating extreme and impractical measures. These men, however, were to be the Bull Moosers of 1912.

The Republican party platform inherited from Roosevelt had specifically promised a downward revision in the tariff. Roosevelt carefully sidestepped this dangerous issue during his administration, leaving the Dingley Tariff, passed under McKinley in 1897, still in force.

The purpose behind introducing a new bill was twofold. In the first place, the Dingley Tariff had not produced enough revenue to run the government; in the second place, it was felt at the time that the tariff rate should provide for the protection of home industry by equalizing the difference between the lower cost of production abroad and that in the United States. It was believed that by inserting a maximum and minimum clause it would be possible, within limits, to adjust tariff rates, irrespective of production cost or discriminatory legislation in foreign countries.

Almost immediately after Taft's inauguration he called a special session of Congress to revise the tariff, and Sereno E. Payne, chairman of the Ways and Means Committee of the House, introduced a tariff bill. Taft realized as well as Speaker Cannon did that "no matter how great an improvement the new tariff may be, it almost always results in the party in power losing the election."

Hearings were held at which Andrew Carnegie and other industrialists testified that no higher tariff rates were necessary to equalize American and European costs of production. This applied to but a few industries. Both Senate and House bills were then sent to the Senate Finance Committee over which Aldrich presided. Without his approval no tariff measure had any hope of success. The Senate Committee promptly made certain articles on the free list once more dutiable, raised rates which had been reduced, and generally restored the reactionary features to the tariff bill. Aldrich approved these amendments, with reservations. Against the vociferous but futile objections of the insurgents, this machine-made bill was pushed through the House and the Senate.

Up to this time no vocal dissent had come from the country at large. Taft, according to his theory that the President should not steer bills through the legislature, waited until the act had gone to conference. He did not approve of many features of the bill, particularly the famous Schedule K on woolens. He believed, however, that the Payne-Aldrich bill was preferable to the Dingley bill, which had become an anomaly. The new measure at least established a Tariff Board to keep track of the relative costs of production and to recommend necessary changes in rates. Taft also approved of the free trade provision for the Philippines. In fact, he believed this bill might break the ground for the general downward trend in rates to which he had on many occasions committed himself. This was at the time when considerable objection was urged against a high tariff because of the high cost of living—sometimes humorously referred to as the cost of high living—a subject much agitated at the time.

Unfortunately for the administration, the self-seeking manner in which sectional and industrial interests had lobbied for rates had aroused the ire of the four able, honest, but radical midwestern Republican leaders.

Taft was perplexed as to what course to pursue. One Sunday in Beverly, a few days before signing the bill, he talked the whole matter over with me. He admitted his dissatisfaction with the bill as it stood.

He summed it up by saying: "I can veto this tariff bill as Cleveland did the one presented to him. Perhaps such an action would make me popular with the country, as it did Cleveland, but it would mean a hostile Congress for the rest of my term. Furthermore, if I should send a veto message, the confidence of the country, which is just recovering from the panic of two years ago, would probably get a setback. More important still, perhaps, is the deficit of $100,-000,000 which can best be made up by the revenue features in the new bill. The Tariff Board and the minimum and maximum features will allow us to make adjustments."

Believing the benefits of the bill outweighed its disadvantages, Taft signed it, but sent a message to Congress explaining his action and criticizing certain of its phases. Nevertheless, the public inveighed loudly against the bill; in its mind Taft had become *particeps criminis*.

The tide of insurgency in the Republican party was steadily mounting, particularly in the West. Some of us who were close to the President believed that if Taft had an opportunity to explain to the Westerners the eventual benefit to be derived from his policies, they would be less likely to block the progress of his legislative plans. To accomplish this it was proposed in 1909 that Taft take a trip through the West.

Taft's friends urged that a bill to give the President a traveling allowance should at once be put through Congress. Political enemies opposed this, basing their arguments partly on the waste of public money and partly on the waste of the Executive's time in what they regarded as a partisan junket. Some of the President's friends suggested that, if Congress would not make this appropriation, they would supply the necessary funds, and that courtesies would certainly be extended by the railroads as they had been in other administrations. But Taft resolutely refused to consider the trip unless Congress would pay every penny of the expenses.

To create support for this measure at Washington, without Taft's knowledge some of us arranged for a concerted demand from clubs, chambers of commerce, and newspapers in the West. Their enthusiasm was so effectual that criticism was stifled and the bill passed.

The President set out on his trip. Among the first stops was Winona, Minnesota, which became famous as the scene of Taft's classic but unintentional blunder on the tariff. His habit was to write his speeches just before delivery, and he rarely read them over. There was little time for composition on the train and, when he reached Winona, he carelessly asserted in his speech that the Payne-Aldrich bill was "the best tariff law the Republicans ever made, and therefore the best the country ever had." Unfortunately, he made this blanket endorsement without forcibly referring to his reservations made to Congress at the time he signed the bill.

Taft realized almost immediately that he had made a definite mistake. I am sure he meant only to say briefly what he had already said to me—that it was the best tariff bill that could be passed at the time.

This speech, coupled with Taft's signing of the tariff act, brought the insurgents in full cry against him.

A few days later, when I saw Major Archibald W. Butt, the President's military aide, who had served in the same capacity in the Roosevelt administration, he greeted me with the remark: "It's too bad you weren't with him. He bubbled all over and has done himself great harm."

Business engagements in California had prevented my accompanying the presidential party on the first part of the trip. Since I was to be in the West, Taft had asked me to see Gifford Pinchot in Los Angeles and try to induce him not to resign as chief forester. Pinchot had tendered his resignation as the result of his disapproval of Ballinger.

The conservation issue and the Pinchot-Ballinger fight gave another ground for attack on the administration by the insurgents. People whose memories reach back to Roosevelt have not forgotten the wave of discussion that swelled in those years over the phrase Conservation of Natural Resources.

The whole matter was exceedingly involved but the main facts were as follows:

Timber, coal, and oil were being rapidly used up; the alarming picture of a starving and shivering population at a time not far distant began to possess the imagination. That there was gross waste in the exploitation of natural resources was a fact, and that America should pause to take stock of the situation was necessary.

Theodore Roosevelt wisely saw the need and acted with decision and energy. Recognizing the professional interest that a mining man has in this subject, he appointed me in 1905 to serve on a committee to suggest revisions in mining law. One of our recommendations at that time was for the leasing, not the sale, of public lands for coal mining. On March 24, 1906, as president of the American Institute of Mining Engineers, I attended a joint meeting of the engineering societies where the subject for discussion was Conservation.

Later, in May, 1908, President Roosevelt called a congress of the governors of the various states and territories to meet at the White House to discuss the whole question of conservation. I represented the mining engineers; in my address I explained the "professional" view: avoid waste and concentrate on utilization.

In June, President Roosevelt appointed me a member of a federal commission, the formation of which had been recommended by the governors. That my own view was consonant with his may be seen by these words from his letter to me:

> Our object is to conserve the foundations of our prosperity. We intend to use these resources; but so use them as to conserve them. No effort should be made to limit the wise and proper development and application of these resources; every effort should be made to prevent destruction, to reduce waste, and to distribute the enjoyment of our natural wealth in such a way as to promote the greatest good of the greatest number for the longest time. . . . There is no break between the interests of State and Nation; these interests are essentially

one. Hearty cooperation between the state and the national agencies is essential to the permanent welfare of the people. You on behalf of the Federal Government will do your part to bring about cooperation.

Another White House meeting was called for January 19, 1909, and on January 18th I gave a dinner at my house to the governors attending the White House meeting. At this point in the history of conservation it should be noticed that the views of Roosevelt were moderate enough to gain the co-operation of the states.

Unfortunately, his secretary of the interior, James R. Garfield, and his chief forester, Gifford Pinchot, waxed overenthusiastic. They came very near taking the position that natural resources were a trust to be held solely for the benefit of future generations, and were not to be enjoyed in full measure by those now living. It was an exaggerated and a sentimental view, but it exactly suited the crusading and capricious spirit of my friend Pinchot.

On the order of Roosevelt many million acres of public land in the West were withdrawn from private development.

All the western states protested against what they considered eastern dictation. Sentiment grew so warm that, at a congress called at St. Paul in 1911, western voters and western governors insisted that their states should have control of the resources within their own borders. They were willing to conserve, but they wanted to conserve for their own citizens and in whatever manner seemed best to them.

Apart from this sectional quarrel, there was a sound objection on economic grounds to the closure of public lands. Individuals and corporations who already owned forests, mines, and water-power sites, it was alleged, were thus given an unfair advantage in protecting them from increasing competition, and so assuring them of larger profits.

My own viewpoint on conservation was neither prejudiced in regard to my personal holdings nor discolored by sentimental preconceptions. The engineer is interested in improving processes of recovering metals from mined ores, and in utilizing to a greater degree the energy stored up in coal and oil.

The mine owner complained of the Sherman Anti-Trust Law because it compelled competition. He was often forced to take out of his property only what could be recovered at low cost. This was called gutting the mine. Also, competition in mining led to overproduction. I was opposed to the drawing of leases that forced the lessee into speedy, incomplete, and uneconomical exploitation. In the development of oil fields I opposed the waste of natural gas. So far as concerned public welfare, the major political aspect of the conservation debate, I favored the intelligent utilization of natural resources when needed by the present or any other generation.

The conservationists were then greatly alarmed by the predictions of oil geologists that the fields would be depleted within a very few years. Since that time geological surveys have led to the discovery of other great oil-producing areas, whose subsequent exploitation has resulted in an embarrassment of riches. The present effort of the oil industry is to limit production, not through fear of the depletion of oil reserves in the near future, but because overproduction has forced oil companies to operate on too low a margin of profit.

As I have described in the preceding chapter, Taft appointed Richard A. Ballinger as secretary of the interior to succeed Garfield. Because Pinchot believed that Ballinger was not carrying out Roosevelt's original program, he considered this appointment as treachery to Roosevelt.

After Ballinger had been in office only a few months one of his subordinates, Louis R. Glavis, was egged on by Pinchot to accuse him of dishonesty in the disposition of Alaska coal lands. Taft asked Ballinger for an explanation, received it, and decided the accusation was groundless. The moment the accuser was dismissed from the service, Pinchot sent in his resignation as chief of the Forestry Bureau. Taft wrote Pinchot a friendly and conciliatory letter: he said that he had personally gone over all the evidence against Ballinger, and that as a lawyer he thought himself better qualified than Pinchot to determine the validity of the charges. His examination of the evidence had led him to exonerate Ballinger. In conclusion he asked Pinchot to withdraw his resignation.

Pinchot had been fishing at Catalina Island. At Taft's request I arranged to meet him at Los Angeles immediately upon his return and forestall any newspaper interviews he might be indiscreet enough to give out.

I asked Pinchot whether he had received Taft's letter. He replied, "It was one of the finest letters one friend could write to another." He appreciated Taft's friendliness, but persisted in his intention to resign. I then persuaded him to go with me to Salt Lake City, where I was to join the Taft party the following day. Pinchot and Taft discussed the matter, but failed to come to an agreement.

Shortly after this Pinchot renewed his public charges against Ballinger, and these led to a senatorial investigation. Though Ballinger was acquitted by the Republican majority in Congress, the Democratic minority were supported by the insurgents in the insistence on his guilt. Ballinger found his usefulness seriously impaired by these attacks and a few months later resigned and went back to the practice of law.

Ballinger's enemies whispered that he had made many thousands of dollars out of his public office, but that accusation I know to be false. Through some of my personal friends who were intimately acquainted with his financial standing, I subsequently learned that he was practically without funds when he left Washington.

I had no reason to feel friendly towards Ballinger. At that time I was interested in an important hydroelectric development in the West which brought me in contact with the Department of the Interior. In the belief that I ought not to be the recipient of favors from an administration in which the President was known to be my personal friend, I did not press my legal claim for permits from the department, and Ballinger on his part did not issue them.

After Ballinger had resigned I explained to him that his timidity and fear of criticism had kept him from doing his full duty towards me. My claims had been approved in principle by his predecessor Garfield and would undoubtedly have been granted had Garfield remained in office.

As for the accusation heard in some quarters that I was interested in the Alaska coal lands for the Guggenheims, that was utterly false. I was no longer connected with the Guggenheims. Furthermore, I had gone on record as urging the withdrawal of the Alaska coal lands from entry. Besides that, I had advocated the construction of railways and their control by the federal government to prevent any possibility of monopolies in the development of the resources of Alaska.

After I joined Taft at Salt Lake City, I accompanied him for the rest of his trip through Utah, Montana, Idaho, Washington, Oregon, California, Arizona, New Mexico, and Texas. Although he had been abroad a number of times, in Europe, the Orient, and the Philippines, Taft had a limited knowledge of the industrial development of the Far West.

In many ways it was a difficult trip, but Taft never lost his good-nature. One of the things not generally realized about Taft—again because of the popular feeling that so large and jovial a man is inclined to be lazy—is that he had an extraordinary ability to work long hours at a stretch in order to finish a task. His power of concentration and of excluding the nonessentials was almost unique. In this way he burned up an enormous amount of energy. One interesting sidelight on this was his need to compensate by taking unusual amounts of food and sleep. I have seen him eat inordinately without any self-consciousness. I have seen him often fall quietly asleep in the midst of a conversation with his friends, not because of lethargy or overeating but because of the fact that he had been concentrating for as much as fifty continuous hours on a given piece of work. On our trip he was often required to stay up until very late to speak from the rear platform of the train to groups assembled to see the President; or, he had to get up at an unconscionable hour in the morning. In these circumstances most people are in a go-to-hell mood; not Taft. He would come into my compartment, which was next to his, and say, "Jack, how are you feeling this morning?" He would then consume his breakfast and start cheerfully on the day's round of speeches and sightseeing.

Particularly on this trip it was an effort to keep Taft running to schedule. First the politicians would have him speak, and then the real estate men would drive us miles and miles over dusty roads through arid country, just to be able to say that the President had been there. Often after such a wild-goose chase I returned in a state of extreme annoyance, but Taft never said an irritable word; he had the greater capacity for swallowing dust.

At Butte, I was able to show Taft something of the copper mining industry. With his usual sense of humor, he expressed himself as doubtful whether the shaft of the Anaconda mine would be big enough to accommodate him, but I assured him that it was sixteen feet square and I thought we could manage to squeeze him through safely. We packed him into the cage. When we reached the bottom of the mine, I showed him how levels were run and timbered and how the drilling machines cut into the solid rock inch by inch.

Taft had never been in a mine before. He was genuinely interested in observing how mining operations were conducted. I did not try to take him over the thousand miles of underground workings, but I did regale him with what I considered astonishing, though accurate, statistics.

His comment at the end of the trip was that of most individuals: "I had no idea what it meant to get the copper out. I had a vague notion that it could be picked up from the ground. Why, it takes tons of rocks to get a few pounds of copper!"

As a matter of fact, the total metal production to January 1, 1934, of the Anaconda Copper Mining Company, including copper, zinc, lead, silver, and gold, had a value of $2,180,000,000, extracted from 150,000,000 tons of ore. To extract this ore, shafts, levels, raises, and stoping were made to an aggregate length of thirty-three hundred miles, or more than the distance across the continent.

A few years after Taft's visit, the agricultural interests for forty miles around Butte banded together to secure an injunction forcing the company to shut down. They complained that the arsenical and sulphuric fumes were killing all vegetation in that huge area. The company was unable to deny the justice of the accusation, but asked for time in which to make remedial experiments, stating that a complete shutdown would entail hardship for many people.

Remembering his visit to Butte and recognizing that thousands depended for their livelihood on this industry, Taft accepted the suggestion of Attorney General Wickersham and appointed a Fumes Commission to make investigations while the company continued operating. Dr. Louis D. Ricketts represented the Anaconda Mining Company, which eventually paid out hundreds of thousands of dollars in a sincere endeavor to solve the problem. Dr. J. A. Holmes represented the government. When these men asked me to act as chairman of the commission, I was glad to serve for the benefit of the industry.

We employed specialists to carry out the experiments. Among them was Dr. Frederick G. Cottrell, who added greatly to his reputation as a chemist by the success of his experiments, which minimized damage from fumes and became the basis for solving similar problems in other smelting centers.

The functions we performed for the Anaconda Company have since been taken over by the Bureau of Mines. There had been much talk of such a bureau, but nothing had been done about it. The attendant clamor over the conservation movement, however, helped to pass the measure through Congress. In discussing the formation of this bureau, Taft asked me whom I would recommend for the post of director. My first suggestion was the labor leader, John Mitchell, who said he could not accept because of his connection with the unions. I then recommended Dr. Holmes, and Taft appointed him.

The duties of the Bureau of Mines now include the treatment of difficult ores, the disposal of by-products, and the development of safety devices for coal mines.

Incidentally, although I did no selfish lobbying, I have not hesitated to use what influence I possessed in behalf of adequate financial appropriations for scientific bureaus, such as the Smithsonian Institution, the Geodetic Survey, the Geological Survey, and the Bureau of Standards.

In May, 1910, I suggested to the President a Department of Public Works, to control the operation of the Panama Canal, the reclamation of swamps and the irrigation of arid lands, the protection of power sites on public waterways, the administration of the Forestry Bureau, and similar projects. My idea was that this department should have charge of the active work of the government in connection with the natural resources of the country, direct all the government's construction and engineering undertakings, and carry out the conservation policy. Taft was interested, but not overenthusiastic. The plan was opposed by Secretary of the Interior Ballinger, and nothing ever came of it. I still believe this to be a legitimate division of executive control and I hope that something will be done about it. Such a department would be of great service in solving problems incidental to the present period of depression.

In Spokane the President made a great speech on conservation; in my opinion, a better exposition of the subject than any Roosevelt ever made. Taft kept strictly to the problem, showed plainly that he knew what he was talking about, and had not been led to his conclusions by a burst of temporary enthusiasm. The President gave all credit to Roosevelt for the initiation of the policy and put himself squarely on record in favor of conservation.

At Phoenix, Arizona, Taft was offered a drink of water from the nearby Hassayampo River. I tipped him off to the legend that he who drinks of the water of this river can never afterwards tell the truth. But he took the risk. There is in Los Angeles a club of several thousand members, known as the Hassayampo Club, which exploits the legend by using the river water for initiating its members. The club members' high standing for probity in the community, however, would seem to disprove the claim of the potency of the water.

At Albuquerque, New Mexico, there was a reception followed by the usual round of oratory. Among the first speakers on the program was Albert B. Fall, prominently introduced as the "senator from New Mexico" should it be granted statehood. The problem of the moment was the proposed statehood of Arizona and New Mexico. Fall began his speech by saying that everybody had heard about the promises presidents were inclined to make on the spot, but he advised the audience not to bank too heavily upon them. When the President returned to Washington he would probably feel differently about the matter.

The audience was hushed with dismay at this open insult. Taft would have been perfectly justified in taking Fall's action as an affront. Instead, he smilingly said he was reminded of the story of an officious young attorney who attempted to lay down the law to the judge. The exposition was so poor that, instead of helping, it endangered his client's case. When the lawyer finished, the judge said, "In spite of your argument, I decide the case in favor of your client." Then Taft went on to state that Fall's injudicious comments had not prejudiced him against the statehood bill; he was still in favor of it and, indeed, shortly afterwards signed the bill.

Before the presidential party arrived in Texas, it had been arranged that the President of Mexico should meet the President of the United States at El Paso. Diaz, then in his seventy-ninth year, made the long journey from Mexico City to the border. For the first time in history the chief magistrates of the two republics were brought face to face.

Unusual care had to be taken to prevent an attempt on the life of either president. Each man had his special secret service and military guard, and the police of El Paso and Juarez had been given special instructions, but further precautions were thought necessary. Major Burnham, my old friend of South African days, at my request had preceded the President's party and organized a number of experienced men who had been his associates in past years—scouts, cattlemen, and customs guards—to help protect the presidents. He had them sworn in as peace officers.

Along the line of march a census was taken of the residents and occupants of every building that faced the route. This area was divided into sections each of which was put under the command of armed deputies. The people in each section were ordered to close and lock all their doors one hour before the procession. Other deputies, stationed in the rear, were ordered to halt anyone trying to enter or leave. As the procession started and the two presidents rode between the crowded lines of people, a space was constantly cleared on both sides, front and rear, so that it would be difficult to make any attempt at assassination with either bombs or firearms.

The peace officers were instructed to keep their eyes constantly on the crowd rather than on the presidents. There was little danger to be apprehended from those who were smiling or chatting with other people. But, if any deputy caught sight of a drawn and set face, he would signal to the next officer, at the same time quietly edging over beside the suspect. While one deputy would engage the man in conversation, and slip his elbow over his arm, the other officer would quickly run his hands over him for weapons, guns, or packages. Many times the suspect never realized he had been one. Over one hundred weapons were gathered in this way, although none of them may have been intended for purposes of assassination. During the day there was but one fatality: a young Mexican boy drove his knife into the heart of another because his view of the Great Diaz was obstructed.

Major Burnham later told me the details of the elaborate care taken, and there is one curious incident which I shall relate. As Burnham was standing near the entrance of the hotel into which the presidents were about to enter, he saw a sinister-looking man writing in a notebook. He gave the secret signal to another deputy, and they closed in. The deputy slipped his arm through the arm of the suspect and at the same moment Burnham grasped his wrist. Quickly flipping over the busy scribbler's hand, Burnham discovered that the pencil sticking out between the first and second fingers was actually the muzzle of a pistol especially designed to be hidden in the palm of the hand.

Although the man with the gun declared he was a newspaper reporter, he was obliged to finish his story in jail.

The meeting of the two presidents had particular political significance. Trouble was already brewing below the Mexican border. If Taft had been killed on Mexican soil, it would have stirred up a tremendous feeling of bitterness in the United States. If Diaz had been killed on American soil, all of Mexico would have been inflamed. Even if the bullet had been fired by one of their own countrymen the people would have been suspicious and infuriated. There were many revolutionists who would gladly have made an attempt on the life of one or other of the presidents.

Taft and Diaz, with their escorts, met in the middle of the bridge over the Rio Grande. After exchanging courtesies, they drove together through the streets of El Paso. In the afternoon Taft returned the visit. Secretary Knox, Archie Butt, and I accompanied him to Juarez to call on the great dictator. When Taft was taking his leave, Diaz asked me to stay and have a chat with him; he assured Taft that I would be conducted back safely.

This was my last meeting with the Eagle of Mexico. His hair was now white, closely cropped, and as in his earlier days, brushed straight up on his well-shaped head. His eyes were still dark, unblinking yet not unkind, bright and full of spirit.

I told him how delighted I was to see him looking so well. He replied that his health was still good, but nothing could alter the fact that he was growing old and rapidly approaching the point where he would lose the grip on affairs that he had maintained so long. He was desperately worried about conditions in Mexico and felt unable to cope with them.

"Mr. Hammond, I should like so much to be able to resign and travel through your great country before I die. However, it seems impossible. I thought I had prepared for my retirement by selecting Ramon Corral as vice-president and my successor, but he is not popular with the people.

"My friends have begged me," he continued, "not to give up office at present. Since I am responsible for the investment of hundreds of millions of dollars of foreign capital in my country, I feel that I must remain at my post until I can secure a competent successor. My chief trouble today is from men whom I have established as governors and other high officials. I am afraid they are taking advantage of the fact that I am too old to get about and ascertain for myself just what they are doing."

After a pleasant hour of informal conversation, he sent me back to El Paso in his own carriage.

The same evening Diaz entertained President Taft's party with an elaborate banquet at Juarez, served on massive old silver plate brought from Mexico City.

After the banquet we returned to our train. Exhausted by the nervous strain of worrying over the safety of two presidents, Archie Butt and I settled into our seats. Like Diaz, Taft had gone through the ceremonies with complete unconcern. He now commented: "You and Archie seem to have been jumpy all day, Jack. What's the trouble? Perhaps a highball would steady you."

Before answering, we gulped down the offered highballs. With a sigh of relief, I then said: "Thank God we're out of Mexico and the day's over. We've been half crazy for fear somebody'd take a shot at you."

"Oh," Taft replied, "is that what's been bothering you? Why should you have worried about that? If anyone wanted to get me, he couldn't very well have missed such an easy target."

CHAPTER TWENTY-EIGHT

Diaz~Taft

WHAT DIAZ DID FOR MEXICO—THE DICTATOR'S DOWNFALL—WILSON'S VIEW OF THE MEXICAN PROBLEM—CANADIAN RECIPROCITY—THE PANAMA CANAL TOLL BILL—BANKING REFORM—TRUST BUSTING—THE RIFT BETWEEN TAFT AND ROOSEVELT—THE POLITIC THING TO DO—A CONVENTION OR A RIOT?—BIRTH OF THE BULL MOOSE—THE GRAND OLD PARTY GOES DOWN TO DEFEAT— TAFT'S NOBLE CAREER AS CHIEF JUSTICE

*T*he Mexican situation was most troublesome to Taft. Almost against his will, he was forced to take cognizance of it. His heart was set on other matters. Canadian reciprocity; banking reforms; the just and wise program he had hoped to carry out to improve domestic affairs were his most immediate concerns. The accumulating danger of trouble on our southern border could not be ignored, however. Mexico was both unstable in character and uncertain in government as my own experience in that country had vividly demonstrated.

Diaz once said to me, "If I could only impress on my people the value of time—as you say in your country, 'time is money'—the development of Mexico would proceed with unparalleled strides."

His critics have said that Diaz mistook the tangible wealth of the country for its welfare, and that its prosperity was one-sided and confined to a small part of the population. Diaz himself recognized this, and was troubled by it, but the fault was not entirely his. Not much improvement in material conditions can be possible so long as the character of the people is what it is.

Industrialism came as a great shock to Mexico. The mestizos and the pure Indians are not conditioned for the exacting demands of modern civilization. They live slowly. The sort of work that Cecil Rhodes drove through in Africa is entirely outside their comprehension, and any dictator who drives them invariably alienates himself from his people. Probably more than any other people in the world they believe that what was good enough for their grandfathers is good enough for them. Even Calles, years later, in his fight to end peonage and to raise his people from actual starvation was able to accomplish little because of the tremendous inertia of chronic racial weaknesses.

Diaz's accomplishment, in spite of three centuries of misrule, was extraordinary, and in my opinion stands without parallel in modern times. Praise is due also to the genius of his finance minister, José Yves Limantour, who, laboring under great difficulties, put the currency on a sound basis and found funds to finance the great projects of the president.

Diaz by main force dragged his people from the darkness of oppression and drew them towards progress. Some idea of the magnitude of his achievements may be gained from the following facts:

Before his presidency there were scarcely any railroads or telegraph lines; one of his first acts was to build thousands of miles of railroads and a network of telegraph lines. There was neither order nor due process of law anywhere and bandits swarmed unrestrained over the countryside. He set up courts of justice and enforced their decrees with inflexible honesty. He formed the rurales, a military police force which cleared the country of highwaymen and public malefactors of every sort. He opened ports, instituted a postal system, built schools, encouraged manufactures, established banks, introduced modern agriculture and industrial methods, patronized the fine arts, supported the professions, and won world-wide confidence in the integrity and good faith of his government. Above all, he fostered trade and commerce by inviting foreign capital to invest in Mexico's great mineral, oil, and agrarian resources.

When he became president in 1877, the country was bankrupt. He left it solvent, with a large reserve, nor did he squeeze this surplus out of the peons as is often supposed. It came directly from the profits derived from foreign investors, and the peons, an incompetent class in the history of Mexico, have never been so well off as under his intelligent and farseeing dictatorship. He made Mexico respected among nations.

With all his accomplishments, however, Diaz overlooked the necessity for the organization and encouragement of liberal groups in politics. Always aware of the general ignorance and excitable temperament of his countrymen, ninety per cent of whom were illiterate, he had felt obliged to suppress all criticism of his government with an iron hand.

As time went on, and the dictator became wholly absorbed in his great schemes for the development of Mexico, his early attitude toward liberal thinkers crystallized into unconscious opposition. He was essentially a man of action; an executive, not a doctrinaire. Like his favorite hero, Bismarck, he had little time or inclination for political philosophy. As a consequence, he came to lean more and more upon the cientificos, or wealthy business men, and to lose contact with the mass of the people.

These cientificos were advocates of modern methods in industry and business. A controlling proportion of them did not, however, apply this scientific progressivism to the government itself. Their attitude towards their own country was in many cases almost entirely self-seeking. The members of this corrupt faction used their influence to bribe officials and to obtain concessions by other dishonest means. In time, they succeeded in completely undermining the morale of the domestic administration Diaz had so carefully built up. Government patronage became the chief source of their prosperity; by a widespread system of interlocking directorates these moneyed men, who should have been the first to lend their support to the government, soon came to exert a sinister influence which in the end brought about its downfall and their own as well.

Diaz eventually realized the harmful nature of this unprincipled element, but it was too late.

In 1911 revolution broke out. The various elements of political thought, which for years had been undergoing a process of fermentation, had united under Francisco I. Madero, a sincere idealist, who was resolved to shake off the grip of the capitalistic government.

The dictator, old, infirm, and entirely out of touch with public sentiment, could not this time suppress a movement which, while ill-advised, represented a genuine conviction on the part of many of the younger generation that Mexico was being mismanaged. Early in his administration he had seen to it that trusted subordinates had been made governors of the various states. These men had been pledged to carry out his policies and to keep him informed. They did neither of these things.

When the revolutionists broke out of Durango and Chihuahua in the north into the more populous south, Diaz vainly endeavored to conciliate them by passing the government on to a successor in orderly fashion. But the Maderistas would have none of this, and on May 11, 1911, he was obliged to lay down unconditionally the power he had held so long.

Though recognizing his defeat, Diaz retained his old courage. When he was being escorted out of the country, his car was held up temporarily on the way to Vera Cruz and a mob of his political enemies threatened his life. It was with the greatest difficulty that this man of eighty-one could be restrained by his friends. Single-handed he wanted to tackle the crowd who were hurling insults at him. No one not conscious of his own rectitude would have dared this.

True to his sterling integrity and honesty, Diaz left office without having laid by a competency for a rainy day. However corrupt his underlings may have been, he himself will always be free of the accusation of graft. He did not run off with the contents of the treasury, as has been the recognized habit of deposed Latin-American presidents. Secretary of State Lansing, who married the daughter of John W. Foster, former minister to Mexico, assured me that the State Department had made a careful examination of Mexican finances and was convinced that the treasury had not been looted; on the contrary, it contained a surplus when Diaz left.

For the four remaining years of Diaz's life, he was supported in Paris largely by the contributions of friends. He died in 1915 at the age of eighty-five. His last words were, "My poor Mexico."

The Mexican revolution of 1911 placed Taft in a difficult position. The lives of many Americans were likely to be endangered by civil war. Furthermore, American citizens had been killed by Mexican bullets fired from across the border, and consequently in the United States a clamor for intervention had already arisen. Taft stated that he did not feel called upon to intervene, but as a precaution ordered the mobilization of twenty thousand troops to guard the Texan border.

His recognition of Madero as constitutional president did not bring peace in Mexico. Madero was impractical and weak and could not control his military leaders. When they began fighting among themselves, Taft put an embargo on the shipment of arms and munitions to Mexico in an effort to deprive them of the means for shedding blood.

In March, 1911, a commercial and industrial congress of the South was celebrated at Atlanta. Taft and Woodrow Wilson, then governor of New Jersey, were there. Incidentally, and with prophetic vision unsuspected by himself, Taft in his speech referred pleasantly to Wilson as the next president.

I returned to Washington on the train with Governor Wilson. We spent the early part of the evening in the drawing room occupied by my wife and myself. I always found Wilson personally charming, and this evening proved no exception. After a pleasant chat he asked to see me alone, saying he wished to discuss with me the President's policy in Mexico, with which he did not agree. We adjourned to the club car.

"In what respect," I inquired, "do you disagree with the President?"

"I think he is making a great mistake in sending troops to the border. What concern is it of ours what Mexico does about her internal affairs?"

"But suppose the President has certain information which you have not? For instance, there may be serious trouble down there in which American lives will be endangered, as well as the lives of foreigners who, under the implication of the Monroe Doctrine, look to the United States for protection. Shouldn't the President be prepared for such a contingency?"

"Now that you've explained it," admitted Wilson, "I can see how the presence of troops might be necessary, but—"

"Then what would you have done in his place?" I asked.

"I would have moved troops in secret, not to the border, but to points within striking distance," replied Wilson.

"But how could that be done without the Mexicans' knowledge? Secrecy would defeat your purpose by giving Mexico ground for suspicion about our intentions. Taft has sent troops openly to protect Americans at the border."

Wilson must have been troubled by the Mexican problem during the night, because he awakened the other passengers with an unearthly Princeton yell. His discussion with a Yale man might have been partly responsible.

Next morning I breakfasted at the White House—Taft had returned by special train—and related my conversation with Wison.

Taft gave the well-known chuckle and said, "I wish he had the Mexican problem on his hands."

Two years later Wilson inherited it.

February 18, 1913, Victoriano Huerta overthrew the Madero government.

A few days before the inauguration of Wilson I gave a dinner to a number of foreign ambassadors in honor of Sir Cecil Spring-Rice at my home in Washington. There were present Bakhmetiev, Jusserand, Bernstorff, Cusani, and Dumba. They had an enjoyable time together, recalling their early friendships as young secretaries in the various embassies of Europe, and addressing each other familiarly as Springy, Baky, Bernie, and Cusi.

Toward the end of the evening the conversation turned to Mexico, and I was asked whether or not President Taft would recognize Huerta.

I replied that the President would leave the recognition of Huerta to "old man Wilson" as he called him.

"Though," I added, "the President has no doubt that Wilson will share his views and recognize Huerta."

Since that seemed the logical policy for our government, all these diplomats hastened to cable their governments. Thereupon Huerta was recognized by all the powers represented at this dinner.

But to the surprise of all Europe, the United States never recognized him. Wilson could not stand the "unspeakable Huerta" and pursued his fatal policy of "watchful waiting."

Before Taft went out of office he offered to give Wilson the benefit of his wide experience and to make suggestions as to how the Mexican situation might be handled. Wilson brusquely let Taft know that he did not care for advice and was prepared to handle the matter in his own way.

My own familiarity with Mexican conditions led me to consider that because of Wilson's failure to recognize Huerta, Taft's over-scrupulousness in deferring to Wilson had proved a mistake. Huerta was at least president de facto and I think should have been given the support of recognition by our government. Moreover, he was at this time friendly to the United States and willing to negotiate for a settlement of our claims against Mexico.

In 1911, at the time of the coronation of George V, I was dining with the King when he received word of Diaz's expulsion from Mexico. At the end of our conversation he said, "Mark my words—Mexico's troubles are just beginning."

In 1924, I was lunching with His Majesty at the Ascot races when he received word of the murder of a British subject by Mexicans. He was visibly affected, and asked, "Mr. Hammond, do you recall my prophecy of twelve years ago about Mexico?"

"Of course," I replied.

"It's come true," he affirmed. "Even after all these years of banditry they haven't a government strong enough to protect the lives of British subjects."

In spite of the time and thought required by the Mexican situation, Taft made great efforts at this time to establish reciprocity with our neighbor to the north. In exchange for the abolition of duties on agricultural products, Canada was to give us free entry for our industrial products. The President was aware, more than most of our statesmen have been, that co-operation and friendship with Canada would be one of the strongest guaranties of our own safety and of the peace of the world.

Philander C. Knox had the idea that, if this treaty were to go through, the friendship between Canada and the United States would be cemented so firmly that a closer Anglo-American accord would naturally follow.

After a long battle against a hostile Congress, Taft succeeded in pushing through a bill to attain this end. In the course of this struggle I was on two occasions asked to serve as unofficial messenger to Premier Wilfrid Laurier and to Governor General Lord Grey, whom I had known intimately when he was an officer of the Chartered Company in the old South African days.

Laurier warned me that the Canadians were extremely sensitive, and asked me to caution Taft "against creating any impression that there is political significance in this treaty. My political opponents are trying to make that an issue."

There was also considerable antagonism on the part of our farmers of the border states. They feared that Canadian agricultural products would flood their normal home markets under reciprocity. This seems to me to have been sectional shortsightedness, because in a few years industries would have sprung up near the border to supply Canada with manufactured goods, and these new centers of population would have furnished nearer and better markets for the farmers. But the people of the agricultural regions could not look ahead.

After Taft had won a hard-earned victory in the American Congress, he was destined to meet defeat at Ottawa. Premier Laurier was in favor of the idea, but opposition rapidly piled up because of incautious newspaper remarks in the United States concerning annexation. The result was that when Canada refused to pass a reciprocity bill, this country considered its friendly gesture had been churlishly received.

As Taft's administration drew to a close in 1912 the question came up as to tolls to be charged for passage through the Panama Canal, which was shortly to be opened. Taft's view, as expressed to Congress, was that, since we owned the canal and since our money had built it, and since foreign governments subsidized their merchant vessels, it was right for us to remit enough on the tolls to our vessels to make up the difference. Also, he thought that coastwise shipping was entirely a domestic matter; as foreign shipping was not allowed to participate in this trade, the United States was merely regulating its own commerce.

Great Britain at once pointed to the clause in the Hay-Pauncefote Treaty which said the canal should be free and open to the vessels of commerce and of war of all nations on terms of entire equality "so that there shall be no discrimination against any such nation, or its citizens, or subjects, in respect to the conditions or charges of traffic or otherwise."

Taft stuck to his interpretation in spite of outbursts of indignation abroad.

A few months later I was talking with Lady Pauncefote, whose husband had negotiated with Hay the treaty which is known by their joint names.

"Of course," she said, "you agree with the stand President Taft has taken on the Canal Tolls question."

"I don't know anything about its legal equity," I answered. "I haven't studied the question particularly, and therefore I suppose I agree with the President."

"Well, he's wrong," she asserted.

"How do you know?"

"Because my husband came back after he had made the treaty and boasted he had outtraded Hay on this point."

Congress finally passed the tolls bill with the coastwise exemption clause, although such lawyers as Joseph H. Choate expressed disapproval. Wilson, who, it is said, had in his early career been touched with Anglophobia, stood in the 1912 election for the bill. Indeed, the Democratic platform itself advocated the exemption of tolls for American vessels. Afterwards Wilson gave in to vociferous English objections and had the clause repealed. This action, he said, "was in accord with justice."

Banking reform was another question constantly agitated during

THEODORE ROOSEVELT (1858-1919)

THE REPUBLICAN NATIONAL CONVENTION, 1912

Taft's four years. During this time the principles and framework of what eventually became Wilson's Federal Reserve Act had been carefully worked out, although the opposition of the insurgent elements was sufficiently strong to prevent its passage.

The actual movement for a unified banking system had begun with the great banking crash of 1907, when banks all over the country suspended payments and had to issue irredeemable currency to meet their obligations.

Senator Aldrich had been profoundly impressed with the idea that something should be done about the banking situation. He introduced and secured the passage of a bill to form a Federal Monetary Commission. At this time Aldrich was beginning to feel the need of accomplishing some great constructive work before leaving office. He was becoming sensitive at being called the head of the System and a reactionary. He bought books and pictures of Sir Robert Peel and Alexander Hamilton, whom he took as his financial mentors.

When the commission was formed, Aldrich took care that no other member should be chosen for his special knowledge of banking. They sailed for Europe to study the banking systems there. On arriving he scattered most of the members of the commission to look over banks wherever they wished. Then—with Henry P. Davison, of the J. P. Morgan firm, George Reynolds, a leading Chicago banker, and A. Piatt Andrew, Jr., assistant professor of economics at Harvard—he interviewed every important banker in London, Paris, and Berlin. He came home with the idea that the American trouble was due to lack of common organization and a common pool of resources. Ours was the only system subject to disastrous panics.

About a year and a half afterwards Davison took six influential bankers down to Jekyll Island off Georgia and there they worked morning, noon, and night for two weeks, whipping a banking bill into shape.

Just at this moment Taft was elected president. He first offered the Treasury post to George Reynolds, who had accepted to all intents and purposes when Taft went off on a trip to the Panama Canal. On his return he learned that when Reynolds informed his bank directors they promptly doubled his salary; consequently, he turned down the Cabinet position.

In the few days that remained before the inauguration, Taft was in a quandary about this appointment. I was in favor of Myron T. Herrick, of Cleveland. Taft finally offered the post to Franklin MacVeagh, who had a wholesale grocery business in Chicago and whose visionary ideas of reform had brought him a certain prominence. Taft wanted someone from the West, and he thought MacVeagh's innocuousness would probably have brought him but few enemies. He had formerly run for the Senate on the Democratic ticket and this was a Republican administration, but the slight anomaly was overlooked.

Taft was increasingly interested in banking reform, but as circumstances worked out his hands were tied. Aldrich naturally looked askance at the impractical MacVeagh, while MacVeagh regarded Aldrich as a sort of antichrist. The result was an impasse, made definite when a Democratic Congress was returned in the 1910 mid-term elections.

As soon as Wilson came in, he called a special session of Congress to put through the Federal Reserve Act, which in almost every way coincided with the Aldrich bill which failed of passage under Taft.

On October 26, 1911, proceedings were begun against the United States Steel Corporation, charging it with being a monopoly, particularly because of its purchase of the Tennessee Coal and Iron Company. This purchase had been made with Roosevelt's sanction during the panic of 1907. I believed with Roosevelt at the time that it was for the national interest that this amalgamation should be consummated.

Mark Sullivan says—in *Our Times*—this was the most important of all the suggested causes of the split between Taft and Roosevelt. The initiation of the suit implied that either Roosevelt had been deceived by the financiers or had been in league with them: "making me out either a fool or a knave," as Roosevelt expressed it. It was not until March, 1920, that the Supreme Court finally absolved the Steel Corporation, "a year after Roosevelt, long since purged of his bitterness toward Taft, had died."

Attorney General Wickersham made the statement, at a White

House luncheon in 1911, that he had started more antitrust suits during the three years Taft had been in office than Roosevelt had in his seven years.

I could not refrain from saying, "George, I don't see any reason for being proud of that record."

I realized that political expediency might require the policy, and understood his aspirations as attorney general to institute more antitrust suits than his predecessor; but it has never been clear to me whether the overrigorous antitrust campaign was forced by the insurgents, or whether it was Attorney General Wickersham's own idea of his duty.

After forty years under the Sherman Anti-Trust Act, the country has now decided that corporations and combinations are by no means the unmitigated evils the reformers of 1890 thought them. Theodore Roosevelt used to distinguish between good and bad trusts. I agree with Franklin Delano Roosevelt, who wisely recognizes the necessity of "combinations in restraint of trade" to prevent the overproduction in agriculture and industry and the evils of cutthroat competition.

In the many party speeches I made between 1908 and 1920, I took the stand that the development of American business and commerce could be carried on most economically if large-scale operation were permitted. Overexpansion beyond the point of economic efficiency would be checked by the operation of economic laws, and much more wisely than by demagogues. Corporations should be judged, not by their magnitude but by their dominant purpose, and their methods, and the manner in which these affect the public welfare.

I suggested that federal incorporation or federal licensing would serve to control one of the chief evils of big business: overcapitalization. No one was more interested than I in destroying dishonest business, but I believed that the ballyhoo of the trust buster was not accomplishing much towards the welfare of industry. Nor, in the end, was the muckraking which came as an aftermath of Roosevelt's period of business reform of much assistance.

In my opinion the animus of Theodore Roosevelt against Taft was at the bottom personal. The rift in the fine friendship had been slowly widening, although I do not recall any one action on the part of Taft which Roosevelt could have construed as a specific personal affront. Until November, 1911, neither had made any public remarks against the other.

But zealots, such as Pinchot, and disappointed friends, such as Garfield, started in almost from the day of the inauguration to work against Taft. Pinchot rushed it abroad to meet Roosevelt when he came out of the wilds of Africa and poured into his ear his own version of the Ballinger episode and accused Taft of being hand in glove with Roosevelt's old enemies in the Senate and House, particularly Aldrich and Cannon.

Roosevelt could never understand Taft's way of doing things. Because Taft felt himself compelled to work with the System, Roosevelt thought he had abandoned the policies they had worked for together. Taft had not changed this program. He was deeply hurt by what he regarded as Roosevelt's unjustifiable coolness and, in his outspoken manner, allowed his friends to hear his comments. These, of course, were promptly reported to Roosevelt, and Roosevelt's were carried to Taft.

The cleavage was clearly marked in June, 1910, when Roosevelt called on Taft at Beverly. I had a faint hope that this meeting might bring the two men closer together, but the conversation never veered from the impersonal. When I saw Taft the following day, he told me of his deep disappointment at the outcome of the meeting. I expressed my regret but also my fear of difficult times ahead in politics.

From my own experience with Roosevelt, I realized how misunderstandings with him could arise in the most unaccountable manner. Shortly after his return from Africa, he made many speeches in New York State on behalf of the Republican party. The National League of Republican Clubs held a meeting at Carnegie Hall in New York City at which Roosevelt was to speak. When he arrived, he was hoarse from his other speeches and asked me in introducing him to express his regret at not being able to make himself heard.

I concluded my introduction with what I considered a pleasant tribute. "I wish to make an apology for the colonel. His voice is bad and you might find it difficult to hear him. But even the 'whisper' of Theodore Roosevelt can be heard around the world."

Roosevelt unfortunately mistook the sentiment I wished to convey. He left the platform without shaking hands with me. As soon as I learned that he was offended I hastened to explain.

He put his arm across my shoulders and said: "Your introduction was most complimentary. I misunderstood at the time what you meant."

My high regard for many of Theodore Roosevelt's admirable traits did not in any way mitigate my disapproval of what I have always considered his unfair treatment of Taft in connection with Taft's acts during his term of office.

A few years ago a well-known newspaper correspondent in Washington, a friend of both Roosevelt and Taft, told me of something that happened just before Roosevelt threw his hat in the ring for the 1912 presidential nomination. It admirably illustrates the difference between the two men. Roosevelt was making a trip through the West. A rousing reception was given him in Wyoming, and a long line of admirers passed to shake hands and greet him.

The reporter, who was standing by Roosevelt's side, whispered that a certain man approaching was a great admirer of the colonel, who undoubtedly remembered him.

The colonel whispered back, "No, I can't recall him."

"He's been at the White House, and lunched with you. His name's Watson."

"Oh yes, I know who he is now. How many children has he?"

"Five. No, he has six—another was born just a few days ago."

When Watson reached Roosevelt, both his hands were grasped and pumped heartily up and down. "My dear fellow, I'm so glad to see you again. I shall never forget the delightful hour we spent together in Washington. How are those five, oh no, I believe you have six children now?"

Watson, who was popular and politically influential in Wyoming, was from that moment an ardent Rooseveltian.

A few months after Roosevelt's tour, the same correspondent went to Seattle with Taft. He was again serving as unofficial introducer. He recognized an old Taft admirer approaching, and whispered, "Mr. President, there's a man approaching whom you certainly remember?"

"No, I don't. What's his name?"

The reporter murmured it in his ear.

Taft reiterated, "No, I don't seem to place him."

"Why, he's dined with you at the White House."

When the man's turn came, Taft took his hand in a friendly way and beamed upon him as he said, "They tell me I ought to remember you but, bless my soul, I cannot recall you at all!"

The former Taft admirer, who was a prominent politician in the state of Washington, went away and turned his strength against Taft.

On one subject Taft and I held decidedly opposite views and I was never able to convince him that I was right. This was the question of woman suffrage. I felt that, aside from expediency, women were entitled to the ballot and for years I had stood for equal rights. Even when the movement was still unpopular I often made speeches in its favor and told my audiences that the franchise for women was not a utopian ideal, and that, in spite of the popular contention to that effect, I did not believe woman would be giving up her prerogatives for her rights.

One afternoon, just before the convention of 1912, after lunching with Taft at the White House, I met a Washington newspaper correspondent who was a loyal friend to the President.

"Is there any truth," he asked, "in the rumor that the President is going to issue a statement that he will make no fight for renomination?"

"Why do you ask that?"

"Well," he said, "the newspaper boys believe it and they're about to give it semipublicity."

"On the contrary," I replied, "I can assure you that, while it is utterly distasteful to him to make that kind of a fight, he told me he was in it to a finish."

My statement was immediately made public. That evening I went to New York for a few days.

When I saw Taft, he said, "Jack, when did I tell you that I was in the fight to a finish?"

I explained to him that as a matter of fact he never had used just those words, but that, knowing him and knowing that he wasn't a quitter, I had merely anticipated his expression. If he had said anything, he would have said that.

He chuckled and said, "Perhaps you exceeded your authority, but it has worked out very well."

Taft then showed me a great pile of letters and telegrams he had received from his Republican friends and partisans, in which they congratulated him for his courageous stand and assured him that they promised undying loyalty since he was in the fight and would not give up.

A few days later, after New York State had elected a delegation favorable to Taft but not actually pledged to him, I was with him and a friend who said, "Mr. President, it must have been a great gratification to you, the way you secured the New York delegation and humiliated Roosevelt in his own state."

Taft replied, seriously: "You're wrong. While the victory is gratifying, it is also heart-rending, because the last thing in the world I wish to do is to humble Theodore Roosevelt. I owe him my nomination and election to the presidency. In spite of what has happened, he is very dear to me."

On November 16, 1911, Roosevelt came out in open warfare against Taft. It soon began to be evident that he would contest the nomination at Chicago the following June. Hughes, who had never been an avowed aspirant, dropped out of the race early. La Follette's attempt to float a Progressive movement, with himself as leader, had failed, for every Progressive preferred Roosevelt. La Follette was used merely as a stalking horse for the greater man and was unceremoniously discarded when he had served this purpose. Roosevelt was as necessary to the Progressive movement as Hamlet is to the play.

Even before the first session of the 1912 convention at Chicago, it was evident that one of the most dramatic events in our political history was about to take place. People were pouring into the city from north, south, east, and west. Hotels were jammed and on the streets were surging throngs. Roosevelt was unable to resist the call of the wild. When a voice from the cheering mob yelled, "How are you feeling this morning, Colonel?" he shouted back, "I'm feeling like a bull moose!"

A little later the stampede for Roosevelt began: it was called the Bull Moose movement.

I was at the Blackstone Hotel. It was so packed that sometimes it took me twenty minutes to make my way through the lobby. I was up very late, often all night, because the real work both before and during conventions is done behind the scenes in the hotel rooms.

According to my custom, I was not a delegate myself. I was, therefore, not subject to the duties of a delegate, such as being compelled to attend innumerable caucuses or be on hand for roll call. This left me master of my own time, and I could use my influence wherever it seemed to me most advantageous.

The convention itself was held in the big sprawling Auditorium on Michigan Avenue, the scene of most Republican conventions. The available seating capacity for spectators was far from sufficient to accommodate the thousands seeking entrance. It was attended by a great number of visitors who had obtained seats through influence with delegates and who followed the proceedings as intently as the delegates did. Some came to see the spectacle for itself; others, the nomination of the candidate; still others were interested in certain planks of the party platform to be adopted.

My wife and I sat in the box of my old friend, Fred Upham, near the stage. Upham was assistant treasurer of the Republican party, which position he had held for many years. Anywhere from thirty to forty people would be crowded in the box at one time. We hardly dared leave the scene of the excitement for fear we might miss something. Pages scurried in and out with food.

We could look down on the tumult. Balconies and boxes flaunted bunting, banners, and pictures of white hopes and dark horses. From galleries and floor came intermittent and inexplicable bursts of applause and song. The din was such that it was difficult at times to hear the speakers on the platform.

The great fight came over the choice of a permanent chairman. If Elihu Root were elected, it would assure Taft's nomination. One by one the contested Taft delegations were seated, and the regulars of the Grand Old Party assumed complete control. The galleries were filled with Roosevelt followers who kept up an incessant cry,

"We want Teddy! We want Teddy!" Senator Jonathan Bourne, of Oregon, had organized this claque.

One now sees in retrospect that the campaign was doomed to end in the defeat of the Republican party. As president of the League of Republican Clubs, I took an active part. Thinking back on the speeches I made, I seem to have spent much more energy in declaiming against Roosevelt than in attacking Wilson.

One reason for that may be found in the fact that Roosevelt was trumpeting challenges which we were forced to answer in kind. Not for him were the insubstantial platitudes of ordinary politics. Though he had fought to lead the whole party in June, as head of the Progressives he was forced to identify himself completely with their radical program. His attack on the political machine coincided with public indignation, and could not be rebutted, since we, too, were saying that the evils of bossism were indefensible. His advocacy of radical principles, particularly the shocking proposal for the recall of judicial decisions, gave us a better weapon, and we used it.

In a calmer moment I would not have complained of the ruthless domination that was characteristic of Roosevelt. Moral force is too rare in this world to be overnicely criticized when it does appear. And I am glad that I did not join with those who referred to paranoias, dementias, and other terrifying psychoses. In describing the "archdeceiver" I did rise once to a poetic quotation:

> "He is the one political Don Juan, who, like the lover in the play, 'speaks the kindest words and looks such things, vows with such passion, and swears with such a grace, that it is Heaven to be deluded by him!'"

I was no defeatist. I insisted in public that Taft would be elected, although I had private misgivings. I was sure the public would not choose Roosevelt but, even so, I had overestimated its intelligence. I said there was no danger that Roosevelt would hurt the party; but he did—he elected Wilson.

What might have happened had Taft been elected is idle speculation. But it seems to me a reasonable supposition that, if Roosevelt had stayed with the party in 1912, he himself would have been nominated and elected by the Republicans in 1916. He would have been an ideal president for the period and, when we finally entered the war, we would have been adequately prepared. There is no doubt that Roosevelt would have much preferred to be a war president for one term than a peace president in perpetuity.

I think Taft was genuinely glad he did not have to assume the burden of another four years in the White House. He had been much distressed by the campaign of personal vilification introduced by Roosevelt.

When Roosevelt and Taft ultimately buried the hatchet and became privately as well as publicly reconciled, Taft came to see me immediately, saying, "I know, Jack, you will be delighted to hear this."

It always gave Taft deep satisfaction to know that this painful quarrel ended before Roosevelt's untimely death.

I have a letter from Theodore Roosevelt dated January 2, 1919. It reached me just after I had read in the newspaper of his death and it must have been among the last he wrote. He wished my wife and me a Happy New Year.

Taft's pleasures were simple, golf and conversation being his chief diversions. He had little time for reading except when he was at Murray Bay in the summer, and then he read mostly biography. Once in a great while he would read a novel, but unlike many of our presidents he never read a detective story. One of his enthusiasms was Patricia Wentworth's historical romance, *The Devil's Wind*. He went rarely to the theater but had violent prejudices for and against the plays he saw.

One day when he was chief justice, Taft and I were walking across the Connecticut Avenue Bridge—now called Taft Bridge, in the renaming of which I was influential. He said, "Jack, do you know what I would like to do this afternoon?"

"Probably play golf," I answered.

"That is out of the question. I would like to see some good play that is free of all sex stuff, something like *Old English* or *Disraeli*. I saw George Arliss in both plays and liked them. I would enjoy something as good as those."

I wrote this to my friend Arliss and he replied that he was highly gratified and hoped that Taft and I would see the moving picture *Disraeli,* which he considered better than the stage play. Excellent as it is, I am not sure that I agree with him.

In some ways I think now that Taft was too straightforward and too high-minded to be a successful politician. These qualities, unless they are coupled with political sophistication, are often detrimental to individual advancement in public life. Taft was one of the truest sportsmen we have ever had in American politics. He took his defeat for re-election philosophically and smilingly, which did much to endear him to the American people.

But when President Harding appointed him chief justice of the Supreme Court in 1921, the country applauded this choice, and he himself rejoiced at the attainment of his life's ambition. His intellectual power and broad knowledge of national and world affairs admirably fitted him for this position. His Lincolnian geniality and charm, which had won admiration and friendship even from those who had been his political enemies, brought a mellower tone to the somewhat austere atmosphere of the bench.

He was without pose and without the craft of the demagogue, and was never guilty of self-stultification. In the few remaining years of his civic service, the debated issues of his presidency were forgotten and he became once more the well-loved Taft who was to possess a permanent place in the affections of the American people.

CHAPTER TWENTY-NINE

Pageantry Before War

TWO SPECIAL DIPLOMATIC MISSIONS—EUROPE
JUST BEFORE THE WORLD WAR—PRECORONATION
FUNCTIONS—SHAKESPEARE BALL—GEORGE V IS
CROWNED—I AM GREETED BY SOUTH AFRICAN
FRIENDS—ON THE ROYAL YACHT—PILGRIM SOCIETY
DINNER—PLANS FOR CELEBRATION OF PANAMA
CANAL — LONDON, BERLIN, ST. PETERSBURG, VIENNA, ROME —
EMPEROR FRANCIS JOSEPH—VICTOR EMMANUEL III
OF ITALY — PANAMA-PACIFIC INTERNATIONAL EXPOSITION

*I*n 1911 and 1912 I had the good fortune to travel over practically all of Europe on two special diplomatic missions. The exceptional advantages this afforded naturally could not be appreciated by me at the time. I visited the capitals of England, Germany, Russia, Austria, Hungary, Italy, France, and other countries. There I met and talked with many people who were vitally to affect the tragic history of the next decade, and I saw things of immediate and subsequent significance. Moreover, although it was entirely unpremeditated, I was able to amplify my background in world economic conditions and politics and to establish contacts which were invaluable to me later when I became engaged in aiding various efforts to found machinery for international arbitration and the maintenance of world peace.

Europe was still colorful with the pageantry of court life and, on the surface at least, was secure, even gay. Prosperity was unequaled. The average man was troubled by only the usual vexations of living. In the pubs in London, the beer gardens in Berlin, the famous restaurants of Vienna,.and the Paris cafés there certainly was no sign of tension. Everywhere there was music, cheer, even complacency.

Yet in the midst of the coronation of George V—the most magnificent England has ever seen, in the official dinners and balls following, and later at the state functions and at the courts of various European capitals which received the members of the Panama-Pacific Commission one might have detected warning notes of political unrest; an unconsidered and truculent remark by the crown prince of Germany, undertones of hostility in Berlin, Count Witte, Russia's greatest statesman, ignored, discouraged, and removed from power by the sycophantic court at St. Petersburg; all this escaped us in the movement and drama of the current scene and seemed important only as we looked at it in retrospect from 1914.

In 1911, President Taft appointed me special ambassador to represent the United States at the coronation, to take place June 22nd. My staff was made up of Rear Admiral Charles E. Vreeland as naval aide; Major General A. W. Greely, the arctic explorer, military aide; and as secretary we had W. Earle Dodge.

My old friend, Mr. Burdett-Coutts, had sent word that he was definitely planning to turn over to us his house at No. 1 Stratton Street. The British government would, of course, have furnished an embassy for the occasion, but we accepted this offer because we realized that it was made not only in token of warm family friendship, but as a tribute to America. It was more than a mere gesture.

The demand for lodgings of any kind in London was unprecedented. Houses were bringing thousands of pounds for a fortnight's rental. One advertisement read: "Room B—handsome well-furnished room with bastion window at corner of St. James's Street and Piccadilly, commanding complete view of the street as procession turns at the corner, and a triple window in Piccadilly, price 200 guineas first day." But our host refused to accept a penny for the use of his home.

I sailed on the *Cedric* early in June and arrived some days before the rest of my party. It was necessary to get my family settled and also to obtain a wardrobe appropriate for the various functions. The latter was no easy matter. We were met at the steamer and conducted to London by our friend, William Phillips, secretary of the American Embassy, whose unfailing kindness and efficiency contributed much to the success of the mission.

We installed ourselves at No. 1 Stratton Street—overlooking the beautiful gardens of Devonshire House—where in the past my wife and I had visited Baroness Burdett-Coutts so many times.

While we were in residence, our official standing was indicated by a sentry box occupied by one of the Royal Guard, with scarlet jacket, black trousers, a pipe-clayed belt, all topped off with a two-foot busby.

In the main hall was another sentry box, framing the figure of Hallett, the hall porter, who used to hop in and out so briskly that the children called him the tree toad.

The Burdett-Coutts home was filled with treasures, and the friends who visited us confessed that they were no longer eager to see the museums of London; they would seem dull by comparison. The presence of several healthy youngsters in the midst of all these rare and antique objects offered dangerous possibilities, exciting as they may have seemed to the children. My wife warned them to be careful in moving about and not to indulge in roughhousing.

Fortunately our host had unusual understanding of children and patience with them. He used to tell Dick the romantic histories of his treasures. One Phoenician carving was dated B.C.; he explained to the boy that that meant it had been fashioned before the birth of Christ. Dick was deeply impressed. That same evening he rushed excitedly out of his bathroom, waving a towel.

"Look," he shouted, pointing to the monogram, B-C. "It's on them all. The towels in this house were all made before Christ."

The old, shriveled custodian took us through the huge cellars, stretching out under the house for more than an acre. They contained innumerable varieties of fine wines and liquors, a large part of which had been laid down in the eighteenth century. We were to give a reception following the coronation. Mr. Burdett-Coutts said: "Here's some eighteen-sixty champagne. I think it would be nice to serve it at your reception."

I hesitated. "But we're having more than a thousand guests."

"Don't be concerned, sir," the little gnome broke in, "we have plenty."

A few days before the coronation I went to Folkestone to rest and await the time of my official reception.

All of the foreign delegations were supposed to gather at Calais, and then to cross the Channel together by special boats. Trains were to be provided to meet us at Dover and to take us to London.

On June 19th, I went to Dover and there met the three men appointed by the British government as my official aides. One of them was Lord Sandhurst. His was the only case, I believe, in which both father and son had been decorated with the Star of India. The others, Lieutenant Colonel B. R. James and Captain C. F. G. Sowerby, I had known in Washington when attachés at the British Embassy. Sowerby came to an untimely end when he accompanied Kitchener on his trip to Russia.

All three were close friends of mine. It was a constant source of entertainment to me to see the mixture of informality and official decorum. Now and then one of them would call me "Hammond," and then, smiling, immediately correct himself with: "I beg your pardon, Your Excellency."

When the special boat train reached London the coach with the American delegation stopped directly in front of the crimson carpet where the Duke of Connaught, the King's uncle, stood. He represented His Majesty on state occasions. The duke, who knew very well that I had been in England for the last ten days, first greeted me in the name of the British government and then, solemnly, but with a twinkle in his eye, asked me what kind of crossing I had had.

I replied, with equal solemnity, that I was a good sailor for whom the English Channel had no terrors.

Preceding the coronation a succession of receptions and state dinners were held. Already potentates, princes, lords, and representatives from almost every country in the world had arrived. The first event was a royal dinner at Buckingham Palace the evening of our arrival. This was "a family affair" of eighty-seven at which the heads of missions were guests. The other members of the various deputations were to gather at nine-thirty and form in line for the procession to the Picture Gallery where each head of a mission was to present the members of his staff to Their Majesties.

After the banquet the men assembled in the smoking room. His Majesty asked me to sit down beside him and we began talking about Mexico and Diaz.

He was so interested in the subject that he failed to notice that we had been left almost alone in the room. Since etiquette demanded that only the King could terminate a conversation, I was unable to suggest leaving, although I feared we were upsetting the routine. At last, a messenger came from Queen Mary to remind the King that she was waiting. He took a short cut to the Picture Gallery where the levee was to be held. I had to follow the prescribed route and join my deputation, but in spite of my best efforts I failed to arrive there in time to take the place in line assigned our delegation.

As I made my bow before the Queen, I apologized for the delay. Always gracious, Her Majesty smiled sympathetically, "I quite understand the circumstances, Mr. Hays Hammond."

The next evening was the occasion of the state dinner, after which the Duchess of Sutherland gave a ball at Stafford House.

One of the most picturesque, memorable, and unique affairs was the Shakespeare Ball given in Albert Hall. We attended as the guests of Mr. Burdett-Coutts. The transforming of this vast but unlovely interior into an artistic Tudor setting for the brilliant scene was of itself an achievement. The great of every branch of art took part in the ball, as well as all of society. As usual in England, the costuming was rich and authentic. Various groups named from Shakespeare's plays gave old Elizabethan dances, and Ellen Terry in one of them shone out with her unsurpassed grace and spirit.

Many of those who had stands or rooms to rent, and also those who had purchased space from which to watch the coronation procession, took out rain policies. June weather in England is proverbially uncertain. Lloyd's rate was twenty per cent for a rainfall exceeding twenty-hundredths of an inch during the twenty-four-hour period.

The arrangements and control of the millions who witnessed the procession on June 22nd and the royal progress the next day were perfect. In fact, the whole coronation was managed with forethought for the last detail and with miraculous precision. Lord Kitchener may not have been the greatest of military men, but in this case he showed phenomenal executive ability.

Early the night before the coronation people from all quarters of the United Kingdom were gathering outside Buckingham Palace. When dawn broke about three in the morning, twelve thousand police and sixty thousand soldiers from every dominion and colony, under the command of Lord Kitchener, took up their stand along the line of march. Anybody still asleep must have been awakened by the royal salute at three-forty-five when, following an ancient custom, the Queen came out on the balcony and looked down at the multitude.

The regalia—including the spurs and sword, the royal robe and the orb, the ring and the scepters, the historic crown of Edward the Confessor—were being carried from the Tower to Westminster Abbey and were guarded throughout the night by the Tower Guard whose duty it is to keep them always in sight. They wore uniforms dating from the time of Henry VIII.

Meanwhile workmen were putting the finishing touches to temporary columns and arches, and decorating them with gilt griffons, red lions, and white unicorns.

Even while this was being done light rain fell so that by morning the colored bunting was streaked. But the spirits of the people were undamped. At intervals there would be outbursts of *Rule, Britannia* and *God Save the King*. All was conducted in an orderly, reverent way. As late as five o'clock in the morning one could still move about easily between Buckingham Palace and the Abbey.

Lord Sandhurst, who was well versed in court etiquette and dress, came about eight o'clock to escort me to the palace. When he entered the study he was attired in a most gorgeous robe with a train fourteen feet long.

"I've never seen anything so magnificent!" I exclaimed. "Let's see you walk around. I want to watch how you manage that train."

He looked at me reproachfully. "God forbid, Your Excellency. Don't ask that of me. My wife has had me parading before the servants for hours. You know we don't wear these more than once in a lifetime."

Each official representative was assigned a seat in a carriage. I was to ride with the French admiral, Fauques de Jonquières, Prince Rupprecht of Bavaria, and Duke Albrecht of Württemberg. When I started to take my place, I found that the seat of honor on the right facing forward, assigned to me as representative of the United States, was already occupied by Prince Rupprecht.

I politely showed the prince my card designating my seat, and intimated that he should relinquish it. He paid no attention, but continued his conversation with the duke. Assuming, for the sake of politeness, that he did not understand English, I made the request in German, and somewhat more emphatically.

To the ill-concealed amusement of the French admiral, Prince Rupprecht then moved, though reluctantly. Obviously piqued, neither of the two Germans paid any attention to me or to Jonquières as our carriage proceeded at a walk. Two independent conversations were carried on during the three-mile course to Westminster Abbey.

This question of precedence may seem a small matter in the light of the democratic usage of the United States, but in those days its implications certainly went deep into the wellsprings of the old-world attitude towards us. Too often England and Continental Europe had patronized us in this respect. And bearing in mind Theodore Roosevelt's unpleasant experience when he attended the funeral ceremonies of King Edward VII as representative of the President of the United States, I determined there should be no repetition. On a visit to England just before the coronation, I had gone so far as to consult Princess Louise, who had later talked to the King and to the Earl of Chesterfield, the lord chamberlain at the time of the coronation. Chesterfield, formerly one of the directors of the Consolidated Gold Fields and a warm friend, not only of mine but of America, assured Princess Louise that we would be shown every consideration.

The survival of ceremonial that dates from the Middle Ages made this coronation the most brilliant spectacle the twentieth century had seen. Some may condemn this pomp and show as economic waste, but in my opinion pageantry satisfies a fundamental human need. Knee breeches do not necessarily change an American into a fawner on kings. The American official costume is, indeed, simple enough. It is so incongruous among velvets, brocades, and jewels that inconspicuousness, the purpose of its plainness, is sometimes lost and the wearer finds himself standing out like a square-rigger in a fleet of battle cruisers.

The morning after the coronation the Hammond family read in the London *Times*: "In the Procession of Royal representatives and guests were the German Crown Prince, conspicuous by his noble bearing, with the Crown Princess, with the Prince and Princess Higashi-Fushimi of Japan, whose Oriental robes contrasted with the plain evening dress worn by Mr. Hays Hammond." The *Times* did me an injustice. I wore the prescribed costume and was not embarrassed by the disturbing thought that American ambassadors were frequently mistaken for waiters owing to the absolute similarity of dress and despite whatever air of superiority they were able to convey.

The Duke of Norfolk, first peer of the realm, was acting as marshal for the complicated coronation ceremony, and the participants conducted themselves as though they were well-rehearsed actors. I, unfortunately, almost missed one of my cues. The secretary of our delegation was to be at the entrance to the Abbey with information regarding the seating arrangements; he was nowhere to be found. Luckily I caught sight of an old friend from the Foreign Office, who was an usher, and asked him where I was to be seated.

"You move right along with the procession until you get as near the throne as possible. Precautions have been taken that no one except His Majesty will occupy that seat."

The vibrant hush inside the huge church, which for centuries has been the burying place of England's kings and distinguished subjects, came as a sharp change from the tumult of the crowd outside, who were shouting continuously, "God save the King." As we went forward it seemed dark at first, in spite of thousands of lighted candles and faint rays of sunlight streaming down from high windows. As our eyes became accustomed to the dimness, we could see the great cross formation of the Abbey, and far down the long narrow nave, the sanctuary and the gold of the altar in the circle of bright lights burning at the rear of the church. In front of the altar stood King Edward's antique chair, and the Stone of Destiny on which so many English kings had been crowned.

We had entered the Abbey in the same order as we had proceeded through the streets: first the representatives of the powers, then the peers and peeresses, followed shortly by the immediate royal family.

As we took our places, pools of light filtered through stained-glass windows, the reflection of the brilliant colors and flashing jewels of the assemblage lay softly on the ancient gray stone walls.

The peers and peeresses sat tier above tier in the transepts and above and nearer the altar were the royal boxes. The tiers as well as the galleries ranging along the nave were draped with velvet hangings of blue and silver-gray. Looking over the crowd, the prevailing colors seemed to be blue, gray, and white, with flashes of scarlet from uniforms and trains and the ceremonial garb of the prelates.

A large choir, drawn from the various churches of London, sang at intervals during the ceremony.

The Queen entered as the anthem began: "I was glad when they said unto me, We will go into the House of the Lord." As the Westminster choirboys chanted, "Vivat! Vivat! Rex Georgius," the King appeared in crimson and ermine, and proceeded slowly to the sanctuary. Their Majesties knelt in prayer, and the crowd became silent.

The Archbishop of Canterbury, standing in front of the altar, began the ritual. He administered the oath, and the King, after kissing the Bible, moved to the coronation chair and was anointed on the crown of his head, his breast, and the palms of both hands. Then came the investiture with sword, spurs, and ring. The imperial mantle was placed across his shoulders, and the orb put in his hand. As he held the royal scepter in his right hand and the rod of mercy in his left, St. Edward's crown was placed upon the King's head by the archbishop. The silver trumpets of the heralds jubilantly rang out, and the bells of Westminster, of London, of England, of the British dominions the world over, took up the antiphonal chorus.

George V ascended his throne. The Prince of Wales kissed him on both cheeks and on the hand. The senior duke, marquis, earl, viscount, and baron then did homage, each on behalf of his order.

After the shorter and simpler ritual of the crowning of the Queen, George and Mary partook of Holy Communion. The great choir then sang the *Gloria in Excelsis* and the *Te Deum*.

Preceded by heralds, yeomen of the guard, standard bearers, court officials, state functionaries, Knights of the Garter, pages, and the Abbey clergy, the King, now in purple velvet, the imperial crown on his head, the orb in his left hand, the scepter in his right, left the Abbey to the triumphant strains of the national anthem.

The ceremony was over. We filed out of the Abbey, in the order of precedence established for the occasion.

I resumed my place in the carriage and the same aloof attitude was maintained by the Germans during the rest of the procession. The South African contingent, about a thousand strong, was occupying temporary stands near the Ritz Hotel. I had known many of them on the Rand, and all of them knew of my connection with the Jameson Raid. As our carriage passed they raised a loud cheer, in which both Boers and Englishmen joined.

At this demonstration, I could not resist turning to Prince Rupprecht and remarking ironically that the ovation must be meant for him. He did not miss the point. Neither he nor the South Africans had forgotten the Kaiser's telegram to Kruger.

Two days later a great naval review was held off Spithead. Great Britain's sea power, augmented by battleships of foreign nations, formed a lane down which the King's yacht sailed, followed by others carrying the coronation guests. Almost deafening gun salutes accompanied the review.

I had been invited to join the King's private party on the *Alexandra,* where I particularly enjoyed meeting the younger members of the royal family. At this solemn moment they were engaged in teasing the Prince of Wales.

They were commenting on the intimate family details of the coronation. Young Prince Henry remarked: "David certainly looked a sight. He was frightfully nervous. He kept fooling with his collar and cuffs as though he thought everybody were looking at him."

No wonder David was frightfully nervous. As a lad of sixteen he was seated in a large chair alone on the dais the cynosure of all eyes until the arrival of the King and Queen.

This was too much for the elder brother. He started after Prince Henry but slipped and sprawled on the deck, to the rollicking amusement of the other children. David braced himself and shouted at his younger relatives. Then he regained his equilibrium and continued the chase.

Simultaneously the crown prince of Germany, insensitive to the humor of this healthy domestic scene, joined the group. He was obviously in a bad temper. We were approaching our battleship, the U.S.S. *Delaware.*

The crown prince made some arrogant remarks about its new basket type of observation mast. He said it was too conspicuous, it would make an easy target.

I retorted that experts on naval affairs did not agree with him. Before the argument could grow too warm, the Kaiser's brother, Prince Henry, arrived. He was head of the German Navy and was able to suppress his fiery nephew by tactfully siding with me. Even so, the crown prince may have been right. Our navy has since abandoned that type of observation mast. The review proceeded without further international incidents. Even the royal children were well behaved!

A few days afterwards, at the garden party at Buckingham Palace, I met Dr. Hillier, a fellow prisoner at Pretoria. He was now respectable; in fact, a member of the House of Parliament. While we were reminiscing, the labor leader, John Burns, approached, and Hillier introduced me.

"Oh," said Burns, "I remember Mr. Hammond particularly well."

"Thank you. I feel complimented but surprised. It has been a long time since our last meeting."

"I never forget a man who has been in prison." Noticing that I did not understand the implications of this statement, he added: "Don't be embarrassed. I've been in jail myself once or twice."

As we three stood talking, Sir Abe Bailey, followed by Sir George Farrar, joined the group. Suddenly, without apparent reason, Burns burst into laughter, stretched out his arms, drew us together, and then whispered, "You see that fellow over there with all those jewels?"

I couldn't imagine what he was driving at.

He pointed to one of the Indian princes, decorated with several ropes of pearls, each pearl as big as a thumb, and with dazzling emeralds, sapphires, and rubies hung about him.

He then pointed in another direction. "See that chap over there? He's a maharaja. God knows how much jewelry those fellows are carrying around. Think of these fortunes in loot and five of us ex-jailbirds let loose in this crowd!"

For ten days we were feted and entertained. One of the most interesting events was the gala performance at His Majesty's Theatre. The King and Queen were in the royal box and the house was filled with coronation guests. Virtually all the theatrical talent of England was represented on the stage.

All the suites, special envoys, and deputations were scheduled to leave Waterloo Station officially on June 28th. Since I was to be the guest of honor of the Pilgrim Society that night, and of the American Society's banquet July Fourth, something had to be done to veil my failure to depart. I approached the Duke of Connaught and asked him how, without infringing any rule of etiquette, I could avoid leaving the country.

He replied that it could be arranged, but that I should have to be conspicuously present in my frock coat and tall hat at the station where I could be seen by newspaper reporters and cameramen at the official leave-taking. I would then board the train, which would stop a few hundred yards down the track to let me out. This all seemed very elaborate but it was carried through and thus, at both my arrival and my departure, official decorum was maintained.

The Pilgrim Society's dinner for me was a delightful occasion. Warmest sentiments concerning Anglo-American friendship were expressed. Arthur Balfour made an excellent speech, in which he pointed out that the best evidence of the sincerity of this friendship was that Americans and English no longer took offense at the jokes perpetrated at their expense by their friends across the water. He was so enthusiastic about it that before the evening was over a Yankee newspaper correspondent said Balfour must be planning to run for Congress.

I replied to Balfour's toast. Augustine Birrell, chief secretary to the lord lieutenant of Ireland, then gave a toast "to the American visitors" to which Chauncey Depew felt called upon to reply.

In spite of the fact that I was not officially present on British soil on the eve of the Fourth of July, my wife and I gave a reception at No. 1 Stratton Street. We had the pleasure of entertaining a great number of Americans as well as many of our English friends. At the stroke of twelve, a band stationed at the foot of the grand stairway, ushered in our national holiday with Sousa's *The Stars and Stripes Forever.*

The next afternoon Ambassador and Mrs. Whitelaw Reid gave the customary embassy reception at Dorchester House, and that night I attended the annual dinner of the American Society at the Savoy. We spent four weeks in Scotland and then returned to America.

My second diplomatic mission during these years was in connection with the celebration of the completion of the Panama Canal. This was of far more than local interest, its importance was greater than most trumped-up world expositions. The international significance of the completion of the canal was apparent, and it was believed that interest could best be aroused by sending emissaries to request the co-operation of European countries. In 1912, therefore, three years before the Panama-Pacific Exposition was scheduled to open, Charles G. Moore, its president, asked me to head a commission for this purpose. He pointed out that my previous business connections in Europe and my having been the President's representative at the coronation would be of value in securing a favorable reception.

I hesitated between my wish to serve California and my desire to take the stump for Taft's nomination, and I wrote to President Taft that I preferred to remain in America to support him in the preconvention activities.

The President replied that he hoped I would go to Europe because it was of the "utmost importance that the European countries be induced to take adequate part in the great memorial celebration . . . in the success of which I am taking more than a mere official interest."

This was true. As secretary of war, he had directed the construction of the canal and, naturally enough, had extended his interest to the celebration of its opening. I then accepted.

Because of this extraofficial interest, Taft issued a presidential proclamation, naming the members of the commission, and thereby giving us a quasi-diplomatic standing. Secretary of State Knox requested all embassies and legations in the countries we were to visit to assure us special governmental courtesies.

In addition to myself, the members of the commission were R. B. Hale, W. T. Sesnon, Rear Admiral S. A. Staunton, and Brigadier General Clarence R. Edwards. Naval and Military representatives

THE PROCESSION ON THE WAY TO THE CORONATION OF GEORGE V

THE PANAMA-PACIFIC EXPOSITION, 1915

accompanied us because of the federal character of our mission. My son Harris and Charles F. Wilson, of the State Department, acted as secretaries.

We sailed for England on the *Mauretania* on April 24, 1912, with a great mass of propaganda literature. In London we made Claridge's our headquarters. Then began once more the round of dinners, banquets, lunches, speeches, and ceremonial visits we had learned to know so well during the coronation; thenceforward these filled every hour of the day and many hours of the night.

Everywhere we received most courteous official attention. We met so many people at different functions that, while we were vitally interested in the world and government affairs, there was little time for anything but the most casual conversations.

We were greeted by the ruler of a country in person if he was in residence; in his absence, by a representative of the government. In hotels we were given the royal suite and walked under yards of canopies and over miles of red carpets. Even station masters greeted us in elaborate uniforms reserved for state occasions. Our official status was in danger of overwhelming our intent.

In England, Ambassador Reid took us first to call on the secretary for foreign affairs, Sir Edward Grey, at No. 10 Downing Street, and in the evening to Covent Garden.

The next day we called on various government ministers, including H. U. Wintour, head of the department on international exhibitions. In the evening, the ambassador gave a dinner for forty, among whom were the Marquis of Crewe, secretary of state for India, Lewis Harcourt, colonial secretary, Sydney Buxton, president of the Board of Trade, Lord Sandhurst, at this time lord chamberlain, and Lord Roberts. Lord Haldane, the secretary of state for war, came in after dinner.

While we were in London, Sesnon called on Lord Desborough, president of the London Chamber of Commerce, Admiral Staunton on Winston Churchill, first lord of the admiralty, and General Edwards on Lord Haldane.

The government gave us a luncheon on the terrace of the House of Commons, with the Rt. Hon. Earl Beauchamp acting as host.

After lunch the speaker of the House of Commons deputed Mr.

Cadogan to escort the commission into the House, where we heard Mr. Balfour in debate on Home Rule. Afterwards "Honest John" Burns showed us through Parliament House and pointed out the room where Cromwell had signed the death warrant of Charles I, and other points of historical interest. He was the best cicerone we had on the trip. It will be remembered that Honest John was the only man to resign from the Cabinet on its vote, at the urgence of Earl Grey, to declare war in August, 1914.

We were granted an audience with King George V, whose cordiality and interest set the tone for our reception on the Continent. Afterwards we were entertained at luncheon by the Earl of Granard, son-in-law of my old friend Ogden Mills.

In London, Mr. Burdett-Coutts gave a tea for the commission. It was pleasant to be back at No. 1 Stratton Street, and to have Hallett pop out of his sentry box just as usual and the handsome major-domo greet me in his dignified fashion.

Our five days' reception in London was extremely cordial, and from every side we heard expressions of keen interest and promises of co-operation. The newspapers were generous in their support and the prevalent atmosphere of goodwill made us feel that we had made a good start.

We went next to Berlin and were met by Messrs. Spencer and Ruddock, secretaries to the embassy, and taken to the Hotel Adlon.

Germany ordinarily encourages exhibitions and had a permanent committee to further and control the multitude of national affairs that are given every year. This committee was exceedingly interested in our proposals because it believed that the Panama Canal had a world significance as an outlet and a means of communication. From an engineering point of view alone the Germans considered it worthy of celebration.

Ambassador John G. Leishman entertained us at lunch at which were present Herr Solf, minister of colonies, and Herr Albert, undersecretary of the interior.

Nevertheless, the reception which was accorded our exposition plans was by no means as warm as we had expected. There seemed to be an undercurrent of hostility. This might have been due to jealousy of England's cordial promises of co-operation. More probably it was a matter of commercial rivalry with American manufacturers, or resentment over the American tariff. But unmistakably the Germans were busy—too obviously so, preoccupied with plans which necessarily excluded all thought of expositions or even courtesy.

Admiral Staunton called on Admiral von Tirpitz and was received politely, but without great enthusiasm. When General Edwards said to the minister of war, General von Herrigen, that Lord Haldane had promised England would be suitably represented, the German remarked with decision, "And so shall we."

The Kaiser was absent in Corfu, but our personal relations with many influential Germans were friendly. At the reception given us by Bethmann-Hollweg there was a brilliant gathering and we enjoyed meeting old friends and making new ones. I remember talking with Prince Lichnowsky, who had just returned from his post as ambassador to Turkey and was to go to London, and urging him to promote friendly understanding between England and Germany which I had always thought a sound idea. He expressed keen desire to effect this.

During our four days in Berlin, we saw thousands of soldiers goose-stepping through the streets. It was evident the Germans had their minds on other things than peaceful expositions. In spite of the official chill, one of our party remarked as the St. Petersburg train pulled out of the station: "It's a good thing we didn't stay in Germany any longer. They might have killed us with that elaborate kindness."

We had some feeling of uncertainty as to our reception in St. Petersburg. Before leaving London, I had been cabled by our Department of State that the efforts of Curtis Guild, ambassador to Russia, had failed to secure Russian support. Though the premier had consented to receive us, no other minister was willing to do so, and the trip to Russia might, in his opinion, wisely be abandoned.

Ambassador Guild joined us in Berlin and explained that, in view of the delicate situation in Russia caused by the abrogation the year before of our commercial treaty, the Russian press was hostile. Members of the commission, he advised, should not talk to newspaper reporters there. He himself planned to remain in Berlin until the mission had finished its alloted stay in Russia, so that his presence might not lend it political significance.

Prime Minister Kokovtzev invited us to his house, making clear that he was receiving us out of courtesy to us as American citizens and not in his official capacity. He then became more cordial and declared there was every reason why the relations between our two countries should be close and permanent; we really had no conflicting interests and more than ninety-nine per cent of our differences had been eliminated. But Kokovtzev at the moment did not see how Russia could participate in the exposition. On the other hand, if a satisfactory treaty could be speedily negotiated, Russia would be glad to exhibit.

The commission was received by Minister of Commerce Timaschev, whose ideas followed closely those of the prime minister, he, too, urging that a new commercial treaty be completed soon.

That same evening Charles Stetson Wilson, the chargé d'affaires, gave us an excellent dinner arranged on a scale of extravagant hospitality. There were many Russians present but only one member of the government, the prefect of police.

The official calls of General Edwards on General Soukhomlinov, minister of war, and of Admiral Staunton on Admiral Grigorovitch met with enthusiastic response and promises that the army and navy would be suitably represented in any international features arranged for the exposition if Russia participated.

Since the Czar was absent in the Crimea, we did not see him.

I returned to my hotel from an official visit to learn that my old friend, now Count Witte, had called in my absence. I hastened to his home and had tea with him. This was the last time I saw him. He was a disappointed, embittered man. The Revolution of 1905 had put an end to his ambitions for Russia's future. Although no liberal in our sense of the word, Witte had hoped to see the Russian Duma's influence replace that of the nobility. Instead, he had had to view a succession of ever more ineffectual Dumas succumb to the reactionary influence of Konstantin Petrovitch Pobedonostsev with his ideal of an absolute autocracy, supreme in church and state. Pobedonostsev was procurator of Holy Synod and virtually ecclesiastical dictator of Russia.

Witte, it has always seemed to me, was the only man who could have saved Russia from the consequences of her bloody revolution. He was the victim of a system against which he struggled in vain. The sinister and all-powerful influence of occultism, fostered by the Czarina herself, was thrown into the scale against him. His position in Russian politics became entirely anomalous. The court regarded him as too radical; the radicals, as too conservative. Although a great statesman, perhaps the greatest Russia has ever produced, in his own country he was unhonored and even abroad had not received the recognition he merited.

The minister of credit, M. Davidov, whom I had met in 1910, gave a banquet for forty guests. I had had some experience with Russian hospitality, but even to me this seemed a gastronomic marvel.

Set out on a long table was the necessary zakousky, an array of irresistible hors d'oeuvres, smoked fish, anchovies, cold meats, caviar heaped in shining gray, red, and black mounds. Punctuating the table like exclamation points, bottles of vodka made from grain, vodka made even from green leaves, alternated with champagne. General Edwards and I, who knew the ropes, were as abstemious as the temptation would allow. The rest of the delegation let themselves go and stood about fairly gorging themselves on the delicacies.

When all the American guests were thoroughly stuffed, one or two approached our host to compliment him on such a superb cold supper. At that moment the great doors behind us were folded back and dinner was announced.

M. Davidov achieved the acme of Russian hospitality—he provided for us the royal boxes at the opera.

Afterwards Davidov asked Harris, who was but little younger than he: "How'd you like to go on a bear hunt? I can get a special train to take us to the Urals. We can have a day's shooting, and then I can arrange for another special train to take you to Vienna."

Harris was reluctant to decline but, in spite of the lavish use of special trains, he was afraid he might not reach Vienna in time to rejoin the party.

We left St. Petersburg at midnight, May 13th, and reached Moscow the next morning.

Someone in the party told the story of two Russian peasants who got on a train together at a way station between these two cities.

One of them said to the other, "Where are you going?"

"Petersburg. Where are you?"

"Moscow."

"Isn't it wonderful that we are on the same train, between the two cities, and traveling together—and that you are going to Moscow and I to Petersburg. What miracles these modern scientists have performed for us."

We stopped off in Moscow only one day to visit the Kremlin, which was closed in anticipation of a visit from the Czar, perhaps a necessary police precaution in view of the activity of the anarchists. As a special courtesy, the prefect of police allowed us to visit the fortress of the Kremlin, its churches, and the treasure room. On my previous visit to Russia I had made many good friends, but they all seemed different now; there was suspicion, tension, and an atmosphere of national distrust. Their gaiety was hectic and their laughter was hollow. The old Russia was dying of her own physical and spiritual inertia.

As the train halted at the small station marking the Austrian frontier, we heard the sound of stringed instruments. On the platform was a five-piece tzigane orchestra, playing its gay gypsy music. Our courier informed us that many years before an Austrian, who had been long absent from his country and was returning home a wealthy man, heard gypsies playing at this very spot. He was overcome with emotion and provided that romany music should henceforth greet every entering train.

We reached Vienna at six in the morning and were met by Ambassador Richard C. Kerens and his entire staff. It was bad enough to arrive at such an impossible hour but to have to struggle into full evening dress when half awake was made bearable only by the comforts afforded by our special train. As we neared each new stopping place we could—if forced to—array ourselves in the proper clothes for any time of day and for any court requirement. It was some satisfaction to know that the welcoming committee was obliged to wear the same formal attire.

Kerens had been most energetic in his arrangements, and we were given a printed government program covering nearly every hour of our visit.

First we called on all members of the ministry and were received enthusiastically. After visiting the Natural History Museum, we attended a luncheon given by Dr. Faber, president of the Austrian committee. We were then taken for an automobile ride to Kobenzl, in the beautiful hills overlooking Vienna. In the evening we sat in the royal box at the Kaiserliche Königliche Burgtheater and from there went to a brilliant reception at the American Embassy.

The death of the king of Denmark, whose body had been found on the streets of Hamburg, necessitated the court's going into mourning. Consequently the invitations issued by Count and Countess Berchtold for a grand reception at the Ballplatz had to be recalled. Berchtold did, however, give us a small and unofficial dinner at his private palace. This gave us the opportunity of frankly discussing world politics. It is remembered by us as a most enjoyable occasion. Berchtold was one of the recognized brilliant statesmen of his time even if he did sign the ultimatum to Serbia in July, 1914.

A state luncheon was given us in the fine old Rathaus. The decorations of the big banqueting hall had been designed and carried out by Joseph Urban, who had been honored by the Emperor for his architectural and stage designs. Later he created magnificent effects of line and color for the Chicago Century of Progress Exposition, but unfortunately he died before he could hear the chorus of praise.

Our luncheon became quite festive. I had written a speech for the occasion and, with the help of our German courier, had translated it into German. I had attempted to keep it in a light vein and felt very well satisfied with my efforts when the audience showed itself highly amused and applauded inordinately.

But later my wife told me that Harris had written her, "Father certainly created an atmosphere of humor, but I am not sure whether the guests were amused at his stories, or were laughing at his German."

The Emperor Francis Joseph, in full uniform, gave us an audience at Schönbrunn. His soldierly bearing belied his eighty-two years.

His manner was most cordial and immediately set the entire commission at ease.

His Majesty had dispensed with the presence of both our ambassador and an interpreter, although we never knew why. He was master of nine languages, but strangely enough, English was not among them. As I was the only one in the delegation who could speak German, I had to assume the burden of conversation. I apologized for not being familiar with the "hofdeutsch" used at court. I explained that my German was the student dialect learned at Freiberg thirty-five years before. The Emperor said pleasantly that he would be glad to hear the studenten-sprache, it would be a relaxation from court German. Thus encouraged I went ahead without regard to grammatical construction to tell him about the prospective exposition.

Dr. Dumba, Austrian ambassador to Washington, told me the Emperor had been pleased with our audience and as a memento of the occasion was sending his autographed photograph to the young man who used studenten-sprache. I was proud to receive this honor from the most formal court in Europe.

In Vienna I was interviewed by a clever newspaper correspondent who cross-examined me thoroughly on American tariffs, always a grievance in Europe. I had a difficult half-hour trying to clarify for his readers the Republican policy high tariffs—perhaps an impossible undertaking.

Our Austrian visit was highly successful and enjoyable. We were shown full official courtesy and were promised hearty support for the exposition.

After four busy days in Vienna, we went to Budapest, where we were met by Dr. Ott, minister of commerce and representative of the city. The next day we were granted an audience by the Archduke Joseph. The Archduke Francis Ferdinand was also present. Two years later his murder at Sarajevo was to precipitate the World War.

After a round of official calls we were given a luncheon by Count Serenyi, the minister of agriculture. The same evening we were guests of the government at a brilliant dinner at the Orszagos Casino, where the minister of justice was the official host. The following day was filled with ceremonious meetings, and in the evening the city

of Budapest was our host for a trip down the Danube to Margaret
Island and a magnificent dinner presided over by Count Apponyi.
The Hungarians justly pride themselves on their hospitality.

The Hungarian government then sent us by special train to Fiume,
then Austria's port on the Adriatic. We spent the day at the torpedo works of Whitehead and Company, and watched with interest
as torpedoes were discharged into the bay for our edification.

It was an overnight trip by steamer from Fiume to Venice. After
a day's sightseeing there, we proceeded to Rome.

Italy was in the midst of the Tripolitan War with Turkey. General Edwards and Admiral Staunton were naturally following its
progress with great interest. I had heard in court circles elsewhere
that Victor Emmanuel III was exceptionally well versed in world
affairs and one of the most brilliant European monarchs, but I was
unprepared for his accurate up-to-the-minute information. Almost
his first words were, "President Taft has lost Ohio."

This referred to the Ohio election of delegates for the Republican
National Convention. He had studied the political map and already
had made an accurate forecast of the effect on the election based on
such incomplete returns. None of us had heard the news, and my
pained expression surprised the king; after his recent meeting with
Roosevelt, he had assumed that all patriotic Americans would be
Rooseveltians.

The gloomy prognostication that the Italian government would be
too preoccupied with its war to bother with commercial questions
was without foundation. The king made the remark that the re-
building of San Francisco after the earthquake and fire was in itself
a triumph sufficient to warrant the celebration, and asked to have
explained many pertinent technical details concerning the operation
of the Panama Canal. These questions might have been expected
from an engineer but hardly from a ruling monarch.

At my last interview with him, in 1926, Victor Emmanuel showed
much interest in my account of the world sources of gold supply.
He then reviewed history and pointed out that after every great
political and economic catastrophe, such as the World War, there
appeared the practice of debasing the coinage, a dangerous practice
indulged in by many governments since 1918.

After our audience the commission was lavishly entertained in Rome and met almost all the members of the ministry and other important personages. Premier Giolitti promised co-operation, and Cardinal Merry del Val, the papal secretary, asked that the commission indicate to him just what exhibits would be appreciated. The cardinal expressed regret that our departure for Paris that evening prevented an audience with the Pope.

From Rome the commission went to Paris where Ambassador Myron T. Herrick took us to call on the premier, Raymond Poincaré, and on President Fallières. We were promised full support on the part of France. The minister of war, Alexandre Millerand, was particularly interested in the canal, since, as he said, he had been minister of commerce during a part of the time the de Lesseps plan was in progress.

He seemed a little surprised that General Edwards asked for military participation, but said he would join if that were being done. Delcassé, minister of marine, promised Admiral Staunton that the French Navy would be represented.

Because of my anxiety to reach the Republican convention in time to support the candidacy of President Taft, I parted company with the commission at Paris; it completed its itinerary before returning to America.

In looking back over the trip, it seems to me that the show of interest we elicited was greater than had been expected. Unfortunately, the outbreak of war in 1914 made it impossible for many of the countries to carry out their participation on the scale they had proposed and hoped for.

On February 20, 1915, the Panama-Pacific International Exposition opened. The buildings were erected on made land by the shore of San Francisco Bay overlooking the Golden Gate. No more beautiful site could have been chosen; at night the fairgrounds were a splash of color, illuminating the sky, while the blue-black hills in the background twinkled with lights, and shining ferryboats scurried across the bay.

During the ten months of its duration over eighteen million people paid admission to the greatest international exposition ever held.

CHAPTER THIRTY

Peace and Preparedness

PEACE MOVEMENTS—TAFT'S INTEREST IN PEACE
SOCIETIES—I WORK FOR THE WORLD COURT—
WOMEN'S PART IN THE MOVEMENT—OUTBREAK OF
WORLD WAR—WOODROW WILSON'S ATTITUDE—HIS
RE-ELECTION—WE ENTER THE WAR—COLONEL HOUSE

As I look back on the years between 1910 and 1919, years crowded with public and private business, it seems to me that the problem of world peace occupied a great proportion of my time and energies. My interest in search of a plan for the peaceable settlement of international disputes became complicated after August, 1914, with the urgent need for preparedness, and after April 2, 1917, with the still more insistent problem of winning the war. But all through this period the underlying and ultimate need seemed to me to be the acceptance of the principle of justice in international relations. I do not propose to go deeply into the history of this movement, nor into the judicial and political arguments in support of it; I want to give merely an indication of the attitude taken by a businessman and an engineer.

These chapters may seem somewhat lengthy to the general reader but the issues discussed have profound importance in the present international political situation. For instance, the activities of the peace movements in this country eventuated in the creation of the League of Nations—an ideal to which Woodrow Wilson dedicated his political fortune and, in a large measure, his life.

The peace movement, under the influence of the Second Hague

Conference in 1907, had produced several propagandist societies, notably those supported and encouraged by Andrew Carnegie. A statesmanlike effort to translate ideals into political facts was made by Taft and Knox in general treaties with England and France, but the Senate refused to ratify them. Taft was greatly disappointed in this failure, but he never gave up his belief that some sort of court of justice could be set up to decide many of the war-breeding questions that arise between nations.

On February 6, 1910, Theodore Marburg, well-known publicist and subsequently United States minister to Belgium, gave a small dinner at his house in Baltimore. Among the guests was James Brown Scott, secretary of the Carnegie Endowment for International Peace, who had been technical delegate to the Second Hague Peace Conference. On this occasion we launched the American Society for the Judicial Settlement of International Disputes. The project was strongly supported by the administration, as is shown by the following quotations from letters read at the meeting.

President Taft:

> . . . If the proposed Court of Arbitral Justice at The Hague becomes an accomplished fact there will still remain the task of securing the adhesion of a number of Powers to the Court, and the very important task of so cultivating opinion in various countries as to incline Governments to resort to the Court when occasion calls for it. There is no other single way in which the cause of peace and disarmament can be so effectively promoted as by the firm establishment of a Permanent International Court of Justice . . . .

Secretary of State Knox:

> By the settlement of controversies susceptible of judicial determination before they have reached an acute stage the causes of war would be minimized and a first step taken toward the gradual decrease of armament . . .

Elihu Root:

> . . . I beg to say to your guests that I sympathize very

strongly with their object and believe that the proposed organization is adapted to render a great public service.

In another passage in his letter, Senator Root made a suggestion in the way of clarification of the society's objectives, which was acted upon:

> I assume that the new organization is to have a definite, specific object which may be indicated by emphasizing the word "judicial" in its title to indicate a distinction between that kind of settlement of international disputes and the ordinary arbitration as it has been understood in the past and is generally understood now.

Other letters expressed approval of the object of this meeting, notably one from Lyman Abbott and one from Woodrow Wilson, then president of Princeton University.

The officers for the new society were James Brown Scott, president; John Hays Hammond, vice-president; Theodore Marburg, secretary.

A statement detailing the purposes and policies of the society was prepared and given to the International News Service, which gave it wide circulation:

> The purpose underlying the formation of the American Society for the Judicial Settlement of International Disputes is promotion of the project to establish a judicial tribunal which will do for the civilized world what the ordinary courts of justice do for the individual and and to encourage recourse to it when established . . . The new society will enter upon no direct propaganda for peace, for arbitration, or for disarmament. Its aim is to advocate the most practical means hitherto devised of settling certain kinds of international disputes without resort to war and to leave to societies organized for that purpose the very useful work of bringing home to men the evils of war . . . Arbitration has been for some time, and will continue to be, of very great value, but it is merely the stepping stone to an institution far more

effective, i. e., the proposed International Court of Justice.

The task before the new society is to show the people of this and other lands . . .

1st. That the movement to reject war as a means of settling international controversies has already become a practical movement, made such by the achievements of arbitration and kindred institutions.

2nd. That the proposed Court of Arbitral Justice offers greater possibilities for the peaceful settlement of international controversies along permanent lines than any existing institutions . . .

The channels through which the new society proposes to work are principally two, viz: the issuing of brief statements of scientific accuracy by the leading men of various countries, and meetings of national scope.

It was now necessary to secure for our society the adherence of men whose names would carry weight with the public, and to enlist financial support. Theodore Marburg wrote to me on April 6th: "We are not deceiving ourselves as to the length or magnitude of our task; it will require many years of active propaganda by printed page and through public meetings before the leading nations of the world acquire the habit of using the proposed International Court of Justice instead of resorting to war."

Today, after a quarter of a century, there is still much to be done: the "magnitude of the task" was not overestimated.

On April 25th I wrote to Marburg:

I spoke to the President last night about the coming Honorary Presidency of the American Society for the Judicial Settlement of International Disputes. He expressed his appreciation of the great importance of this work, and predicted success of the object which we are all making an effort to attain.

He also said that it would give him great pleasure to accept the post of Honorary President if he could do so with propriety, and that he would speak to Knox about it.

Secretary Knox approved and President Taft became honorary president. Woodrow Wilson was asked to become a member of the Advisory Council but declined.

It was thought desirable also to interest officials in Mexico and Canada. In June the secretary of state of Mexico, Señor Enrique Creel, accepted my invitation to become an honorary member We asked President Taft to invite President Diaz, Sir Wilfrid Laurier, and Earl Grey, governor general of Canada, for our coming annual meeting in December, but he could not see his way clear to issuing so official a request. We did not secure any of them, but Earl Grey sent me this telegram:

GREATLY REGRET IMPOSSIBLE ACCEPT YOUR MOST KIND
INVITATION DECEMBER FIFTEEN   SYMPATHIZE HEARTILY
WITH ALL YOUR HOPES AND WISH YOU THOROUGHLY
SUCCESSFUL GATHERING
                                        GREY

The December meeting was addressed by President Taft, Jules Jusserand, the French ambassador, Joseph H. Choate, Charles Eliot, and others, and was considered a success. I was made president, and Simeon E. Baldwin, governor-elect of Connecticut, became vice-president.

In 1911 our society joined the American Peace Society in a national Peace Congress held at Baltimore in May. The situation in China was a disturbing one at the time, and in the course of my address I advocated the neutralization of China, and the guaranteeing of its integrity by the great powers. At that day none of us would have believed that within three years the Belgian neutrality treaty would become a mere "scrap of paper."

Whether or not this venture on shaky ground was wise I do not know. I remember asking Dr. Wu, the Chinese minister, Charles R. Flint, Paul Morton, E. H. Harriman, and a few others to a dinner, where our discussions were to be strictly confidential. In our conversation about affairs in China, Dr. Wu said that China was able to take care of herself and was at the time organizing a large army. I asked him whether it might not be better for China to continue her traditional peaceful policy, spend her hard-won revenues on internal development, and allow the powerful nations of the world to guarantee her sovereignty. To neutralize China would be advantageous to Europe, because, I pointed out as tactfully as possible, China might, if armed, become a threat to other nations.

"Quite true," said the minister, "that is good business, good diplomacy, and good politics; but could we trust you Western nations?" He went on to say that he was reminded of the fable *The Kite and Pigeons,* the moral of which is that "they who voluntarily place power in the hands of a tyrant or an enemy must not wonder if it be at last turned against themselves." He elaborated this by adding, *"Timeo Danaos et dona ferentes."*

When I was in London at the coronation of King George V, I attended the Pilgrims' Dinner and made an address on international amity. A. J. Balfour, I found, was enthusiastic in the cause of peace and made a telling speech on the value and practicability of a World Court.

Our society continued to hold public meetings and to issue quarterly pamphlets which were widely distributed. Annual conventions were held, I believe, up to the sixth one in 1916; the one planned for 1914 had been omitted at the request of our president, Charles W. Eliot. He characteristically wrote to the Executive Committee, "Events more effective than talk this year."

Another echo of the uncertainties of this first war year is found in Elihu Root's reply to Marburg's request that he become vice-president of the society for 1915 and, in regular course, president in 1916: "I shall be happy to act as vice-president for the year 1915. The question of the presidency for 1916, however, I think better be held in abeyance at present. That is a good ways off and I am not at all sure how I shall be situated at that time."

The society decided to concentrate its efforts on just one point— to gain support for the idea of an international court. There was no dissension in its ranks. It is true that some men, notably President Eliot, believed that force would be necessary to make effective the awards of such a Court, but the accepted official attitude was that the moral weight attaching to the Court's decisions would be sufficient to ensure their compliance; furthermore, that to advocate

THEODORE MARBURG

ANDREW CARNEGIE (1837-1919)

the sanction of armed force would raise such objections that our more modest aim would be nullified. We steered clear also of extreme pacifism, such as was being preached by more radical groups.

In place of the annual convention, a Peace Platform meeting was held at the Metropolitan Temple in New York on December 27, 1914, directed by John Wesley Hill and the International Peace Forum, of which I was vice-president. In my address I emphasized the similarity of the World Court to the United States Supreme Court. The analogy was not original with me, but it seemed a simple and familiar idea to impress upon the popular mind.

A day or two later, after talking with Marburg, I issued a call to a number of prominent men to meet me at lunch at the Midday Club on January 4, 1915. There I explained my idea of making an intensive campaign for the World Court through popular meetings and newspaper publicity. I did not consider that this activity would be regarded by anyone as in any sense unfriendly to the American Society for the Judicial Settlement of International Disputes, on the Executive Committee of which I continued to serve. (I did feel that that society's unwieldy title, suggesting a somewhat academic and "intellectual" tone, handicapped its effectiveness.) The outbreak of the World War had, it seemed to me, made it advisable to find a new approach to the problem. It furnished a concrete example of the failure of the old folk-ways of nations, and pointed the lesson that civilization must find its *modus vivendi* under Justice, impartial and recognized. Agreeing on the value of a new society under a new name, and of renewed and intensified effort, we proceeded to organize a World Court League and take it before the country.

I found enthusiastic support among my friends, many of whom were already working for the Court idea. Root declared for us, and Taft, whom I went to New Haven to see, agreed on the plan of a general campaign. In order that we might work in harmony with the Wilson administration, James Brown Scott interviewed Secretary Lansing and secured his approval. But we were unable to gain a public adherence from President Wilson. His reply of February 3rd said in part:

> I think it would be unwise for a member of the Administration to appear at a public meeting called for the advocacy of some particular measure of international organization, just at this juncture . . .

Marburg took the President's refusal quite to heart. In a letter written to me on February 8th, accompanying a draft of the President's letter, he wrote: "I enclose copy of a very disappointing letter from the President . . . You were right; I should have gone to see him in person."

Certain men we had hoped to have with us in a congress at Cleveland, planned for May, failed us. President Lowell, of Harvard, declined,

> . . . not through a lack of faith in the importance of an International Court of Justice . . . my objection to being on the general committee is that I got uncomfortably caught once in a peace movement, where I find that the names of the Trustees are being used for proposals which they have had no chance to consider, and which some of them, at least, do not approve; and I feel very shy about adding one's name to a movement in which one had not the time to take an active part. If I could be in Cleveland in May, it would be a very different thing.

Later, Lowell became actively identified with us in the League to Enforce Peace.

Joseph H. Choate's letter of refusal written April 8, 1915, is also interesting:

> I think there is no need to attempt to prove to the world that the people of the United States wholly approve of the project of an International Court of Justice, and I do not think the time has come to take any action that would be effective towards its prompt establishment, while the war is going on. The American public, in my opinion, does not need to be roused to a consciousness of the possibilities that lie in the creation

of such a court, and the discussion of it at such a congress in the midst of the war will receive no attention from the nations who are engaged in the war, and who will probably settle the terms of peace without assistance from outsiders.

Of course, Mr. Choate knew as much as I did about the weight of America's influence abroad, but my opinion was at variance with his. I felt, and often said, that America's irreproachable neutrality, her conspicuous advocacy of peace, her commanding position in finance, industry, and commerce, her freedom from political alliances, her cosmopolitan population had ordained her by Providence to take the lead in the peace movement. Time proved that our influence as one of the combatants was in some respects dominant at the Peace Conference, but I believe that our advice would have been listened to even if we had taken no part in the war, provided we had created from a military point of view a strong position. It seemed eminently reasonable and probable that a carefully thought-out plan proposed by the United States and overwhelmingly supported by its citizens would be welcomed by the nations of Europe when the war was over.

Our minimum plan was for the creation of a World Court to deal only with justiciable questions, and for the creation of an assembly, or Council of Conciliation, to deal with nonjusticiable questions if only to ensure delay and the publicity which a hearing would produce. This plan was so simple as to cause some men to say that it was unnecessary to undertake a campaign to persuade Americans that it was good.

Harold Howland, of the *Independent,* thought a postcard sent through the mails, or the simple creed thrown on the screen before motion picture audiences would be sufficient. Some thought the nations at war would have no time to listen, and they were to a degree right. Archbishop Ireland replied to my letter, saying that he did not have "much confidence in movements proposed at the present time." Jacob Schiff thought that the "first thing is to bring to an end the present conflict." Samuel Gompers, after consulting the Executive Committee of the American Federation of Labor, replied, "I am not in sympathy with some of the projects." Oscar Straus approved but ended his letter with these words, "whether amid the awful clash and brutal noises of war men have ears to hear or not at the present time is a question which doubtless has had your consideration." Nevertheless, our World Court League grew rapidly by the accession of those who believed in the value and feasibility of our program. During the two years of its greatest activity, the officers were:

John Hays Hammond, *President*
Alton B. Parker ⎫
Bainbridge Colby ⎪
Charles Lathrop Pack ⎬ *Vice-presidents*
D. D. Woodmansee ⎭
Henry Clews, *Treasurer*
Emerson McMillin, *Chairman of Executive Committee*
John Wesley Hill, *General Secretary*
Charles H. Burr, *Executive Secretary*
William W. Wilson, *Recording Secretary*
William Howard Taft, *Honorary President*
Charles W. Fairbanks ⎫
Oscar S. Straus ⎪
Lawrence Y. Sherman ⎬ *Honorary vice-presidents*
Woodbridge N. Ferris ⎭

The limited object of the World Court League was defined thus:

> To advocate, and by agitation and appeal, to secure the support of all peoples in the establishment of a World Court for the settlement of all justiciable questions of dispute that may arise between Nations . . . a rational alternative to war.
>
> Until the efficiency of an INTERNATIONAL COURT has been recognized by the laws and practices of civilized Nations, the League likewise recognizes the right of every Nation to adopt adequate measures for National Defense.

The clause on preparedness expressed our sense of the danger to America of a spread of the European war, and our insistence that to plan for a reign of justice was not inconsistent with a vigorous defense program.

Our plan of operation was to hold public meetings throughout the country for the purpose of securing the adherence of clubs, chambers of commerce, state legislatures, and the masses. During February, March, and April we carried on a whirlwind campaign in the East and as far west as St. Louis. John Wesley Hill, as field agent, made the arrangements for meetings; and he, Henry Clews, Senator Lawrence Y. Sherman, of Illinois, and I addressed them. This initial campaign culminated in the First World Court Congress at Cleveland, May 12-14, 1915.

The congress was well organized and largely attended. Newton D. Baker, then mayor of Cleveland, greeted the assembly in an eloquent address. The subject of ex-President Taft's principal address was "The United States Supreme Court the Prototype of a World Court." Emerson McMillin and Theodore Marburg spoke on "The Composition of an International Court"; Henry Lane Wilson, on "Limitations of Jurisdiction." Judge Alton B. Parker, Warren G. Harding, Bainbridge Colby, and I, as president, on the practical value and feasibility of a World Court. These and other speeches were listened to with enthusiastic interest; the newspapers and later the magazines rendered excellent service in publicizing our proceedings; the officers and delegates were encouraged to carry on. The employment of sanctions to enforce decisions of the Court was rejected. My presidential address contained this expression of opinion:

> "As to the judgment of the court or the order of the Council of Conciliation, many of us believe that all nations would respond to the dictate of a World Court or a Council of Conciliation, irrespective of the exercise of any constraining influence other than that of the public opinion of the rest of the world.
>
> "This program, I believe, is practicable, whereas, it is very doubtful if we could obtain the agreement of the nations to the exercise of military force to compel obedience to the orders of the Court or Council in case of non-

compliance. This, however, would probably be a future enlargement of the power of the League.

"But this meeting has to do only with the creation of a World Court.

"A World Court would, in time, undoubtedly become representative of a world interest, subordinating the narrow interests of any particular nations to the welfare of humanity at large. The judges would become world judges, animated by the highest patriotism—the welfare of mankind—not a tribunal prepossessed with national bias.

"Many of us believe that the World Court can be established by the time of the termination of the present European War in connection with the discussion of the terms of peace. So, then, *in time of war let us prepare for peace, that in time of peace we shall not again have to prepare for war.*

"The belligerent nations at that time would, we believe, be willing to subordinate minor differences of opinion for the realization of this ideal, which they will regard as indispensable to their welfare. Since they all suffer from the evils of a great war, all neutral nations should make an insistent demand for the establishment of such a Court. Neutral nations have a common peril. In a World Court they would have a common safety."

Several interesting incidents occurred during the progress of the conference: A group of Polish patriots submitted a petition that we take up the question of Polish independence. A delegation of Zionists set forth reasons why Palestine should be made the seat of the Court. J. B. Livesay proposed a "Peace Society of the World."

On May 6th, Dr. Jeremiah W. Jenks and I had a conversation with Dr. Bernard Dernberg, the reputed unofficial spokesman of the Kaiser in this country. Dr. Dernberg knew of the event planned to terrorize the world on the following day—the torpedoing and sinking of the *Lusitania;* nevertheless, he calmly assured us that the Kaiser and the German people were in favor of a World Court!

In its meetings in 1916 the World Court League proposed to lay special emphasis on the study of the nature and the development of the United States Supreme Court, a study which should reveal useful analogies for an international court. A minor convention was held at Louisville, Kentucky, in April, and a special effort was made to secure favorable resolutions from state legislatures. The Second Annual Congress was held in New York on May 2-4, 1916. I wrote to Colonel House in April, explaining our program and assuring him that the war and preparedness issues would not be raised, and then asked that he get President Wilson to speak. Colonel House replied, "It is impossible for the President to make any commitments at present."

The World Court League now had the valuable assistance of an active and enthusiastic Women's Committee with the following officers: Miss Mabel T. Boardman, president; Mrs. Champ Clark, Mrs. Henry Clews, Mrs. Lindley M. Garrison, Mrs. John Hays Hammond, Mrs. Charles Evans Hughes, Mrs. Thomas J. Preston, Mrs. James Speyer, and Mrs. William Howard Taft, vice-presidents; Mrs. Alice Fisher Harcourt, secretary.

Our discussions were not so much on the desirability of the Court, for the public mind had really accepted that, but rather on its feasibility. As the *World Court Magazine* put it, the problem was no longer one of pure ethics; it was a problem of practical operation.

Taft discussed with great acumen the initial jurisdiction of a World Court, and the ways in which its jurisdictions could legally be extended so as to give it latitude for really effective ruling. General Leonard Wood spoke on the issue of preparedness: "Our country should be prepared to take its part with force when reason fails; there is nothing in the constitution of the Court which makes—or should make—its members pacifists." Senator Warren G. Harding said, "Yes, I believe in a World Court, I am very enthusiastic about it." My own emphasis was placed on the need for raising international questions out of the field of diplomacy and conciliation and arbitration into a field where not national but human welfare would be the first consideration: when a World Court became representative of genuine world interest, that is, of justice, nations would not be fearful of submitting disputes to its decision.

At the end of May our society joined with the League to Enforce Peace in their first assemblage. Our aims were to some extent the same, though it is significant that James Brown Scott, secretary of the Carnegie Endowment for International Peace, refused my invitation to speak at the assemblage on the ground that he could not lend, by his presence, support to the *Enforcement* aspect of the program. In taking this stand he was true to the principles of the Second Hague Conference and to the position of Andrew Carnegie.

Through the efforts of our Judicial Settlements Society, the Republican National Convention, in June, 1916, adopted a plank favoring a World Court, and the inclusion of it in Hughes's speech of acceptance. During the campaign I spent much of my time on political matters and eventually resigned the presidency of the World Court League.

The third peace movement in which I took an active part was Theodore Marburg's League of Peace, or League to Enforce Peace. As I served on the Executive Committee and then on the International Committee, from its beginning in 1915 up to 1919, I shall review briefly its history in so far as I personally know it.

Theodore Marburg gave a dinner at the Century Club in New York, on January 25, 1915, and there proposed a League of Peace. I could not be present but I was on hand at the second meeting, January 31st. The program included the World Court plan as its first step and then proceeded to put "teeth" into the Court, as I shall show later. Although I never could conscientiously advocate its more extreme measures, it contained so much that I agreed with that I gladly joined, served on its committees, and made speeches on those phases which I thoroughly believed in. I had the sincerest friendship for, and confidence in, Theodore Marburg, and the League was his greatest effort in the cause of peace. The two volumes of his *Development of the League of Nations Idea* give the full story, and form an important chapter in modern history.

The setbacks the League was destined to suffer were indicated in its early days. Theodore Roosevelt's reply to Marburg was, "But our prime duty is ourselves to be prepared." James Brown Scott said, "I do not see how we are justified to advance proposals—which we know would not, indeed could not, be accepted by our country." Marburg, Howland, and I were appointed to consult James Bryce, whose reply was that "a cautious and limited scheme has a better chance than such a large one as would satisfy you and Mr. Root and our British group." Howland, on the other hand, expressed the growing opinion that "The Hague Conventions are now in the scrapheap. They lacked the compelling force to make them effective under the conditions which existed, just before the outbreak of the Great War" and that a League of Peace will have to contain a "guarantee to be maintained when necessary by the use against offending nations of the united force of the nations of the League." *Quot homines tot sententiae.*

After several discussions and the examination of the criticisms, the Executive Committee agreed on a platform. Whereas the first proposal included the setting up of a League Police Force to compel obedience to the decisions of the Court, the committee decided to drop this provision as being too radical an invasion of national rights. It was hoped that the defenders of the two long-standing clauses of American foreign policy—"Monroe Doctrine" and "No Entangling Alliances"—would thus be placated. The name of the organization was decided on: The League to Enforce Peace. Preparation was made for the public inauguration of the League, and on June 17th a great meeting was held at Independence Hall in Philadelphia.

The platform was written by William Howard Taft, then the League's president.

> The principles and project of the League to Enforce Peace, as projected by the American Section of its promoters, are few and simple. Shortly stated, they look to the peaceable procedure for the hearing and decision of all international controversies, to be enforced by the joint power of the nations of the world. The force is to be applied in securing the due process under the agreements of the League. It does not extend to the enforcement of the judgment or recommendation of compromise which shall be the result of the hearing. The essence of the plan is the delay and deliberation involved in orderly procedure for the hearing and decision of the controversy. It is thought that most wars can be avoided by such a procedure, and the force is to be applied against the premature hostilities of any na-

tion which violates its plighted faith under the League by beginning war before the procedure of hearing and judgment has been completed.

On September 17th the Executive Committee passed the following resolution: "Efficient preparation for adequate national defense is in no way inconsistent with the purposes of the League, but on the contrary is essential thereto." Those who lived through the war years will remember how necessary it was at that time for our League to dissociate itself from the less conservative and more sentimental and visionary peace societies. As it was, our society was frequently misunderstood, and repeated pronouncements had to be made in the effort, not always successful, to assure the public that we were not "pacifist," "pro-German," or utopian. In the official announcement for the First Assemblage at Washington in May, 1916, A. Lawrence Lowell wrote:

> It is emphatically not a "stop-the-war" movement, neither is it an "anti-preparedness" organization, nor is it a "peace-at-any-price" endeavor. It represents an earnest effort by practical men, to secure joint action by the principal nations, after the close of the European war, looking towards the establishment of more permanent peace by the use of economic and military force.

Though I had failed in April in my effort to get President Wilson to attend the World Court Congress, the negative I received seemed to be due to the President's being overwhelmed with business and not to any unfriendliness. I knew, at any rate, that Colonel House was favorable, and we all felt that Wilson's speech at Des Moines on February 1st gave ground for thinking he was ready to espouse our cause openly:

> "I pray God that if this contest have no other result, it will at least have the result of creating an international tribunal and producing some sort of joint guarantee of peace on the part of the great nations of the world."

This statement I copied out and enclosed with a letter I wrote House on May 17, 1916:

There is to be a meeting of the League to Enforce Peace on May 26th and 27th at the New Willard Hotel, Washington. I am enclosing a tentative program for that meeting, also a descriptive pamphlet showing the object of the League.

At a meeting the other day a committee of the League discussed how best to present an invitation to President Wilson to speak on this occasion: and before sending an official invitation to the President they wished to ascertain whether or not it will be possible for him to accept it, knowing his urgent official engagements. I told them frankly that I did not know how far President Wilson would commit himself to the use of arms to compel signatory powers to the League to submit their controversies to a Court before commencing hostilities. I did say, however, that I believe that he could, consistent with his other declarations on the subject of a World Court, go so far as to advocate a policy of nonintercourse with a recalcitrant nation in such a contingency.

Mr. Theodore Marburg, one of the members of the Committee, gave me a quotation from a speech of President Wilson which I enclose.

Would you please let me know whether or not you can be of service to the League in this matter, and whether I should arrange to have an invitation extended to the President through you, or whether it would be better to send an invitation directly to the President. Your kindly offices will be appreciated by the members of the League and myself.

The World Court League, of which I am president and of which I spoke to you, has for its object the establishment of a World Court at the opportune moment. Our League relies for the enforcement of its decrees upon the pressure of the sentiment of the world, rather than the application of physical force. Both Leagues are agitating the establishment of a World Court.

Would you kindly let me hear from you by telephone

or send me word where I may call to see you, should
you wish to discuss the matter further.

This time we were successful. President Wilson attended the
meeting of May 27th and stated that the United States was ready
to take its place in "an universal association of the nations . . . to
prevent any war begun either contrary to treaty covenants or without warning and full submission of the causes to the opinion of the
world."

"I cannot tell you how pleased I am with your speech last night,"
Colonel House wrote the President the next day, "it will be a land-
mark in history."

By this time the League had been supported by resolutions passed
in several state legislatures I had addressed on the subject, and it
seemed opportune to secure a resolution from Congress. Marburg
and Taft suggested to Wilson, therefore, that he have proposed in
Congress an administration measure favoring the League. Wilson
said that would not do, because of the opportunity it would offer
for speeches against the measure on the floor. Taft agreed with
Wilson, and Marburg reluctantly gave up the idea.

During the year 1916 our Committee on Foreign Organization
proceeded to enlist the interest of the countries of Europe, those at
war and the neutrals. Our literature was translated into several
languages and sent to government officials and prominent persons.
Marburg had been in France and England, from February to April,
and had opened the question of the League with many influential
people. Sir Edward Grey, shortly afterwards created Viscount Grey
of Fallodon, was strong in his support, and his successor in office,
Arthur J. Balfour, was hardly less interested. Correspondence was
carried on with European chancelleries and we had conversations
with foreign ambassadors at Washington. The result was encouraging. While the almost universal reply was to the effect that
cabinets were too much engrossed in the immediate problems of
the war to give proper attention to a plan for peace after the war,
the League was accepted "in principle," and that was really all
that could be expected.

As a crowning move in this international campaign we proposed
to send Taft to Europe as our emissary. England was particularly

anxious to have him come for the moral support of his presence. He was, of course, to talk with individuals only, and in the capacity of a private citizen; no attempt was to be made to promote inter-Allied conferences. Taft was persuaded to undertake the mission and went to President Wilson to ask his opinion. Wilson's answer was that he did not like it at all, and Taft replied, "Thank you, that ends it." The project was abandoned.

It began to be clear that unless Congress, and particularly the Senate, was in favor of the League the whole movement would be futile so far as American participation was concerned, and from 1916 on we determined to concentrate our efforts on the Senate and the House. Sir Edward Grey, on February 19th, expressed the fear that "the U. S. Senate will not adhere, which would make of the League merely a concert of the powers of Europe."

After we entered the war, like the other warring nations, we had to concentrate our efforts on winning it. The League should, however, as Glenn Frank said in an appeal to the members on April 24, 1917, meet its new obligations, which were to keep clear in the public mind that we were fighting for future security. The phrases of Wilson, "Make the world safe for democracy" and the "League of Honor," indicate the accord between us and the administration. The League had from its very foundation recognized the necessity of a policy of preparedness for defense, and throughout the two years of war supported the administration in its vigorous prosecution. On May 16-17, 1918, we held a memorable meeting in Philadelphia, the theme of which was, "Win the War for Permanent Peace."

That our work was of interest to the administration may be gathered from my letter to Taft, July 27, 1917:

My dear Bill: The other night dining with Colonel House I had a chance to discuss with him the future of the League to Enforce Peace, and he expressed the wish that I should arrange a meeting some time in the near future, when mutually convenient, with you, President Lowell, myself and him, to discuss certain features of the plans. I believe that Colonel House can be and would be of great assistance to us if we take the trouble to enlist his co-operation . . .

Synchronized with all my work for peace, and arising out of it, was the debate between the pacifists, in the invidious sense of the term, and the advocates of preparedness, a controversy in which I was necessarily active.

Before the outbreak of the World War, all of us who were identified with peace movements called ourselves pacifists. But with the appearance of peace societies of the nonresistant order, it became necessary to distinguish between the peace-at-any-price groups, among whom Henry Ford, Dr. David Starr Jordan, and Jane Addams were prominent, and the groups that considered adequate national defense consistent with the advocacy of peace.

As the war ran on into 1915, many Americans became concerned over the state of our army and navy. A grudging Congress had starved both, and the war waging in Europe had not roused either Congress or Cabinet to action. The soothing reply to questions was that the national defense was adequate—a reply that was contradicted by both army and navy and, as later became obvious, by the facts. The administration. in its official insistence on neutrality seemed bent on proving its neutrality by being unprepared. Not even the sinking of the *Lusitania* on May 7, 1915, brought any change in the official position.

At this juncture Henry A. Wise Wood came to see me, and after our talk I took steps looking to the building up of the nation's defenses. What these steps consisted of, and the results that followed upon them, were explained in a letter Wood wrote me four years later, September 24, 1919:

Professor William H. Hobbs, of Ann Arbor, Mich., is bringing out a book entitled "Leonard Wood and the Preparedness Movement," which gives a history of both. I have supplied Hobbs with a great deal of data concerning the latter, among which is a reference to the exceedingly important part you played at a critical moment in 1915. Hobbs recounts this incident in the following words:

"A month after the *Lusitania* outrage the Conference Committee on National Preparedness was organized among the defense societies with Henry A. Wise Wood as chairman. The wisdom of this union of effort was at once to be proven, though the facts which we are here to present have not before been given to the public. The chairman of the Conference Committee was a friend of John Hays Hammond and both were during the summer the neighbors of Colonel House at his home near Cape Ann, Massachusetts. Since House was the unique confidential friend of the President, Wood made a strong appeal to Hammond to see if he could not through House get the President to move in the now desperate matter of our national defense. This Hammond did, but with no other result than a suggestion from House to get in touch with the Secretary of War. This failing to bring results, the appeal was renewed by Mr. Wood, though in a different way. In a personal letter he writes:

I hunted up Hammond and told him something really had to be done, saying that the sentiment for preparedness was rising so rapidly throughout the country that the inactivity of the administration would soon become a public scandal, and that the Democratic party would have only the President to thank if it should be utilized by its political opponents. I suggested that Hammond see House again and point out to him the *political* danger into which the President was running because of his refusal to take the steps necessary to prepare the Army and Navy for active service. Hammond said that he would act at once, and did. He saw House and told the latter that unless proper defensive measures were at once taken by the administration the President might expect the Republican party to make a political issue of Wilson's inactivity. Hammond told House that while the Republican party would not wish to make political capital out of such a matter, Mr. Wilson was so shaping affairs that the Republican party in order to fulfill its duty would be compelled to attack him for his dereliction. This, Hammond told me, greatly aroused Colonel House, who said that he would write at once to the President, at Cornish, and recommend that something be done. Immediately after Mr. Hammond's action came Mr. Wilson's half-hearted request for recommendations by the General Board of the Navy and the General Staff of the Army.

"These requests for reports on what was necessary for the National defense were sent from Cornish on July 21st and the reports of the two Boards were submitted to the President on July 30th. The reports of these expert Boards, containing, as they did, such vitally important information for the safety of the country, were not given to the public. In the public mind was the question, 'Was the President right when he assured the joint houses of Congress, and through them the nation, that they had been misinformed and that the national defense was already secure?' or did a desperate condition exist such as General Wood, Admiral Fiske, Congressman Gardner, and a number of former Secretaries of War had asserted? If these latter were right and the President wrong, it was obviously necessary to at once utilize every available agency to the end of supporting representatives in Congress when that body should meet and take up the consideration of the necessary appropriation bills."

Professor Hobbs will be glad to have you add any further matters that you have in mind, or to make such corrections in the above as you may deem necessary. My own view is that it was your action that turned the President from one course to the other and thus was a major influence in inaugurating our active military preparations.

This account agrees in substance with my recollection of the matter. I have only to add that Mr. Wood asked me to take the chairmanship of a defense committee, which I refused on the ground that to do so might handicap the cause since my son, John Hays Hammond, Jr., was at that time negotiating the sale to the government of his invention to control boats by radio.

Colonel House and I had been friends in our Hopkins Grammar School days in New Haven when he was a classmate of my brother Bill. Although Colonel House had been for many years a summer resident near Manchester (only a few miles from Gloucester), I had not seen him until after the inauguration of President Wilson when House dined with me at my summer home. At that meeting he told me that he was called "the John Hays Hammond of the Wilson administration." I said, "I hope you will have more influence with President Wilson than I had with President Taft; I failed to use such influence that perhaps I should have exerted."

As will become more and more apparent with the passage of years, Colonel House has been one of the greatest influences behind the scenes of American politics, and of world statecraft as well.

During the war Colonel House's cottage at Coolidge Point was a veritable "hub of the universe": every important diplomat who came from Europe was sent by President Wilson to consult with the colonel.

House has often been called "the man of mystery." There is nothing mysterious about him. He is a man without the usual pecuniary interests in life. The fact that no one can accuse him of private or selfish concern in his actions gives him great power and freedom of opinion. He has never liked publicity, which frees him from suspicion of greed for the limelight. He seldom appears in public. Today he sits in his home and receives, one after another, the great men of the world who use him as intermediary and spokesman because he is that most unusual phenomenon—a man without self-interest. He is actively behind the scenes in Franklin D. Roosevelt's administration, admittedly concentrating his keen analytical powers on international problems.

In the formation of the Wilson Cabinet, House was more influential than any other of Wilson's political advisers. In his *Intimate Papers,* House has understated the part he played in the Wilson administration. This I know, for it was my privilege to be his confidant in many instances just before and during the period of the World War.

When I first approached him on the subject, Colonel House assured me that he was in favor of preparedness and had given such support as he could to General Leonard Wood's citizen training camp at Plattsburg. At his suggestion I went to Washington and saw Secretary of War Garrison, who said that he had already taken steps to make the army more efficient for warfare. I talked with several other high officials, and also with Samuel Gompers, with whom I arranged a conference in a drawing room on the train between Washington and New York. At first he refused his cooperation, urging that preparedness was a militaristic aim that might be used later on to dragoon labor. Fortunately, before we reached New York, my arguments prevailed and Gompers became an important factor in the preparedness movement, as shown by his unswerving loyalty to the cause and by his splendid record during the war.

On my return to Gloucester I discussed the subject of preparedness with Secretary of the Navy Daniels, at a dinner at my home, August 25, 1915. Secretary Daniels at that time favored the idea of increased efficiency of the navy, though only a short time before he had made the public statement that the navy was already adequately prepared.

In the fall of that year I was a guest of Senator Frank Newlands, of Nevada, at a small lunch in San Francisco, attended by Senator Oscar W. Underwood, of Alabama, Senator Phelan, of California, and Norman E. Mack, Democratic National Committeeman for New York.

We discussed the national election to be held in 1916. I was the only Republican present, but we were all old friends and the discussion was perfectly frank.

I told Senator Underwood that I thought the Republicans would win, on the issue of the tariff. (At that time the Underwood Tariff was in effect.) Senator Newlands interrupted the argument by saying: "Jack, you are entirely on the wrong track. The tariff will cut no figure in the next national campaign. The people of the country are strongly opposed to our being dragged into the World War, and President Wilson will have a War Program in the campaign on the slogan that he will keep us out of war."

Although Mr. Wilson, on a speechmaking tour in January, 1916, uttered sentiments in favor of preparedness (at St. Louis, declaring for "incomparably the most adequate navy in the world"), he afterwards soft-pedaled, probably on political advice and carried on the campaign of 1916 as forecast by Senator Newlands. Private individuals and societies were left to agitate for preparedness. The Republicans used the issue as one point in criticism of the Democrats, and I remember that Vice-President Marshall, in his defense of Wilson in the *Forum* of July, 1916, could only weakly say that it ill befitted the secretaries of the Taft administration to criticize. As if nothing had happened between 1912 and 1916!

The League to Enforce Peace had a joint meeting with all the defense societies, and its speakers, myself included, took occasion to emphasize the need for preparedness. I made a point of it in my political speeches before various audiences: before the National Republican League in conference in Washington, December 13, 1915; before the Detroit Board of Commerce on December 27, 1915; and at the National Republican League Convention at Chicago, June 6, 1916. I reviewed the whole problem of preparedness, answering objections as well as I could, before the National Civic Federation at Washington on January 18, 1916. In January, 1917, Governor Whitman appointed me New York's delegate to the Congress of Constructive Patriotism held in Washington.

The "pacifists" were claiming that the defense movement was being fostered by the manufacturers of munitions, who were making vast profits out of the war and hoped to make still more. The point was an awkward one and gave rise to the proposal that private profit should somehow be taken out of the business. Colonel House had in mind this sort of solution when he wrote, apropos of measures that ought to be taken after the sinking without warning of the *Arabic* on August 19, 1915:

I would begin preparations for defense and for the war, just as vigorously as if war had been declared. I would put the entire matter of defense and the manufacture of munitions in the hands of a non-partisan commission composed mostly of business men—men like John Hays Hammond, Guy Tripp, and others of that sort.

Just before the election, on a New York-Washington train, I met the German ambassador, von Bernstorff, whom I knew very well. He asked me what I thought would be the result of the election. I replied by asking for his opinion, adding that I felt sure he favored the re-election of President Wilson. He wanted to know on what grounds. I said: "Because it is to the advantage of Germany that America does not join with the Allies, and Germany depends on Wilson to keep America out of the war. Furthermore, even if we are forced into the war on the side of the Allies, President Wilson's opposition to a preparedness program will ensure diminished efficiency in our support of the Allies." Naturally, von Bernstorff revealed nothing.

The failure to prepare during the years 1915 and 1916, up to the time of our joining the Allies (April, 1917), undoubtedly resulted in the loss of many precious months in equipping our nation to take part effectively in the early stages of our military campaign abroad. I think it is agreed that, had we been thoroughly prepared for war, it is quite likely that Germany would have refrained from some of the acts that caused us to declare war. In any event, it is certain that had we been properly equipped when we joined the Allies the war would have ended considerably sooner than it did and there would have been the saving of many lives and the costs of war. As General Wood said, "It is better to be ready for war and not have it, than to have war and not be ready for it." But alas! Woodrow Wilson yielded to political expediency.

CHAPTER THIRTY-ONE

From the World Court to the
League of Nations

THE anniversary of Armistice Day should stir us to great exultation of spirit, because of the proud recollection that it was our precept and example which had, by those early days of that never-to-be-forgotten November, lifted the nations of the world to the lofty level of vision and achievement upon which the great war for democracy and right was fought and won. Although the stimulating memories of that happy time of triumph are forever marred and embittered for us by the shameful fact that when victory was won—chiefly by the indomitable spirit and ungrudging sacrifice of our incomparable soldiers—we turned our backs on our associates, refused to bear any responsible part in the administration of the peace, or the firm and permanent establishment of the results won by the war at so fearful a cost of life and treasure, and withdrew into a sullen and selfish isolation which is deeply ignoble because manifestly dishonorable.

With these words Woodrow Wilson began his last statement to the American people—his radio address on the eve of the fifth anniversary of the Armistice.

History offers few episodes more tragically bewildering than this, in which Woodrow Wilson points the finger of scorn and shame at the country he had led in a valiant war and had attempted to make responsible for an enduring peace.

When the end of the war was almost in sight, it seemed to me that the foundations of the League might be begun immediately. On October 29, 1918, I wrote ex-President Taft:

> President Wilson and Lord Bryce, it seems, are opposed to the creation of a League to Enforce Peace before the end of the war. It has always been my belief that such a League already established would be able to render great service in the settlement of many of the important details relative to the terms of peace, and it seems to me that the nucleus of such a League now exists in the Allied Nations. The Allies should create this League either independently of, or with the co-operation of the Neutral Nations, after which the present Enemy Nations should be invited to join the League. As the result of their experience in the present war the Allies should be able to devise an effective League. This League should assert jurisdiction over all Nations whether members of the League or not when the safety of the world is involved. Germany's Allies in this war would undoubtedly avail themselves of the opportunity of joining such a League, and however Germany might resent the League having been started without consulting her, she would eventually also find it to her interest to join it.

I sent a copy of the letter to Marburg, who replied under date of October 31st:

> Dear Jack: . . . I was also pleased to see your letter to Mr. Taft. You of course know that some few of us have been urging just this thing for a year past, having the hearty support of the French group in this movement. I fear that owing to President Wilson's attitude there is little hope of the project being realized, the more so because events connected with the war are moving so fast.
>
> But everything is working out just right. The great aim of the war, you no doubt agree, is the destruction of Prussianism, which can be accomplished effectively only by the German people themselves. President Wilson has risen wonderfully to the demands of the moment by emphasizing this side of it in his recent messages. It looks now as if we really would have revolution in Germany. If we get it everything else will be plain sailing. Without it we could not get an effective league and the future of the world would indeed be gloomy—the maddest kind of military preparation all around. . . .

Colonel House with remarkable discernment and vision advised President Wilson to go to Europe after the Armistice to size up the situation for himself and become acquainted with the leading European statesmen. He further urged him not to participate personally in the Versailles Conference but to return to the United States and from Washington direct the American representatives. This would undoubtedly have given Wilson far greater influence in the proceedings of the Conference.

House suggested that Taft and Root (or Taft and some prominent Republican senator) be on the American commission with three Democrats appointed by Wilson, one of whom should be a member of the Senate. Taft and Root would have added great strength, not only because of their wide experience in European affairs but because of the high esteem in which they were held by their countrymen. Instead, Wilson appointed his secretary of state, Robert Lansing, Colonel House, Tasker H. Bliss, and Henry White, all of whom were regarded by the country as affiliated with the Democratic party, with perhaps the exception of Henry White who was at the most a lukewarm Republican and whom the Republican leaders regarded as a Democrat.

Since the President decided to act in person at the Peace Conference, these men had no standing other than as his personal assistants, to be ignored or dismissed at his will. Their names had not been submitted to the Senate for confirmation. The President in this fashion organized his Peace Mission only a few short weeks after the country had been chilled, even in the midst of victorious advance on the western front, by the dictum that "if you wish me to be your unembarrassed spokesman in affairs at home and abroad, I earnestly beg that you express yourselves unmistakably to that effect by returning a Democratic majority to both the Senate and the House of Representatives." This appeal was resented not only by the Republican party which had rendered patriotic service to Wilson in the winning of the war, but by the country at large as evidenced in the return of a Republican majority in Congress.

Wilson sailed for Paris, December 4, 1918. With Colonel House in Europe, jealous and self-interested advisers began to influence the President that he should be on the ground himself in order to maintain his ideas and—I say it with some hesitation, but believe it to be true—for his own exaltation.

Before sailing Wilson boasted that he was to match wits with the statesmen of Europe. He little realized that he was to sit in a game of poker with a "cold deck" provided by the conferees.

The League to Enforce Peace was now placed in an awkward position. In the first place, we were kept in the dark as to the course of negotiations for a League of Nations; in the second place, when news did come the clauses providing for drastic sanctions to be employed against recalcitrant members of the League went further than our League to Enforce Peace had ever advocated. In both these difficulties, however, the League to Enforce Peace supported the President blindly and loyally. When opposition began to appear, both Taft and Marburg stood staunchly and wholeheartedly by the Wilson program. Some of us could not do so.

On January 5, 1919, at the Maryland convention, the League to Enforce Peace passed a unanimous resolution in support of Wilson in his efforts to get a League of Nations established. A cablegram was sent from the convention to Wilson assuring him that the sentiment of the country was behind him and that the recalcitrant senators must eventually dissent from their opposition to the League of Nations. I did not agree with these views and opposed sending the cablegram but without avail. I offered controversial material in my own speech in the following points: Do we need a League of Nations? If so, what power are we willing to delegate to such a League? What steps must be taken to create the League?

To the first question the answer was "Yes." To the second I showed a "reservationist" attitude: "If the authority delegated to the League in the enforcement of its decrees by armed intervention is considered too far-reaching, the authority might, I believe, be curtailed in some respects without seriously impairing the potency of the League."

In answering the third question I was more sharply critical:

"Now what are the best steps to be taken for the creation of a League of Nations? The present is not the time for partisan politics, and I have, I am glad to say, not seen, as yet, any disposition on the part of statesmen of either party to make a League of Nations the football of politics. But, in the consideration of the supreme problem of world peace, it is the duty of those who have given the subject careful consideration to speak frankly and fearlessly, if such expression of views will be of ultimate assistance in the promotion of this all-important movement.

"It does not seem that we are proceeding along the right lines—certainly not on the lines of least resistance—to attain the creation of a League of Nations. For obvious reasons, the nations of Europe, who have paid such a great price to 'save democracy' and to whom the menace of war is more imminent, will be more ready to accept a subordination of their national sovereignty to consummate the project of a League of Nations than will the people of the United States. It is among the people of our own country that a campaign of education must be carried on.

"In all probability, at the Versailles Conference the European representatives will be empowered to conclude a treaty creating a League of Nations without reference to further sanction by their respective governments. In this respect, our delegates to the Peace Conference will be, unfortunately, seriously handicapped in their negotiations, inasmuch as any treaty they may make on behalf of our country would be merely tentative—subject to ratification by the United States Senate. The Senate may, perhaps, at times deserve criticism for ultraconservatism and for its reluctance to admit of any encroachment upon its prerogative as a party to our foreign treaties. I hold no brief, but as regards the present attitude of the Senate with reference to the proposed League of Nations, we surely cannot censure it in so far as it is noncommittal, nor for its refusal to give its endorsement *to plans of which the Senators themselves have not been apprised.*

"The proper procedure would be the development of some plan which would receive the endorsement of the Senate in advance of its submission to the other nations. A plan having this sanction could then be presented as the American Plan, the principles of which had already been accepted by the Senate, and which would have the approbation of the people of the United States.

"We should not be deterred by a false sense of delicacy in requesting from President Wilson and the American Peace Delegates an outline of their plan. If it meets our approval, we should take immediate steps to present our recommendations to the Senate, backed by whatever influence we may command, with the view to obtaining its endorsement and its co-operation.

"Inasmuch as the League to Enforce Peace has given to this subject more consideration than any other American organization, and has had, moreover, the advantage of the collaboration of the best minds of this country, its intervention in this matter could not reasonably be regarded as officious. This course would undoubtedly facilitate an understanding between the Senate and our Peace Delegates, thereby expediting definite and definitive action. Otherwise, the creation of the League of Nations would be subject to delay which would be from every point of view highly undesirable. . . ."

It is true that in giving carte blanche to the President in its resolution the convention discounted my objections, but I submit that my criticism touched on political realities as proved by the subsequent history of the League of Nations in the Senate and before the American people.

One of the very few in the audience to sympathize with my attitude was Major Fiorello H. La Guardia, who had just returned with a distinguished record in the World War.

On January 30th, I wrote to Theodore Marburg:

. . . I fear the President is not making the progress that we wish in connection with *his* League of Nations. Of course, it is most difficult to get the unadulterated truth from Paris through the press which is still virtually under censorship. It will be a great misfortune for the world unless some kind of a League is established to eliminate the causes of war. You see now the futility of soliciting the cooperation of Senators in a scheme of which the promoters themselves are so ignorant. Team-work is the only method by which anything could have been accomplished, and President Wilson is not strong on team-work. The day of dictation has passed in November last on the day of our Congressional Election . . .

On February 13th, Marburg wrote me:

> I wrote you a post card from the station last night suggesting that, after all, you carry out the plan of having a few Senators at the dinner at your home tomorrow night.
>
> I had with me last night only Senator McCumber and Mr. J. J. Rogers of the House, who, I understand, had a good chance of becoming Chairman of the Committee on Foreign Affairs for the House in the coming Congress. Francis B. Loomis also joined us. The little talk was exactly right, the Senator and Mr. Rogers participating freely and both accepting the program which you and I stand for, i. e., force limited to compelling inquiry, plus the various institutions we plan to set up. We were at it until quarter past eleven and canvassed the subject pretty well. . . .

With the work of the Peace Conference partly done, Wilson returned to America, arriving February 23rd. He then entertained the Senate Foreign Relations Committee at the White House, and discussed with them the draft of the League of Nations Covenant as it had been submitted to the Peace Conference on the eve of his leaving Paris. Although the document was not then submitted for the action of the Senate, more than one-third of the members of that body took the initiative in warning him of their opposition to the plan of the League of Nations as he had approved it. This was a sufficient number to prevent the ratification of the Treaty. To these Mr. Wilson gave public answer as he again took ship for Paris, March 14th. "When that Treaty comes back, gentlemen on this side will find the covenant not only in it, but so many threads of the treaty tied to the covenant that you cannot dissect the covenant from the treaty without destroying the whole vital structure."

The day Wilson sailed for Paris, a message came to me from the editor of the New York *World* asking that I telegraph him for publication in the *World* my views "as to desirability of League of

Nations," and any suggestions or criticisms I might care to make with respect to the "pending draft of the League's provisions." I give my reply in full for the light it throws on my drift into the "reservationist" camp:

> My political affiliations are Republican, but I regard a League of Nations as a national and not a partisan matter. Politics must be entirely dissociated from the problem of World Peace. I am an earnest advocate of the creation of a League of Nations, properly constituted, believing that such a League of Nations would have prevented the recent great World War. The advocates of a League of Nations realize that no political organizations can do more than minimize the possibility of war. I do not believe that our Nation should endeavor to maintain an attitude of "splendid isolation" as to World politics. Our detached position, geographical and political, did not suffice to keep us out of the recent war. We are now a World Power and have world-wide interests. While we should aim to minimize "entangling alliances," we must, nevertheless, be ready to assume our international responsibilities if we are to insist upon our national rights.
>
> A speedy settlement with Germany and her allies is of paramount importance, in view of the disturbed political and economic conditions of the world. To effect this speedy settlement, it is necessary that the Treaty of Peace with Germany and her allies should be separate from the Treaty creating a League of Nations.
>
> I am opposed to the pending draft of the League of Nations. It is loosely phrased and generally ambiguous. Moreover, where the meaning is clear, it is in many respects highly objectionable.
>
> For example, under article 10, the United States would be committed to "preserve, as against external aggression, the territorial integrity and existing political

independence of all states members of the League." This means preserving the status quo of the whole World, which is an onerous obligation and the observance of which might in the future become highly undesirable. Our obligations should be confined to an agreement not to invade the territories of the members of the League. The League should, however, undertake to protect the territorial integrity of the newly constituted Nations under the mandatory system, with such power to readjust territorial boundaries as future experience might necessitate in the interest of justice and of peace.

A permanent court to try justiciable controversies should be definitely established in the Treaty creating the League of Nations. Otherwise, a separate Treaty will be necessary to establish such a tribunal. The members of the League should be compelled to submit all justiciable questions to this court.

While article 13 contains a provision that the contracting parties will carry out in good faith any award that may be rendered by a Court of Arbitration, article 15, which provides for the reference of disputes to the Executive Council or the Body of Delegates, contains no similar provision, except that the contracting parties agree not to go to war if the decision of the Executive Council or the Body of Delegates is unanimous.

Article 16 assumes vague obligations and requires both clarification and limitation.

As to mandatories, the United States should not only be willing to assume, but should insist upon being, the mandatory in the case of the need of a mandatory for the Western Hemisphere. Under the proposed constitution, the United States would not be compelled to assume any mandatory, but I believe if the constitution of the proposed League were satisfactory in other respects, the responsibility of a mandatory would not be an insuperable objection.

There should be in the constitution, a specific exclusion of the Monroe Doctrine in its broadest implication and the question of immigration and of tariffs and other domestic questions should be also excluded from the jurisdiction of the League.

As I interpret article 8 as to disarmament, the objection against it seems hypercritical, inasmuch as the extent of military equipment is a matter to be determined by the respective governments themselves in the first instance. It is true that thereafter the forces shall not be exceeded without the permission of the Executive Council. The self-enlightened interest of the respective members of the League would eventually dictate a common policy as to disarmament.

As the League is a matter of experiment, the contracting powers should have the privilege of withdrawing from the membership any time after a period of ten years.

It must be conceded by all that ententes and alliances, with their secret treaties, espionage, and nefarious diplomacy, have utterly failed. Let us try a League of Nations. The infamous Holy Alliance is no precedent to quote in opposing a League of Nations. The World will certainly not go back to competitive armaments in the future to maintain World peace, but the proposed draft must be made more clear, more specific, and amended in many particulars.

Marburg was not in agreement with my stand for reservations. After reading a copy of my telegram to the *World*, he wrote me (April 7th) avowing unqualified support of the Wilson program:

I quite share the view that the convention could be improved by certain amendments and we may of course look forward to such improvement as indicated by the Paris dispatches. I would have been willing, however, to accept the document just as it was, feeling the following to be a fundamental thing, namely, that practically the whole world, cooperating, is pretty sure to be governed by reason and to do justice. Personally, I should go so far as to say that I would be satisfied to have the United States go into a rough agreement to cooperate in this way through a central council without any written document whatever. I shall not, however, inflict you at this time with an argument on this line . . .

Woodrow Wilson did bring back in July the kind of treaty he said he would when he sailed in March, to submit to the Senate for the "advice and consent" of that body.

The Senate's opposition to the United States joining a League of Nations became more formidable as the subject was agitated. Many of us began to realize the impossibility of committing any future national administration to the plan of the League of Nations as approved by President Wilson, since whatever commitments the Wilson administration might make, even if approved by the Senate, would be liable to repudiation under certain contingencies by succeeding administrations.

To ensure a League of Nations compatible with our political institutions and the spirit of the nation, Senator Lodge, as chairman of the Foreign Relations Committee, had moved the approval of the Versailles Treaty, including the League Covenant, but with certain reservations as a *sine qua non* of the United States joining the League.

After weeks of acrimonious debate in the Senate, the President met with the Foreign Relations Committee on August 19th, and two weeks later set out to carry the fight to the country. It was soon reported that the senators who trailed him were gaining the larger and more responsive audiences; and it became apparent that "the irreconcilables," the "pygmy men," the "jaundice-eyed Bolsheviks of politics," as the President had variously called his opponents, were probing the deeper instincts and sensing the sounder traditions of American political life. Doubling back from the Pacific coast, on September 26th, near Wichita, Wilson's health snapped, and with drawn shades at which the nation gazed sympathetically his train carried him back to Washington.

On November 19th, the Lodge motion to ratify the Treaty with reservations was defeated by a vote of 55 to 39. On the previous day, President Wilson had addressed a letter to the Democratic leader, Senator Hitchcock, in part as follows:

> In my opinion, the resolution in that form does not provide for ratification, but rather for nullification. I sincerely hope that the friends and supporters of the treaty will vote against the Lodge resolution of ratification. I understand that the door will then probably be open for a genuine resolution of ratification.

"Thus urged," says Colonel House in the *Intimate Papers,* "the Democrats voted with the 'bitter enders,' defeating ratification. Had the Democrats disregarded the President's wishes, and voted for ratification, including the Lodge resolution, the treaty would have been ratified by a vote of 81 to 13."

A few days before Viscount Grey of Fallodon, then serving as special ambassador to the United States, sailed for England early in January, 1920, he lunched with me at my house in Washington. After lunch I took him and the other guests, Colonel George Harvey, Senator Brandegee, my son Harris, and Lord Glenconner (who died shortly thereafter and whose widow Viscount Grey subsequently married,) up to my study.

We discussed the approaching presidential election, and I voiced my fears that there would inevitably be an acrimonious discussion of the League of Nations question in which criticism of England's "six votes to our one" and other objections would be violently debated.

At that time I was in favor of entering the League of Nations with the Lodge reservations, and I think Colonel Harvey probably would have agreed with me, but Senator Brandegee was unalterably opposed to entrance in any way, shape, or form. I therefore asked Viscount Grey whether it was true (as Wilson had said) that modifications or reservations on our part would be totally unacceptable to our late allies. Colonel Harvey took up the question with alacrity and pressed Viscount Grey with great adroitness to issue a public statement on his return to England. This statement was to be to the effect that he (Grey) understood that the above impression prevailed in America, through statements of President Wilson, but that, on the contrary, such reservations as those proposed by Senator Lodge would be entirely acceptable to the Allies, and consonant with the Covenant of the League and the Treaty of Versailles.

Viscount Grey naturally declined to commit himself at this time, but later in the afternoon, when I was having tea with him at the British Embassy, he told me that upon reflection he felt sure he would be able to make such a statement as we requested, and that he could probably work out the details on shipboard.

Three days after his return to England, Viscount Grey was in Paris reporting to the prime minister and Lord Curzon, who were attending the first session of the League. On the 22nd, the King gave audience to Grey and the prime minister; and on the 31st, the London *Times* began a lengthy editorial with the significant sentence, "We publish a communication today which is probably unique in the history of diplomacy." "Lord Grey, who until recently was the British Ambassador to the United States, and who technically still occupies that position," continued the *Times*, "now feels it his duty to make public his views, and what he believes to be the views of the American people, upon the subject of his mission."

Viscount Grey ascribed the status of the Treaty in the Senate to two underlying causes: 1. A real conservative feeling for the traditional policy of the nation; 2. The provision of the Constitution under which the Executive and the Legislature have separate functions in treaty-making. "Let us first get rid of one possible misunderstanding," the statement says. "No charge of bad faith or repudiating signatures can be brought against the action of the United States. The Senate, by the American Constitution, is an independent body, an independent element in the treaty-making power. Its refusal to ratify a treaty cannot expose either itself or the country to the charge of bad faith or repudiation."

On February 6th, George Harvey wrote me, reviewing the discussion that had taken place at my home and giving further details about how Grey's historic statement came to be made:

... Grey certainly did go through in fine shape, didn't he? When you come to think of it he carried through the programme outlined to the very letter, even to the time when the presentation of his views would prove most effective. It is really quite gratifying to recall that, after having thrashed out every detail of the reservations, and somewhat to his surprise, I suspect, finding that there was nothing but the friendliest of feelings toward England on the part of those of us here who were fighting the League, as we believe justifiably, he turned to me and said, "But what can I do? My hands seem to be tied." And I replied that the greatest service he could render his country and our country and the entire world would be by announcing shortly after his return home that his Government fully appreciated the natural apprehension felt by our people in making so radical a departure from their age-long traditions and that with this knowledge his Government stood ready to accept the Lodge reservations. "Would you not," you remember he asked in return, "cooperate in according our self-governing Dominions the recognition which they thought they had earned?" You will recall how pleased he seemed when I replied that, in my judgment our people were quite as friendly disposed toward the Dominions as they were towards the Mother Country itself and it was simply a question of framing a provision in such a way as to give them all they were entitled to, while maintaining for our own country moral and numerical equality with the Empire as a whole. This did not strike him as an insuperable obstacle and since it seemed to be the only one, he should concentrate his efforts on his way home in striving to find a solution which might be satisfactory and even welcome on all sides, even going so far as to add that personally he would be glad to have us have as many or even more votes than Britain if that would tend to cement our friendship because he did not believe we would ever disagree on anything of consequence.

There was much more of course, especially with reference to the remark of King Edward to Von Meyer, printed recently in *Scribner's,* of which apparently he had not heard, as constituting in my judgment the true and wisest policy respecting the future relations of England and America. If, however, it should seem desirable to work out something more definite, the only association of nations into which the United States could possibly enter would be one based upon law and not upon force . . . in a word, along the Hague lines, insuring application of justice after full hearings by an impartial tribunal through resolute enforcement (by whatever means required) of all decrees rendered.

You will remember how he came as near clapping his hands as one could expect and responded enthusiastically, "Why, that is what I want. That is what we all want!" And then he frankly agreed that an aspiration to that end would be the Chief justification of America entering into an engagement in the hope that out of it, through the working together hand in hand of England and America would evolve the true solution of peace without tyranny.

Well, in any case, Grey certainly far more than fulfilled expectations and it begins to look as if the settlement of the whole business dates from your luncheon. It was a good party anyhow and one well worth remembering . . .

"The settlement of the whole business" did not turn out as Harvey surmised. But Viscount Grey's statement had the immediate effect of undermining Wilson's dictum that the Treaty must be ratified, as it was commonly expressed, "without the dotting of an 'i', or the crossing of a 't'." Grey's insight, common sense, and understanding were pleasing to conservatives in America, but Wilson, wrathful, made sharp reply. It was felt on all sides that the Lodge motion could be passed any time within a few hours, if the President would give the lead. "Mr. Wilson is the man," a leading editorial read, "who threatens to block the way. He can do so only by degrading his presumably democratic office into a personal autocracy."

The Senate, under the suspension of its rules, voted to reconsider the Lodge resolution. Mr. Wilson remained obdurate, however, and on March 19th the Senate voted to send the Treaty back to the President without its approval. Wilson had resolved that the presidential canvass of 1920 should be a "great and solemn referendum" on the Treaty. Upon this issue his party suffered overwhelming defeat. By the mandate of that election, not only was the issue of the League of Nations buried beyond hope of resurrection for at least decades to come, but solemn warning was served that no supergovernment which would involve, even in a remote degree, the derogation of their national sovereignty would be tolerated by the American people. That may again be regarded as an established principle of governmental policy in our foreign relations.

As Viscount Grey came down the gangplank at Southampton after his visit to America, he was greeted with the cry that he might become president of the League of Nations. "I thought that was to be President Wilson's job," he retorted in disclaiming for himself visions of such grandeur and power.

When Clemenceau visited this country in 1923, he expressed to me a good deal of bitterness towards Wilson, and blamed him for everything that had gone wrong at Paris. *Et tu, Brute!*

Venizelos had been spoken of by Wilson as one of the ablest men at the Peace Conference. When I saw the Greek statesman in California in 1922, he had lost whatever admiration he may once have had for Woodrow Wilson. He blamed the failure of America to join the League of Nations on the obstinacy of Wilson in defending his own point of view.

Although the Grey statement had modified the harsh judgments of many European statesmen, the French continued intemperate in their condemnation of the United States for failure to live up to the agreement which Wilson *ultra vires* had made at Versailles.

On Armistice Day, 1923, an admiring throng gathered informally in front of the Wilson residence in Washington. The ex-President appeared before them and imperturbably avowed

"I am not one of those who have the least anxiety about the triumph of the principles I have stood for. I have seen fools resist Providence before, and I have seen their destruction, and it will come upon these again, utter destruction and contempt; that we shall prevail is as sure as that God reigns."

Viewed with the perspective of events since the war, it seems that the World Court idea, because it was less ambitious, was the more practical and possible of realization. A Court, limited wisely in jurisdiction, supplemented by a Council of Conciliation, seemed feasible and had won wide popular support. But the World Court was tied into the Covenant of the League of Nations as inextricably as the Covenant was tied into the Peace Treaty.

President Harding initiated the effort to extricate the Court from the League, so far as our adherence was concerned, by his proposal of February 24, 1923. Secretary of State Charles Evans Hughes devised four conditions for our entrance, and Coolidge, upon his accession to the presidency, urged action along the lines of the Harding-Hughes formula. After numerous modifications, this formula gave way to a Resolution for entrance to which five reservations were attached, and after passing a cloture rule, the Senate finally, on January 27, 1926, voted by a large majority to join the Permanent Court of International Justice.

Article 14 of the Covenant of the League of Nations reads as follows:

The Council shall formulate and submit to the Members of the League for adoption plans for the establishment of a Permanent Court of International Justice. The Court shall be competent to hear and determine any dispute of an international character which the parties thereto submit to it. The Court may also give an advisory opinion upon any dispute or question referred to it by the Council or by the Assembly.

At just this time, the Council convened to consider Germany's application to join the League. From Geneva, Sir Austen Chamberlain made bold to proclaim that the Senate Reservations would require the revision of the Statute under which the League had established the Court. That was discouraging. Presently there came another and more ominous interposition, in the overwhelming defeat for renomination of William B. McKinley in the Illinois primary election. McKinley was the first of the pro-Court senators to go before his constituency after the Senate had voted to enter the Court. The Coolidge administration, taking warning, deftly turned its attention to another undertaking, deriving from Chicago, and soon to be heralded as the Kellogg-Briand Pact to outlaw war. In these circumstances, no question was to be raised about the status of our adherence until after the presidential election of 1928.

Meanwhile, the Council of the League, acting upon the Chamberlain position, named an Advisory Committee of Jurists to revise the Statute of the Court. Elihu Root, who had served on the original committee that had written the Statute in 1921, was again invited to serve. The Council then asked this Advisory Committee also to resolve the problem created by the Senate Reservations, which had been slumbering nearly three years in the archives of the League at Geneva. The Council promptly approved the report of the Committee of Jurists, clarifying the Senate Resolution, which report has come to be known as the "Root Formula." President Hoover thereupon directed our representative at Geneva to sign for the United States the Protocol of membership in the Court, and then urged the Senate to accept the Root Formula. But Mr. Hoover was unable to induce the Senate to take such final action.

Although the Democratic platform of 1932 declared for the Court, the administration of Franklin D. Roosevelt had not moved formally in the matter up to the end of 1934. But on the reassembling of Congress in January, 1935, the thirteen-year-old controversy over the United States entering the Permanent Court of International Justice was reopened on January 9th and the Senate Foreign Relations Committee ordered the World Court protocols favorably reported. It declared once more for the doctrine of the long-disputed Reservation 5 which says the Permanent Court of International Justice "shall not, over an objection of the United States, entertain any request for an advisory opinion touching any dispute or question in which the United States has or claims an interest." This reservation adopted nine years ago by the Senate was rejected by other nations signatory to the Court. Whether these nations will now admit us to the World Court is as yet a matter of doubt. Whether the people of America are eager to join the World Court is in my mind a matter of even greater doubt.

Seemingly ineradicable suspicions, such as that the Court is a "back-door" entrance to the League, that the Court is under the political domination of the League, that war debts and domestic policies of immigration, tariffs, etc., might be subject to its adjudication, continue to militate against final favorable action by the Senate. While it cannot be denied that there has been some ground for suspicion, it is my judgment that the Root Formula adequately protects our domestic interests and concerns but guards against our becoming involved in the League. If we are to join any Court set up by the League, our sense of self-respect should restrain our seeking further protection than the Root Formula attaches to the 1926 Resolution of the Senate.

Were, then, the efforts put into propaganda by our peace societies, particularly the World Court League and the League to Enforce Peace, all pure waste? I think not. At the opening of the century Lord Salisbury predicted of the advocates of arbitration: "Future ages will look with pity and contempt upon those who could have believed in such an expedient for bridling the ferocity of human passions"; and now Spengler grimly warns that "we have entered the age of world wars. It began in the nineteenth century, and will outlast the present, and probably the next."

Notwithstanding the undeniable affirmation which these woeful years give to such pessimism, I cannot give up hope.

There have been gains, even if they do not as yet quite balance the losses. The voluntary efforts of these societies succeeded in making our citizens think in larger terms than before, to see that international problems affected them too. The Ideal of Peace was upheld by the press, the pulpit, the platform, and devoted political leaders. Under the impulses and stresses of war, Woodrow Wilson attempted to carry these aims and ideas to levels to which our nation could not climb; to force them upon peoples whose age-old racial hatreds, deep-seated political animosities, and violent economic antagonisms found them unprepared for such assents among themselves or for submission to sanctions imposed by others. Surely America, in declining to follow paths so precipitous, cannot be charged with disclaiming such honorable part in the world as befits the genius of her people and the traditions of her existence as a nation. On that path my country had never faltered. It has been the bungling statesmanship and not the lofty idealism of Woodrow Wilson that I have criticized. Confessedly, he may some day be remembered as a Messianic prophet. Colonel House still maintains that the League of Nations is Woodrow Wilson's greatest work. It may be so . . . I have my doubts.

CHAPTER THIRTY-TWO

Wilson and Harding

*W*ith the election of Wilson I lost interest in politics for the time being. I left Washington for New York, and did not return to the Capital until we entered the war in 1917, and then I bought a home there.

In the beginning I was not unfriendly to Wilson. I liked him personally and I told my Democratic friends that I thought the party had put up a surprisingly good candidate. Many of my friends admired Wilson greatly, though I was inclined to regard him as somewhat of a doctrinaire.

When I first met Woodrow Wilson in the winter of 1908-9 he was president of Princeton University. He was in Bermuda con- valescing from a recent illness and my wife and I were there for a rest. We were together for several weeks, and Wilson shared our table in the hotel dining room during this interval. We saw him several times a day and greatly enjoyed his society. His discussions with me were invariably concerned with the way political organizations were run. My practical experience in the recent Taft campaign had given me insight into this subject. I remarked to my wife that I thought Wilson had the political bee in his bonnet, though his interest might have been purely academic.

Thereafter not unnaturally I followed Wilson's career with interest.

On February 3, 1906, at a dinner given to Woodrow Wilson at the Lotos Club in New York, George Harvey, the editor and publisher, had "nominated" Wilson for the presidency. He had "discovered" Wilson—though later Harvey declared that Woodrow Wilson had "discovered" himself—at his inauguration as president of Princeton University in 1902.

After the Lotos Club dinner, Harvey, a past master in the promotion of political candidates, gave much thought and publicity to grooming Wilson for the presidency. Through his efforts Wilson became recognized by the Democratic leaders of the country as "presidential timber."

Harvey realized that the election of Woodrow Wilson as governor of New Jersey was an important step to his nomination for the presidency, and it was through his initiative and political skill that Wilson was elected governor in 1910. Also, Harvey recognized the futility of advocating the nomination of Wilson for the presidency in 1908, as Bryan at that time practically dominated the Democratic party and was the inevitable choice as nominee.

Nineteen-twelve was the psychological year: Wilson had made good as governor, and there was the split in the Republican party owing to the Roosevelt-Taft fight. The result was the election of Wilson to the presidency.

Shortly before the nomination of Wilson, Harvey and "Marse Henry" Watterson, editor of the Louisville *Courier-Journal,* who had been his enthusiastic supporters, were discarded by Wilson at the suggestion of other political advisers who asserted that they were too closely connected with Wall Street—an allegation which then as now struck terror to the heart of every office seeker who hoped to obtain the suffrage of the voting public.

Colonel Edward M. House had picked out Wilson when he was governor of New Jersey as the outstanding Democratic presidential possibility. House had been slower to declare his adherence than Harvey, but when the campaign opened he threw himself into it heart and soul. Wilson realized that House had no ax to grind, and turned to the colonel with a trust and affection he showed no other man.

House once said in the course of their ripening friendship, "Isn't it remarkable that we have become so well acquainted in so short a time and have so many views in common?"

To this Wilson replied: "I don't think so. There is no beginning to a friendship such as ours. Our meeting merely gave it expression."

During Wilson's first presidential years, I was in sympathy with many of his domestic measures, particularly the Federal Reserve Act. On the other hand, I disapproved heartily of the Underwood Tariff which in 1914 threatened to bring on a financial panic. This was averted only by the outbreak of the war. I was totally out of sympathy with his policy of unpreparedness, and especially with his treatment of Mexican affairs. He showed no more knowledge of the Mexican problem than he had displayed in our conversation on the train in 1911.

Just before House went abroad at the outbreak of the war, I asked him about the Mexican situation. He said, "Nothing will be done until I get back from Europe."

The Mexican situation became acute during his absence, however. Americans were being murdered, among them some fine young engineers who at one time or another had been in my employ. It was an open season on Americans. Posters were up in Tampico and elsewhere, saying now was the time for all good Mexicans to get rid of Americans. Not a single German, and, up to this time, not a single Englishman had been murdered.

The Mexican government still professed a desire to have mining operations continue, as this was an important source of revenue. A half dozen American engineers returned to the mining districts under a promise of protection by the Mexican government, and with assurance of our own government as to their safety. They were stood up against a wall and shot by "revolutionists" and still no step was taken by the American government. Wilson steadfastly adhered to Bryan's policy of hands off and to an exchange of ineffectual letters of protest.

I could keep silent no longer and made several speeches roundly criticizing Wilson.

When House returned, he said, "I hear you've been attacking the President on his Mexican policy."

"I certainly have," I replied. "I couldn't stand by and say nothing while Wilson permitted open murder of American engineers in Mexico."

From this time on Wilson and I had little to do with each other, although Colonel House and I have remained close friends.

In 1916, I attended the Republican convention at Chicago, again in a private capacity. Though Roosevelt's bolt from the party in 1912 had not been forgotten by the Old Guard, it was my opinion that by concentration on the preparedness issue alone he could heal the break and win strong support. Certainly his vigor would be welcome after Wilson's academic calm.

I found myself practically the only one of the old Taft men who had a favorable word to say for Roosevelt's candidacy. There were many misgivings as to his ability to carry the country. The most important of these was the antagonism roused among the German-Americans by his denunciations of their Fatherland.

My reply to this was: "Oh, well, if Roosevelt were the candidate that would be forgotten in a month or two. He would get out there in the German districts and in no time have Roosevelt-German clubs parading for him."

Those who knew Roosevelt realized the truth of this statement, but I soon found that party bitterness remaining from 1912 was an insurmountable obstacle to his nomination.

When I was convinced that the convention was strongly in favor of Charles Evans Hughes, I advised my friends among the Roosevelt faction to turn their strength to him and stop their talk of secession. I warned the Roosevelt supporters again and again that they were doing great injustice to their leader by trying to push him as candidate for a third party. "If he goes into the fight, he will beat Hughes but he can't be elected. So there will be another term of Wilson."

Roosevelt was reached by long-distance telephone and informed of what was going on. A few days after my return to New York, Mrs. Roosevelt invited my wife and me to Oyster Bay, to have a talk with the colonel. In greeting me he put his arm on my shoulder with his characteristic gesture of friendship, and said, "John Hays, I have to thank you for the good advice you gave my friends at Chicago."

I replied, "Colonel, of course you understand that I was supporting the Roosevelt of 1916, and not the Roosevelt of 1912?"

"Yes," he said, "I understand that. I remember how you denounced me four years ago. But you were then acting as Taft's friend, and I could not have asked your support at that time. Indeed, I respect you for your loyalty to him and for your frankness with me."

At the conclusion of the conversation, Roosevelt told me he intended to support Hughes. This was his first intimation of what he was going to do.

"That's the decision I expected you'd make, Colonel, but none the less it's gratifying to hear it from your own lips."

I at once reported the colonel's decision to Hughes, at the Hotel Astor. He was pleased and relieved.

During the campaign I saw Hughes at frequent intervals, and spent much time at Republican headquarters in New York. Hughes really possessed a charming personality to those who knew him, but this was not apparent in his platform manner or on public occasions.

William R. Willcox was selected to manage Hughes's campaign. Willcox and I resembled each other so closely that our pictures were often interchanged in the newspapers. I was also frequently mistaken for him by heelers, who are always conspicuous at campaign headquarters and whose special interest lies in the anticipation of political favors to be bestowed.

Whenever these spoilsmen caught sight of me they would approach one by one, shake my hand effusively, and say, "You won't forget me, will you, Mr. Willcox?"

"Oh, no," I replied, "I've a good memory. I certainly won't forget you."

After the election, I laughingly told Willcox that perhaps it was better for his peace of mind that Hughes had been defeated and that he could not be called on to keep his "promises" to this hungry mob of political job seekers.

Apropos of promises, I am reminded of a story told me by Senator Stephen B. Elkins, of West Virginia. Once while traveling on a stagecoach in the West, he noted that at every change of horses his driver's friends would remind him not to forget the pup he had promised them. It seems the driver owned a very fine bitch that was about to have a litter. By the time the long journey was ended, the driver had agreed to give a pup to at least a hundred friends.

Elkins said to him, "How on earth can you let every one of those fellows have a pup?"

The old driver grinned and replied, "Well, it's a mighty damned mean fellow who wouldn't 'promise' a friend a pup."

Hughes was defeated for the presidency because of the way he mishandled California. The state had been normally Republican in national elections, but by an inexcusable blunder it went Democratic in 1916, though by a small margin.

Hughes unfortunately visited California while a bitter fight was being waged in the primaries between the rebellious Senator Hiram Johnson and the regular Republican faction. Johnson had controlled state politics for many years through his machine and, in spite of being apostate at times, was fairly certain of renomination.

Hughes was met at the state line by a delegation of Republicans who were leading the campaign against Johnson. Shortsightedly ignoring the significance of the local political situation, Hughes allowed himself to be completely identified with Johnson's enemies, thus inadvertently appearing to take sides against Johnson. During his stay in California he neither met Johnson nor made any overtures towards him.

Johnson won the renomination, and also triumphed at the ensuing election. But his supporters, filled with resentment at the treatment accorded him by the anti-Johnson group, split the Republican vote. This, in turn, lost Hughes the State of California and the presidency.

Another political mistake was the sending of a group of wealthy eastern women to California to urge the women of that state to vote for Hughes. In my absence, my wife had been invited to join this expedition. Using her own good judgment and her knowledge of California affairs, she declined the invitation. She told the committee it was the height of folly for eastern women, who had never been allowed the vote, to presume to instruct the women of California as to how they should exercise the franchise which they had possessed for years.

When I learned this fateful car had started west, I suggested to Willcox that he contrive to lose the ladies somewhere in the wide open spaces until such time as they could do no harm.

This was not considered practicable, and the original program was carried out. The spirit in which the women voters of California received the advice of those from the East amply justified my wife's predictions.

I deplored the defeat of Hughes, not only for partisan reasons but because I was convinced he would have taken measures to prepare our country much more efficiently than Wilson for the war into which I believed we were inevitably drifting.

As a practical man, I had no sympathy with Wilson's effort to avoid issues by phrases, such as "too proud to fight" and "watchful waiting." I did not question his high ideals as to world peace, but I considered them not only unworkable but also unattainable. Moreover, the methods he employed to secure his ends were in my opinion lamentably wrong.

During Wilson's second term I was naturally an outsider so far as administration matters were concerned. But there was one incident in which I had a personal interest. In the winter of 1920, President Wilson sent the name of Bainbridge Colby to the Senate for confirmation as secretary of state in place of Lansing. Colby was a prominent New York lawyer who had originally been a Roosevelt man but had gone over to Wilson in 1916. I had been associated with him in various political and civic activities and therefore knew him well. Our many talks about our foreign policy,

NATALIE HARRIS HAMMOND

WILSON AND HARDING

especially with reference to Russia and Mexico, had given me a high opinion of his knowledge and judgment.

There was considerable opposition to his appointment by the Republican members of the Foreign Relations Committee, due largely to the charge of alleged unprofessional conduct made against Colby by Herbert Parsons, Republican congressman. Although this accusation proved utterly groundless, several of my Republican friends on the committee which was to pass on Colby's fitness for confirmation still hesitated.

I interviewed Knox, now back in the Senate, about Colby's appointment. He said: "Well, it probably won't make much difference who's secretary of state. Wilson intends to run that department himself."

My response was: "From intimate knowledge of Colby's character, I feel sure that not even the President of the United States can use him as a rubber stamp. In politics he has always been hard to drive tandem."

Colby's appointment was confirmed. Immediately afterwards he came to thank me for the influence I had exerted in his behalf.

"Bainbridge," I said, "you have the ability to make a splendid secretary of state for a short time, and to establish an enduring reputation in that office. My fear is that President Wilson will put pressure on you to adopt policies which will not be to your credit if you follow them. Though I realize, of course, that if you try to be independent, you'll run the risk of being dismissed."

"Don't worry about that, Jack," he replied, "I've taken my house for only six months!"

Colby renewed the lease, and in spite of his independence was secretary of state until the end of the Wilson administration. He then formed a legal partnership with Wilson, which was soon terminated by the breakdown of Wilson's health.

It was during the early part of 1914, after I had visited Thomas Nelson Page at Rome, that I first met Lord Northcliffe in Paris. We were staying at the same hotel and occasionally played golf together and spent several pleasant evenings in general political discussions.

I asked Northcliffe why it was that Great Britain had not tied up Italy with the Allies, as Italy's treaty with Germany was soon to expire. I told him that I had found the Italians in government circles very friendly to England. Northcliffe replied that overtures had been made to Italy to prevent Italy tying up again with the Triple Alliance, but without avail. I said that was quite true, but unfortunately, the overtures were made through France, and France and Italy were not altogether friendly because of their disputes about territory in Northern Africa. Besides this, there was no love lost between Italy and Austria. "Irredentism" aggravated this situation. I told Northcliffe that I felt something could be done. Of course, I was not anticipating the war which came so soon afterwards. He said: "I will give you a letter to Sir Edward Grey [at that time foreign secretary of England] and I will write him privately."

I went from Paris to London to spend a few weeks before returning to America. There I had a confidential talk with Grey and found him very much interested in the Italian question.

When I next saw Viscount Grey in Washington in 1919, he said: "Hammond, suppose I had told you when I last saw you in England in 1914, that within six months England would be fighting in France against Germany, and that within three years America would have two million soldiers joined with the armies of England, France, and Italy, what would you have thought?"

"Of course," I said, "I would have replied that the prophecy was absolutely ridiculous."

"That would have been my opinion, and yet," said Grey thoughtfully, "both of these things have come to pass."

I recall a story that Northcliffe told me about Maximilian's invasion of Mexico. He said the most regrettable part of it was that the basis for the invasion was commercial and sordid. It was inspired, he said, by the Duc de Mornay and unscrupulous financiers in Paris, who were interested in being repaid for the Mexican bonds they had purchased.

When Northcliffe came to America in 1917 as representative of the British War Cabinet, he visited me in Gloucester. I asked him whether the World War might not have been prevented if Grey had notified Germany definitively that if she moved into Belgian or French territory, England would join France. Northcliffe was of that opinion. This is also the theory of Lloyd George as related in his memoirs.

I gave a dinner at Gloucester in honor of Lord Northcliffe and invited Calvin Coolidge, then lieutenant governor of Massachusetts, Governor McCall being away at the time. Before dinner was announced, Northcliffe began to question Coolidge insistently but tactfully concerning the opinions of certain influential people in America. All he elicited in return was a succession of monosyllabels. Observing the heavy conversational weather, I cheered Northcliffe by telling him he would be seated next to Mrs. Coolidge at dinner and would be sure to find out all he wanted to know. The result was very gratifying to him.

I recall that at the solicitation of several of Colonel Roosevelt's friends I asked House to suggest Roosevelt's name as the head of the commission the President was sending to Russia at the time the Kerensky government came into power in 1917. Elihu Root had been spoken of in that connection. I was a great admirer of Root but I thought Roosevelt better qualified for the emergency since he would be much more aggressive and forceful. Indeed, I said that he would probably revive the Russian cause by personally leading its troops on the battlefield, whereas Root would talk over the head and understanding of the average Russian. House agreed with me, but when he suggested the appointment of Roosevelt, President Wilson went up in the air. It was not that he failed to recognize the force of my argument; it was because of the pettiness he often showed in treatment of those who had previously offended him.

The Root Commission was a failure.

After the last session of the Paris Peace Conference, Colonel House returned to his country place at Manchester. A few days later he lunched with me at my home, Lookout Hill, and told me I would probably be interested to learn why the newspapers were reporting that the friendly relations previously existing between Woodrow Wilson and himself had ended. He began by stating there had never been a serious difference between them nor had they ever exchanged an unpleasant word.

"Probably it would have been better for both President Wilson and you," I remarked, "had there occasionally been heated arguments between you."

"No," he replied, "I know what you have in mind. You think it might have cleared the atmosphere. But I don't agree with you. Had I not minimized and disregarded differences of opinion on certain subjects, I should not have been able to accomplish other measures which we both thought of paramount importance."

To my knowledge there were many instances in which House's views differed from Wilson's and in which subsequent developments proved House the wiser man.

In a previous chapter I have alluded to the advice House gave Wilson as to his and Wilson's participation in the Versailles Conference. Later this advice was urged by those of Wilson's entourage who were unfriendly to House as evidence that House had his own ambitions to serve.

This was not all. An unfortunate article had appeared in the European newspapers the day of Wilson's arrival in Paris on his second trip to the Peace Conference. In it was included the statement that "what Colonel House thinks today, Wilson does tomorrow."

Wilson was led to believe by those jealous of House that this article had been inspired directly by the colonel or by his friends.

This charge was not only untrue, it was entirely foreign to House's attitude towards Wilson, which had always been one of self-subordination. House never had the opportunity to discuss the subject frankly with the President.

Shortly after the appearance of this article, Wilson returned to make his great but losing fight to have the League of Nations ratified by the Senate. He sadly needed the wise counsel of Colonel House during this period. Had House still enjoyed the President's confidence, all his influence would have been exerted towards having the Lodge reservations accepted by Wilson, rather than to risk the utter defeat of the Wilson plan at the hands of the Senate.

The ultimate cause of the break was probably due, as House himself asserts, to the jealousy of a small circle around Wilson which shut him off from his friends.

According to House's statement in the *New York Times,* July 26, 1934: "The bedroom circle kept him apart from me and kept me apart from him. My letters never reached him; no messages were ever sent to me."

In 1920 I was one of General Leonard Wood's active adherents. Since I was an old friend of his family, I felt privileged to state frankly to him my views on matters affecting his candidacy. In the first place, I advised against his coming forward too aggressively; also, I and others cautioned him against extravagant pre-campaign expenditures. He did not follow this advice and, as it later turned out, the reckless use of funds in his campaign was one of the most forceful arguments urged against his nomination at the convention.

While characteristically hesitant about declaring their positions, many of the leading politicians expressed their admiration for Wood. Several said definitely they were for him. I encouraged Wood with this information.

It was shortly after this that the unfortunate selection of Frank H. Hitchcock as his campaign manager became known. I warned Wood that this would estrange many men who would be influential in the coming convention. I referred him to Taft or Hughes if he doubted the wisdom of my advice.

Wood replied: "It's too late. I'm under obligation to make this appointment. The men who are putting up most of the money for my campaign have made it a condition that I choose a practical politician as my campaign manager. They insist Hitchcock fills the requirements. In addition, he can secure the vote of negro delegates from the South, a role in which he specializes."

"You'll lose by it," I told him.

I arrived at Chicago a few days before the convention was scheduled to begin. Since this was my fourth convention, I was well acquainted with the leading politicians. When the Hitchcock appointment was verified a number of them told me plainly they would not support a man who had had the bad judgment to select Hitchcock as political manager, and thereby had obligated himself to give Hitchcock a Cabinet position.

Alice Longworth, who for some years past had been familiar with Hitchcock's political activities, says in her book, *Crowded Hours:*

> When General Wood got to Washington he told me that King's activities were too secret and devious, and that he had had to get rid of him. [At that time John King of Connecticut was General Wood's political manager.] When I had talked with General Wood in August, Frank Hitchcock's name had come up, and I had warned the General to avoid having much to do with him, as he was just as devious as King, without being in with powers that counted. However, that warning was wasted words, and he proceeded to take Hitchcock as his manager.

Senator Warren G. Harding telephoned me the morning he decided to become a candidate and asked for my support. I told him I had not known he was in the field; on the contrary, public statements made by him had led me to believe that he was intending to run again for the Senate. I said I had already committed myself to Wood.

He then sent two of his supporters, Harry Daugherty and Mont Reilly, to see me. We agreed that none of the principal candidates —Wood, Lowden, Harding—was likely to go to the convention with a majority of pledged delegates. Daugherty asked me whether, if the proper time came in the convention, Harding could count on Wood's support, provided Harding would throw his support to Wood if the current ran the other way.

I replied that, of course, I had no authority to speak for Wood on this matter, but there was always a possibility of an understanding later should the occasion arise.

George Harvey and I had secured rooms not far apart in the Blackstone Hotel. We were together a good deal during convention week and obtained much inside information as to political doings. On Thursday there had been several ballots for presidential nomination—Governor Frank Lowden, of Illinois, and General Wood were the favorites, with Senator Harding trailing.

On Friday evening Harvey told me there was to be a conference of the leaders of the convention in his suite and invited me to be present. I did not attend the meeting because I had been reliably informed that both Lowden and Wood would be eliminated by those who controlled the political destiny of the candidates. Up to this time Harvey had been friendly to Wood's nomination.

Influential Republicans were threatening to create dissension if Wood should receive the nomination. One of the chief reasons advanced for this was the too-liberal campaign expenditures made by his adherents in securing delegates. There was no insinuation of corruption, but influential party men of Senator William Borah's type thought a heavy outlay of money in selecting the presidential candidate would establish a bad precedent.

Lowden's campaign was criticized because of the charge of political graft on the part of two or three of his delegates. Lowden was absolutely innocent, of course, but it was feared that possible scandal would prevent his election even if he were to receive the nomination.

Harvey came to my room about three in the morning and told me that the leaders had decided to promote the candidacy of Harding and that after two or three perfunctory ballots, purely for appearance' sake, Harding would receive the nomination.

Early next morning I went to Wood's suite. He was there with Mrs. Wood and Nicholas Roosevelt. After telling him of Harvey's plan to nominate Harding on the third ballot, I said, "It's all up."

He replied: "I don't believe it. I've just seen Frank Hitchcock. He says we have the votes."

"I still say I'm right. Don't rely on Hitchcock's estimate of delegates favorable to you."

Wood was troubled, but still confident. He kept repeating: "I can't believe it. You don't mean to tell me that my friends are going to desert me?"

After the third ballot someone from the auditorium telephoned Wood's suite. I answered the phone and a voice came over the wire, "Harding has just been nominated!"

While the news was not unexpected, the necessity for repeating the message to Wood was none the less unpleasant. "General, Harding has been chosen."

Wood said bitterly: "It's another 1912 business. It's the same old thing."

So loath was Wood to accept the fact of his defeat that he hesitated to sign the congratulatory telegram to Harding which Nicholas Roosevelt had prepared. He said he could not understand why certain men, whom he named, had first professed undying loyalty to him and then had betrayed him. His indignation and bitterness were not directed against Harding, but against what he regarded as treachery on the part of some of his own friends.

I told him with some cynicism that the loyalty of the soldier, which leads him to fight to his death in defense of a position assigned to him, need not be looked for in politics; expediency, not loyalty, is the fundamental tenet of the politician's creed.

Immediately upon his return to Washington, Harding came to my house and told me, "If Wood had taken your advice, he would have secured the nomination."

"How do you know what I advised?" I asked.

"I had a good intelligence department," he replied. "You warned Wood against attacking me in Ohio and Lowden in Illinois. Didn't you tell him to get busy elsewhere and let Lowden and me fight it out in our own territories?"

"That's true," I admitted.

"Well, he made a bad mistake in tackling us in our own states. He could hope to win only a few delegates there, while making enemies of the rest."

Although I had been a Wood supporter, I had grown very fond of the Hardings during the years we had been neighbors in Washington. I could not fail to appreciate Mrs. Harding's clever and forceful character. While Harding was acting as temporary chairman of the 1916 convention, my wife and I sat next to Mrs. Harding in her box. During the senator's speech, her lips formed each syllable as he pronounced it. We could not help harboring the suspicion that she had assisted in its composition.

A few months after Harding's inauguration, I started on a long-contemplated trip to study political and ecoṅomic conditions in the Orient. My first stop was to be Japan. I studiously avoided taking with me letters to government officials or other prominent Japanese. By keeping free of all obligations, governmental or otherwise, I hoped to obtain accurate information for myself rather than to see Japan through the show windows usually provided for official visitors.

Among my first callers was M. Otagawa, a Japanese of high social position and one of the distinguished mining engineers of the country. I had met Otagawa in America several years before and had extended him some professional courtesies. Through him I came in contact with many leading Japanese engineers and businessmen with whom, as a private citizen, I had the opportunity to discuss the economic conditions of Japan and the Orient generally, as well as the political relations between our two countries.

I criticized Japan's excessive expenditure on naval armaments, offering the opinion that this would almost certainly be construed as an unfriendly and perhaps a hostile move against America. There were no other great naval powers against whom Japan might need to prepare. Germany had no navy, Russia had no navy, and the other nations could not endanger her, with the exception of Great Britain, and Great Britain was Japan's ally. I pointed out that the huge sums of money Japan was expending on a navy might much better be diverted to the expansion of her merchant marine.

While in Tokyo, I discussed this subject with Baron Shibusawa, the J. P. Morgan of Japan; he was a gentleman of the old school, a lover of peace, an admirer of the United States. He was a Confucianist and was pleased when I discussed with him the similarity between the Golden Rule of Confucius and that of the Christians.

I also had a talk with Premier Hara, a few days before his assassination. He expressed himself as in full accord with the facts and conclusions I advanced on Japanese-American relations.

It was interesting to ascertain the Japanese attitude towards the Naval Disarmament Conference shortly to be held in Washington, particularly as I knew that our government was apprehensive lest Japan would not be represented.

I wrote in detail to Senator Knox, saying that Japan could not afford to be absent on that occasion. All that would be necessary to ensure her attendance, I said, would be the presence of a mere coolie claiming to represent China, in which case Japan to save her face— a paramount consideration in Oriental politics—would be compelled to send a representative to Washington. No coolie plenipotentiary was needed—Japan attended the conference.

A severe attack of ptomaine poisoning prevented my getting back to Washington, as I had hoped to do, for the conference. It also prevented the continuation of my trip to Korea, Manchuria, and China as planned.

I returned from Japan the latter part of October and decided it was wiser to remain in California for the winter than to risk the Washington climate. When the conference ended in February, I was well enough to be in San Francisco to attend a banquet given the Japanese delegates on their way home. I made an address presenting the views I had previously expressed regarding our relations with Japan.

During the ensuing weeks, I discussed the Japanese question before several of the Chambers of Commerce in California, and stated that Japan's geographical situation, and her progressiveness and energy, entitled her to an important share in the opening up of Manchuria and Eastern Siberia, and that America ought to co-operate with her towards that end. Jealousy, it seemed to me, should not be allowed to appear in our relations with Japan, and it was especially shortsighted to antagonize the country by tactlessness.

I firmly believed in John Hay's open-door policy in China; at the same time, I felt that it ought to be made somewhat more flexible. In respect of Asiatic immigration into America, I thought it should not be allowed, but considered the question ought to be so handled as not to wound the susceptibilities of a country with whom it was essential to be friendly.

I had on several occasions made clear my position on the immigration question to Ambassador Ishii, who was a frequent guest at my house in Washington. Ishii suggested that the problem might be economic and inspired by the labor organizations of California. My reply was that, while this was partly true, Californians themselves were unanimously opposed to immigration of Oriental peoples; they recognized that the races did not assimilate, and dreaded the outcome of possible miscegenation.

In the face of my outspoken sentiments, I have always been regarded by the Japanese press and officials as a true friend of Japan.

When staying in Santa Barbara, California, during this winter of 1921-22, I occupied a cottage in the grounds of the Hotel El Mirasol. The bungalow next to mine was divided for two families. My son Harris and his wife occupied one half of it, and Eleutherios Venizelos and his bride the other half. Both M. and Mme. Venizelos spoke English perfectly and we all enjoyed our association with them. Venizelos had just been run out of Greece by his political enemies, and was awaiting an opportunity to return. He invited us to visit them in Athens, and when I asked, "When do you expect to be there?" Mme. Venizelos replied, "Oh, about May"—and sure enough they were.

One day Venizelos called on my son, saying that he was moving from the bungalow into the main building of the hotel. "I wish to explain," he said, "that it is not because of uncongenial neighbors, but there have been persistent rumors that an attempt will be made to bomb my cottage. It is close to the road and is not therefore as safe as rooms in the other building. I have paid little attention to the rumor, but should the bombing occur you and your wife might become the innocent victims, and it does not seem fair that you should be exposed to a possible calamity of this kind. That is why I am moving to the main building." This, I think, is evidence of the consideration of a real sportsman.

When I returned to Washington in the spring of 1922, I made no secret of my disappointment at the result of the Disarmament Conference. First I told President Harding, and after his death, President Coolidge and other officials that in my opinion we had made a great mistake in sinking a navy *in esse* in exchange for the promise of the British Admiralty to destroy the blueprints of contemplated additions to the fleet. My criticism at that time may not have been popular, but I believe that subsequent developments have shown that, so far as American naval interests were concerned, the

Washington conference must now be regarded as an egregious failure.

Because of my interest in the development of the Orient, and in the political situation in the Far East, President Harding offered me the ambassadorship to Japan. I declined because I wished to remain with my family and friends in my own country.

While I saw but little of Harding socially during his administration, except when my wife and I were guests at White House functions, I was often with him in connection with my duties on the Coal Commission.

In common with people of Washington generally, I, of course, heard allegations reflecting on the President's private life. No doubt, many of these reports were true, though some were probably greatly magnified; the President was doing credit neither to himself nor to his administration. It was soon evident to all except President Harding himself that certain members of his entourage were thoroughly unscrupulous. They were imposing upon his good-nature and abusing his confidence for their own profit. Harding was generous to his friends, but much too easygoing and trustful. The motives of these intimate friends should have been irreproachable, inasmuch as they reflected the attitude of the President on important governmental measures.

Believing as I did in Harding's personal honesty, and that the scandals of the administration were entirely the result of his faith in his friends, I had much sympathy for him, though my admiration naturally was greatly diminished. On several occasions I spoke quite freely to him on this subject, but it was impossible to convince him that he was being betrayed.

I saw Harding a day or two before he left for his Alaskan trip, and he impressed me as being seriously perturbed. What I subsequently learned made me certain that he was beginning to lose confidence in some of his trusted associates. I am sure that if he had lived to return to Washington, there would have been a general housecleaning and the corrupt leaders among his intimates would have been summarily dismissed.

Harding did not have the qualities of greatness but there have been many other presidents lacking in such qualities to whom, nevertheless, the nation has reason to point with satisfaction.

President Harding's good-nature and kindliness are illustrated in a small way by the story of the Live Wire Club. When I called on him one day, he noticed the button in my coat lapel and asked me the meaning of the emblem—a bolt of lightning. "Mr. President," I replied, "that is the emblem of the most exclusive club in the world."

"Tell me about it."

This was the story.

A few months before, I had gone to the Berkshires to call on my friend, Dr. Samuel W. Mixter, a renowned surgeon of Boston who had a beautiful estate on which he raised a herd of pure-blooded Guernseys. The entire village, consisting of some hundred people, was in his employ and looked up to him with pride and some awe. I arrived early and, finding him out, strolled about the grounds and the village. I climbed over the low stone wall of the village graveyard, read epitaphs for a while, and then sat down against the wall.

While I was enjoying a smoke, I heard boys' voices calling out coaxingly, "Here, Spot! Here, Rover! Here, Sport! Here, Towser!"

I looked over the wall and saw four youngsters eight to ten years of age—but only one dog.

I hailed them. "Hello, fellows. Where are all the dogs?"

"There isn't but one," was the reply.

"But I heard you calling so many different names I thought you had at least four or five."

"No," the biggest lad said, "we only found this dog last night and we don't know his name, so we're calling him all the names we can think of to see which is the right one."

I couldn't help them out but we chatted for some time. During the course of our conversation I asked what they did, to which the spokesman replied that their club was out for a hike.

"Your club must have a name even if the dog hasn't," I said.

"Sure it has."

"Well, what is it?"

"It's the Live Wire Club."

"How many members have you?"

"Just the four of us."

"That's a pretty small club. Why don't you take in those boys?" I asked, pointing to two other youngsters across the street.

"There are only four offices in the club and so we can't take in anyone else," they explained.

I asked who was president, and the youngest spoke up and said he was. The next one was vice-president, and the next secretary.

"Then I suppose the big fellow must be treasurer?" Yes, he was. "And how did he get that office?"

"He wanted to be treasurer, and so we let him have it," said the president.

"How much money have you in the treasury?"

"Two dollars."

"Shh!" I whispered. "Don't talk so loud. Someone might hear you and rob you."

But they were prepared for that possibility. They explained that the treasurer hid the money in a different place every night.

"Well, boys, how about electing me a member of the club?"

They hesitated a little and then the treasurer answered, "But there isn't any office for you."

"That's easy," I said. "Why not make me high private? That's the most important office in a club, and such a club as yours needs a high private."

And so I was duly elected to the Live Wire Club.

It was nearly lunch time, so I asked, "Can you tell me who has the best meals around here?"

Four hands simultaneously pointed to Dr. Mixter's house. "Everyone says that they have grand food there."

"Well," I said, "in that case I believe I'll go over and see if I can't get something to eat."

"But you don't know him," they objected.

"That makes no difference, I'll go and try. Come along and we'll see."

We reached the house, the boys remaining at a respectful distance, and I was admitted much to the amazement of my fellow club members. Dr. Mixter was much amused with the account of my adventure. After lunch, I found the four little fellows again and took them for an automobile ride about the country.

President Harding was greatly interested in the story. "I like those boys," he said. "You'll have to get me elected."

I told him I would take the matter up with the other officers and let him know. In due time I notified him that he had been elected honorary president of the Live Wire Club. He sent the boys an autographed photograph and a friendly letter thanking them for the honor.

In the summer of 1923 President Harding set out for the West and Alaska. He asked my wife and me to accompany him, but my duties as chairman of the Coal Commission prevented.

Before leaving, President Harding informed me that George Harvey was going to resign as ambassador to the Court of St. James's, and he desired to appoint me in his place.

I was highly complimented, and said I would consider it. London was very attractive to me, but the English climate was bad for my wife's health and I should not care to go without her. In any case, nothing could be done until his return from Alaska.

Harding died at San Francisco, August 2nd, on his way back to Washington. After the President's body had been brought to Washington there were special services at the Capitol. Mrs. Harding telephoned and asked me to come to the White House and accompany the mourners from there.

After the burial of the President at Marion, Ohio, Mrs. Harding returned to "Friendship," the home of Mr. and Mrs. Edward B. McLean in Washington. She at once sent word that she would like to see me. I arrived at eleven in the morning, and she related in detail the various incidents of her trip west with the President. She was obviously in great distress of mind, and after luncheon I suggested to the McLeans that I had better leave. But Mrs. Harding begged me not to go, and I stayed with her until late after dinner, hearing again the details she had previously related.

Because of the persistent insinuations that have been uttered against Mrs. Harding by scandalmongers, I should like to say that there can be no possible doubt of her deep and genuine grief over the death of her husband.

CHAPTER THIRTY-THREE

Washington—Coolidge and Hoover

*I*t was most fortunate for the country that a man of Calvin Coolidge's type succeeded to the presidency. He had an estimable record for probity and executive ability during both his Massachusetts governorship and the vice-presidency. Sitting in at Cabinet meetings during the Harding administration had given him special knowledge of national problems.

His slightly rigid personality manifested caution and sanity. His eccentricities were safe ones. There was no derision in the anecdotes that were told of him, and the laughter of the people at hundreds of Coolidgisms only served to increase their belief in him as a wise and forceful leader. After the miasma of suspicion created by the scandals of the Harding administration, the country soon showed implicit confidence in Coolidge.

Shortly after Coolidge became president, Senator Brandegee and George Harvey both told him that Harding had offered me the post of ambassador to England. Dr. Morton Prince, without my knowledge, went to see Senator Lodge, who wrote to Coolidge recommending me as "widely and favorably known" and in a marked degree *persona grata* to England. Since many political favors had already been awarded men of Massachusetts, he added that I, though a resident of that state, was really a western man.

President Coolidge appointed Frank B. Kellogg to that post.

When I returned to Washington from our summer home in Gloucester a few weeks later, the President asked me to dinner. When we went upstairs to smoke, he said he wanted to explain why he had not appointed me.

"No explanation is necessary, Mr. President," I assured him. "You're not bound by acts of your predecessor, and I feel no resentment."

"Yes, I know," he replied, "but Harding offered you the position, and I know you're qualified to fill it properly. Yet if I had given another important post to a Massachusetts man, the politicians in Congress would have raised an outcry. With the President, the speaker of the House, and the majority leader in the Senate, the secretary of war, and the ambassador to Italy, all from Massachusetts, they would be likely to object if the biggest plum in the diplomatic service were to go to that state also. Had the vacancy occurred a few months from now, when I expect to have a stronger grip on the political situation, I should have appointed you notwithstanding."

He then added, "However, there will be other things of importance coming up, and I shall be glad to give you something that will accord with your deserts."

I was somewhat irritated at this method of expression and replied that I had never sought any political reward.

He assured me that political considerations were not in his mind, and the matter was dropped. Later, when there was a vacancy, he offered me the ambassadorship to Italy. I appreciated the honor, but was unable to accept.

I have already explained my feeling about officeholding and presidential appointments. And I do not regret the circumstances that forbade my filling such posts.

The one place, with the exception of the English ambassadorship, that I would have accepted gladly was that of secretary of commerce. I had no private interests which would have made it embarrassing for me to serve in that position, and the whole problem of business and trade, both foreign and domestic, was one that I had been studying for many years. I saw an unusual opportunity to build up a department which at that time was not flourishing. Harding told me that personally he would be glad to offer me the position, but he was advised of the necessity of strengthening his Cabinet by the selection of Herbert Hoover, who had certain political support. The choice was a wise one, as later events proved. Hoover not only brought strength to the party organization, but his conspicuous success in the office was recognized by the country at large.

One of the first important issues to confront Coolidge after Harding's death was the coal crisis. In October, 1922, President Harding, on the authorization of Congress, had appointed a United States Coal Commission composed of the following members: George Otis Smith, director of the United States Geological Survey; Clark Howell, of Georgia; Thomas R. Marshall, former vice-president; Judge Alschuler resigned, and Edward T. Devine was appointed in his stead. The members of the commission made me chairman.

The action of Congress was taken because of the strike of union coal miners in that year, the second since the war. The function of the commission was to discover what could be done to cure the almost continuous crisis in the coal industry. Within the allotted period of a year, we had to assemble our facts and set forth our recommendations in the form of a report, which meant much hard work. The situation in the coal industry was exceedingly complicated and the evidence had to be gathered from many sources.

Our meetings, however, were not taken up exclusively with serious matters. Tom Marshall was a good storyteller, and had a habit of relating humorous anecdotes which, though amusing, threatened to block the transaction of business. I decided that if this flow of wit could be curtailed, we would make better progress, so I purchased a large clock and placed it where both Marshall and I could see it. After that, even when he was fairly launched into a story, one significant look from me at the clock would effectively silence him.

The feeling between mine operators and labor representatives often became tense. When a disputed point threatened an outburst that might embarrass everybody present and retard the proceedings, I would studiously avert my eyes from the timepiece. Marshall, with admirable tact, would then lead us past another difficult corner by telling some apt story at which the miners, operators, and members of the commission would laugh heartily together.

At the conclusion of our labors, the commission presented me with a gold desk clock to commemorate this piece of minor diplomacy.

During the months of intimate association, I came to know Marshall well and to have not only a deep affection but a genuine admiration and regard for him. I considered him one of the most level-headed and upright men in public life.

He was probably the most popular vice-president the country has ever had, more so perhaps than Theodore Roosevelt when he was in that office. Like James Whitcomb Riley, George Ade, and Booth Tarkington, Marshall was a Hoosier and his wit had that pungent quality that seems almost a part of the flat accent of Indianans.

He was quiet, unassuming, and kindly, but once having entered a conversation, he always had something important to say. To bring out points he was making, he drew on his great stock of amusing and original stories; his epigrams were, of course, famous. But he was not a slap-the-back politician. His humor had its roots in deep, fertile soil.

In Washington he had a host of friends and we considered ourselves fortunate in having him and Mrs. Marshall as frequent guests. In my opinion, and to edit one of Marshall's best-known remarks, "What the country needs is more men like Tom Marshall in its government."

The Coal Commission's full report of three thousand pages was printed by the government; a one-volume summary was published in 1925 by Williams and Wilkins under the title, *What the Coal Commission Found.*

We did not solve the coal problem, nor did we expect to. In presenting our report we uttered the warning that the solution of the coal problem could only grow out of a sustained and thoughtful effort over many years by the public, by Congress, by industry, and by students generally. The problem is almost unbelievably complex and there is no easy short-cut to a solution.

This is not the place for an analysis of the report, though two of the principles underlying it may be mentioned. The first of these is that the coal industry is clothed with a public interest, which means that it is not possible for the nation to sit idly by while operators and miners fight each other to a standstill. The government has a right to supervise and to regulate, though fixing of prices and wages was not advised, nor was compulsory arbitration. Furthermore, the collection and publication by the government of data showing costs, profits, and wages, and the airing of the points in dispute in a labor crisis, would, it was thought, bring to bear an enlightened public opinion that neither disputant could afford to flout.

The second principle is in a sense the corollary of the first. We recommended that the responsibility for the smooth running of the industry should lie within the industry itself; we felt that legislative action would tend to diminish efficiency rather than increase it, and that private development, if carried on honestly and as a quasi-public utility, ought to be encouraged. There was in the published figures an implied warning on the monopolistic control of the anthracite fields and the artificially high prices maintained there, particularly for coal used in domestic consumption. The deplorable condition of labor, both union and nonunion, was pointed out in no uncertain terms.

Gifford Pinchot, then governor of Pennsylvania, was eager to gain political prestige by having the difficulties in the coal region adjusted through his intervention. It was, of course, natural that he should be keenly interested, since the scene of the coal trouble was in his state. Interviews had appeared in the press in which he was represented as announcing that he was going to offer the government a solution of the coal problem. When the question was brought before President Coolidge, he agreed with the members of the Coal Commission that the settlement should be effected through the federal government.

When Pinchot approached him for an interview the President immediately notified me by telephone that Pinchot had volunteered his services and wanted to talk the situation over with him. "I've invited him to lunch tomorrow, and since you're better acquainted with the technical and economic problems than I, I'd like you to be present."

"All right, Mr. President," I said, "I'll be glad to come." I then said that Pinchot was an old friend of mine, that I admired him in many respects, but that I did not agree with all his policies.

I added that I was sure Pinchot would bring a plan of his own and suggested that, before Coolidge saw him, he read the Special Report just completed by the commission.

The President not only welcomed this idea, but asked me to bring the report to the White House at once. After reading it, he approved our conclusions and recommendations.

Pinchot and I were the only guests. The conversation during lunch was entirely social. The moment we reached the President's study after lunch, I pulled from my pocket the report Coolidge had already read, and handed it to him, saying: "Mr. President, the commission has studied the conditions in the coal industry with great care, and considers this report covers the situation. After you've examined it, I'm sure Governor Pinchot will wish to read it also."

I had seen Pinchot's hand go towards the pocket where I assumed his own plan reposed. I had beaten him to the draw.

For form's sake, Coolidge glanced briefly over the report and then handed it to Pinchot. As soon as I saw Pinchot had finished, I said, "Don't you agree that this covers the situation?"

The governor had to admit he approved the report, with the result that the coal crisis was met by the Coolidge, and not the Pinchot, plan.

President Coolidge many times referred to this as our "coup."

Pinchot endorsed the commission's report in a statement to the press. At his request, I supplied him with all our data and sent two assistants to Harrisburg to explain technical points.

My next connection with the coal problem was in October, 1923, when I was appointed chairman of the Executive Committee of the New England Governors' Fuel Committee composed of Governors John H. Trumbull, of Connecticut, Ralph O. Brewster, of Maine, Alvan T. Fuller, of Massachusetts, John G. Winant, of New Hampshire, Aram J. Pothier, of Rhode Island, and Franklin S. Billings, of Vermont.

The price of anthracite at the time was excessive and the supply uncertain. We urged that operators and miners in the Pennsylvania fields find some means of furnishing New England with sufficient coal at reasonable prices. We warned them that otherwise New England would turn to oil and bituminous coal. Later figures show that the use of substitute fuels has greatly increased, and Pennsylvania no longer enjoys her fuel monopoly of New England.

The International Conference on Bituminous Coal was held in Pittsburgh in November, 1926, under the auspices of the Carnegie Institute of Technology. Thomas S. Baker, president of the institute, and leading scientists from England, France, and Germany were present. Utilization of coal to provide expanded markets was the primary object of the conference. Considerable discussion was devoted to methods of producing oil and gasoline from coal.

As chairman of this conference, I stressed once more the need for a government study of the economics of the coal industry, and particularly for better protection against the prevalent waste in the mining of bituminous coal. The industry had been for a long time one of the major economic national problems; there was constant overproduction, coupled with intense market competition, and a plethora of miners for whom remunerative employment could not be provided.

In 1924, President Coolidge had asked me to represent him at Tallahassee, on the occasion of the centennial of the first meeting of the Legislative Council of the Territory of Florida. The most interesting part of the assignment was my contact with William Jennings Bryan in the last phase of his extraordinary career.

In my opening speech I extended the good wishes of the President to the people of Florida. Bryan then made a short address in his usual flattering and flowery manner, in which he congratulated the President on having selected me as his representative on this occasion.

"There could be," he said, "no more fitting choice, since Mr. Hammond is known as one of the great Americans who have developed resources in other lands, to the advantage of the people of those lands, as well as of his own country."

Senator Fletcher leaned over to me. "Bryan must have changed his views about Americans being interested in the development of foreign countries. When he was secretary of state, he used to call them all 'unprincipled exploiters.' "

At the termination of the speeches, I accepted Bryan's invitation to lunch. He began at once to regale me with a list of the marvelous opportunities Florida offered as a field for profitable investment.

"In what particular line?" I asked.

"Real estate," he replied.

"But," I said, "is it better in that respect than Los Angeles?"

"Oh, yes," he assured me, "far better. I'll give you an illustration. About ten years ago I bought some land in the Miami section. The other day I sold part of this land for eight times what I paid for the whole."

"That's certainly a good profit," I admitted.

"Oh," he said, "I expect to do much better than that with the rest of the property."

"Well," I replied, "all this seems to resemble what we, in the days of frenzied finance, used to call 'unearned increment.' "

Bryan changed the subject. He knew I had often heard him inveigh against profits made from real estate.

On my return to Washington I related this incident to President Coolidge. His answering smile was equivalent to the laugh of an average human being.

"I think I can cap that story," he said. "Dawes was in here a few days ago and told me he had recently seen Bryan in Florida. The Great Commoner had shown him his property near Miami and told him his investments would return him a profit of several hundred thousand dollars. Dawes then said to Bryan: 'That's a new idea for you. When we were young lawyers in Nebraska, you challenged me to debate on whether any man should be allowed to acquire a fortune of more than a hundred thousand dollars. How does that fit in with your present bank account?'

"Bryan's reply was, 'Circumstances alter cases.' "

Speaking of altered circumstances, my introduction to aviation and the active interest I have since taken in it comes as a far cry to the enthusiasm I felt as a boy, greeting the Pony Express, a contemporary marvel of transportation.

When Charles A. Lindbergh was on his way back to America after his epoch-making flight to Paris in May, 1927, the commissioners of the District of Columbia formed a reception committee to greet him on his arrival at the Capitol. I was asked to become its chairman and take the responsibility, on behalf of the people of Washington, of providing a fitting welcome and entertainment.

My own interest in aviation dated back to the time when, at the Metropolitan Club in Washington, I used to meet S. P. Langley, then head of the Smithsonian Institution. He was full of strange ideas about flying machines. In those days his theories were regarded as too visionary for serious attention, but I used to listen with interest to his lengthy disquisitions and predictions as to what he was going to accomplish in aviation.

When gasoline engines were invented a few years afterwards and the Wright brothers used them as airplane power plants, Langley's ideas were proved sound. I was struck with the difference between the talkativeness of Langley and the taciturnity of the Wright brothers. On the occasion of their receiving from President Taft the medals Congress had voted them, it was with the utmost difficulty that I could induce either of them to utter a word.

On December 15, 1925, I gave a dinner to a group of men actively engaged in promoting commercial air transportation. They had approached me with the idea that I might assist them in getting a measure passed by Congress which would secure government aid in the construction of beacon lights and landing fields for the guidance and convenience of pilots.

I had invited to the dinner those representatives of aviation companies and also government officials whose influence would be of most service in furthering the plan. The dinner was successful and the passage of the bill proved to be a long step in the advancement of commercial aviation.

I like to fly as a passenger. In fact, when a doctor tells me that altitude might dangerously affect my heart, I usually am able to find another who will reverse the decision. With this aviation background, my connection with the welcome accorded Lindbergh proved one of the memorable incidents of my life in Washington.

The haste with which we were forced to complete the reception plans meant strenuous work. But by the day before he was to arrive everything was settled, except the all-important question as to where and how the President and Lindbergh should meet. At the last committee meeting, I asked Postmaster General New, the government's representative on the committee, what the wishes of the President were.

"I don't know," he replied.

"But Lindbergh's going to be here tomorrow."

"The President doesn't want to be bothered with details," New assured me.

Saying I would return in a few moments, I got into my car and drove straight to the White House.

At the executive office, I was told by the staff that the President was not receiving anyone.

"Is anybody with him?"

"No."

I started for the door determinedly, and the executive clerk at once volunteered, "I'll take your card in."

"You won't have to," I responded, and walked into the inner office.

I found the President seated at his desk. I apologized briefly for my intrusion and reminded him that Lindbergh would arrive within twenty-four hours and that it was no longer a question of details but of making the final plans.

Then I asked him where he wanted to receive Lindbergh. He replied, "At the White House." This meant the temporary White House in Dupont Circle, which was serving while the national mansion was undergoing repairs.

"Bring him to lunch," said the President.

This arrangement struck me as unfair to those who would be marching in the parade that had been planned, and also to the thousands of spectators who would be kept waiting in the midday heat while Lindbergh was lunching.

"What will Lindbergh do for lunch then?" asked the President.

I suggested that I might take him one or two sandwiches, which was all he had on his transatlantic flight, or I might send a radio message asking him to have his lunch on the *Memphis* before landing.

"All right. Notify me when he reaches the grandstand, and I'll go there to receive him," said Coolidge.

My answer to this was that courtesy demanded he should be there first to receive Lindbergh. He finally acquiesced.

The weather was extremely hot. I hated to think of this young man, especially with the arduous program ahead of him, being subjected to the discomfort of the stiff and heavy colonel's uniform the army had prepared for him. I knew that one of the St. Louis backers, who had made this flight possible, was going down the river to meet the *Memphis* and was to take the uniform with him. I suggested that he lose it if possible.

The arrangement of the meeting between Lindbergh and his mother, Mrs. Evangeline Lindbergh, was one of my duties. I promised her that if she wished to accompany me to the *Memphis,* there would be no newspaper photographers on board to witness the greeting.

It proved difficult to get through the crowd of officials, congressmen, and others with special passes to the Navy Yard. Only the fact that we were in a White House car enabled us to edge our way finally to the dock. I escorted Mrs. Lindbergh to the captain of the *Memphis* and waited at the foot of the gangplank.

After a few minutes, Lindbergh with the President's aide, followed by Mrs. Lindbergh and the secretaries of war and navy, came down the gangplank amid the deafening uproar of whistles, bells, shouts, and cheers. Colonel Lindbergh, his mother, the President's aide, and I started off in the White House car and joined the long parade.

When Lindbergh appeared in a neat blue business suit, I was not surprised. As we were driving along to the grandstand near the Washington Monument, I asked him why he was not wearing the uniform. He smiled in his disarming manner and said: "Fortunately I couldn't get into it. I don't think I could have survived wearing it in this weather."

Each morning the papers printed his program for the day and, acting on this information, thousands of people would stand patiently for hours hoping to catch a glimpse of him.

As he rode from place to place, without a hat, he remained unaffected so far as anyone could see. He seemed to look on the entire performance as an interesting phenomenon, something apart from himself and having no connection with his astonishing achievement.

At the end of two days, Lindbergh was to fly to New York, where another reception awaited him. Since his arrival at Washington, my telephone had been ringing constantly with personal messages from my friends Grover Whalen and William H. Woodin, heads of the New York committee of reception, imploring me to see to it that he departed on schedule. Having witnessed the mad enthusiasm with which he was being greeted in Washington, I realized even better than they what the New York welcome would be like. Consequently, at six o'clock on the morning of his departure, I called at the temporary White House and took him to a breakfast tendered him by members of the different aeronautical associations.

The previous afternoon I had accompanied Lindbergh to Bolling Field while he inspected the *Spirit of St. Louis* and found the plane in perfect condition. That morning, however, he found that through carelessness of those in charge the plane had not been placed in the hangar and during the night a severe storm had rendered it unfit for flight. At the last moment, a plane of a type Lindbergh had never seen or flown before had to be substituted. He had no time to make his customary thorough inspection or even a trial flight.

When Lindbergh left the field, I was standing near Major F. Trubee Davison, assistant secretary of war, who, shocked at the angle and speed of the take-off, exclaimed, "My God! What a risk!" and turned his head away. Davison had been in the Yale aviation corps during the war and had had a serious accident.

A few months later the papers told of how Lindbergh started to fly to Portland, Maine, and was caught in such a heavy fog that it had taken him several hours to find a landing place. I knew that he was doing some work at the time for the Guggenheim Foundation, and I wrote my friend Harry Guggenheim that Lindbergh had already won his reputation for courage; if anything should happen to him now, aviation would be given a tremendous setback. It would be much better if he were to devote himself to conservative rather than risky flights.

Lindbergh came to see me shortly afterwards in Washington, and told me that Harry Guggenheim had showed him the letter. "I'm going to take your advice," he said.

In February, 1929, when President-elect Hoover was vacationing at Miami for a few weeks, and I was not far away at Palm Beach, he invited me to a luncheon party. One of the first persons I saw there was Lindbergh.

As soon as we had greeted each other, he remarked in some embarrassment: "I'm afraid you've lost confidence in me. You see when I was out in California the army planes were having maneuvers and one of the pilots was killed when flying in formation with two other planes. I felt I had to substitute for him and I may have taken risks, after I told you I wouldn't."

Lindbergh invited Hoover and me to make a flight with him that afternoon. I noticed that Hoover seemed hesitant about accepting, and to keep him from feeling embarrassed, I told him that, as the future President of the United States, he had no right to take chances with his life; that his doing so would be regarded as bravado. He was obviously relieved at my suggeston.

Mrs. Alvin T. Hert, a prominent member of the Republican National Committee, was also a guest. She remarked that Lindbergh was the only person with whom she could be induced to fly and asked whether she might go up with us. When the plane took off there was a full passenger list, including Mrs. Hert, Mrs. Henry Rae, and several other women. Mrs. Hert sat rigid with closed eyes and turned a deaf ear as I endeavored to beguile her with a description of the beauties of Biscayne Bay seen from the air. When we landed, she was the first one out of the plane. I congratulated her on her heroism.

It was not until we were safe on earth again that I related Hoover's account of the famous French aviator who shortly before had made a demonstration flight in Brazil with a party of Brazilian officials. The plane had crashed in landing, and all had met a tragic death. I told her that even Lindbergh had on several occasions been forced to seek safety with a parachute.

She looked at me dubiously and then remarked, "I wouldn't have missed this trip for a million dollars, but it would take a lot more than a million to get me up in a plane again."

In spite of the honors which had come to Lindbergh since the first Washington reception, he had not changed. A characteristic action of his turned my admiration into warm affection for him.

When he made his goodwill trip to Mexico—which not only achieved its purpose but also won him a bride—he had only two days in which to get ready. Inasmuch as I knew he personally supervised all flight preparations, and consequently had his hands full, I was greatly surprised when, at dawn of the day he was to leave, the doorbell of my house in Washington rang and I was told Colonel Lindbergh was downstairs.

Grasping my hand hurriedly, he said, "I'm off in half an hour, and I hadn't a second until now to come and have you wish me good luck."

When later he went to Panama to establish a route for the Pan American Airways, he wired me to join him as a flying companion. Unfortunately, I was at Gloucester and could not reach Miami, the starting point, by the date set for his departure.

Looking back on the Coolidge administration, I find it difficult to estimate either the man or his work. Despite the fact that I saw a great deal of him, I never felt close to him. Few people did. As I have said before, I considered him the man of the hour. And while many people attribute the financial collapse of 1929 in part to some of his policies, I consider the justice of this debatable. I would ask them if these same policies had not been their own.

There is no doubt that in his hour he was one of the most popular presidents we have ever had. And I imagine that part of the resentment which even today is directed towards him is due to the fact that thousands of his former constituents believe that, had he chosen to run again, he would somehow miraculously have saved their personal fortunes and the country from the depression.

To me, as a Westerner who had grown to pride himself on his knowledge of the psychology of that part of the country, one of the most amazing things about Calvin Coolidge was that he came to supersede even Theodore Roosevelt in the popular affections of the West.

Everything about Roosevelt had been the antithesis of Coolidge: his strenuous activities, his love of exciting adventures, his physical daring, his aggressiveness, and his ebullient manner. It has always seemed phenomenal to me that Coolidge, without any effort on his part, could have won the West. It may perhaps be explained by the fact that the West admired Roosevelt as an *individual* and Coolidge as a *president*.

Those who knew the political game considered Coolidge one of the shrewdest politicians among our presidents. His reluctance to commit himself when it was not necessary, his taciturnity, and his mannerisms help to build up this picture. In my contacts with him I became conscious that these characteristics were real and not legendary.

When he first came into office, I was still chairman of the Coal Commission. Almost daily we would have a smoke and a chat together.

Knowing that Coolidge was a very good judge of cigars, I sent him a box of particularly fine ones with my compliments. I received a note of appreciation. The next time I saw the President, I found him smoking a cigar which had the familiar aroma of my own brand. As I sat down, he opened a drawer of his desk and held out a box of cigars.

I leaned over and eyed it critically. One glance convinced me he must have taken literally Tom Marshall's witticism about the country's need for a five-cent cigar. I smiled, and said, "No, thank you."

Coolidge grinned in response, dipped again into his desk, and brought out my gift box. "Come to think of it, you sent me these. Try one."

I accepted.

The anecdotes about the Coolidge thrift are innumerable. It is said that in his boyhood he could make a worm last longer as fish bait than could any of his companions. About the best of these stories was told me by a newspaper correspondent who was one of three to interview him when he was lieutenant governor of Massachusetts.

It was an exceedingly stormy day. One reporter arrived a few moments ahead of his confreres.

Mrs. Coolidge, always thoughtful and generous, noticed how wet and cold he was, and considerately remarked, "Calvin, I think Bill needs a drink of whisky."

"All right! Give him one," said Coolidge.

Bill had finished his drink by the time the other two reporters arrived. Mrs. Coolidge poured out drinks for them also, and was about to give Bill another when Coolidge interjected hastily, "Oh, no! Bill's already had his."

Coolidge never could be forced to talk. The old story is true of the woman who sat next to him at dinner and wagered that she could get him to converse. "Mr. President," she began, "I have a bet that I can get you to talk to me."

Coolidge hesitated a moment and then replied quietly, "You have lost."

There were evidently times when, like Macaulay, Coolidge had brilliant flashes of silence and yet there were times also when, although he could not be called exactly loquacious, at least he became a most interesting conversationalist. My own experience warrants this statement. Often, after he had finished his work at the executive office and his desk was clear of official data, I dropped in and had most enjoyable talks with him.

He was logical in his theory of the value of silence. As he once remarked to a friend, "Well, after all, you'll have to admit that what I didn't say has never cost me anything."

I remember one illuminating conversation I had with him after the Teapot Dome scandal became public property.

"Mr. President," I said, "you sat in here with Harding's Cabinet. You must have seen a lot of Fall. Did it ever occur to you that he was a scoundrel?"

"Never," was the succinct reply.

"Would you ever have thought he could have been bribed?"

"Never."

"Wouldn't you have thought he was the sort of man who would have been so insulted by an attempt at bribery that he would have knocked the offender downstairs or kicked him out the door?"

"Yes."

At that laconicism I gave up.

Coolidge was exceedingly fortunate in not being in the White House when the storm ultimately broke. He conveyed to me at the time, more or less inarticulately, and he closed his autobiography with this sentiment:

> My election seemed assured. Nevertheless, I felt it was not best for the country that I should succeed myself. A new impulse is likely to be beneficial.
>
> It was therefore my privilege, after seeing my administration so strongly endorsed by the country, to retire voluntarily from the greatest experience that can come to mortal man. In that way, I believed I could best serve the people who have honored me and the country which I love.

In retrospect, I am impressed not so much with Coolidge's lack of foresight as with that which characterized our financial leaders, the bankers. Their judgment proved no better than that of the man in the street, and they failed utterly to realize that the bubble of fictitious prosperity was soon to be pricked. If any voices of protest and warning were raised, they were either inaudible or disregarded.

No doubt most of the justifiable disgust of the people with bankers came from the fact that in investing and losing other people's money (and indeed, to a certain extent, their own) very few of them had direct and accurate knowledge of the things in which they were investing, and in many cases their advisers and agents were both dishonest and incompetent. Even in the best of all possible worlds, it is not always wise to buy and sell goods you have never seen.

Our failure to recover more rapidly from the depression was founded, I believe, on this—and on the fact that our country still has little confidence in its leaders either political or economic. They had been tried and found wanting.

During the years in which my connection with politics was most active, and especially in my work with the Coal Commission, various of my opinions on capital and labor crystallized. But even before

MRS. EVANGELINE LINDBERGH, CHARLES A. LINDBERGH, AND MYSELF

CALVIN COOLIDGE (1872-1933)

this—believing, as I do, that every citizen should take an active part in civic matters—I had always been glad to donate my services where I considered they could be of use.

After the death of Grover Cleveland in 1908, I was asked to join the National Civic Federation as his successor to serve as "representative of the public" on one of the committees. The organization was politically nonpartisan, and included representatives of capital, labor, and the public. Its president at that time was Seth Low, formerly president of Columbia University; later Judge Alton B. Parker served. Ralph M. Easley was its secretary and its moving spirit. Its various committees were active in collecting data concerning many of the problems that affect the citizen, in making a careful study of them, and in advocating reforms. These committees studied and reported on the problems of Americanization, public education, taxation, judicial procedure, uniform state laws, trust regulation, Workmen's Compensation Act, and many purely economic and social questions.

The Women's Welfare Department of the federation, of which my wife was chairman for some time and Miss Gertrude Beeks (later Mrs. Ralph M. Easley) was secretary, was interested not only in women employees but in the welfare of employees in general.

The federation was not reformist in the radical sense. With a membership drawn from all classes of people, it necessarily preserved a balance of common sense and avoided extremes. It was conservative enough to wish to preserve the broad principles underlying Americanism.

It was customary for the officers of the federation to have luncheon meetings once or twice a month at some downtown club in New York. These were attended by many leaders of finance and industry. August Belmont, for example, was conspicuous for the splendid service he rendered up to the time of his death. Samuel Gompers, John Mitchell, and other labor leaders were usually present. The public did not realize that the frank discussions of our committees quietly composed many a difference before it could grow into an open dispute or strike. Gompers once remarked that he found the meetings of great service because they showed him the point of view of the employer, and the employers acknowledged the value of the information about labor matters which they secured from him.

Some of my friends outside took me to task for my association with labor leaders, and once a reactionary coal mine operator reproached me for the sympathy I had expressed for organized labor. In the presence of several prominent industrial leaders, I replied that organized labor was needed to protect the workingman against organized capitalism.

"There must be organization, and you men pursue a mistaken policy in fighting Gompers and Mitchell, who are conservative and patriotic, and are guiding labor with sanity and wisdom. Gompers is not a Socialist, and is energetically opposed to Communism. He has kept organized labor out of the hands of the radicals. Organized labor we will have. You must take your choice between the conservative Sam Gompers and the radical Bill Haywood."

Gompers was the best labor leader we could have found in those days. He stood out against the arbitrary, narrow, and selfish employer, and against the militant radicals in his own party. He used the weapon of the strike only as a last resort and settled many differences before they came to an issue. He broke many an outlaw strike by vigorously and decisively exercising his power as a dominant leader. The regard which the National Civic Federation had for him, a regard which had grown during twenty years' association, was given expression in a memorial meeting held in 1924, in memory of Samuel Gompers and August Belmont, both of whom had recently died.

I remember one occasion when the cigars were passed after dinner. "Try one of these, Sam," I requested.

Gompers picked up one, sniffed it, and a pleased expression spread over his face as he said: "I certainly will. You know I was a cigar roller once. This is one cigar that I hope I'll enjoy. Try one of mine!"

"Well, Sam, you may have been a cigar roller once but you're certainly the best-dressed man here tonight."

He smiled. "If labor didn't think I more than adequately represent it, it would never forgive me."

As a matter of fact, he was always immaculately attired. He met everybody on a plane of equality, with the complete and justified assurance that he was their mental equal. He had an essential humanity which gave him understanding of all, rich or poor, educated or illiterate. His oratory was effective but unaffected, illustrated with homely anecdote and pointed witticisms. He was an artist in playing on the bass string of human experience.

One of my prized possessions is his photograph on which he wrote, "To the most conservative, practical, radically democratic millionaire I ever met, John Hays Hammond, with the compliments of Samuel Gompers."

As Gompers and Mitchell knew, I am a friend of fair labor. I have often said that, were I an employee I would join some labor organization.

I believed in the Railway Brotherhoods and also in the American Federation of Labor under the guidance of such a man as Samuel Gompers. I supported both organizations as valuable parts of our industrial system. On the other hand, I had no use for the radicalism of the I.W.W., of which I had had experience in the Coeur d'Alene and Cripple Creek.

When I later discussed this aspect of the labor question with Samuel Gompers and John Mitchell, both admitted the unusually serious features of the Coeur d'Alene trouble. They confessed they had been wrong in sympathizing with the Western Federation at that time; their subsequent difficulties with Haywood and Orchard disclosed to them the true nature of the situation.

The lesson from labor strikes, as I see it, is that no organization, whether labor or capital, industrial or social, economic or spiritual, can succeed or even continue to exist unless it is founded upon fair intent and is conducted in the main by honest leaders. This truth applies equally to a nation, a trades union, a bank, or a church. If a government does not honestly and speedily enforce the laws made to protect both individuals and corporate bodies against attacks on life and property, it invites disaster upon itself.

My own interest lay primarily in the relations between employer and employee. As a mining engineer I had come in close contact with a type of workman perhaps the most difficult of all to handle because of his independence. I understood the miner, and his problems, and had a good deal of sympathy with his point of view. I was instrumental in securing the passage of legislation for the protection of the miner, and advocated workmen's compensation laws and the minimum wage, and other beneficent measures.

Gompers, curiously enough, was opposed to the movement to set up a minimum wage, fearing it would tend to become a prevailing wage.

I did not fall into the error of class antagonism. The close contact a mining engineer must necessarily have with his men doubtless keeps him democratic. I never lost my liking for cranks and odd characters in general, as they have afforded me amusement and sometimes indeed valuable suggestions.

Though I always kept on friendly terms with workmen, I also understood the point of view of the employer. I early became identified with large corporations and the management of successful companies, and later counted among my friends the great promoters and capitalists of the country. I saw that capital, too, has its rights and minimum wage; that is, the rate of interest necessary as guarantee before the investor can be expected to risk his money in an enterprise.

It is true that capital has often exceeded its rights, and by exercise of its power grasped inequitable rewards. I believe that some method should be devised to prevent such evils as overcapitalization, both in public utility and in private corporation. The recently revealed corruption in some large corporations calls for reform. The public should not be forced to pay for services and products in excess of value received, nor should the credulous investor find that he can hope for no return on his investment unless labor is sweated.

During the Taft, Harding, and Coolidge administrations, my family became more and more intimately involved in the social life of Washington. While we never found it quite so fascinating as the same type of life in London, we felt it was far more interesting than similar aspects of living in any other American city. Washington is, I think, one of the most beautiful cities in the world, especially at Eastertime, with the gorgeous cherry blossoms, Rock Creek Park and the lovely green lawns with beds of multicolored flowers set aside for the public, monuments, buildings, drives along the Potomac, and Georgetown, Arlington, and Mount Vernon only a short distance away.

While the whole make-up of Washington life is complex, it is also in a sense simple, and while, of course, in the days of which I am writing, there was a considerable amount of hospitality on a lavish scale, charming and equally memorable were the simple entertainments given by people of modest means. One of the most admirable characteristics of Washington social life is that money doesn't count as it does in other American cities. In this it resembles London.

The social scene is composed of various groups. Centering in the White House is the administrative and diplomatic life, and on down the line the whole parade of governmental officeholders. I may be prejudiced, but it seemed to me that members of Congress, senators in particular, do not measure up to the intellectual capacity of those who served two or three generations ago. Nevertheless, they are a hard-working class and when one considers Congressional nonentities, one must remember bankers, lawyers, businessmen, and indeed, mining engineers.

The army and the navy add a certain glamour to various dinners and parties. Not only those occupied actively in the army and navy departments are present, but also many men who have served with distinction in one or other of the services and who have, as is their custom, made their residence permanently in Washington.

And there is that other large and select group known, with kindly humor, as the "has-beens," passé politicians, former congressmen and senators, retired diplomats, and more and more people from other parts of the country who come to Washington to spend their later years in a life which offers them contacts both democratic and stimulating.

No description of the character of Washington life would be complete without mention of the "Cave dwellers." They are the real Washingtonians. For many generations their ancestors have lived there, some of them in Georgetown, even before the founding of Washington. Feeling themselves the real aristocrats, they do not seek society, and patronize somewhat the shifting governmental population.

Since the World War, I am glad to observe that American women are becoming "internationally minded"—which must be pleasing to my friend, Nicholas Murray Butler—and the Washington women are particularly fortunate in having the opportunity of acquiring interesting and reliable information about world conditions through the Monday Talks on "Affairs Political and International" of Miss Janet Richards, who is justly known as the Dean of Lecturers on Current Events.

One of the more vital groups in Washington is that composed of the scientific and literary men, many of whom are world famous. During lunch at the Cosmos Club, it is possible to hear conversations dealing with every phase of the world of scholarship and science.

Many of these men are connected with the Smithsonian Institution, Bureau of Standards, Carnegie Institute, the four neighboring universities, the Congressional and Carnegie libraries, the various other branches of science and learning. Unfortunately the members of this group are conspicuous by their absence from most society functions. An innovation that would contribute much to the social and intellectual life of Washington would be dinners given by the President to notable people of the Capital other than high government officials.

President and Mrs. Franklin D. Roosevelt are, to a degree, aware of this and in this respect are following the traditions of Theodore Roosevelt. They have frequently entertained writers, artists, scientists, sculptors, and scholars, and have been subjected to undiscerning criticism. American politicians have always been notoriously afraid of men possessing sound and proven knowledge. In England a procedure such as this has always been taken as a matter of course. On the other hand, in the transaction of the affairs of the government, the designation of power to people, whether intellectuals or politicians, who have not demonstrated their ability and honesty seems to me to be dangerous.

Anyone living in Washington cannot fail to be both irritated and impressed by some of the irksome duties imposed by its custom.

For example, the presidential handshaking seems a great imposition on our Chief Executive—surely an onerous and unnecessary obligation. The right arm of the President, which is sworn to maintain the Constitution of the United States, has often been seriously impaired for efficient service by this senseless business. Witness the case of President Coolidge, who was once forced to carry his arm in a sling for several days from too constant and strenuous handshaking. I understand that at the New Year's Day reception at the White House this has been discontinued. Surely the reception itself clearly shows our democratic spirit, and the handshaking is unnecessary at that time, as well as when the President meets organizations, societies, groups, and committees from all parts of the country.

As all old Washingtonians know, precedence at government functions, and even at conventional private entertainments, is often a matter of considerable embarrassment to the host or hostess. It is probably necessary, however, as its effect dignifies and preserves respect for the custodians of our government. Democratization of governmental functions would perhaps tend to lessen respect for those occupying high positions. On the other hand, an American citizen who holds no official position—though highly important in the life of the nation—may feel himself socially handicapped on these distinguished occasions when he finds himself assigned, perhaps, "below the salt." Only recently I learned that, etymologically, the word "idiot" signifies "a person who is not in the government service."

It must be extremely monotonous for Cabinet officers and their wives to be repeatedly huddled together at the White House, and other places—but the more philosophical "grin and bear it." And if their constant neighbors required by custom prove deadly dull, they get their conversational relaxation elsewhere. At any rate, this is Washington!

I feel quite certain that the men of any family prominent in Washington social life cannot have failed to notice and deplore some of the senseless and irksome duties imposed upon women: for example, the survival of the incessant paying of formal calls, the almost daily task of leaving cards at innumerable front doors—surely a sad waste of time and cardboard, and quite ridiculous as a custom. But I believe that the women of present-day Washington are fast discarding this form of etiquette, which must be a relief to all concerned.

After we came to the Capital to make our home, my wife and I found great pleasure in the dinner parties, the old-fashioned elegance of entertainment, and above all in the fact that we discovered ourselves making new friends, interesting friends, and warm friends.

Emily Beale McLean was one of our close friends; she was a great hostess. Her Sunday luncheons at "Friendship," her semicountry home on the edge of the city, were memorable. Although they were formal and much thought must have been given to their arrangement, they seemed almost impromptu. No fewer than a hundred guests were invited for each occasion, and even at the eleventh hour one might ask the privilege of bringing any number of out-of-town friends. Small tables, at which there was no question fortunately of precedence, seemed to appear as if by magic for a last-moment influx. Delicious food, accompanied by her celebrated mint juleps, was abundant. This hospitality was very gracefully carried on by her daughter-in-law, Evelyn Walsh McLean, for many years.

Among the elaborate dinners at which I was a guest was that given by Colonel Robert M. Thompson several years ago at his home in honor of some members of the Greek royal family who were visiting in Washington. I was asked to take in Lady Sarah Wilson, widow of a British army officer, Colonel Henry Wilson. She was a well-known sportswoman, a great traveler, and a woman of interesting personality. As we sat at table she remarked on the contrast between the luxury of the present appointments and the primitive simplicity of the meal we last had together, nearly thirty years before. The dinner to which she referred was one which she and her husband and I had had when they were visiting Jameson's camp on the veldt, just before the Boer War. Jameson had run short of provisions when I reached his camp after an inspection of some mines, and as I was on my way out to Bulawayo, I divided with him all of the food I had left. So there on the veldt in Jameson's camp we dined that night on game and canned goods.

Another Washington friend of ours, made through old family ties, was Princess Cantacuzene, the granddaughter of President Grant. She naturally had nothing but abhorrence for the violence of the

Bolshevik government, a viewpoint with which I fully agreed, as did most informed Americans with the exception of the rankest ideologists.

On the question of the recognition of the U.S.S.R. I did not agree with Senator Borah. Later I came to see that despite his predilection for the Soviet government he could feel sympathy for the unfortunate sufferers in its terrorist regime. The incident that convinced me occurred at the time the Soviet government had decided to execute several Roman Catholic priests. Senator Borah and I were in my study when Judge Alton B. Parker, president of the National Civic Federation, telephoned asking me to be one of a hundred Americans to sign a cablegram of protest against the execution of these priests. I readily consented, of course, and urged the senator likewise to send a cablegram, saying that a protest from him would be more potent than Judge Parker's petition. He flatly refused because the priests had no business taking part in Soviet politics. As he left my home I followed him to the door in an endeavor to appeal to his humanity. I pointed out that he could not rest easy with the thought that innocent priests were suffering when his name might save them. Half an hour later Borah telephoned me from his house saying: "Colonel, you are right. I have sent the cablegram."

William E. Borah, during the Republican administrations, was undoubtedly the outstanding figure in the Senate. His enemies characterized him as one

> Stiff in opinions, always in the wrong,
> Was everything by starts and nothing long;

but even his political enemies had to admit that he was a factor to be reckoned with because of his unimpeachable integrity, his political courage, and of the fact that he was an indomitable fighter and an orator with "the applause of listening senates to command." Borah undoubtedly was "the big bad wolf" in the Coolidge and Hoover administrations. He has put Idaho on the map politically and it has never been marked "a windswept plain."

Viscount Grey of Fallodon, my old friend, was in Washington as special ambassador in 1919, and I have told of the luncheon at which we urged him to make a public statement regarding the Lodge reservations to President Wilson's League of Nations. Another time when he was dining with me in Washington, he told a story which he said was the most remarkable example of true sportsmanship he had ever known. Two of the major native tribes in New Zealand were incessantly warring against each other, much to the annoyance of the white residents, and a representative was sent out by the British government to investigate. (My recollection is that Grey himself was the British representative.) Having decided in favor of one of the tribes, he reported that if properly backed by the government it would be able to conquer the other and establish peace. The government sent what it considered a sufficient supply of arms and ammunition to enable its champion to defeat the enemy, who possessed only primitive weapons.

After a few months the government was surprised to receive a request for more guns. They were sent with some reluctance, but when a third request was received for still more guns, the representative was sent out again to investigate. He found the native chief and asked why he needed so many rifles, saying that the great King had at first sent all that were thought necessary. The chief expressed his thanks for the many guns he had received but said that he did not use all of them. Very much surprised, the representative asked him what he had done with the rest. The old warrior replied, "We divided them with our enemy because they did not have any guns." After telling the story, Grey said, "And we call those people uncivilized."

From the time when I first collected stamps as a boy in San Francisco until late in life I did not have the time nor the inclination to indulge in hobbies. But during the years I did develop one other hobby—and that, too, collecting. I collected people, in a sense, people I had met and admired.

It has been my privilege "in the day's work" to meet many of the leading men of my time. On the walls of my study in my Washington home I have what is regarded as a unique collection of autographed photographs, numbering over eight hundred. They represent, so my friends tell me, at least one-half the men of my day who have controlled the destinies of nations.

Charles Coffin, the great genius who was responsible for the development of the General Electric Company, had not been photographed since childhood, but just before his death he was persuaded to have one taken for my collection. He, Myron T. Herrick, and I were a trio bound together by the closest ties of friendship.

In all my collection of famous individuals, the only one I have not known personally was Abraham Lincoln, whose picture was given me by his son, Robert Todd. It is an etching which he declared was the best of all the likenesses of his father.

Bob Lincoln, whose home was one of the most picturesque in Washington, liked to talk of his father, and after our golf at the Chevy Chase Club, he would visit the "nineteenth hole" at my house, and relate stories about him. I remember his telling how his father composed the Gettysburg Address on a sheet of wrapping paper while the train was on its way from Washington. He told me that once when he returned from Harvard to spend his vacation at the White House, certain officials came to him and asked him to complain to his father about Salmon P. Chase, secretary of the treasury. Chase, they said, was considered disloyal to the President, and everyone in the executive office knew it except the President himself. That night when he was studying in his room his father entered and Bob told him what he had heard. The President said, "Well, I have Chase's resignation in my hand." Bob said, "Of course, you will accept it?" The President replied, "Of course, I shall not."

He then asked for writing materials and wrote a note declining to accept Chase's resignation. To Bob's question why he was taking such action, he answered: "He is much safer in my Cabinet than he would be outside." Lincoln's action is known to history. In 1864 he appointed Salmon P. Chase chief justice of the Supreme Court, in which he served creditably until his death in 1873. The story has been told often before but it was interesting to hear the details from Bob Lincoln, as he told me in the presence of Colonel Chase, a descendant of Salmon P. Chase. It had been said that similar considerations—namely, it is safer to have your opponent in the fold than out—largely determined the appointment of William Jennings Bryan to the Cabinet of Woodrow Wilson.

The photograph of Blasco Ibañez recalls to mind an amusing incident which shows that all great men are not recognized generally as such. We had entertained Ibañez at our home for several days, and found him an interesting and brilliant guest. After his visit my wife made a trip to Philadelphia, and remembering that she wished to get some more of his books, went into Wanamaker's Department Store. She asked the young clerk in the book department if he had any Ibañez. Somewhat confused and puzzled, he said: "Madam, you may find them in the underwear department." Evidently something resembling "Ypsilanties" was in his mind.

One of our closest friends in Washington was Senator Frank B. Brandegee of Connecticut, and I have always felt a distinct personal sorrow at his suicide, October 14, 1924. He was a fine, honest man doing real patriotic service. He was one of the outstanding figures in the Senate and was leader of the "irreconcilables" who opposed our joining the League of Nations. Brandegee had invested heavily in real estate near Washington and, although he was losing money currently, later the properties became highly profitable. He was embarrassed by the fact that he had borrowed small sums of money from his friends and could not repay it in the allotted time. Naturally, his friends did not expect or want him to pay until he could do so conveniently, but he became hypersensitive in the matter.

The day before Brandegee committed suicide I called on him. He was a bachelor and lived alone with his servants in a gloomy brick house. He was not in good health and had been deeply affected by the death of his sister a few years earlier. Added to this, he had recently consulted an eminent surgeon in New York who told him that before long it would be necessary to amputate one of his legs. This was enough to break the most resolute spirit. I found Senator Brandegee quite depressed and most difficult to cheer, but before I left we had a good reassuring talk. I asked him to come home with me to dinner, but he declined saying he had an appointment with some real estate men. Then I asked him to come up the next night when George Harvey would be with me; he accepted.

Brandegee did not arrive for dinner, nor did I hear from him. I worried about him. Early the next day as I was getting into my automobile to call on him, William, my chauffeur, said: "Mr. Hammond, I want you to know how sorry I was to hear about Senator Brandegee's suicide." I was shocked. I had not seen the papers and this was the first I had heard of the tragedy.

Brandegee left a note addressed to his butler; this was characteristic of his consideration and affection:

> Dear George: I enclose $100 for you and $100 for Emma and Rufus. I am in the bathroom on the top floor nearest 18th Street; the top floor, the floor above the one I sleep on. If you and Lundy come up there, beware of the gas. Goodbye.

In spite of the fact that the convention of 1920 was my last, I did have an indirect connection with the candidacy of Hoover in 1928. During that winter, Frederic C. Walcott later United States senator from Connecticut, who was prominent in pressing Hoover's candidacy, came to Ormond Beach, Florida, where I was spending the winter. He asked me whether, in my opinion, Hoover should announce his candidacy in the near future or, as had been suggested by some of his political advisers, wait until shortly before the convention.

I thought it was absolutely necessary for Hoover to lose no time; I advised that he make his announcement at the earliest possible moment. When Walcott asked me whether this was not somewhat different advice from that given by me to General Wood, I explained that the circumstances were different. Wood had had many rival candidates while Hoover so far had virtually none. Walcott reported my conversation to Hoover, and my plan was adopted.

A few months before Chief Justice Taft's death, he and Walcott were present at a luncheon I gave in Washington. Walcott told Taft that Hoover and he had just seen General Charles G. Dawes, and Dawes had said that Hoover had had a narrow escape, for if he had not announced his candidacy the very day he did, Dawes himself would have been in the field. Dawes would have been a powerful contestant. Owing to his friendship for Governor Lowden, Dawes had not pressed his own candidacy, but when it began to appear that Lowden would have little chance for the nomination, he found that he could count on Lowden's support. He was then, he told Hoover, on the point of announcing his position and entering on a vigorous campaign for delegates. Sure of Ohio and Illinois and several other states, he would have had a good chance of defeating Hoover.

My first intimate contact with Herbert Hoover was just before we entered the World War, when he was in charge of Belgian Relief. The Rocky Mountain Club gave him a dinner. Funds for the relief work were not being collected in anything like the volume needed, and Hoover was asked to make an appeal to our members, and through them to citizens at large. This appeal was successful in gaining the support of our club. In two months, three million dollars were raised for the Belgian Relief, more than had been secured the previous year. For ten years the club had been collecting a reserve fund to be used in erecting a new building, but this appeal was so cogent that by a unanimous vote the entire fund was to be donated to help feed the starving people of Belgium.

One might think that western men, being used to traveling lone trails, would lose something of gregariousness, but it is not so. The Rocky Mountain Club of twelve hundred members, which maintained an "oasis" in New York for "roundups" and "stampedes," is evidence of the persistent desire even among Westerners to flock with their kind.

Our purpose was to promote good fellowship among our members and to bring about a greater solidarity between eastern and western states. The cosmopolitan nature of our membership list was shown by what happened one evening when a dozen or so mining engineers were talking after one of our banquets was over. These banquets were regarded by all who attended them as among the most enjoyable in New York.

While we were having a last smoke the question came up as to what countries we had all visited. We produced a large atlas and, just as my brother and I used to do with the counties of California, picked out the countries which had been visited by some member of our party. When the checkup was made, we found there wasn't a country on the face of the globe which one member or the other had not set foot on in the course of his professional work.

During the World War the Rocky Mountain Club rendered distinct patriotic service in entertaining and caring for soldiers of regiments raised in the western states, en route to the battlefields of Europe, and in caring for them on their return to New York after the war, before they departed for their homes. The wives of the members formed a committee, of which my wife was chairman, and they worked diligently for the boys.

After this last roundup, the money received from the sale of our real estate holdings was turned over to the American Institute of Mining and Metallurgical Engineers as a gift to be expended under its direction. We considered the institute the most worthy heir of the principles and spirit of the Rocky Mountain Club. The first work of this fund was the publication of a scholarly book, *The Porphyry Coppers,* by A. B. Parsons, secretary of the American Institute of Mining Engineers. In making possible the publication of this book and others to follow, the Rocky Mountain Club continues to live.

Our active members were representative western men living in New York, who were identified with the development of the West; our associate members were the governors of western states, and mostly mining men living in the West whose business brought them frequently to New York. From 1907, when it was founded, to the "last roundup" in 1928, I had the honor of being the club's only president.

The late "Ike" Hoover, of the White House staff, says, "Coolidge perhaps did less work than any president I have known; Herbert Hoover the most work."

Coolidge was not lazy; he had his departments well organized with capable men at their heads. I never saw his desk cluttered with papers, and in that I recognized he was a good executive.

Hoover came into office under far more trying conditions. He had taken his position as a Cabinet officer more conscientiously than is usual, attending strictly to business and not indulging in social life. Indeed, he rarely went out.

He was inducted into the presidency under most adverse conditions. As I told him on one occasion, he had built up a Frankenstein for himself, for it is undoubtedly true that the prosperity—whether fundamental or not—developed during Coolidge's administration was in a large measure due to the financial ability of Andrew Mellon and to the commercial ability of Herbert Hoover.

While I saw Hoover occasionally in the executive office as well as at White House social functions, I did not enjoy the intimacy with him that I had enjoyed with his predecessors. As president he was, in many ways, a lonely man. Even Taft, who had been the constant adviser of Coolidge, was never called to the White House by Hoover for conference, nor did Hoover avail himself of the political experience of Calvin Coolidge. It was unfortunate for Hoover that his enthusiastic followers of the younger generation associated with him in his relief work had made him appear to the public as somewhat of a superman—an impossible role to maintain. Then, too, Hoover was handicapped by the fact that he relied too much on "yes, yes" men for advice.

My estimate of Hoover is that he possessed executive ability to an exceptional degree, but lacked the qualities of leadership. This explains in a measure his failure to secure the co-operation of the public, Congress, the politicians, and the press—all essential elements in the successful carrying out of his policies.

The four years of Hoover reminded me of Ovid's remark that "an army of stags led by a lion would be more formidable than one of lions led by a stag."

CHAPTER THIRTY-FOUR

Trekking De Luxe

TRAVEL EQUIPMENT—RENEWING OLD FRIENDSHIPS—
EUROPE'S PREDICAMENT—INEFFECTIVE PEACE
PACTS—FRENCH-GERMAN SITUATION—WE TAKE A
CRUISE TO THE MEDITERRANEAN—MY DAUGHTER
IS BRIDESMAID AT AN EGYPTIAN WEDDING—MUSSO-
LINI AND THE POPE GRANT AUDIENCES—LATIN
AMERICA—THE MONROE DOCTRINE—WE HAVE AUDI-
ENCE WITH THE KING AND QUEEN OF SPAIN—THE PHILIPPINES

During the administrations of which I have written in the preceding chapter, and in view of a life which, to this point, must appear unrestful in its constant motion, it may seem logical that I would settle down in my home in Washington or Gloucester and be content to retire in a definite and fireside manner. Indeed, in thinking about it, it does seem reasonable.

But travel was my busman's holiday and an enthusiasm which my entire family either inherited or acquired. Having in the past journeyed perforce through many countries of the world and having come to know a cosmopolitan and broadly scattered group of peoples, I felt a natural impulse in the years after the war to revisit places I had known, to scrutinize altered political, economic, and social conditions and to find out what had become of old friends.

No doubt, were it still necessary to get about on burros, aboard sailing vessels, in Cape carts, droshkies, buckboards, on snowshoes, and in uncomfortably primitive railroad trains I would have reconsidered this strong inclination and my zeal would have abated.

To me, traveling on business has always been one thing; traveling without the urgency of business, quite another. I am reminded that my trips to investigate properties and development possibilities were often the despair of my wife. I hated to be encumbered and usually went off with one large valise, or preferably a duffel bag. Coming home ordinarily with more rock specimens in my bag than wearing apparel, and those rocks frequently wrapped in my very best clothes, was an eccentricity that never met with her complete approval.

On the other hand, in recent years when I started out on a recreation trip, I wanted to take along as many as possible of the household. In fact, had it been even remotely possible, I probably also would have taken my entire library and all the movables, and even our lares et penates.

In making such trips I carried with me books relating to the different countries which I was to visit and these I studied assiduously. Comfort was to me the first consideration. In addition to these impedimenta, my family and I had a fixed habit of aggravating our burden with all sorts of objects at each stopping place, and we would often arrive back on shipboard with a number of individual, carefully wrapped purchases, and the prized autographed photographs. All of these things brought about perpetual confusion among the servants. And I can say with some assurance that the family is remembered in one way or another in a number of distant ports and railroad stations. In later years, my secretary, Griffin, added final touches to traveling de luxe. I relied on him in the purchase of tickets and securing comfortable accommodations on steamers as on trains, and to keep an eye on all trunks, valises, holdalls, suitcases, bags, and boxes. He justly prides himself on never having lost an article.

Attached to my entourage were a maid and a valet to complete the vicious circle, not for swank, but as indispensable to the Sybaritic mode of travel into which we had gradually drifted.

Speaking of traveling de luxe: a few years ago when lunching with the officers of the British South Africa Company in London I was urged by them to revisit Rhodesia to see the wonderful progress that had been made in the development of the country. In a casual way

I inquired as to the comforts of hotel accommodations there. This provoked considerable amusement among my friends who remembered the hardships I had uncomplainingly experienced in the pioneer days. It must have occurred to them that I was getting very soft—which was indeed the case. Alas!

The spring, summer, and part of the fall of 1924, I spent in Europe, accompanied by my wife and my daughter Natalie. In spite of the depression abroad, it proved to be an enlivening trip, particularly since we met such a wide range of interesting personalities. We stayed in London several weeks meeting old friends. Natalie was presented at the first Drawing Room held that year by King George and Queen Mary, who entertained us also at luncheon at the Ascot races. And, on a gala occasion, the Duke of Connaught took us to the Wimbledon Exposition. One particularly interesting event I recall is when I was a guest at the magnificent banquet given to Ras Taffari by Lord Granard in the name of the British government.

Ras Taffari was then the reigning prince of Ethiopia (Abyssinia). He has since ascended the Gold Throne of David as Emperor Haile Selassie I, King of Kings of Ethiopia, Elect of God, Conquering Lion of Judah, and Light of Ethiopia. He claims royal descent from King Solomon and the Queen of Sheba, without benefit of clergy.

In recent years this sovereign, who seemed a quiet, unpretentious gentleman when I met him, has been affording the press opportunities for amused comment through his grandiose styles of entertainment and his quixotic statesmanship.

Through an interpreter I managed to tell Ras Taffari—and he seemed much interested—of the reopening of the great mines of his ancestor, King Solomon, in Rhodesia and of the immense wealth being taken from the ancient workings.

For several years I used to broadcast a graduating address to the high school and college classes throughout the United States on "Essentials of a Successful Career," and generally ended my address with the quotation about the plucky cowboy:

> Life ain't in Holding
> A good Hand
> But in Pla-ing
> A Pore Hand Well.

While in London I was asked to broadcast a similar address to the youth of the British Isles. It happened that my broadcast was to take place on a Sunday evening. When I submitted in advance copy of my address to those in charge of the program, I was told that I could not use that motto as the pious audience in Scotland would be scandalized at a reference on *Sunday* to card playing.

On this trip we visited Berlin. There we again saw the British ambassador to Germany, Lord D'Abernon, and his beautiful and charming wife. I had the opportunity to meet interesting German statesmen and economists, among them Secretary of Foreign Affairs Stresemann and Dr. Hjalmar Schacht, the eminent German financier. I also met the members of the Dawes Commission who were working on the Dawes Plan.

A most interesting luncheon was given us by Count and Countess von Schoen. Count von Schoen was at that time in the Foreign Office. Countess von Schoen and her sisters, Mrs. Harold Walker and Mrs. E. R. Finkenstaedt, of Washington, were noted southern beauties. This occasion was also my first meeting with Baron Ago Maltzan. The countess told me privately that Baron Maltzan, one of the undersecretaries of foreign affairs, had been offered the ambassadorship to the United States, but was hesitating about accepting.

I brought up the subject as tactfully as possible in my talk with him. He admitted that he was considering the post but was disinclined to accept, as he believed it was too soon after the war for a German ambassador to be favorably received in Washington. He asked my opinion. I told him that I thought he was wrong; if he would go to Washington in the proper frame of mind, I was convinced he would be given a cordial reception. I urged him then and on subsequent occasions to accept, and he finally did. He proved to be democratic, that is, a good mixer, making friends particularly with the newspapermen. This quality made him a popular ambassador. I had the pleasure of giving the first large dinner in his honor in Washington, and later help him to find a place for his summer embassy at Magnolia, on the North Shore of Massachusetts. Our acquaintance developed into a most pleasant friendship.

He came to see me just before he sailed to spend the summer at home. He planned to visit many parts of Germany in the short time at his disposal. When I asked how he could possibly cover so much territory, he said: "Of coure, by airplane," and added that aviation was so far advanced that flying was perfectly safe, and no one had ever been killed in a plane of the company he was to use. Unfortunately, the first exception was his own case: he and the best pilot of the company met their death on one of these flights. So my farewell "auf Wiedersehen" was not to be realized.

In visits to the capitals of England, France, Switzerland, and Germany and in discussions with men of authority in different governmental and private capacities I was beginning to get a clearer picture of the current political situation in Europe and to reaffirm ideas I had held during the years when I devoted much of my time to international peace work—ideas which later events have developed into more or less definite convictions.

When I entered Freiberg in 1876, Bismarck was at the height of his power. It was his policy to let England and France fight it out for territory, while Germany intensified her internal industrial development.

It was not until the latter part of the eighties that Germany became territory-conscious and overzealous in her aim to secure a place in the sun. As a consequence of this policy she felt compelled to build a navy and a merchant marine on a parity with other great powers. This naval ambition created political unfriendliness between herself and England, and this was accentuated when Germany declined the invitation of Winston Churchill on behalf of England for a naval holiday.

In my former visits to Berlin over a period of years, I had observed the increasing hostility growing out of this rivalry. The sudden presence of a militant Germany among the contenders for territorial expansion inevitably led to clashes and tariff wars with England and France, which in turn brought about other disputes and accentuated national hatred, and finally to the World War.

I talked with statesmen in France, and later with Stresemann in Germany, of Briand and Stresemann's aim to establish an economic accord among the European nations by the creation of a United States of Europe. When Briand asked Stresemann for his offhand comment on this plan, Stresemann said: "Start from the one inevitable manifestation of European unity, I mean Industry . . . It is obviously the only escape from the chaotic and impossible industrial relations of today—from the artificial segregation by customs barriers of forces that are striving to combine."

Briand brought his proposal for a United States of Europe before the council tables of practical statesmanship and won for it approval in principle from all the nations of Europe that are members of the League. Since 1930 the Committee for a European Union set up by the League has met regularly to formulate plans, the details and scope of which are common knowledge.

Foremost among the economic measures to bind these nations together would be the leveling of tariff barriers among themselves and the removal of quotas, embargoes, and other strictures now bewildering producers and paralyzing the commerce of Europe. Thus there would be created a great zollverein providing a free internal market comparable to the domestic market upon which the prosperity of the United States of America has been built. Commerce on such a scale would call for a unified system of money and the stabilization of banks of issue. This should mean an end to periods of false prosperity such as recently afflicted both Europe and America, prosperity which consisted largely in buying and selling money, or more exactly in the creation and selling of credit, which ultimately took on the nature of counterfeiting on a colossal scale. Finance could then again be surbordinated to and made to serve the needs of production and distribution.

By such a plan racial jealousies would become less acute in the realization of a community of economic interests. It would do much towards the economic stabilization of the world and building up a prosperous economic entity that ultimately would prove of advantage to the United States, Great Britain, and other great commercial nations in that eventually it would afford a market within its own boundaries which does not obtain at present owing to the lack of purchasing power and the low standard of living of the industrial and agricultural population. By developing an important trade from other countries it would help to create markets; it would, by increasing their purchasing power, benefit the nations outside of the United States of Europe. There certainly would be no opposition to such a plan on the part of the United States or Great Britain. We have established a high tariff policy in our own country, and Great Britain, at the Ottawa conference, gave to her dominions and colonies a preferential tariff which in many items becomes a prohibitive tariff against other nations.

It would seem to me reasonable to hope that the nations that would be members of this contemplated United States of Europe would be willing to make extreme concessions of their political and economic interests in order to establish such a zollverein, or trade league.

The League of Nations, Locarno, and the Kellogg-Briand Pact, admittedly, have not proved sufficient to reassure the world as to peace, although they have greatly contributed to peace-psychology which has tended to restrain overt acts of hostility.

And yet, in view of the recent developments in Europe, it seems incredible that practical statesmen have been considering and working chiefly towards this objective, knowing how hopelessly improbable its accomplishment is.

By the stipulations of Locarno both Germany and France have bound themselves to respect and to preserve the boundary line drawn at Versailles between Germany and France, and Great Britain and Italy have engaged to go to the defense of either nation should that boundary, a rampart of hatred for thousands of years, be violated by the other.

The keeping of this faith, already strained, nevertheless remains the supreme test of the civilization of the French and German people. It is a key to the peace of the world. Whether so precious a heritage shall be preserved rests now with the wisdom of French and German statesmanship.

As to the French-Italian situation, I am still of the opinion expressed to Lord Northcliffe and to Viscount Grey in the early part of 1914: it is unfortunate that better understanding does not exist between those two countries.

It seems obvious that the quandary in Continental Europe today is that there can be no economic recovery until political controversies are adjusted, and political controversies cannot be adjusted until economic conditions improve. This is the vicious circle. I feel that no solution of this problem has been effected through the League of

Nations nor by the various financial and political expedients. The Dawes Plan and the Young Plan, heralded by Europe and the world as instruments to bring about economic recovery, have both failed in the realization of their objectives. D'Abernon, Dawes, Schacht, Young, and countless others have been tireless in their efforts to repair the springs of economic difficulty. They and their various plans and accomplishments were the best expedients at the moment and at least helped to postpone the crises of 1924 and 1929.

There is less security for the world today than there has been at any time since the Armistice. And yet, if war is to be avoided, some economic plan must be worked out and followed. To me and to most thinking men, war as a policy is insanity. While it is impossible for anyone to predict what is going to happen to Europe or, as the days go by, confidently to hope for the maintenance of peace, nevertheless the present outlook is more reassuring.

We had returned to the United States by way of London in time for me to take an active part in connection with the election of President Coolidge. But in the spring of 1926, my wife, my daughter, and I again had a touch of wanderlust and started out on another trip. This time we went through the countries on the Mediterranean, including Spain, Algiers, the ruins of Carthage—"*delenda est Carthago*"—in Northern Africa, Greece, Turkey, Palestine, and Egypt. Major and Mrs. Burnham joined us at Gibraltar from their trip around the world and went with us to Egypt, our first visit to that country.

We made a trip to Luxor and arrived on the first rainy day there had been for many decades. We spent several days in the Valley of the Kings, visiting the tomb of Tutankhamen, which was just being excavated, and other points of interest.

I have many friends in the diplomatic corps of foreign countries, among them Yousry Pasha and Samy Pasha, successively Egyptian minister at Washington. Loutfia Yousry, daughter of the former, went to school with Natalie and came often to our house. When we started on our trip to Egypt, Samy Pasha, then minister to Washington, gave me a letter to Hassanein Bey, a writer and explorer of note and the son of the sheik of a powerful Bedouin tribe.

I found Hassanein Bey an attractive man of high culture. He had been educated at Oxford, and spoke English with a decided Oxonian accent. Major Burnham was with me at the time I presented my letter of introduction and the three of us discussed the gold ornaments in the Cairo Museum, and particularly those from the recently discovered tomb of Tutankhamen. We also talked of the possible location of the gold fields from which the ancient world derived its gold supply, and I became more than ever convinced that much of the gold had been brought to Egypt from Rhodesia.

By arrangement, I was presented to King Fuad I and enjoyed my talk with him about conditions in Egypt and the development of the country. He was democratic and jovial and given to making "wisecracks," but he showed that he could be serious when discussing the future of his country. He was greatly impressed with the possibilities of railroad development in North Africa which would connect up with Cairo, and also the improvement in aviation which would bring Egypt nearer to the nations of Europe and easier of access for tourists.

Several years later at a garden party given by King George V in London, I saw King Fuad again; he reaffirmed his optimism as to the future importance of Cairo as a resort for foreign visitors.

After my audience with King Fuad, Hassanein Bey expressed his regret that he could not show me more attention during the next few days, but told me with some diffidence as befits a prospective husband that he was to be married. He said the young lady—the party of the first part—was the daughter of a former Egyptian minister to Washington. I asked the name and was delighted to find that it was Loutfia Yousry. Hassanein Bey, who saw his fiancée almost immediately after I had taken my leave, told her of my daughter's presence in Cairo. That same afternoon Natalie received a letter from Miss Yousry, welcoming her to Egypt, and asking her to call and see her without delay, as she was for the moment confined to her harem.

My daughter telephoned her and then went to have dinner and spend the evening with her. When she had not returned at a late hour I became anxious and went to the palace to call for her. I must say that it took courage, but of a different sort from more harrowing adventures I have had in mining camps. At the entrance I was stopped by two imposing eunuchs, and by others, again, at the door. Finally, I was admitted just in time to see a bevy of charming young women scampering up the broad stairs on which they had been sitting talking, when my sudden appearance startled them. However, I succeeded in finding Natalie.

She was asked to be a bridesmaid at the wedding, and since an American girl is seldom present at a marriage ceremony of that kind, I think her description will be of interest.

> The marriage in Egypt is complete after the act of marriage has been signed. The husband and wife could, if they wished, immediately assume marital relations; yet, it is often the custom that they live apart for a month or more while their furniture and trousseau are arranged. After that period and without any new formality, the couple assume the relations of husband and wife. It is on this occasion, however, that the festivities are generally given.

> The civil ceremony was performed one Sunday evening at the palace of Princess Omar Hallim. The house, a free translation of Italian and Arabic architecture, opened on to a large palm-bordered garden, across which one saw against the stillness of the desert the Pyramids of Gizeh.

> I had been asked to appear at Loutfia's apartment in the palace punctually at nine, and to wear a green evening gown. When I arrived she was being dressed by two Sudanese women. She wore a lace coif, and a medieval tiara of sapphires and diamonds. Her eyes were outlined with kohl. Three of her four cousins also wore green evening dresses. Later I learned that I had replaced the fourth, in the wedding ceremony. We descended a curving flight of alabaster stairs. In the hall below were the women of the diplomatic corps, and of the Egyptian court. No men were present. The hall which we crossed was lighted by flares held by nautch-

girls in magenta skirts and vermilion boleros. We stood
at the side while Loutfia mounted a low dais at the end
of the room. On the dais were two massive chairs inlaid
with ebony and gold. On one of these she sat. Faintly
and at a distance one heard a native stringed orchestra.

Hassanein Bey entered, after a minute's interval, with
Yousry Pasha. He wore "tails" and a fez. He advanced
to the dais, kissed first the back of her wrist, then her
forehead, and seated himself beside her in the second
chair. No other ceremony took place. They rose and
left the hall, scattering tiny gold pieces to the crowd.
Hassanein Bey and Yousry Pasha rejoined the men in
another part of the palace, while the women danced
together till the buffet supper was served in the garden.

Later I had tea several times in the harem with Loutfia and her cousins, Wahid and Gina. For my benefit
they spoke French, though together they conversed in
Arabic. Most days were spent in the pleasant loggias
of the palace, a special hour being reserved for the visits
of Hassanein Bey. At half-hour intervals Turkish
coffee was served, and they smoked incessantly. With
a few exceptions their only outings were at a Cairo
night-club, which was put at the disposal of the women
of the court one day a week. On these afternoons they
danced together, eagerly learning the latest European
steps. What other excursions they wedged into their
routine existence I could not say. But there was a court
fortune teller who appealed greatly to their supersti-
tions.

Loutfia's grandmother had two hundred slave girls
in her harem, and lived in strictest seclusion. Footmen
and chauffeurs are always eunuchs, and the royal automobile is a long vermilion affair, with two of these
gorgeously caparisoned Sudanese on the box.

The reader will not blame me for envying my daughter her
glimpse of the life that goes on behind the mysterious walls of the
East.

From Egypt we went to Sicily, then to Italy. In Rome I was granted an audience by Mussolini. After being passed through several anterooms, I was admitted into a long room at the end of which sat the Great Dictator on a dais. As I approached him he fixed his eyes on me in the penetrating way peculiar to him.

It is said that this slow approach is arranged not so much for his physical protection, as for the purpose of disconcerting the interviewer. During his progress up the length of the room, the visitor forgets the set speech he has prepared and is likely to say something closer to his real thoughts. And, of course, the setting is arranged to make Il Duce very impressive indeed.

When I reached the dais Mussolini gave me the Fascist salute. I thanked him. He then asked me with surprise if I did not recognize it. I said that I did but could not understand why I was accorded the honor. Smilingly he said that he had been informed that I, on a certain occasion (referring to the Jameson Raid), had had the courage to go to jail for my political convictions. That was true, I replied, but in this respect he had me at a disadvantage, since he had gone to jail on several occasions for the same reason. He laughed at that and asked me if this was my first visit to Rome. I told him that I had been to Rome several times before but that, having just returned from seeing something of the wonders of the ancient world, the Pharos of Alexandria, the Sphinx, and the Pyramids of Egypt, I was anxious to see one of the wonders of the modern world, which he personified.

He seemed pleased at this; being encouraged, I told him that I considered his action in establishing the Fascisti comparable to the deed of the famous Dutch boy who inserted his arm in the hole of the dike to prevent inundation of the country; that his heroic action had prevented the inundation of Italy, France, and other European countries by the wave of Communism already started by the Bolsheviks.

I asked if any provision had been made for the maintenance of the Fascisti should Italy be unfortunately deprived of his beneficent dictatorship. Mussolini informed me that one of my Italian friends, who had spent many years in America, would call on me at my hotel that evening and give me a clear understanding of this subject.

My friend assured me that after Mussolini there would be no deluge. I was not entirely convinced, however, that the optimism expressed by him was justified, for I believed it was Mussolini's great personality that enabled him to carry out his Fascist movement. The Celtic people are deeply impressed, I believe, by the personality of their leaders whose influence transcends the inherent importance of the principles they represent. In contradistinction, Anglo-Saxons are more imbued with the principles underlying any reform movement. With them leaders may come and leaders may go, but the spirit lives on and there is a persistent determination to carry out the movement initiated by the leaders.

Mussolini gave me a signed photograph of himself for my collection. I have not seen him since but have kept directly in touch with him through my son, Jack, who installed for him a selective system of radio which he uses in communicating with his representatives in Italy and Africa. For this service my son was decorated by Mussolini with the order of a Grand Officer of the Crown, an exceptionally high honor.

My wife, my daughter, and I were granted a private audience with Pope Pius XI, the third pope my wife and I had met. My friend, Taft, had written Cardinal Gasparri, the all-powerful papal secretary. Through him and Cardinal Bonzano, with whom I first became acquainted when he came to Washington as papal legate, they had made the arrangements for our audience. Bonzano had been a missionary priest in India and China and possessed a remarkably deep and fine religious sense. He had great intelligence and breadth of mind, and was a most accomplished gentleman. As cardinal, he successfully presided over the Eucharistic Congress in Chicago. Though he was in poor health at that time, his spiritual energy never faltered. He was on the way, it is said, to the very highest office in the church, when he died.

From Rome we went to the French Riviera and while at Cannes I met King Gustaf V of Sweden, one of the most democratic of the reigning monarchs of Europe. He told me that his son, the crown prince, was soon to visit America and he would be greatly obliged if I would see that he received a "rousing good welcome for which the

Americans are noted." I promised King Gustaf that I should see that his wishes were carried out.

When Crown Prince Gustaf Adolf arrived in Washington, shortly after we returned from our trip, I gave an afternoon reception at my home in his honor, and invited the leading newspaper correspondents, assigned to duty in Washington, to meet him.

In showing the crown prince through my gallery of autographed photographs he commented on the remarkable collection of famous men. I asked him if he would kindly give me a photograph of himself to be placed with those of other royalty, which he had already seen in our drawing room. He demurred at my suggestion at first, and then said that if I considered him qualified he would much prefer to have his photograph on the walls of my study among the men of "real achievement" rather than with royalty. The newspaper correspondents heard his remarks and were so impressed with his democratic spirit that immediately after the reception they telegraphed his conversation with me to their papers throughout the United States. They all agreed that the crown prince was a "real fellow" and his photograph now hangs among the "men of achievement" where it rightly belongs.

My last trip of importance was to South America with my wife in December, 1929. From there we went to Portugal and Spain.

I was particularly interested in the study of the economic conditions of Brazil and Argentina, countries which I had not visited. This was to supplement my knowledge of Latin America. Besides this I was desirous of obtaining firsthand information regarding the iron deposits in the state of Minas Geraes, in one of the companies of which I have a substantial interest. The Minas Geraes deposits are probably the most extensive of high-grade iron in the world but at present cannot be developed economically on a large scale This is due to the lack of coke and of an adequate supply of charcoal for treatment locally. Added to this economic obstacle, there is no market for iron in Brazil. For these reasons it is necessary to transport the crude ore to the United States or to Europe for treatment. The inaccessibility of the iron deposits precludes shipment of the ore to meet the present competition of other countries.

The area of Latin America (South America, Central America, Mexico, and the Caribbean islands) is approximately that of continental United States and Canada combined, with a population nearly equal that of the United States.

At first glance, because of the size of its population and great extent of undeveloped territory, one is favorably impressed with the potential markets in Latin America. But a closer study shows that of this large population not over ten per cent possesses purchasing power of any significance and that a large part of the territory is valueless for both agriculture and mining.

Indians and negroes constitute the mass of the population. The Indians live in the interior under conditions bordering on destitution. The negroes, originally slaves from Africa, are confined to the Caribbean islands and the coast of Central and South America. Their wants are few and their means scant even for the bare necessities of life.

The general opinion prevailing abroad is that Latin-American countries have unbounded natural resources, development of which would add greatly to the purchasing power of their peoples and in that way open up important markets for the rest of the world. I do not concur in this opinion as I regard the outlook as pessimistic, and find confirmation of my viewpoint in Frank Tannenbaum's recently published *Whither Latin America?*

Broadly speaking, the west coast of South America exports minerals, mainly copper, nitrates, tin and, in an increasing degree, petroleum; Central America and the Caribbean mainly bananas, coffee and sugar; and Mexico, silver and oil. The east coast of South America exports mainly coffee from Brazil, and cereal and meat products from the Argentine and Uruguay. This regional specialization can best be illustrated by citing the commonly known facts of the Latin American foreign trade. In six of the countries coffee constitutes more than 50 per cent of the total export. These countries are Brazil, 65 per cent; Colombia, 65 per cent; Costa Rica, 63 per cent; Guatemala, 79 per cent; Salvador, 93 per cent; and Haiti, some 80 per cent. . . .

Excessive dependence upon unitary export items is not confined to agricultural products but also holds for mineral exports. Bolivia depends for 72 per cent of its total export upon tin, and 74 per cent of Venezuela's exports is crude petroleum.

Thus, at least 15 countries are dependent for the major part of their export trade upon some single item. . . .

Since these countries have no monopoly of any of these items their export trade is obviously precarious, and without a favorable trade balance there can be no import trade of importance.

In its agricultural exports Latin America meets with severe competition from many other countries. Besides this, since the World War, European countries that formerly constituted an important market for agricultural products have been developing in an important measure their own agricultural resources to supply their domestic needs.

There does not seem any likelihood that Latin-American countries will be able to expand their home markets to the extent of justifying any considerable agricultural or industrial development. This, because it is impossible adequately to increase the purchasing power of local consumers. There will, however, be a tendency to develop home industries on a small scale to supply the urgent needs of commodities they will be unable to import as their export trade balance diminishes. And in pursuance of the policy of economic nationalism which they have recently adopted an import trade will be further restricted.

While there is the possibility of an interchange of goods with adjacent states, unfortunately physiographic conditions make transportation difficult, putting this trade under a severe economic handicap.

I agree with H. F. Bain and T. R. Read in the opinions expressed in their recent publication, Ores and Industry in South America, that the potential mineral resources of South America have been greatly overestimated.

The nitrate industry, hitherto the backbone of the fiscal system of

Chile, is becoming less important owing to synthetic processes now employed elsewhere in the production of nitrogen.

The development of new deposits of copper or other minerals is not probable, in the near future at least, as a result of keen competition resulting from overproduction of these commodities in other parts of the world.

There is, of course, the likelihood of the development of new oil fields in certain parts of South America which would increase the export trade, but in that case, too, there would be formidable competition for markets by other fields more favorably situated.

In the development of the mineral industry of South America as well as that of other parts of Latin America, most of the capital required has thus far been supplied by investors from the United States. For the most part these investments have not proved sufficiently remunerative to attract new capital. Nor do the political conditions of South America in general provide an incentive for investors.

The Pan American Union in Washington has done much to promote friendly understanding between the United States and the sister republics of Latin America, yet there is an abiding lack of wholehearted confidence on the part of Latin America in our integrity of purpose. The sister republics are both jealous and suspicious of our power and wealth. They do not comprehend the Monroe Doctrine and its implications. In spite of the fact that by virtue of the Monroe Doctrine our nation has at various times rendered inestimable service to Latin America in frustrating the aggression of European powers, the doctrine has not been favorably regarded by those countries. Our threatened intervention in behalf of Mexico, which prevented Maximilian from establishing a monarchy, has not earned for us the gratitude of that country.

Again, we rendered a service by our intervention in behalf of Venezuela against what President Cleveland regarded as aggressive action by Great Britain. This friendly act, too, was soon forgotten. These are but a few of many instances of the kind. Nations have short memories for favors received. We cannot blink the fact that Americans of *North America* are not popular with South Americans and Central Americans. South Americans in particular object to the citizens of the United States referring to themselves as "Americans" and not as Americanos del Norte. Much of the antipathy is to be ascribed to the insidious propaganda of our commercial rivals who have stigmatized the Yankees' activities as imperialistic, imputing ulterior political motives.

Latin Americans are a peculiarly sensitive people, with a highly developed racial and national pride. I have had many discussions of the Monroe Doctrine with leading statesmen of Latin America and am convinced that its modification would eliminate much misunderstanding. Within the past few years there has been what is practically a repudiation of our former policy regarding our rights and duties under the Monroe Doctrine. In this we may have gone too far. In one respect it certainly will not be to the advantage of Latin America as it will, in a large measure, prevent future investments of American capital in the development of those countries. Furthermore, I believe that later it may result in considerable embarrassment to our government in that we cannot consistently intervene for the protection of the lives and vested interests of other nationals who have hitherto relied upon our government under the implication of the Monroe Doctrine to perform this service.

We left Buenos Aires and arrived in Portugal in February, 1930, where I had the opportunity to get firsthand information regarding operations of a tin dredging company in which I was interested. After several days' motoring through Portugal we went to Seville to see the Ibero-Americano Exposition. The American representative at the exposition was none other than my old friend, Thomas E. Campbell, former governor of Arizona, and a most capable representative he was. He, with Mrs. Campbell and Richard Ford, the American consul, met us on arrival and contributed greatly to the interest and pleasure of our visit.

To me the most interesting exhibits of the exposition were the documents of Columbus, with the original contract between him and Ferdinand and Isabella in their handwriting. In this contract Columbus stipulated that he should be full admiral in the Spanish Navy, governor general in the newly discovered world, and that he should receive one-tenth of all the findings. His first expedition was successful in the discovery of the New World and he became a hero, and received as a reward, it is said, the sum of about three hundred and twenty dollars. From his third voyage he was returned in chains; after his fourth, having opened a new empire to Spain, he died poor and neglected at Valladolid.

All this early historical data about Columbus made me interested in getting other information about the expedition from the original documents which are stored in the Casa Municipal ó del Ayuntamiento (City Hall). During several hours I spent at the Ayuntamiento I was shown many interesting documents dealing with the discovery of America and was informed by the custodian that the actual money expended for fitting out the first voyage would be equivalent to about three thousand dollars of American money today. Of course, much of the labor was donated, as well as food and supplies. The custodian assured me that there was no foundation for the story that Isabella had pawned her jewels to outfit the expedition, for as he said, her jewels had already been pawned for other purposes.

After several weeks in Seville and vicinity, we went to Madrid where we were entertained by our friends, Ambassador Irwin B. Laughlin and Mrs. Laughlin, and Mr. and Mrs. Walter Schoellkopf. Mr. Schoellkopf was first secretary at the American Embassy. Through the ambassador we had the opportunity of meeting many interesting Spanish people, prominent socially and politically.

While we were in Spain the king and queen granted my wife and me a private audience; we were shown into the queen's personal reception room. We had known her father and mother and other members of her family and had many intimate mutual friends in England. My wife and I stayed a long time, as it was in the forenoon and we were the only visitors. Suddenly realizing this, I said: "Your Majesty, I am afraid that we are keeping you longer than our appointed time. You must have other engagements?"

My wife smiled: "Your Majesty, my husband has probably forgotten the etiquette for occasions of this kind."

The queen replied laughingly: "He is quite right, but I still have plenty of time and I will serve notice when I must go."

After "notice was served" we were escorted to an audience with King Alfonso. It is well known that he is unusually democratic and absolutely free from all conventionality. He asked me if I had been to Seville to which I replied in Spanish: "Quien no ha visto a Sevilla no ha visto maravilla."

Alfonso told me that his royal position was very irksome; it was impossible for him to play polo, his favorite game. It seems the court objected to his taking such risks, and this he highly resented. But he said: "Perhaps they are right. I have broken every bone in my body, and some of them several times, at polo or other dangerous sports. They regard it as not only perilous, but beneath the dignity of a king to play any more." I believe he was sincere in his feeling of the arduous nature of kingship and in his distaste for its unpleasant royal inhibitions.

Later at the Escorial, where each royal coffin is placed in a white marble vault or sarcophagus, I noticed particularly that there was no space provided for future kings and queens of Spain, with the exception of Alfonso XIII and his queen. I remember the passing thought that perhaps this was an omen that at some future date Spain might be a republic. The king's popularity was great up to the time of the revolution; in fact, it was said that, should Spain become a republic, the king would be its first president. Unfortunately this did not prove true; when revolution did occur, shortly after my visit, Alfonso was compelled to abdicate in order to avert bloodshed, and to join the ranks of other royal exiles.

Sidney Franklin, the young Brooklynite who achieved a reputation as a matador in the bullrings of Mexico and Spain, and later in the motion pictures, was in Madrid at the time of my visit. A number of businessmen of the American colony gave a lunch in my honor at which Franklin was present. After lunch some of the newspapermen introduced him to me. I was surprised to see a youth with a face "unusually kind." Being reassured on the part of the newspapermen that this was really the great American bullfighter, I said: "You do not seem to me like a man who would enjoy killing a bull. You have a very kindly look on your face and might well be taken for an official of the Society for the Prevention of Cruelty to Animals." "Well, sir," he replied: "I'm looking at *you*, but you should see my face when looking at an infuriated bull." He spoke feelingly, for he had recently been seriously gored in the bullring.

The minister for foreign affairs at this time was the Duke of Alba, the descendant of a long line of Spanish noblemen and the foremost grandee of Spain. He was wealthy, highly cultured, a world traveler, a great sportsman, and thoroughly familiar with America, where we had many friends in common. He invited me to luncheon and showed me over his beautiful palace in Madrid, with its treasured documents of Columbus, Cortez, and other makers of Spanish history. The duke told me that he had been drafted for his position very much against his wish; that he had no experience in state affairs as his whole life had been devoted to sports. He hoped to be able to "muddle through," but also hoped the king would not find him satisfactory and would soon "fire" him.

I expressed surprise that Americans receive such cordial treatment in Spain.

"Of course," he replied, "you have in mind the late unpleasantness between our countries?"

"Yes," I said, "the Spanish War."

He went on: "The Spanish people are philosophical. They lost the war, but after thinking it over, they came to the conclusion that it was a blessing in disguise.

"It had been a very heavy drain on the mother country to administer the Philippines and Cuba, not only in money but in soldiers, and the people of Spain were tired of having their sons drafted to suppress revolutions in those countries. Realizing this, they feel grateful to the Americans for having relieved them of this burden."

The pertinence of this idea for America is becoming obvious in its sponsorship of the Philippines.

Many of us have changed our former views about the Philippines. Some years ago I had alluring visions of America as an economic empire and regarded the Philippines as the stepping stone to the development of Oriental trade; today this does not fit the American spirit, which holds such retention as undesirable and autocratic. The maintenance of benevolent relations with the Philippines is regarded by many as a duty we assumed in accepting the islands as a protectorate after the Spanish-American War, but they feel that aside from this our policy should be to accede to the request of the Filipinos for complete autonomy.

That the Philippines are as yet wholly unfit for independence was recognized by General Wood, Henry L. Stimson, Nicholas Roosevelt, and other authorities "whether from the viewpoint of instructed public opinion, preparedness for defense, or a common language."

In his report to the secretary of war, General Wood stated that "To turn these islands over to self-government would mean the betrayal of our trust and would plunge twelve million people into dire disorder and strife. For it would result at once in serious clash between the Moros and the Christian Filipinos. Such a step would, in short, defeat true independence both economic and political."

Nevertheless, American public opinion strongly inclines to the granting of complete independence to the Filipinos. If this is done, there should be a distinct understanding that when we withdraw we absolve ourselves from all further responsibility and in no wise commit ourselves to protect the Filipinos from aggression by any other nation or to intervene in their internal affairs.

In view of the increasing conflict of interest with Japan, the Philippines are to be considered as the heel of Achilles in the maintenance of our military position in the Pacific. This is undoubtedly a scuttling policy, but in the circumstances seems inevitable. We should now concentrate on making Hawaii a Gibraltar as the basis of naval operations to ensure the protection of our Pacific Coast states against an invading enemy.

CHAPTER THIRTY-FIVE

Spreading Interests

Our machine civilization has been wrought by the engineer, who contrives its apparatus, utilizes and harnesses the physical and chemical forces of nature, and exploits the resources of the earth. All that he designs and invents and exploits redounds in the end to the public benefit.

My business career began as a mining engineer. But when I had reached a certain proficiency and standing in my profession, I was tempted to branch out in other fields of engineering activities. The technical knowledge for carrying out these new ventures was at my command through the services of younger men. My experience guided and tempered their enthusiasm.

The science of engineering covers not only mining for metals but the production of all other forms of wealth from the earth. Those portions of the globe which for eons had remained comparatively barren and useless now are being transformed into a blessing to man.

The idea of irrigation and reclamation, later so publicized by Theodore Roosevelt, had taken possession of my brother William's imagination as early as 1891. He had established himself in the pleasant little town of Visalia, California, in the semi-arid San Joaquin Valley which stretches for miles between the Sierra Nevadas and the Coast Range. He believed that, if water could be delivered to the farms of the valley at reasonable rates, it would bring about an agricultural revolution. In association with A. G. Wishon, his partner in the local water company, and Ben M. Maddox, the owner-editor of the Visalia *Times,* he worked to bring his theory to realization.

It was no simple matter to obtain water in the San Joaquin. There was in the valley no sufficiently large or dependable river from which a supply could be brought by canals. Wells had to be driven sixty to a hundred feet below ground to find the water table. The soil was rich, but rainfall was irregular and occurred only during the winter. Grain was about the only crop that could be raised, and the profits from this were small and uncertain.

My brother had seen what Captain A. J. Hutchinson, pioneer farmer, had done to his arid acres at Lindsay in the foothills not far from Visalia by attaching a six-horsepower engine to a pump. Hutchinson was raising oranges, lemons, olives, grapes, and all sorts of vegetables. It seemed to my brother that an abundant water supply would transform the entire countryside into a paradise.

Bill tried to interest San Francisco and Oakland capital in building a power dam on the Kaweah River and bringing electricity by long-distance transmission line from Mount Whitney to operate irrigation pumps in the San Joaquin Valley. They listened to him with interest, and said they did not care to invest at the moment; apparently they were too polite to call him visionary for entertaining such an idea. Having failed in America to obtain the funds necessary to launch the project, Bill as a last resort came to see me in London in 1898.

The idea of going into the public utility business had never occurred to me but I could see that my brother's scheme had possibilities. I had known the valley since boyhood and the fact that another brother, Richard, had done the surveying gave me added assurance.

"Jack," urged Bill, "we already have options on the water sites and

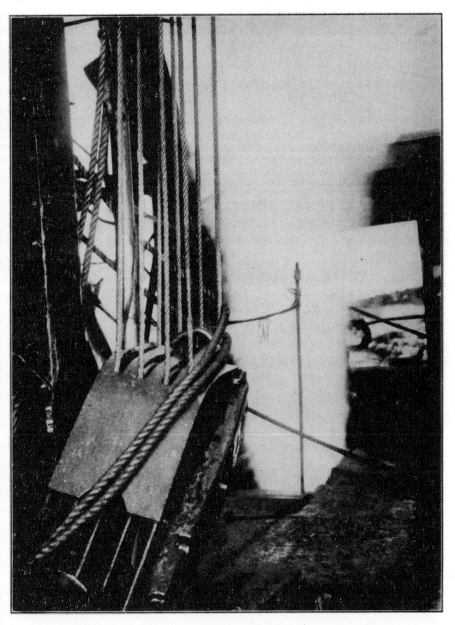

A STRIKE. THE DISCOVERY WELL IN THE KETTLEMAN OIL FIELDS,
MARCH 21, 1927

White gas that precedes the gush of crude oil

THE DISCOVERY WELL, NORTH DOME, KETTLEMAN HILLS

The oil production of this field from the time of its discovery, March 21, 1927, to December 31, 1934, was approximately 19,590,000 barrels, and the gas production within the same period was approximately 660,000,000,000 cubic feet, from which 18,300,000 barrels of casing-head gasoline were extracted

the rights of way. As you know, we have a soil and climate that will grow anything. Whenever we drill a well we strike water, and all we need is the power to pump it. Gasoline and steam engines work, but they're too expensive and can serve only a few acres each. With cheap electric power available, thousands of acres will go into cultivation."

"But can you send electricity as far as that?" I asked. "It's never been done before for irrigating purposes, has it?"

"No, but we have an engineer who guarantees it can be done," he replied. "Robert Doble. He'll build the power house at Mount Whitney and bring the current the necessary thirty-five miles. This will put all of Tulare County within reach of our feeder lines."

"How about customers?" I queried again. "There are practically none in the valley."

"We'll have to build ahead of them and take a chance," he told me frankly. "Once the electricity is there for delivery, the settlers will follow."

On the night Bill arrived in London, Leopold Hirsch dined at my house. During the dinner he and my brother talked about American affairs and California. Hirsch was so impressed by this conversation that he took me aside after dinner and asked me all about Bill. I assured him that my brother had earned such a reputation for honesty and sound judgment that throughout the San Joaquin Valley many bitter disputes were taken to him for arbitrament rather than to the law courts.

I told him about the Mount Whitney project, which Bill and I had agreed should be financed by private capital and not offered to the public. Hirsch expressed great interest and, when I informed him I was thinking of putting money into it, said he would like to discuss the matter a little further with my brother. He might even want to have an interest in it himself.

The next day I told Bill I would supply half the funds required and would assist him in raising the balance among my friends in London. Naturally, I had Hirsch in mind.

I made an appointment for the two to meet again, and the banker agreed to underwrite the other half of the funds required. So simply was the Mount Whitney Power Company launched.

Bill strongly recommended that both Hirsch and I buy land in the valley. He felt sure that it would greatly increase in value and that we could realize more quickly on this investment than on the hydro-electric plant.

Shortly after my return to America I purchased the Hirsch interest in the Mount Whitney project and became its sole backer. This put a heavy financial burden on me and I was unable to make the land purchases urged by my brother.

Before I bought Hirsch's interest, Bill had given us another oppor-tunity, to make an investment in an oil region that was being de-veloped in Kern County not far from Visalia. We were so favorably impressed that we authorized my brother to secure options on pos-sible oil-bearing land in the district, which at that time could be acquired on very reasonable terms.

After the options had been secured, Hirsch and I sent an English oil expert to examine the territory. Unfortunately the expert made an adverse report and we abandoned the project. Not long after, however, one of the large oil fields in California was opened up by local capital, encouraged by quick and enormous profits from recent oil strikes.

The construction of the Mount Whitney powerhouse and trans-mission line went steadily forward. On June 26, 1899, the motors began to hum at the Lindsay substation, the first time electric power had ever been used for irrigation purposes in California. Until this moment only our own little group had been convinced that the idea was financially sound or technically feasible. As the switch was thrown and the water began to flow, one of the skeptical spectators exclaimed, "By God, it does do it, don't it?"

At Lindsay, our first outlet, ten growers made contracts at once, the entire load aggregating only one hundred and seventy-five horse-power. But within the next few years thousands of acres of idle land were brought under cultivation. In 1914 fifty thousand acres were irrigated by power from our lines. In a district where even in successful seasons wheat had brought a profit of no more than fifteen dollars an acre, orange, lemon, walnut, and olive groves now flour-ished, splendid vineyards covered the hillsides, and peach and prune orchards were coming into bearing. Some of these crops were giving a profit of a thousand dollars an acre; undeveloped land, selling in the nineties at ten to fifteen dollars, now brought several hundred dollars an acre. From 1893 to 1900 there had been a loss of $600,000 in assessed valuation of Tulare County property. This loss was turned into a gain of $30,000,000 by 1914.

Abundant wealth was being created from the soil by cheap power. Money was pouring into the valley. Lindsay, which, in 1899, consisted of a small railroad station, a schoolhouse, and the home of Captain Hutchinson, had grown to be a prosperous community of four thousand inhabitants. Visalia, the county seat, had tripled its former population of twenty-five hundred. Through my representations to E. H. Harriman, the Southern Pacific Railroad had built an electric spur line from Visalia to Lemon Cove, one of the pioneer towns of the citrus fruit development, and had thereby greatly improved transportation facilities.

A dozen years passed before other electric companies followed our lead. They realized that profits would be slow and did not foresee the large amounts of current which must ultimately be used by this type of enterprise.

In 1916, the Southern California Edison Company desired to obtain a market for the electric power it had developed in the upper Sierras. Its offer for the Mount Whitney Company was so attractive that we decided to accept. When the transaction was made public, we were gratified at the receipt of a telegram from the head of the Railroad Commission of California, which has jurisdiction over all public utilities in the state, that our company was the best operated in California.

Through association with the Mount Whitney Company, I became interested in developing the Pitt River hydroelectric supply, and I personally financed this work. The Pitt River had previously flowed over a circuitous course around a mountain. Our plan was to tunnel a passage near the top of the mountain, and divert the flow of the river to a point on the opposite side several hundred feet above the old bed. From this end of the tunnel the water would be conducted by huge pipes to a powerhouse below.

The engineering difficulty in building the tunnel was the presence of thermal springs which, if encountered, might at any moment flood our workings. From surface indications it was evident that the ground might prove so porous that difficulty would be found in making the walls of the tunnel stand up.

We took the risk, drove the tunnel through some thousand feet of rock, and proved that the undertaking was practicable.

This flow of water was capable of developing from one to two hundred thousand horsepower, and was destined to be one of the cheapest producers of electric current in California. It was a magnificent project. My chief difficulty came from the fact that it was located on government land. Though no one else had seen fit to undertake this work, the Department of the Interior insisted that it be done at such a rate that I could not afford to comply with government specifications. I was forced to sell out to the Pacific Gas and Electric Company of San Francisco, a company which uses it now as one of the most important sources of hydroelectric power for San Francisco.

Among other electrical engineering enterprises in which I had a large interest was the Yosemite Power Company, which furnished electric current to the farmers of various irrigation districts. This company owned some old and valuable water rights, and was eventually sold at a good price.

In 1908 I bought Lake Eleanor in the Sierras with a view to developing its potential one hundred thousand horsepower. When San Francisco launched the Hetch-Hetchy project to bring water from the Sierras a hundred and sixty-seven miles distant, Mayor McCarthy came to see me and said that Lake Eleanor was indispensable to their plan. He urged me, as a civic duty, to sell at a fair valuation. I agreed to let Lake Eleanor be embodied in the Hetch-Hetchy plan.

Looking back upon these early enterprises in the public utility field, it is interesting to see how their original promise has been fulfilled under the management of those to whom I sold. Today they form most important integral parts in the great network of public utilities in California.

The trail-blazing work on the Mount Whitney project was purely of an engineering nature. In an irrigation venture in Mexico we had to meet pioneer problems more typical of the frontier.

In 1909, Major Burnham said to me: "Mr. Hammond, I have something that'll interest you. I've picked up an option on the water rights of the Yaqui River and some three hundred thousand acres of land from my friend, Davis Richardson, of Los Angeles. The soil is sixty feet deep and there's not a pebble in it. Once this valley is irrigated, it'll be one of the garden spots of the world."

Curiously enough, the potential value of the Yaqui Valley had been pointed out to me many years before by my father-in-law, Judge Harris, who had owned a large plantation in Mississippi before the Civil War. He had passed through a part of the valley in 1882 on the trip from Guaymas to join our family at Alamos, and had recognized its agricultural possibilities.

The delta of the Yaqui River consists of two thousand square miles of rich alluvial soil, brought down through the ages from the surrounding mountains. The Yaqui Valley itself is enclosed on one side by the Bacotete Mountains and on the other by a sixty-mile coast line on the Gulf of California. Through this valley runs the Yaqui River, hundreds of feet wide when the snows were melting on the mountains but shrunken to a trickle during the summer. If the water could be impounded in a storage dam somewhere in the upper courses, it could be released gradually for irrigation purposes.

Along the river, and generally on its northern side, lie the eight Yaqui pueblos of four square leagues each, or about one hundred and eighty-five thousand acres in all. The portions of these pueblos watered by the overflow of the river were being cultivated after a fashion by the peaceable Indians who owned them. These Indians were called Mansos to distinguish them from the fighting tribes of the nation, the Bronchos. The rest of this inherently rich valley was covered with chaparral and cactus.

Knowing that Burnham was not likely to be overoptimistic, I immediately started preliminary investigations. His claims proved conservative. I then went to Harry Payne Whitney, outlined the proposition to him, and as usual found him a ready listener. Together we took up the option on this acreage.

A. P. Davis, whose work in Russia has already been described, was sent to determine the engineering problem. He made a highly favorable report. An ideal site for a storage dam was found about one hundred miles from the northern borders of our concession. It would make a lake several miles wide and sixty miles long, lying between the pine-clad slopes of the Sierra Madre Mountains. In addition to a supply of water sufficient to irrigate the entire valley, this would furnish fifty thousand horsepower, enough power and light for the whole district and the neighboring mines. So beautiful was the country around the proposed site of the lake that we had visions of its becoming a pleasure resort where the settlers in the Yaqui could spend the hot summer months. It was but a few hours' trip from the valley by motor.

According to the Davis plan the river bed would serve as a canal until it reached our property. At this point we could build a diversion dam to check the flow of the water and send it into the headgates of our canal system. Then, because of unusually favorable topographical conditions, the water would flow by gravity south and west over practically the entire Yaqui Valley.

We lost no time in buying an additional nine hundred thousand acres of land contiguous to that already acquired and in every respect equal to it. This also would come under the proposed water system.

When we had completed the purchase, our acreage covered an area the size of Rhode Island. None of this property was obtained by free land grant; all was purchased from the Mexican government or from private owners. None of it lay within the eight Indian pueblos.

We estimated twelve million dollars as the cost of building the entire system. Before making any attempt to raise this money, we used our private funds to construct a temporary diversion dam and some hundreds of miles of canals and laterals. Seventy thousand acres were ultimately brought under cultivation. The amazing diversity and abundance of the crops convinced us that this agricultural area equaled or even surpassed the world-famous Imperial Valley of California.

The climate of the Yaqui was incontrovertibly better than that of the Imperial Valley. There were no rains during the winter. The days were warm; the nights were cool but without frost. Fruits and vegetables invariably ripened some weeks earlier than did similar crops in Southern California.

Under W. W. Mackie, who was recognized by the government as an authority in the agricultural development of the arid regions of the West, we established a thousand-acre experimental station. Here we grew oranges, grapefruit, cotton, rice, alfalfa, and garvanza beans.

At first everything seemed to favor us. While our plans were yet maturing, the Southern Pacific Railroad, passing along the northern boundary of our property, completed its line to Mexico City. We would not only have this terminal as a ready market for dairy and farm products, but freight rates to the large American cities were identical with those from Southern California, an important advantage to the Yaqui settler. We also located ports within our own territory from which the products of the valley could be shipped to foreign countries by way of the Panama Canal.

One of the most alluring aspects of this venture was the water rights to the Yaqui River. Our concession gave us the right in perpetuity to charge fifty cents per acre foot on all water furnished for irrigation purposes. Since on the average each acre used from four to five acre feet a year, this would have assured a handsome return to us at an unusually low cost to the settler.

Whitney and I were so impressed with the attractions of the Yaqui Valley that we bought many thousands of acres with the idea of forming a winter colony of our friends. There Whitney also planned to raise polo ponies and race horses.

The valley offered many inducements to sportsmen. Nowhere had I seen wild game in such abundance. There were duck, dove, and quail. In the mountains and foothills were bear, deer, peccary, and puma. According to the famous sportsman, Professor Holden, the Gulf of California was an angler's paradise—better than Catalina. Mighty Nimrods and Izaak Waltons could shoot without let and fish without hindrance. There were oysters, delicious bivalves, in abundance, and, believe it or not, they grew on trees.

Over the savannas beautiful wild stallions and mares galloped up to neigh at the intruders. From the great caves of the Bacotete Mountains, filled with countless tons of guano, millions of bats poured out like black smoke from a chimney.

When my son Harris made his first visit to the valley, he found a reception committee which had been camped in the dust and heat for hours. In its midst was an old gentleman in a frock coat, green with age. Battle-scarred from innumerable Indian raids, Don Tomas Sexton's lean weather-beaten frame was still erect in spite of his sixty-odd years.

He had heard that Mr. Hammond was coming to inspect the valley. All that afternoon Don Tomas followed Harris around like a hungry dog until the latter became restive under the intent gaze. Finally the old man buttonholed him and whispered mysteriously,

"You have a secret I want to know."

Harris replied mildly, "I haven't any secret."

"Yes, you have!" Sexton insisted.

"No, I haven't! I don't know what you're talking about!"

"But you must have! I remember you as a young mining engi-. neer at Alamos in 1881. You're not a day older than you were then."

Don Tomas believed I had drunk at the fountain of perpetual youth. At the time of this trip to Mexico, Harris was just about the same age I had been at the time of my meeting with Don Tomas so many years before.

When Harris said he was my son, Don Tomas was at first incredulous. Then a little shadow of disappointment clouded his countenance, but he took the news like the soldier he was.

By 1912, just as we had reached the point where we felt justified in going into the money market to secure capital for completing the project, the long series of Mexican revolutions began. The first serious effect upon us was the uprising of the valley Indians who had hitherto been an excellent source of labor supply. Inspired by the Bronchos, and by false promises of local Mexican revolutionary leaders, they formed bands and began to raid our settlers.

Annoyed by the inability of the Mexican government to control the Yaqui, I suggested to the government that Major Burnham and I go into the Bacotete Mountains and bring out every hostile entrenched there. My plan was to give each family a plot of land in fee and supply water to irrigate it. There was a change in government, however, and my offer was not accepted. These Indians would have provided a constant and efficient supply of farm labor.

The Bronchos had been supplied with arms by both sides in the

WELLS AT THE DOMINGUEZ FIELD

The Burnham Exploration Company have drilled 137 wells in this field

BULOLO DREDGE, NEW GUINEA—AN EXAMPLE
OF MODERN MINING TECHNIQUE

*This and three other dredges have been brought in from the seacoast 100 miles distant
and over a mountain range more than 5000 feet high by this fleet of three airplanes*

Mexican revolution, but had refused to fight for either. From the seventy-foot watchtower at Esperanza, our headquarters, the lookout could see the dusty war trail running down the center of the valley. One spring day a mounted band of Yaqui were observed moving rapidly towards the barricade. Waldo Sheldon and Cappy Jones, the two young Yale graduates who were in charge of the Hammond ranch, served out rifles to the peons and warned the outlying districts by telephone. The fighting lasted a few hours and several settlers were killed. When they found they could not make any impression in our defenses, the Yaqui withdrew, abandoning their dead and wounded.

Less than a month later they were again on the warpath. This time we were prepared. But they had learned their lesson, and detoured around the ranch in going down the valley.

Although on each occasion the pioneers succeeded in clearing the valley of Indians, crops were ruined, cattle stolen, and the experimental station buildings burned. The destruction of seven years' statistics on seeds and plants gathered from all corners of the world was an irreparable loss.

Johnny George and Bill Franke, two of Harris's associates, were running a store at the town of Yaqui. The constant raids taught them caution. Late one oppressively hot August night, Johnny was sitting alone in the store going over his books. Suddenly he heard what he thought was the report of a 30-30. He dropped instantly to the floor and crawled halfway under the desk. He waited and waited but nothing happened. Finally the torture of this cramped position became worse than the anticipation of what might occur if he showed himself. With infinite caution he rose, glancing warily around. At his feet was a little rivulet. His eyes followed it to the shelf, and there lay the shattered remains of a soda water bottle which had been exploded by the heat.

These young storekeepers were constantly called upon to meet emergencies. One afternoon a group of thirty or forty Yaqui came around the corner of the corral. Since the Yaqui never wore distinctive signs when on the warpath, the two boys had no way of telling whether their intentions were friendly or otherwise. But, from their taciturn and sullen manner, there was every reason to fear they were looking for trouble. The Indians crowded into the store. The odds against the boys would have been too great even if they had been able to reach their guns.

Johnny, who had a charming personality, spoke to them pleasantly in Spanish. For fifteen minutes the Indians milled around indecisively, and then one of them approached the counter, threw down a coin, and said, "Cigarettes."

Johnny placed a package on the counter before the Indian, and picked up the coin. He pressed the keys of the cash register, the numbers flew up, the drawer opened, and the bell rang.

The Yaqui, startled out of his impassivity, pointed and asked, "Que es este?"

Johnny explained that it told how much money went into the drawer, how much the article cost, and how a little record was made of the transaction.

The Indian was doubtful but interested. After a moment's thought, he threw down another coin, and, without picking up the first package of cigarettes, ordered another.

Again the numbers flew up, the drawer opened, and the bell rang.

The Indian beckoned to his companions and they swarmed about the machine, fascinated. All of them began to make purchases, watching each movement of the register with unblinking curiosity. They bought sixty dollars' worth of goods, and then, excited and happy, left with the promise to come back again soon.

Years afterwards I told this story to John R. Patterson, president of the National Cash Register Company. He was so delighted with it that he promptly used it in the company advertising. In his opinion there could be no more impressive testimonial from the poor Indian "whose untutor'd mind" beheld in this handiwork from Dayton, Ohio, a veritable deus ex machina.

We could have coped with the Indian menace, but the instability of the various Mexican governments made it impossible to protect our settlers. With the whole country disintegrating, and lawless desperadoes roaming about in search of plunder, any attempt to interest American or foreign capital in our enterprise was hopeless, and the Mexicans themselves had none to offer.

The final blow fell in 1917 when President Carranza passed the agrarian laws prohibiting the sale of land to foreigners. From that moment the colonization plan became inoperative. We carried the property until 1930, when it was sold to the Mexican government.

To Mexico the project would have meant the employment of labor in great numbers, warranted the collection of high taxes solely needed by the republic, and the development without expense to her of an agricultural project on a scale unparalleled in any other part of the North American continent. Although we were much disappointed at being prevented from carrying out an enterprise of such inestimable value, we wish every success to the present Mexican government which is about to start development of the Yaqui Valley along the original plans.

Mining for metals and mining for oil involve different specialized sciences. The name "black gold" applied to oil means only that the flow of riches derived from the wells is comparable to that secured from the gold mines. My own training and experience as a mining engineer caused me to take a lively interest in oil development.

In the winter of 1910 I was about to go to Mexico City when Harris suggested that I look into the oil developments in the Tampico region on the east coast. That district offered excellent opportunities, he said. After leaving Mexico City, I got in touch with Ricardo A. Mestres, who for some years had been consulting expert for Lord Cowdray's famous Aguila Oil Company in Tampico.

Mestres was half English and half Spanish. His father died when the boy was only fourteen, and Ricardo had begun to support his mother and sisters by taking charge of the billiard tables in one of the Tampico saloons. Being exceptionally intelligent and energetic, thoroughly honest and brave, he had ultimately risen to an important position in the oil industry.

Mestres offered me an option covering 167,000 acres, scattered in large tracts from the Panuco River to the Tuxpam. We took over his entire acreage and made him general manager and gave him a substantial interest. We then went to the Consolidated Gold Fields of South Africa for capital; this company purchased ten thousand of our acres in the Panuco district. Mestres assumed full charge of the exploitation and development of its Transcontinental Oil Company. Our company was called International Petroleum. For several years little was done except to keep our properties intact.

In 1916, just as we were about to begin developing our holdings, we received news of Mestres' death. This was a great personal, as well as business, loss to all who knew him.

Harris, who had managed the Mount Whitney Power Company from 1914 to its sale in 1916, was now free to devote all his time to our oil venture. I formed a million-dollar syndicate to carry on active exploration work, and in the beginning of 1917 put Harris in charge.

Prior to the Carranza regime it was the custom for oil companies to buy land outright at low prices and pay no royalty on oil production. After talking things over, we had agreed to reword all our previous purchase agreements by inserting royalty clauses. In this way the former Mexican owner would enjoy considerable profit whenever we struck oil. As a result, there were few potential oil properties in Mexico that were not offered to us in preference to any other company. This was our reward for treating owners justly when we were under no legal obligations to do so.

One day the oil companies in the Tampico field received notice from Pelaez, a bandit leader, that the monthly government royalty on oil production would be collected by him. His troops were in control of the district in which we were operating. The oil companies knew the Mexican government would not credit us with this illegal tribute on account as taxes, but we also knew that the wells would be burned by the bandits if we did not pay. We all made a virtue of necessity and the first month turned many thousands of dollars over to Pelaez. As expected, the Mexican government promptly notified us that it did not consider our obligations discharged. When nothing was paid to Pelaez the second month, he gave all the companies seven days to pay, announcing that at the end of this period he would act against any company he might catch operating.

Our company had used Mexican labor in the oil fields wherever possible, and when Mexicans proved their ability we had promoted them. This seemed to us good policy as it allayed any ill feeling against us as foreigners and gained us their loyal support.

Many of our head drillers, camp bosses, and other workers were stockholders in the company. We wired them from New York to use their own judgment as to what they should do, and enclosed a copy of Pelaez' proclamation. All the companies prudently closed down, except the Mexican Seaboard Oil Company—as International Petroleum was now called. When Pelaez rode in with his men, he found the Seaboard doing business as usual.

He demanded of the Mexican who met him, "Let me see your camp boss at once."

"I'm the camp boss," was the reply.

"You are? I never heard of a Mexican being in charge of a mine before!" exclaimed Pelaez in surprise. "Well, didn't you get my orders?"

"Yes," admitted the camp boss, "but many of the Mexicans here are stockholders, though we are men of modest means. We could not believe that this order included us. Moreover, we have instructions to feed you and your men and make you welcome."

Pelaez could not afford to antagonize the Mexican element, from whom his followers were recruited, so he allowed the Seaboard to continue operations.

During the enforced absence of the other companies from the field, we drew from the common pool two and one half million barrels of oil that were sold at $1.10 a barrel. This was a handsome profit on the stock we had given the men.

At Chereras we had a great loading rack that could fill three Standard Oil tankers at one time. A pipe line connected it with the storage tanks on land, which had a capacity of a million barrels.

From Chereras to the camp we had built a twenty-one-mile narrow-gauge railroad which was used to transport materials and gold coin for payrolls. José and Pedro, two Mexican brothers who had charge of the payroll train, had handled several million pesos for us without losing a centavo.

It was the custom to notify the camp by telephone the moment the train left Chereras. If it was a few minutes late, a car of armed men would be sent to meet it. One day in 1921 the usual message came that the train had started. When it was five minutes overdue, our manager tried to call Chereras and found the telephone line had been cut. Within a few moments the manager, accompanied by guards and the camp doctor, was on the way down the line. In twenty minutes the relief came upon the twisted, splintered wreckage of the light train. It had been literally blown to pieces by dynamite. Of the crew of seven men only José showed signs of life. He was badly broken by the explosion and shot through the chest.

The doctor reported that José's wounds must prove fatal, but that an injection of adrenalin might bring him back to temporary consciousness. The drug was administered.

In a few moments the doctor leaned over him to inquire: "Can you tell us who they were? Were they masked?"

"One was El Diablo," came the dying man's whisper. "He put his foot on my chest to shoot me. I saw the patch on the bottom of his shoe. It was three-cornered."

The manager knew that El Diablo had been hanging around the camp and would naturally have been observed carefully by anyone as conscientious as José.

In their wanton brutality and their desire to kill and leave no witnesses, the bandits had prepared so heavy a charge of dynamite as to defeat their own purpose. The gold coin had been so twisted and scattered by the violence of the explosion that little had been recovered in the few minutes before the arrival of the camp guards.

At the time of the dynamiting, Harris was in California with me. After a hasty discussion, we agreed that he should see President Obregon at once to ask whether the law against the carrying of arms could not be modified so that we might clean the bandits out of the district.

Harris described the outrage to Obregon and then added firmly, "We can't expose our men to this sort of thing, and we want to get the bandits no matter whether they're American, English, French, German, or Mexican."

Obregon replied, "You're the first man who has ever admitted to me that a bandit could be anything but Mexican."

He thereupon gave the company permission to arm its employees and also the right to call on the local garrison for help.

Acting on this authorization, we procured the services of seventeen men who had spent years with the Texas Rangers and similar bodies in hunting down criminals. They had been trained to act on the command, "Get your man, dead or alive."

After drifting around for two or three months at the bandit hideouts in Tampico and Zacamixtl, they began to pick up information here and there as to El Diablo's whereabouts. One day there came a tip that El Diablo was in a Tampico saloon. Our man suspected a trap, but he entered. As the door swung shut behind him, El Diablo and the two men with him opened fire from their table at the side of the room. When the smoke cleared the Texan walked out unharmed; the three bandits were dead.

This started real war.

The bandits were eventually tracked to their retreat in the mountains, where they had a supply of dynamite, rifles, and ammunition. With the explosives cached there, the Texans blew up the whole place.

After the death of El Diablo, a fine-looking young American assumed leadership of the gang. Lacking the necessities of life and war, the leader came in the night to the camp of one of the Panuco oil companies. Pounding on the door of the superintendent's shack, he called out, "If you don't open the door, we'll shoot it down." He was answered by a burst of gunfire which killed him and scattered his men. For several days the bandit leader's bullet-riddled body was exhibited in Tampico as a warning to evildoers.

By the end of two years our men had killed thirty or forty bandits. The spirit of the rest was broken and they wandered off. Life and property in our district were once more safe.

After discovering and developing the famous Toteco pool, the Mexican Seaboard extended its operations to California and to the equally famous Kettleman Hills field in Kern County, near Bakersfield. The geological formation there indicated oil, although the drilling of several dry holes seemed to disprove its presence. Even at a depth of six thousand feet, no traces of petroleum had appeared and drilling had been abandoned.

In a *Popular Science Magazine* article, Ray Lyman Wilbur, former secretary of the interior, said: "So finally came Harris Hammond, son of John Hays Hammond, who decided to plunge for the fluid gold where others had failed. He drove a well 7000 feet deep, at a cost of $250,000, and found incomparably greater wealth than his father had in South Africa." The secretary of the interior particularly approved of the manner in which the gas was conserved. The Mexican Seaboard Company had not only brought in the richest oil field in the world, but had supplied Northern California with natural gas.

When the Mexican revolution of 1923 broke out, Obregon had no money to pay his soldiers and could obtain no arms because of the United States embargo on the shipment of munitions into Mexico. We heard that Obregon had tried to borrow money from other oil companies. Finally one of his emissaries came to see Harris, who at once telephoned me in Washington.

I told him that if he could advance the money I would go at once to Secretary of War Weeks and explain that Obregon had been legally elected president and had been recognized by our government. Unless he could at once secure arms from the United States, anarchy would once more be let loose in Mexico. Moreover, if de la Huerta should win, relations between the United States and Mexico would be imperiled because of the rebel's well-known unfriendliness to our government.

Upon learning that the administration had already turned down de la Huerta's request for guns, I urged Secretary Weeks to send down airplanes or anything else in the way of fighting equipment that might help Obregon to win.

Weeks assured me of his sympathy with my views. I then called upon President Coolidge and told him: "We'll be the laughingstock of the world if we don't send guns to Mexico. Look what happened when Wilson refused to support Huerta. If we allow Obregon to be overthrown, we shall be put in a ridiculous position as we have already rendered him some aid and are committed to his cause. We've simply got to keep Obregon and Calles in power in spite of the revolution!"

Coolidge assured me of his determination to support Obregon to the full extent of his power.

The money was supplied and the embargo was lifted.

When the fighting was about to begin, we received a telegram to the effect that "General Obregon was taking the field to defend President Obregon." We were sure President Obregon could have no better defender than himself in the role of general. The money was paid back in full by rebating the taxes due the government by the company, and Obregon was successful in putting down the rebellion.

My second venture into oil took place in 1919 through the Burnham Exploration Company. Major Burnham, who was visiting me in New York, had been deploring the inactivity of the Yaqui project.

"Major," said Harris, "since you have so much time on your hands, why don't you try scouting for oil? You were a scout before most of the oil prospectors were born, and if you'll have a try at it, we could likely get hold of a profitable field to develop."

The idea of action appealed to Major Burnham, and the syndicate was formed, with Harris as president and Burnham as field manager.

In the course of two years Major Burnham examined properties in several states and took options in various sections of California. After a personal examination of these, Harris selected one property in the heart of the producing area of the Los Angeles basin. According to all geological indications, it seemed the most promising. As in the case of Kettleman, the field had already been tried and abandoned. The Union Oil Company had given up its options, and the Standard Oil of California had done the same after drilling two unsuccessful wells.

Major Burnham's son Roderick, "Rick" Templeton, and other geologists familiar with the structure recommended it strongly and were satisfied that the Standard Oil drillings had been no fair test of the field. Finally E. A. McKenna, the consulting geologist of Seaboard, made an exhaustive examination which resulted in thorough approval and recommendation of the structure. Harris and I then put up part of the money necessary to acquire the property, and, by telegraph, obtained the rest from Ogden Mills and Harry Payne Whitney.

While we were negotiating for the land, our intentions leaked out and we found ourselves bidding against Dutch Shell Oil and Union Oil, both of which companies wanted a footing in the field. A tripartite arrangement was accordingly made. We and the Union were to have a one-half undivided interest each, and the Dutch Shell a certain specified area for itself.

The first well, put down jointly by the Union Oil Company and ourselves in this Dominguez Hill field, came in at the rate of fifteen hundred barrels a day. Ever since then, the property has been one of the most highly valued fields in California.

The Mexican Seaboard Oil Company and the Burnham Exploration Company were exceedingly successful and are still earning. The Seaboard, between 1920 and 1930, paid off all its bonds and their interest, the value of the bonds being $10,700,000, and paid over $11,500,000 in dividends. The Burnham company, from 1923, its first year of operation, to 1933 inclusive, paid off its $1,000,000 worth of preferred stock with a bonus of ten points and during this ten-year period paid $10,240,000 in dividends.

It is estimated that the available oil still underground in the Dominguez Hill field runs from two hundred to four hundred million barrels.

One of the interesting features of the acquisition of this property was the fact that Major Burnham, who had been all over the world seeking his fortune, returned to find wealth in the very place where as a small boy he used to graze cattle, and shoot game which he sold to the neighboring mining districts to support his widowed mother and infant brother.

There are phases of development work in the Dominguez Hill field that are worth mentioning because of their bearing on oil recovery the world over. For a number of years, in various oil fields of the United States (exclusive of California), processes had been devised with a view to increasing oil production by the injection into the field of gas, compressed air, or water. Each field presented a problem in itself and several different processes were used successfully in Ohio and Oklahoma.

In the early part of 1925 the officers of the Burnham Exploration Company sent their engineer to consult with the Union Oil Company as to the possible application of the injection process in the Dominguez field. As a result of several conferences and many tests, we adopted a process which I believe had never been used in the state of California. This is the process of gas injection. The gas is taken from the well, the gasoline extracted, and the gas then driven by huge compressors into the oil-producing formation. There it again absorbs the oil locked in the sands and conveys another load to the surface. This invention has made possible the recovery of many millions of barrels of oil that otherwise never could be recovered.

CHAPTER THIRTY-SIX

In Retrospect

*A*s I look back over these eighty years, it seems to me that I have been fortunate, most fortunate, perhaps, in the family into which I was born, the family I helped to found, and the friendships I have formed.

In two other things I was fortunate: that I was able to choose during college the life course I wanted to pursue and that I married early and had the responsibility of a family.

I have made more than a fair amount of success according to the world's standards, but I hope this has not been at the cost of sacrificing the finer quality of life. Even in my later years I have been busy and it seems to me that most of my leisure hours were occupied with things other than dolce far niente. Now and then, of course, I was able to sandwich in relaxation between business and other activities, but I have not often enjoyed a real vacation as is the habit of most businessmen of today.

In contemplating the writing of this book and, after a great deal of hesitation, in undertaking it, I have come to realize that perhaps because my life has been so active, retrospect is not particularly natural to me.

The world into which I was born was one where driving power and physical energy were essential to survival. Frontiers were being extended on every hand. On many of these I lived and encountered adventure. This seemed but part of the day's work. I recognized adventure, of course, when it came, but whatever elements of romance may now seem to surround those episodes are due to my seeing them as a whole, rather than as a disconnected series of events. And in later years I was not insensible to the drama that was coming into business and political affairs. I lived in it while it was unfolding; when it was over I did not forget it, but the conscious memory was displaced by the immediacy of other things to be seen and accomplished.

I have led such an active life that I have had literally no time and no desire to keep a diary wherein I might jot down the facts which the average traveler observes automatically. One may be a guest at a dinner where the conversation proves so enthralling as to make one oblivious of the food. One may travel through the countryside and be so absorbed in a problem as not to know whether the road is rough or smooth. It is possible to have one's attention so fixed on a definite goal that it overshadows everything else.

The reader may feel that in telling this story I have left out certain human values. This may be true. The momentum of events has carried me along and I have detailed incidents as they came to mind. In looking back on my life I realize that my truly happy hours of recreation seem always to have been spent with my wife and children.

I have talked little of home or homes. And yet, to men who are forced to spend a large part of their lives in out-of-the-way places, family life is of far greater importance than to others.

In this respect I was particularly fortunate. My wife possessed the gift, with sometimes but few facilities at her command, of creating the background essential to our family life. She never allowed the unsettled character of my activities or her own various interests to interfere and she made a real home for us in many parts of the world. She had feminine methods of accomplishing this and one of the cleverest was her ability to appeal to our appetites. She was not only a good cook herself, she could teach others how to cook. In kitchens the world around she provided the favorite dishes of the family. In Mexico we would find awaiting us at dinner Maryland beaten biscuits; in Johannesburg, spoon bread—real delicacies to one of southern rearing.

In every mining community there are many young engineers, married and unmarried, and in our various homes they found welcome. Under my wife's sympathetic guidance they soon forgot any shyness and talked at length of other days, the theater, music, their homes and families. As a result, they felt less lonely and not quite so far from things dear to them.

Our third abode in Washington—this time really our own—delightfully situated on Kalorama Road was purchased in 1917. Here we spent many busy and interesting winters (until my wife's death in 1931). My own children had by this time grown up and I became friends with those in my neighborhood as I was conscious of missing the cheerful society of the very young.

I owned some vacant lots across the street from our house where children of the neighborhood used to congregate. I made it into a sort of community playground for them. I fenced in sand piles and put up swings for the smaller ones, and benches for their nurses. To the older boys I gave baseball bats and gloves with the strict proviso that they should not use them until the "kids," as they scornfully called them, had gone home. I spent many delightful and refreshing hours in the companionship of these children—we became real pals.

One day when walking near our house I saw a small boy lying flat on the sidewalk, screaming at the top of his lungs, while his nurse with soothing words vainly endeavored to induce him to move. Having many times heard the same sort of cry from my own children I knew that he was not hurt; he was merely indulging in a fit of temper.

"What's his name?" I asked the distracted nurse.

"John."

"John, did you see that big black bear run across the street!" I exclaimed.

The crying suddenly ceased, and John's face was lifted from the sidewalk as he asked, "Where?"

"It's too bad you've been making such a noise. You must have scared him away. There he goes around the corner! Come on, maybe we can catch up to him."

Hand in hand we started after the bear, but we never caught up with him. But John had forgotten his troubles and, after we bade each other a cordial farewell, he allowed his nurse to take him peaceably home.

The next day I received a letter from Mrs. Franklin D. Roosevelt, thanking me for the service I had rendered her family. From that time on young John Roosevelt and I were friends. He and an older brother often visited me at my house. Before an expected call, I would bury a few pennies and nickels in the back yard. They would come armed with buckets and shovels, and, under my instruction, would start digging like true miners. Great was their excitement and elation when they came upon the bonanza.

The three of us once went on a pleasant expedition to the zoo. After gazing for some time into bear pits and monkey cages, I asked John, "Have you ever seen a ship of the desert?"

"No," replied John thoughtfully.

"You don't mean to tell me you've never seen a ship of the desert? And your father is assistant secretary of the navy?"

They were indignant at their father's failure to keep them up to date on nautical matters.

"Well, come on with me then."

I led them to the camel yard, explained to them why these animals were called ships of the desert, and told them stories of camels I had seen in my travels.

"We're going right home and ask father if he's ever seen a ship of the desert," John declared.

Following up my affection for children and my delight in their society, it was not unnatural that I should undertake some work in behalf of the boys of the country.

I believe that some of the most valuable supplements to the system of public education, and the upbuilding of character, are in the Y. M. C. A., the Boy Scout movement, and the Boys' Clubs of America. The latter organization—until recently called the Boys' Club Federation—was founded in 1906 and for many years has had my friend William E. Hall as its president; it has been my privilege to serve under him as vice-president for about fifteen years. Nearly two-thirds of the boys in our country have been classed as "underprivileged." They are born in humble homes where family life is unattractive and sometimes pernicious; they are able to take advantage of educational opportunities to only a limited extent; they are often handicapped by prejudice of race or religion; and they make up the sad army of juvenile delinquents. Yet, if I were to select a team to compete in the battle of life, I should unhesitatingly select boys of this class. They are intelligent, self-reliant, and used to hardships. They are not "bad boys," but good boys doing the wrong things, and have never had a fair chance in life. I have often said this when talking to them. Ninety per cent of the criminal class is drawn from this great two-thirds of America's boyhood—this undernourished, undefended majority. We really cannot pretend to be amazed at crime waves and the degeneracy of which newspapers make a daily chronicle. The cause is not obscure nor difficult to locate.

An appalling and pitiable fact in the crime situation is not that hordes of bandits and gangs of racketeers swarm the city and defy suppression, but that the *offender is often only a boy*—a boy who has been denied the opportunity of developing good character in proper environment.

Former Police Commissioner Whalen, of New York City, recently said: "One of the tragedies of the crime problem of today is the extreme youth of the criminal. Of all persons arrested last year 44 per cent were under the age of twenty, and 60 per cent of all holdups were committed by youths between the ages of sixteen and twenty."

It was to offset this menace that the Boys' Clubs of America was founded. Branches have been established in 134 American cities with a membership of 240,000 divided among 260 clubs. The average club numbers 940 boys. Its aim is to provide the poorer, more congested districts with clubhouses which will offer wholesome mental and physical activities.

CAPTAIN HOWARD BLACKBURN (1863-1932)

GLOUCESTER HARBOR FROM LOOKOUT HILL

The enormous success of the clubs in dealing with these boys may be attributed to the fact that they have shrewdly capitalized the gang interest which is strong in every boy. Youth, after all, learns largely from youth. It will not learn voluntarily from moral precept, but once arouse in a group of youngsters interest in their grown-up contacts with young men, who will sanely embody a boy's admiration for daring and adventure, and the youthful pack is headed in the right direction. Hero worship is an inherent part of a boy's life. The man chosen by a boy as a type of hero exerts a vast influence on his life. We must counteract the evil influence of the racketeer and the bandit. If no other associations with elders are granted them, can they be blamed if they emulate these men?

Lewis E. Lawes, warden of Sing Sing Prison, says: "Boys' Clubs cost $15.00 per capita per year, whereas it costs $400.00 to maintain an inmate at Sing Sing for that period."

These clubs have made an amazing record in reducing juvenile delinquency.

I feel no disgrace in having been involved in the following episode as reported in *Fortune:*

JOHN HAYS HAMMOND TAKES THE COUNT

An unusual pugilistic upset was recorded when John Hays Hammond, vice-president of the Boys' Club Federation, was knocked out by Walter Brady, eight year old champion pugilist of the Boys' Club of Washington, during the first round of a challenge bout at the formal opening of the new sixty thousand dollar gymnasium of the Washington Boys' Club on Tuesday evening, November 9th. The vanquished boxer admitted that he was beaten in a fair fight with the exception that young Brady assured him before the fight that he would not "hit him hard."

In reviewing our lives at this period I remember that my wife was continually engaged in work of civic and philanthropic nature. Her charity list was not long. She would find something worth remedying, raise the money needed, and administer it personally. She never stopped in the middle of an undertaking.

If her interest was a hospital or a charitable home, she would frequently drop in and talk to the doctors, to the directors, and to the inmates so that there was always the direct personal touch.

During her term as chairman of the Women's Welfare Department of the National Civic Federation she was active in a move to improve the living conditions in the federal prisons, and particularly in the one first called to her attention in Washington and known as the "D. C. Jail." She interested her friend George W. Wickersham, the attorney general, and took him to visit that notorious prison. They found that the gallows stood at the end of the dining room, covered with a scant curtain. On the days of execution the prisoners ate their breakfast in the corridor. The men lived in tiny cells that had no running water; there was no outdoor exercise for women. The prisoners were fed like animals, and were grossly maltreated. As a result of her efforts, conditions were radically improved.

She established and was for five years president of the Women's Evening Clinic in Washington, which was free to the poorest and charged fees from ten cents to a dollar for workingwomen. In 1914, through her influence, the first woman interne was appointed in Garfield Hospital. It was at that time a very difficult matter to gain recognition of this kind for the woman physician.

As was natural, her thought was often directed to the welfare of children. The War Children's Christmas Fund owed its success to her ability as an organizer. The result of her efforts, aided by a corps of volunteer workers, was the shipment to Europe before the Christmas of 1915 of a large quantity of clothing, food, and toys, which was distributed without racial distinction among the children of all the warring nations.

My wife then undertook the direction of the Militia of Mercy which devoted itself to caring for poor children of Boston and New York who had been crippled by the infantile paralysis epidemic of 1916. These are only a few of the philanthropic interests that occupied her time and energy.

In 1912 my wife organized the movement to erect the Titanic

Memorial, to commemorate the bravery of the men who sacrificed their lives "that women and children might be saved."

The response to the appeals of the Woman's Titanic Memorial Association was remarkable.

Benefit performances of various kinds, given in different places, added substantial sums. Of these the most notable was a benefit that took place in December, 1912, at the Century Theatre, in New York. My sister expressed its spirit in these words which appeared on the outside of the program:

GREATER THAN SELF, STRONGER THAN FATE,
HEROIC SOULS ASK OF US NO TRIBUTE BUT REMEMBRANCE.

Over three hundred of the leading actors and actresses gave their services with the usual warm-hearted, generous response of that profession to all appeals for charity. The organization of the benefit was in the capable hands of Daniel Frohman. He suggested to my wife that it would be advisable for her personally to enlist the interest of Charles Frohman, as he felt sure that many of the artists then under his brother's direction would gladly appear if Charles were willing.

My wife then called on Charles Frohman and was received with the utmost courtesy. He was in a jocular mood, and her glowing praise of the heroism of the men who had gone down on the *Titanic* was met by a facetiously expressed doubt as to their being entitled to the honor of a monument.

I am inclined to think that Mr. Frohman was favorably impressed as he continued to rally her in regard to her warmly expressed admiration for the bravery of men in general, in order, I suspect, to draw her out.

Finally he remarked: "Well, personally, I should have shoved my way to a lifeboat and got into it." But, he soon ceased to joke, and gave his promise to aid the benefit—a promise generously fulfilled in his contribution of talent.

A few years later, as everyone remembers, Charles Frohman intrepidly faced death on the sinking of the *Lusitania*. His last words have been widely quoted: "Why fear death? It is the most beautiful adventure in life."

With the co-operation of Major U. S. Grant III, in charge of public grounds and buildings, Congress finally appropriated a site in Potomac Park in Washington, and in 1931 the beautiful monument designed by Mrs. Harry Payne Whitney was unveiled. The President, the secretary of state, many officials and statesmen were present, with a great crowd of representative citizens. Mrs. Taft unveiled the monument. On one side are inscribed the following words:

TO THE BRAVE MEN WHO PERISHED IN THE WRECK OF
THE TITANIC, APRIL 15, 1912. THEY GAVE THEIR LIVES THAT
WOMEN AND CHILDREN MIGHT BE SAVED. ERECTED BY THE
WOMEN OF AMERICA.

There is every year an exodus from Washington, New York, and other large cities, of all who are not bound by their official duties to remain and swelter in the unpleasant heat. My wife and I were anxious to find a place where the children could spend their long vacations. In the summer of 1903 we chartered a boat and cruised along the coast from Long Island to Bar Harbor, looking at various sites, always anxious to avoid such enervating routine as one finds in Newport and other fashionable resorts. Finally, we decided on Gloucester, Massachusetts, because it was a town of fishermen—men whose rugged character reminded us of communities we had known and loved in the Far West. We built a home, and called it "Lookout Hill."

Even in the midst of affairs of business, which did not entirely cease with the summer, I was able to spend more and more time with my wife and youthful family. On many long walks through the woods, I taught Natalie woodcraft, and we spent many afternoons swimming, sailing, and fishing, pleasant and healthful diversions for both of us. When she was six she had already begun to be interested in drawing, and we always encouraged her. At the age of eight she wrote an ambitious romance entitled *The Adventures of Sir John Hammond* and illustrated it profusely. The unconscious humor of both text and pictures put a severe strain on the polite seriousness of her family readers. Since then her work has been shown and sold in many art exhibitions both here and abroad, and her designs for theatrical sets and costumes have been used by Nazimova and for special performances at the Guild Theatre.

Harris, Jack, and Dick spent most of their time sailing around the harbor in their boat, the *Swallow*. Three times they won the Massachusetts championship for boats in that class.

Dick became a skilled sailor and, at the beginning of the World War, turned naturally to the navy. He and three college friends were commissioned by the government to do night patrol work on the Cape Ann coast, where German submarines were getting their fuel supply. Dick knew every channel and rock in this section and could navigate without lights.

The boys were so conscientious in the discharge of their duty that they would board any suspicious-looking vessel they encountered and, unless the skipper could prove to their entire satisfaction that his business was harmless, they would order him summarily in to the port authority at Boston. More often than otherwise the irate captains were able to prove complete innocence of intent. But the boys continued to do their duty as they saw it.

I fitted up a laboratory for Jack on the Gloucester grounds. There he used to carry on experiments in boat control by radio, alarming and mystifying both natives and summer people who observed his boat careering around the harbor without anyone on board.

My summers would probably not have been so peaceful had I known all that was going on at the laboratory.

There was in the cove an old fisherman called Joe Adams, who had been more or less adopted by the boys. In his declining years, he used to place lobster pots a few yards from the shore. Usually, before starting out, he took a few drinks. From the terrace the boys would watch him make his uncertain rounds during which he sometimes pulled up the same pot several times within the hour.

Jack and Harris one day laid a homemade mine about a hundred yards offshore, which Jack was going to try to explode by wireless. They didn't know much about explosives then, and put in far too big a charge. Harris was to be stationed at the door of the laboratory to sound a warning should any boat approach too near the mine. After pulling the switch a dozen times without anything happening, Jack buried himself in the complicated wiring, and called Harris inside to help. Finally Jack said: "I have all the connections made. This time the infernal thing is sure to go off. I'll pull the switch when you get outside, and then I'll run out to see the fun."

When Harris returned to his post, he saw old Joe calmly pulling up a lobster pot directly over the mine. Just as Harris yelled to Jack, "Hold everything," there was a terrific detonation. Joe and his boat rose fifty feet on a trumpet of water, capsized, and came down in a shower of lobster pots, boulders, seaweed, rocks, and fish.

In three jumps Harris reached the rowboat at the foot of the little cliff and battled his way out among the waves to rescue Joe who was splashing about in a half-drowned condition. Harris hauled him in, thankful to see he was not hurt.

When Joe had partially caught his breath, he gasped, "God-amighty, did you see what happened to me? I went up right top of a big wave."

"Nonsense, Joe," Harris said. "We've been watching you for the last quarter of an hour. I saw you lean over to pull in that lobster pot and you fell in."

"But I felt it," Joe insisted. "My boat's all broke up! As I went up, I could see right over the top of the house."

"You're crazy," Harris insisted, this time with some show of justice, since the top of the house was a hundred feet above the water line. "You must have kicked the boat as you fell. I think you've had a few too many drinks."

The people of Gloucester heard the noise of the explosion but thought it was probably blasting in the near-by Rockport quarries. The boys comforted Joe and bought him a new rowboat.

To his dying day Joe thought he had been the victim of a hallucination. But once in a while he would mutter to himself, "I know damn well the ocean blew up."

In 1913, Jack explained his ideas about remote control by radio to the secretary of war, Lindley M. Garrison, and to the chief of coast artillery, General Weaver. The general promised to come to Gloucester when Jack was ready.

Two years later the first demonstration took place. With no one on board, a motorboat was run across the harbor to the breakwater and around the spar and back, a course of three miles. The experiment was perfectly successful. Eventually the potential range of control was increased to thirty miles.

Later the government's interest lay in the application of remote control of torpedoes. Jack was using his boat as a theoretical torpedo, which, of course, could run only on the surface. By further development he was able to control the U.S.S. *Iowa* without anyone on board, at a distance of several miles. The *Iowa,* discarded as a warship, was used in this instance for target practice.

Our cautious government refused to accept his invention until he perfected his methods so that torpedoes could be directed at the standard depth, though this was not contemplated (indeed, not regarded as possible) in his original agreement with the government. These inventions now constitute an important part of our naval equipment.

In connection with his radio researches Jack obtained most important patents for receiving and broadcasting and these he sold to the Radio Corporation of America and became its consulting engineer.

There were two fishing boats in Gloucester which interested my family very much. Both were owned by Captain Lemuel Spinney. One of them had been named the *John Hays Hammond* and the other the *Natalie Hammond.* There was great rivalry between my daughter and myself as to which would return first from the Grand Banks and which would have the larger catch. With the telescope we would watch the boats making harbor and then telephone to the pier to find out which had won. I jokingly accused Captain Spinney of knowing we had bets up on the result, and therefore of unduly favoring the *Natalie Hammond.* These boats were regarded as "lucky" boats, but in reality Captain Spinney was the best fisherman in Gloucester. He had picked crews who would not return until their cargoes were complete, although many other vessels in the fleet would come back with half a load. My namesake was torpedoed in the North Sea by the Germans, when it was used by the Allies in the World War.

Among the residents of the North Shore were people I had known in Washington and elsewhere. A few of my Massachusetts friends occasionally assumed an attitude of friendly superiority towards me, because of my western birth. The chief offender was the late Major

Augustus P. Gardner, congressman from my district. "Gussie" and I often used to speak on the same political platform. At times he would point to the fact that every drop of his blood was Puritanic blue. He was trying to make me feel a rank outsider in.the Bay State, although it had been my legal residence since 1903.

On one occasion Gussie went too far. When I spoke, following him, I said that in my opinion my distinguished friend was not entitled to special commendation for having been born in Massachusetts. That event was merely an accident of birth. On the other hand, I had been born in California, lived in many parts of the world, and after attaining an age of discretion and mature judgment, had of my own volition chosen Massachusetts for my permanent residence. Gussie appreciated the point.

I had really enjoyed sailing and fishing with the children. Later when I bought a yacht, the *Atreus,* for longer trips it seemed that every time my wife and I took a cruise something happened to shorten our trip. Even when we took the smaller children with us on the *Atreus* for an extended cruise, invariably their nurses were seasick. I began to feel that yachts were fools' paradises, but I used the *Atreus* advantageously for business purposes. When compelled to be within reach of my office in New York, I would take members of my staff with me, spending the evening on the boat working out engineering problems.

During one of our cruises we anchored off Coney Island. Among the guests were Baron Rosen, Dr. Morton Prince, R. D. Evans, Finley Peter Dunne (*Mr. Dooley*), and Major Burnham.

Baron Rosen was the Russian ambassador and accompanied me on many trips on the yacht. He was an excellent raconteur, and a man of extensive diplomatic experience. Of all the diplomats I have met, I consider that he was best qualified to comment on international questions. We were somewhat shocked when he ridiculed the open-door policy of John Hay which we had unquestioningly accepted as one of the Ten Commandments of international relations. Rosen claimed that it had not settled the Japanese question in any way. He prophesied, however, that the Japanese would unobtrusively creep up inch by inch until they had taken possession of all the Asiatic coast opposite their islands. With the recent establishment of Manchukuo his prophecy has come true.

Dunne was an occasional visitor at Lookout Hill and I came to know something of the rigors of the newspaper "copy date." He could never finish his material on time. I have often sat up late with him, urging him on by various methods, then sent off his material by automobile to Boston to make a late train to his New York publishers.

Dr. Morton Prince of Boston, charming and well-informed gentleman as well as great psychiatrist, was a very dear friend of the family. One of the chief ambitions of Dr. Prince's life was to beat Charles Francis Adams at sailing. They both owned boats made by the same firm and of an identical type. They raced constantly but, so far as I can learn, Prince never once took a race from Skipper Adams.

One of the visitors who always received a hearty welcome at Lookout Hill was Moreton Frewen of London, noted bimetallist and an intimate friend of Justice Oliver Wendell Holmes. On our way to the Myopia Club for lunch one day Frewen and I stopped to invite Holmes to join us.

He regretfully declined, saying, "I have to prepare an opinion immediately, and much as I should enjoy being with you I cannot spare the time."

Frewen, with his extraordinary persuasive powers, finally induced Holmes to accompany us. But Mrs. Holmes said, "Oliver shouldn't be going, but, since he is, I want you to promise you'll get him back here sharp at three o'clock."

We were so engrossed in enjoyable conversation that our promise to Mrs. Holmes entirely slipped our minds. After tarrying long over lunch we motored to the Eastern Yacht Club at Marblehead for further refreshments. About six o'clock we boarded my boat and sailed to Lookout Hill, arriving just in time for dinner. It seemed quite natural that the justice should remain.

We had not been long seated at the table when I was called to the telephone. It was Mrs. Holmes, who indignantly upbraided me for having failed to return her husband at the promised hour. She said she had been telephoning all up and down the North Shore trying to locate him.

We guiltily bolted our food and hurried to his home. I had not the courage to face Mrs. Holmes, so I abandoned the justice on the door-step and beat a hasty retreat. The only notice she would take of me for a long time thereafter was a formal and reproachful nod.

Holmes was unrepentant, and professed never to have forgotten his truancy. Whenever we meet he refers to it as "that red-letter day."

My first lessons in golf were received in England under the tutelage of Lord Lorne, later Duke of Argyll. When I came to America, I was told that I should have to forget all I had learned abroad and begin over again. The professional at the Myopia Club told me patroniz-ingly that I would never make a good golfer. Disappointed, I asked why he had not told me so before giving me lessons.

To console me, he replied: "President Taft is no better than you are."

"That's a comfort, anyhow," said I. "How do you explain our inability to master this difficult sport?"

"The reason is," he explained, "that the brains of both of you are always working on so many things that you can't concentrate on the game."

Taft used to carry a score book with him, which I, in an unguarded moment, had presented to him. Whenever I boasted of some par-ticularly fine record I had made, he would pull out this book and check me up.

Our favorite playing ground was the golf links at the Myopia Club. The name of this club was selected because several of the leading incorporators had been myopes. Among the many people who ques-tioned the origin of the name was a certain party of New Yorkers who were being driven out from Boston. They were asking each other what the derivation of "Myopia" might be.

Amid a chorus of "Search me" and "Darned if I know," the driver interpolated, "Beg your pardon, sirs, but the word myopia is derived from the Greek *myein,* to close, and *ops,* meaning eye, hence near-sightedness."

"You get inside, and I'll drive," retorted one of the New Yorkers, who possessed a sense of the fitness of things.

There was one hole on the Myopia course which used to give Taft particular difficulty. I dubbed it the President's bunker, because it had been devised, so the story goes, by Herbert Leeds, chairman of the golf course committee, especially to vex the President and vex him it did. Leeds was an alumnus of Harvard and up to the time of his death had no use for a Yale man, not even if he was President of the United States.

Taft was bent on getting around under one hundred. All the club members had bets on his score, offering odds against him. As Myopia golfers will attest, ninety-eight on their course is fully as good as ninety on any ordinary links. I shall never forget one particular day when Taft came to lunch at Lookout Hill. When I met him at the door, he was bubbling with good-humor and was chuckling so merrily that I was sure he had some joke on me.

"Well, Jack," he announced jubilantly, "I've gone around at Myopia in less than one hundred. My score this morning was ninety-eight."

Major Archibald Butt's famous *Letters* make me out more of a duffer at golf than I am willing to admit. Even so, I regarded Archie as one of the most tactful men I have ever known. No one not possessing that quality could have retained the friendship of both the Tafts and the Roosevelts during the trying years of their estrangement.

As to the revelations which came out in his book, they are more valuable for small incidents and sidelights on character than for any knowledge imparted as to serious matters. Butt used to gather up the scraps of conversation which fell his way and report them without a full understanding of the background. This makes them somewhat misleading to the credulous reader. Charles D. Hilles, who succeeded Charles D. Norton as secretary to President Taft, wrote me recently that he "considers the inaccuracies to be innumerable and inexcusable." Butt's comments are, to say the least, indiscreet, distorted, and often far from kind.

When the news first came of the sinking of the *Titanic,* on which Archie was taking a long overdue vacation, I telephoned Taft to ask whether there was any reason to hope that Butt had been saved.

"Not the slightest chance," he replied. "Archie would be the last man to leave the ship."

Golf was a great pleasure to me so long as my health allowed me to play. I was sorry when I had to give it up, although I never played more than an average game. Arthur T. Hadley, for example, was not particularly enthusiastic about my golfing abilities. Once when I ignominiously missed a drive, he burst forth in impromptu rhyme:

> I thought I saw a friendly soul
> Whose face beamed mirth and jollity.
> I looked again: He's missed the ball
> And only hit the tee.
> "Now how," said I, "could anyone . . ."
> "You go to hell," said he.

In the fall of 1913, I was in the midst of an extended tournament with Thomas Nelson Page when his appointment as ambassador to Italy threatened to cut it short.

Page at once declared: "We mustn't let the unkind intervention of affairs of state interfere with our golf. Let's settle this matter in Italy. I could then prove to you once and for all that I could beat you."

This was a challenge not lightly to be disregarded. I went to Rome for the winter. Since it must be admitted that this pretext for a vacation was somewhat flimsy, I ostentatiously left my own golf kit at home. I knew that I could borrow clubs from Colonel Dunn of the American Embassy, and the true nature of the trip would not then be quite so apparent; certainly less embarrassing to me in case of defeat.

In the end I was able to satisfy Page that his advantage over me was not so great as he had assumed.

It was at the Myopia Club that George Harvey brought about a reconciliation between Senator Beveridge and me after we had fallen out several years before during Taft's administration owing to political differences. Harvey, who was visiting me at Gloucester, told me that Beveridge was anxious to make up. This pleased me greatly, and I enjoyed the renewed friendship up to the untimely death of this remarkable man.

But Beveridge never made up his quarrel with Tom Marshall, whose sense of humor sometimes carried him further than he had intended. For example, once when Senator Beveridge, up for re-election, was covering Indiana in a whirlwind campaign of eloquence, he declared that if the voters would send him back to the Senate, he would put Indiana on the map.

Marshall could not resist this opening. He commented: "I agree with Beveridge. If he were elected, he would put Indiana on the map, but the area would then be marked 'windswept plain.'"

Beveridge never forgave him.

The country at large did not agree with Marshall's characterization of Beveridge: it recognized that he was a brilliant, upright, and courageous statesman, and a historian of marked ability.

Albert Beveridge's direct and serious nature sometimes prevented the exercise of his sense of humor. Once, after an after-dinner conversation, there was some discussion of his *Life of John Marshall*, which had just appeared.

Aware of the antipathy of Beveridge for Tom Marshall, I said, "Albert, I think the writing of the life of Marshall was magnanimous on your part."

He looked at me in his characteristic way to search for my meaning, then he exclaimed: "Why, Jack! What do you mean? You don't really think I wrote the life of Tom Marshall, do you?"

At my look of pretended bewilderment, Beveridge, obviously annoyed, stalked into another room. The others appreciated the joke, and one of them followed Beveridge to remind him that I had already read much of the manuscript before publication and naturally was well aware that his hero was John, not Tom.

The last time I saw Beveridge, shortly before his death, he brought to my home some chapters of the biography of Lincoln which he was then writing. We spent the afternoon discussing the book. I remember vividly his telling me that he had greatly changed his views about the South. He admitted that, although he had been raised in an abolitionist atmosphere, a close study of the conditions preceding the Civil War convinced him that the South had had much right on its side, and that, in many respects, the North had been too intolerant.

The harbor life of Gloucester added to my love of the place. I enjoyed chatting with the old sailors as much as I did with my other friends. I used to go to Captain Blackburn's store on Main Street and get him to tell about his extraordinary life. In 1883, at the age of twenty, his dory was separated from its schooner in an icy norther off the Grand Banks. He was forced to sit four days looking at his dead dory mate frozen on the seat in front of him. When he realized that his own hands were freezing, he curved them around the oar handles so that he could continue to row after the hands themselves became immovable. Ultimately he came safe to land but lost his fingers and one foot.

Despite this crippled condition, he never gave up his life as a sailor and continued to complete daring and incredible voyages. Some years later, in a small schooner, with a limited crew, he sailed around the Horn to the Klondike to prospect for gold, but was forced to give up the undertaking because of his health. In 1899 he sailed alone in a thirty-foot sloop from Gloucester in New England to Gloucester in Old England. He was one of the most undaunted sailors America has ever had and I have seldom enjoyed exchanging yarns with anybody so much. I was proud to be one of the honorary pallbearers at his funeral, with Captain Bob Bartlett, Commander Donald B. MacMillan, Sir Wilfred Grenfell, Charles Francis Adams, and others.

I look back with the greatest pleasure on the hours I have spent with other old Gloucester fishermen. In the winter of 1910 several of these old fellows appeared before the district court and pleaded guilty to vagrancy. Without other means of gaining food or shelter, they were seeking some sort of sustenance in the poorhouse for the winter. In Washington, I read about this in the papers and got in touch with Judge York, Dr. Dickswell, Fred Shackelford, and others who were interested. We established a home to provide for these old fishermen. I learned to appreciate the fine traits of these men who were given refuge there. Often it was exceedingly difficult to persuade them that they were too old to stand the hardships of deep-sea fishing. Their truck garden faced the sea, and from there they could watch with their telescopes for the fishing vessels as they left and entered the harbor.

Sailors, like miners, are notoriously spendthrifts and these of Gloucester were no exception. They would arrive at the Home in a destitute condition. Because they no longer went to sea, and there was no chance of their reaching the traditional sailors' grave, they had a great dread of potter's field. For that reason I provided a cemetery near Gloucester where all could be assured of decent burial. Above the gate is inscribed:

AND HERE REST, BRAVE TOILER OF THE SEA,

SLEEP UNDISTURBED.

GOD'S PEACE BE WITH THEE.

Many of the inmates were choosey about the location of their graves. There were two in particular, bunkies since boyhood, who quarreled daily and, I fear, nightly, but who exacted from me a promise that they might be buried side by side.

Like the old prospectors of the West, they were given to enlarging upon their experiences. I used to slip them a little grog and a pipe of tobacco and then start them off spinning yarns. Each of the yarns would grow somewhat better than the one just told. But when they overstepped the bounds and the yarn became too fantastic, the size of the fish too large, or description of some strange sea serpent or "queer doings" in foreign lands became utterly preposterous, I would raise my hand in protest and say: "Wait a minute, boys! Not quite so fast! Remember, I can tell some 'tall' stories myself."

ACKNOWLEDGMENTS

The stanza from Kipling's "The Burial" is reprinted by kind permission of Mr. Kipling.

"Ghost Town," from Let Us Dream *by Don Blanding, copyright, 1933, by Don Blanding, is used by permission of the publishers, Dodd, Mead & Company, Inc.*

Bibliography

BOOKS COVERING THE PERIOD

BAKER, HERBERT, *Cecil Rhodes, by his architect.* London: Oxford University Press, 1934.

BLAKE, WILLIAM P., *Tombstone and Its Mines.* New York: Cheltenham Press, 1902.

BRYCE, JAMES, *Impressions of South Africa.* New York: The Century Co., 1897.

BURNS, WALTER NOBLE, *Tombstone, an Iliad of the Southwest.* Garden City, N. Y.: Doubleday, Page & Co., 1927.

California State Mining Report. Ninth Annual Report.

CANFIELD, CHAUNCEY L., *The Diary of a 49r.* San Francisco: M. Shepard Co., 1906.

CURLE, J. H., *The Gold Mines of the World.* New York: Engineering and Mining Journal, Inc., 1902.

DEWAAL, D. C., *With Rhodes in Mashonaland.* Cape Town: J. C. Jusa & Co., 1896.

Economic Geology (Magazine), May, 1930.

GARRETT, F. E., *The Story of an African Crisis.* Westminster: A. Constable & Co., 1897.

HALL, R. N., *Great Zimbabwe.* London: Methuen & Co., 1905.

———, *Pre-historic Rhodesia.* London: T. F. Unwin, 1909.

———, and NEAL, W. G., *The Ancient Ruins of Rhodesia.* London: Methuen & Co., 1904.

HATCH, F. H., and CHALMERS, J. A., *The Gold Mines of the Rand.* London: Macmillan & Co., Ltd., 1895.

HOLE, HUGH MARSHALL, *The Making of Rhodesia.* London: Macmillan & Co., Ltd., 1926.

IMPERIALIST (Dr. Jameson), *Cecil Rhodes, a biography and appreciation.* London: Chapman & Hall, 1897.

IRELAND, ALLEYNE, *The Anglo-Boer Conflict.* Boston: Small, Maynard & Co., 1900.

KEANE, AUGUSTUS HENRY, *The Gold of Ophir.* London: E. Stanford, 1901.

KRUGER, PAUL, *The Memoirs of Paul Kruger.* New York: The Century Co., 1902.

LAKE, STUART N., *Wyatt Earp, Frontier Marshal.* Boston: Houghton Mifflin & Co., 1931.

LYMAN, GEORGE D., *The Saga of the Comstock Lode.* New York: Charles Scribner's Sons, 1934.

McDonald, J. G., *Rhodes, A Life*. London: P. Allan & Co., 1927.

Maclaren, J. M., *Gold*. London: The Mining Journal, 1908.

Mitchell, Sir Lewis, *The Life of the Rt. Hon. Cecil J. Rhodes*. London: E. Arnold & Co., 1910.

Neville, Mrs. Amelia R., *The Fantastic City*. Boston: Houghton Mifflin & Co., 1932.

O'Meara, James, *Pioneer Senators*.

Phillips, Sir Lionel, *Some Reminiscences*. London: Hutchinson & Co., 1924.

———, *Transvaal Problems*. London: J. Murray, 1905.

Pioneer Miner and the Pack Mule Express, The. California Historical Society.

Report of the Select Committee on the Jameson Raid in the Territory of South African Republic. Printed by order of the House of Assembly, July, 1896. Cape Town: W. A. Richards & Sons, Government Printers.

Rickard, T. A. (editor), *Economics of Mining*. New York: Hill Publishing Co., 1907.

Slocum, Capt. Joshua, *Sailing Alone Around the World*. New York: The Century Co., 1900.

Truscott, Samuel J., *The Witwatersrand Goldfields Banket and Mining Practice*. London: Macmillan & Co., Ltd., 1898.

Williams, Gatenby, *William Guggenheim*. New York: Lone Voice Publishing Co., 1934.

BOOKS AND PERIODICALS MENTIONED IN TEXT

Almanach de Gotha.

Bain, H. F., and Read, T. R., *Ores and Industries in South America*. New York: Harper & Brothers, 1934.

Bent, James Theodore, *The Ruined Cities of Mashonaland*. London: Longman, Green & Co., 1892.

Beveridge, Albert J., *Life of John Marshall*. Boston, New York: Houghton Mifflin Co., 1919.

Bible.

Burnham, Frederick R., *Scouting on Two Continents*. Garden City, N. Y.: Doubleday, Page & Co., 1926.

Butt, Archibald W., *Letters of Archie Butt*. Garden City, N. Y.: Doubleday, Page & Co., 1924.

Churchill, Lord Randolph, *Men, Mines, and Animals in South Africa*. London: S. Low, Marston & Co., Ltd., 1897.

Colvin, Ian, *The Life of Jameson*. London: E. Arnold & Co., 1922.

Corning, Frederick G., *A Student Reverie*. New York: The De Vinne Press, 1920.

Bibliography 781

DAVIS, RICHARD HARDING, *Soldiers of Fortune*. New York: Charles Scribner's Sons, 1902.

D'ABERNON, LORD, *An Ambassador of Peace*. London: 1929-1931.

FITZPATRICK, PERCY, *The Transvaal from Within*. New York: Frederick A. Stokes Co., 1899.

HAMMOND, NATALIE HARRIS, *A Woman's Part in a Revolution*. New York, London: Longmans, Green & Co., 1897.

History of the Texas Rangers.

HOBBS, WILLIAM H., *Leonard Wood*. New York, London: G. P. Putnam's Sons, 1920.

HOUSE, EDWARD M., *Intimate Papers of Colonel House*. Arranged as narrative by Charles Seymour. Boston: Houghton Mifflin & Co., 1926-1928.

John Hays Hammond's Report.

KESSLER, CAMILLUS, *At the Bottom of the Ladder*. Philadelphia, London: J. B. Lippincott Co., 1926.

LONGWORTH, ALICE ROOSEVELT, *Crowded Hours*. New York: Charles Scribner's Sons, 1933.

MARBURG, THEODORE, *Development of the League of Nations Idea*. New York: The Macmillan Co., 1932.

MARVEL, IK, *Reveries of a Bachelor*. Philadelphia: D. McKay, 1850.

MILLIN, SARAH GERTRUDE, *Rhodes*. London: Chatto & Windus, 1933.

PARSONS, A. B., *The Porphyry Coppers*. New York: Published by the American Institute of Mining and Metallurgical Engineers, sponsored by Rocky Mountain fund, 1933.

POTTER, ELIZABETH, and GRAY, M. T., *The Lure of San Francisco*. San Francisco: P. Elder & Co., 1915.

PRESCOTT, WILLIAM HICKLING, *History of the Conquest of Mexico*. New York: Harper & Brothers, 1843.

RANDALL-MACIVER, DAVID, *Mediaeval Rhodesia*. London: Macmillan & Co., Ltd., 1906.

RICKARD, T. A., *Man and Metals*. New York: Whittlesey House, McGraw-Hill Book Co., 1932.

SCHREINER, OLIVE, *The Story of an African Farm*. London: Hutchinson & Co., 1910.

——, *Trooper Peter Halket of Mashonaland*. Boston: Roberts Brothers, 1897.

SIRINGO, CHARLES A., *A Cowboy Detective*. New York: J. S. Ogilvie Publishing Co., 1912.

——, *History of "Billy the Kid."* Sante Fe, N. M.: The Author, 1920.

STEAD, W. T., *Americanisation of the World*. New York, London: H. Markley, 1902.

——, *If Christ Came to Chicago!* Chicago: Laird & Lee, 1894.

STEAD, W. T., *Letters from Julia.* New York: John Lane Co., 1907.

SULLIVAN, MARK, *Our Times, The United States 1900-1925.* New York: Charles Scribner's Sons, 1928-1929.

TANNENBAUM, FRANK, *Whither Latin America?* New York: Thomas Y. Crowell Co., 1934.

United States Army Register.

What the Coal Commission Found. Report of commission appointed by President Coolidge.

WILLIAMS, BASIL, *Cecil Rhodes.* London: Constable & Co., 1921.

Fortune; Forum; Independent; National Geographic Magazine; Pall Mall Gazette; Popular Science Magazine; Review of Reviews; Saturday Evening Post; South Africa; World Court Magazine; Yale Literary Magazine. Courier-Journal, Louisville, Ky.; *Daily Mail,* London; *Globe,* New York; *Herald,* New York; *Standard and Diggers News,* Johannesburg; *Star,* Johannesburg; *Sun,* New York; *Times,* Johannesburg; *Times,* London; *Times,* New York; *Times,* Vasalia, Calif.; *Tombstone Epitaph,* Tombstone, Ariz.; *Volksstem* (Boer newspaper).

Index

Index

GOLD

HISTORICAL AND ECONOMIC ASPECTS

An Arno Press Collection

[Bonus, Petrus of Ferrara]. The New Pearl of Great Price. 1894

Emmons, William Harvey. Gold Deposits of the World: With a Section on Prospecting. 1937

Father Coughlin on Money and Gold: Three Pamphlets. 1974

Gold and Silver in the Presidential Campaign of 1896. 1974

Gold Mining Company Prospectuses. 1974

Hammond, John Hays. The Autobiography of John Hays Hammond. 1935. 2 volumes in one

Johnson, Obed Simon. A Study of Chinese Alchemy. 1928

Letcher, Owen. The Gold Mines of Southern Africa. 1936

Nesbitt, L[ewis] M[ariano]. Gold Fever. 1936

Ogilvie, William. Early Days on the Yukon and the Story of its Gold Finds. 1913

[Preshaw, G. O.]. Banking Under Difficulties or Life on the Goldfields of Victoria, New South Wales & New Zealand. By a Bank Official. 1888

Rickard, T[homas] A[rthur]. Man and Metals. 1932. 2 volumes in one

Russell, Henry B. International Monetary Conferences. 1898

Seyd, Ernest. **Bullion and Foreign Exchanges Theoretically and Practically Considered.** 1868

Speculation in Gold and Silver Mining Stocks. 1974

Taylor, F. Sherwood. **The Alchemists:** Founders of Modern Chemistry. 1949

United States Congress. House of Representatives. Committee on Banking and Currency. **Gold Panic Investigation.** 41st Congress, 2d Session, House Report No. 31. 1870

Weaver, James B. **A Call to Action.** 1892